MW00565334

Art on Campus:
The College Art Association's
Official Guide
to
American College and University
Art Museums and Exhibition Galleries

Edited by John J. Russell and Thomas S. Spencer

2000

Published by Friar's Lantern, Inc.
P.O. Box 641, 1900 Monkton Road
Monkton, Maryland 21111
Telephone: 410-472-3748   Telecopier: 410-472-3774
E-Mail: flantern@aol.com

Front cover:

Auguste Rodin - *St. John the Baptist Preaching*, bronze, 1878-1880. Gift of Dr. and Mrs. Meyer P. Potamkin. Trout Gallery collection. Photograph courtesy of Trout Gallery, Dickinson College, Carlisle, Pennsylvania.

Hugo Schieber, *Head of a Woman*, 1920, gouache on board, 29 x 23 3/4 inches, gift of Dr. Lee Goldstein, Housatonic Museum of Art. Photograph courtesy of Housatonic Museum of Art, Housatonic Community College, Bridgeport, Connecticut.

Guido da Siena, *Annunciation*, Italian, 13th century. Tempera on panel, 35.1 x 48.8 cm. The Art Museum, Princeton University, Caroline G. Mather Fund (144). Photograph courtesy of The Art Museum, Princeton University, Princeton, New Jersey.

Archibald J. Motley, Jr. - *The Jazz Singers*, c. 1937, oil on canvas, 32 x 42 inches, WPA. Permanent collection, Western Illinois University Art Gallery. Photograph courtesy of Western Illinois University, Macomb, Illinois.

Back cover:

Ngiraibuuch, storyboard relating myth of Chief Koror receiving a gift of stone money; Palauan. Isla Center for the Arts collection. Photograph courtesy of Isla Center for the Arts at the University of Guam, Mangilao, Guam.

Guy Carlton Wiggins - *Brooklyn Bridge in Winter* (1920), oil on canvas, 20½ x 24¼ inches. Gift of W.T.S. Johnson, University of Cincinnati Fine Arts Collection. Photograph courtesy of DAAP Galleries, University of Cincinnati, Cincinnati, Ohio.

Circle of the Antimenes painter, Greek, attic black figure amphora, height 15½ inches, c. 539-520 BC. Purchase of the Friends of Art Acquisition Fund, The Christian A. Johnson Memorial Fund, the Walter Cerf Acquisition Fund, and the Memorial Fund, Middlebury College Museum of Art. Photograph courtesy of Middlebury College Museum of Art, Middlebury, Vermont.

Published by Friar's Lantern, Inc.
P.O. Box 641, 1900 Monkton Road, Monkton, Maryland 21111.

Library of Congress Cataloguing-in-Publication Data
Russell, John J., 1945-, and Spencer, Thomas S., 1946-
Art on Campus: The College Art Association's Official Guide to American College and University Art Museums and Exhibition Galleries,
1st edition.
Includes index.
ISBN # 0-9667144-0-7

First Printing, 2000
Printed and manufactured by Automated Graphic Systems
Cover design by Jeff Jones, Put-It-In-Print (Dickerson, MD)
Mapping software licensed from Cartesia Software

2

Table of Contents

Table of Contents, cont.

Foreword

The College Art Association was honored to have been approached by the editors of this volume to act as sponsor of this guide to American college and university museums and galleries. It is therefore with great pleasure that we announce the Association's sponsorship of *Art on Campus*.

CAA, founded in 1911, played a major role in establishing principles of art historical scholarship and in distinguishing from one another the serious aspects of what was then broadly referred to as "art education" - namely, history, criticism, pedagogy, and creativity/art making, while numbering representatives of all these constituencies among its members. From its inception, CAA has been a national organization responsive to cultural and professional diversity. Of the 108 members listed in 1913, nearly half were women; artists and art historians employed both in the academy and the museum were represented in the association from the beginning.

As the visual arts and scholarship in general blossomed in the United States during the 1930s and 1940s, so too did the College Art Association. Likewise, both major constituencies of CAA - artists and art historians working in the academy and museums - grew dramatically at this time. In the 1930s, the New York Federal Art Project of the Work Projects Administration (WPA) was headquartered at the College Art Association offices. CAA also circulated exhibitions and scheduled lectures by leading artists, art historians, and critics. In the 1950s, CAA joined with the American Association of Museums, the Association of Art Museum Directors, the American Federation of Arts, and Artists Equity Association in a project that lasted a decade, entitled "The Museum and the Artist", a thirty-page paper containing the recommendations of the committee that was formed "to consider the mutual problems of museums and artists".

CAA has continued to grow an average of more than 5 percent a year and currently has over 14,000 national and international individual members and nearly 2,000 institutional members. Although approximately 15 percent work full time in museums and 75 percent are employed in the academy, many professors serve from time to time as guest curators in museums and galleries; and, of course, the work of all CAA artists and art historians relies on that of museums and galleries. As an indication of the importance of this mutually beneficial relationship, CAA is an affiliate of the American Association of Museums (AAM), and the Association of College and University Museums and Galleries is an affiliate of both CAA and AAM.

In recognition of the interdependence of museums and the academy and the roles that CAA members play in both, CAA proudly supports this guide. Furthermore, we commend editors John J. Russell and Thomas S. Spencer for undertaking such an ambitious project and producing this comprehensive, useful, and handsome guidebook.

Susan Ball
Executive Director

Editors' Introduction

Why devote a guide exclusively to college and university art venues? While many college and university spaces show a span of classic artworks including famous, important, and rarely traveled works, there is more to consider. With their primary focus on teaching and the exploration of the boundaries of knowledge, college and university art museums play a distinct role in the American visual art community. The traditional art museum preserves and frequently canonizes merely the work of recognized artists, and the commercial gallery is motivated by profit; in contrast college or university galleries are principally motivated by the desire to promote intellectual inquiry. Their collections and exhibitions are developed with the ultimate goal of enhancing the perceptual and conceptual abilities of the visitor. In some respects, college or university galleries are comparable to laboratories, positioned to experiment, to take risks, to show work by emerging artists that merits scrutiny, but is not currently commercially viable or is too unfamiliar and controversial to be shown in a museum.

While a few of the college and university art museums (Yale, Chicago, Berkeley, Williams, Miami, etc.) are well known and offer permanent collections that are comparable in size and quality to those of major urban museums, many other intriguing facilities do not receive the attention they deserve. For example, the museum at Amherst College boasts a high-quality and comprehensive collection of American art. Middlebury has a small, but fine collection, housed in an architecturally significant facility. The collections of smaller, or less prominent, institutions often constitute a unique resource by their focus on a particular artist, genre, or theme. For example, the permanent collection of St. Mary's College (California) features an extensive collection of paintings by William Keith, and Saginaw Valley State University (Michigan) is home to the Marshall M. Fredericks Sculpture Gallery. Other "hidden treasures" abound, for example: Scripps College's Scripps Ceramic Annual, the longest running exhibition of ceramics in the United States, and Bradley University's National Print and Drawing Exhibition.

We believe that this book fills a need long-felt by the American art-loving public for a comprehensive guide to American college and university museums and exhibition galleries that is portable, readable, useful, attractive and comprehensive. Our book is neither a coffee table art book nor a periodical guide to temporary art exhibitions. Rather, it is intended to enable the art lover to plan more productive and enjoyable excursions by providing essential information on institutions, their collections, and activities.

It is unique in its scope, focusing on over 700 institutions. No other source contains detailed information on nearly so many institutions. We have sought to be as inclusive as possible, the thought being to permit the reader to decide not to visit a museum, which he can do only after being made aware of its existence. To this end, we have included not only traditional art museums with permanent collections, but also galleries that present only temporary exhibitions.

Our book is "current" in that it provides complete and accurate basic information about each organization. It also describes the museum's collection and the facility itself, in many instances illustrating one or the other with a color photograph. These descriptions and illustrations not only help the reader to place the museum as to type, but also, along with facts about annual attendance, gallery size, membership availability, and other topics, permit the reader to make qualitative and quantitative judgments about it. Of course, the sophisticated museum-goer knows that such a process is not without its dangers; there are hundreds of wonderful small and, sadly, sparsely attended college art museums in the United States.

Finally, a few words about accuracy are in order. First, space limitations have prevented us from setting forth in as much detail as we would have liked certain particulars regarding facilities and operations. For example, a museum listed as accessible to the disabled may be only partly so. Second, some attendance figures may include persons attending related facilities, such as theatres. Third, some institutions listed have not responded fully to our repeated requests for information, perhaps in a few cases resulting in publication of dated or misinterpreted information. Fourth, we have chosen to not include specific information on the scheduling and nature of temporary exhibits in the belief that such transitory information is most reliably gained by contacting the institution directly, or visiting its web site, as close to the time of a proposed visit as possible.

We have made every possible effort to verify the information contained in this book, by sending each facility a questionnaire, making follow-up telephone calls, visiting web sites, and checking a number of secondary sources. Nevertheless, the data in this book can be no more accurate than that which we have received (we hope no less accurate), and therefore, when in doubt, the reader should contact the museum directly. We apologize for any inconvenience caused by errors in this book, whatever the source. We also welcome suggestions from those who use this book regarding institutions that should be added or other changes that would make future editions more useful.

John J. Russell and Thomas S. Spencer
Monkton, Maryland
November 1, 1999

How to Use This Book

We have approached questions of design and organization in this book from the point of view of the reader; ease of use and accessibility are our paramount concerns. To that end, we have tried to be consistent in format and to avoid unnecessary and annoying abbreviations as much as possible, even though to do so uses more space on the page.

The main body of the guide is organized alphabetically by state and then community. Each state listing is preceded by a map, which indicates the communities in which museums/galleries may be found. (Maps for the metropolitan areas of Boston, Los Angeles, New York, Philadelphia, and San Francisco appear after their respective state maps.) The number in parentheses after a community indicates the number of facilities listed in this guide in that community; the absence of a number means that there is only one such facility listed. The maps are intended merely to indicate the approximate location of communities with museums or galleries, in order to assist the reader in planning excursions, not to function as detailed roadmaps. (As an aid for the visitor, many college and university web sites contain detailed travel directions, often accompanied by maps.)

Facilities are arranged alphabetically under the community in which they are located. If there is an initial "The" in an institution's name, it is ignored in determining entry order. ("The University of Arizona Museum of Art" falls under U, not T.) Also, "St." is alphabetized as "Saint" and "Ft." as Fort. ("St. Louis University" sorts as "Saint Louis University".)

Among entries, information of a type always occupies the same position. The symbol ⓒᴬᴬ, immediately following a facility's name, indicates that the school held institutional membership in the College Art Association in 1999. Contact information immediately follows the organization name, followed by data on admission fees, attendance, year established, availability of membership, accessibility to the disabled, and parking arrangements. If the facility itself does not maintain an internet site, we have provided instead the college/university home page address because information on the facility and its current exhibition schedule may often be quickly found in the institution's art department and/or general calendar web pages.

Next is information on hours of operation. The data following "Open:" are the regularly scheduled hours of operation. Following "Closed:" are the exceptions to the hours shown in "Open:", such as holidays. Please note that if an institution is regularly closed on Mondays, it will be shown as "Open: Tuesday to Saturday"; Monday would not appear under "Closed:", as it is understood in the "Open:" section.

"Facilities:" and "Activities:" have been designed to allow the reader to skim the listings for a particular piece of information without having to read the entire text. The categories in bold type are in alphabetical order followed by specific information in parentheses when appropriate. For instance, if one wishes to know which museums have libraries, simply scan under "Facilities:" in each entry. You might find for example "Library (12,000 volumes; non-circulating; Tues-Wed, 11am-1pm)".

This is followed by information on the institution's publications. Finally, there is a more detailed description of the facility, designed to give the reader a "feel" for the institution, its permanent collection, and exhibitions.

The Index, in addition to the formal name of each institution, includes cross-references to facilitate finding the entries of organizations for which the proper name is unknown. For example, "(The) University of Arizona - Center for Creative Photography" may also be found in the Index under "Arizona, University of - Center for Creative Photography", "Center for Creative Photography - University of Arizona", and its acronym, CCP.

We encourage users of this guide to contact us with any suggestions for improving the organization and presentation of data in future editions.

Editors' Suggestions

In preparing this guide, we have concluded that there are many museums throughout the United States that are not sufficiently appreciated by the museum-visiting public. This conclusion is based largely on a comparison of the museums' reported attendance and their descriptions of their holdings and facilities provided to us. With respect to some institutions, we know from first-hand experience that they deserve greater attendance. With respect to others, their questionnaires caught our attention, making us want to visit them ourselves. Rather than housing encyclopaedic collections, many of these institutions have a more narrowly defined focus, assembling with a clear eye meaningful and provocative collections and exhibitions. Perhaps some museums are more concerned with the quality of their collections than they are with self-promotion. In other cases, geography no doubt adversely affects attendance. In any event, we present below our list of less-visited (that is, with fewer than 50,000 reported visitors each year) but intriguing institutions and invite our readers to test the wisdom of our choices. We stress that our list is both non-exhaustive and to some extent subjective; all of us (readers and editors) would benefit from your informing us of our more glaring omissions. There certainly will be space (and probably sufficient reason) to make the list larger in future editions.

California
 Mills College Art Gallery (Oakland)
 Scripps College -
   Ruth Chandler Williamson Gallery (Claremont)
 St. Mary's College - Hearst Art Gallery (Moraga)
 University of California, San Diego -
   Stuart Collection (La Jolla)
 University of Southern California -
   Fisher Gallery (Los Angeles)
Connecticut
 Housatonic Community Technical College -
   Housatonic Museum of Art (Bridgeport)
 University of Connecticut -
   William Benton Museum of Art (Storrs)
Delaware
 University of Delaware - University Gallery
   (Newark)
District of Columbia
 American University - Watkins Gallery
   (Washington)
Illinois
 Governors State University -
   Nathan Manilow Sculpture Park
   (University Park)
Indiana
 Valparaiso University - Brauer Museum of Art
   (Valparaiso)
Iowa
 Coe College - Galleries (Cedar Rapids)
 Cornell College - Armstrong Gallery
   (Mount Vernon)
Maine
 The Bates College Museum of Art (Lewiston)
 Colby College Museum of Art (Waterville)
Massachusetts
 Amherst College - Mead Art Museum (Amherst)
 Brandeis University - Rose Art Museum
   (Waltham)

Michigan
 Saginaw Valley State University -   Marshall M.
   Fredericks Sculpture Gallery   (University City)
Missouri
 Saint Louis University - Museum of
   Contemporary Religious Art (St. Louis)
Nebraska
 University of Nebraska-Lincoln -
   Great Plains Art Collection (Lincoln)
New York
 Colgate University - The Picker Art Gallery
   (Hamilton)
Ohio
 Capital University - Schumacher Gallery
   (Columbus)
Pennsylvania
 Bucknell University - The Center Gallery
   (Lewisburg)
 La Salle University Art Museum (Philadelphia)
 Ursinus College - Philip and Muriel Berman
   Museum of Art (Collegeville)
South Carolina
 Bob Jones University Museum and Gallery
   (Greenville)
Tennessee
 Fisk University - Carl Van Vechten Gallery
   (Nashville)
Texas
 Southern Methodist University -
   The Meadows Museum (Dallas)
Vermont
 Middlebury College Museum of Art (Middlebury)
Virginia
 Hampton University Museum (Hampton)
 Mary Washington College Galleries
   (Fredericksburg)
 Randolph Macon Woman's College -
   Maier Museum of Art (Lynchburg)

Alabama

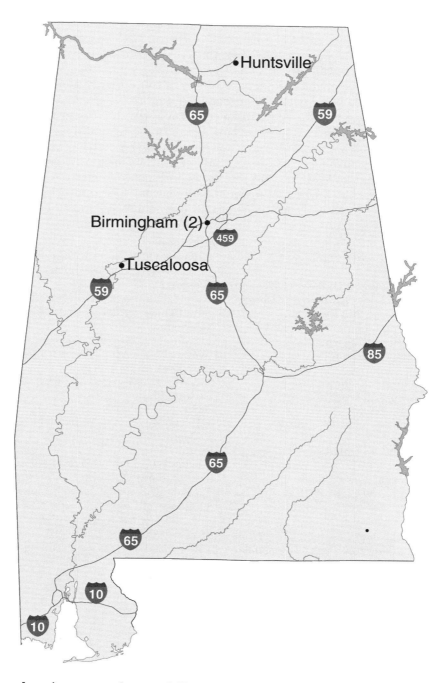

The number in parentheses following the city name indicates the number of museums/galleries in that municipality. If there is no number, one is understood. For example, in the text two listings would be found under Birmingham and one listing under Tuscalossa.

Alabama

Birmingham

Birmingham-Southern College - Durbin Gallery (C4A)
Kennedy Art Center, 900 Arkadelphia Road
Birmingham, AL   35204
Tel: (205) 226-4926
Internet Address: http://www.bsc.edu/arts/durbin/default.htm
Admission: free.
Open: Monday to Friday, 9am-4:30pm.
Facilities: **Exhibition Area.**
Activities: **Temporary Exhibitions.**

The Gallery presents traveling, faculty, and student exhibitions. Annual events include the Southeast Regional High School Art Competition, the senior art exhibition, and a juried student art exhibition.

University of Alabama at Birmingham - Visual Arts Gallery (C4A)
University of Alabama at Birmingham, 900 13th St. South
Birmingham, AL   35294-1260
Tel: (205) 934-4941   *Fax:* (205) 975-6639
Internet Address: http://main.uab.edu/show.asp?durki=1925
Curator: Ms. Antoinette Nordan
Admission: voluntary contribution.
Attendance: 5,000   *Established:* 1972   *Membership:* N   *ADA Compliant:* Y
Open: Monday to Thursday, 1pm-6pm; Sunday, 2pm-6pm.
Closed: New Year's Day, ML King Day, Independence Day, Labor Day, Thanksgiving Day,
        Christmas Day.
Facilities: **Gallery; Temporary Exhibition Space.**
Activities: **Films; Guided Tours; Lectures; Traveling/Temporary Exhibitions.**
Publications: collection catalogue (annual); posters.

The Visual Arts Gallery features a changing series of exhibitions of contemporary and historical art by internationally known artists, as well as by students and faculty. The gallery also maintains a permanent collection primarily of works on paper dating from the mid-18th century to the present and of works by faculty and students.

Huntsville

University of Alabama in Huntsville Gallery of Art (C4A)
Department. of Art and Art History
Huntsville, AL   35899
Tel: (205) 890-6114   *Fax:* (205) 890-6411
Internet Address: http://www.uah.edu/colleges/liberal/art/gallery.html
Admission: free.
Established: 1975   *Membership:* N   *ADA Compliant:* Y
Open: Call for hours.
Facilities: **Architecture** (Greek Revival church, 1840's).
Activities: **Films; Lectures; Traveling Exhibitions.**

The Department of Art and Art History directs and operates two gallery spaces on campus. The galleries play host to a yearly series of exhibitions of the work of local, regional, and national artists. In addition, the galleries are used for annual student exhibitions, senior student solo shows, and faculty exhibitions. The original UAH Gallery of Art, a one-room church built in the Greek Revival-style (circa 1840), was donated to the University in 1973 and was renovated by UAH students in 1974. A second gallery area is located in the UAH University Center and has 500 square feet of exhibition space.

Tuscaloosa

University of Alabama - Sarah Moody Gallery of Art ⒸⒶⒶ

College of Arts and Sciences, 103 Garland Hall
Tuscaloosa, AL   35487-0270
Tel: (205) 348-1890
Fax: (205) 348-9642
Internet Address:
   http://www.as.ua.edu/calendar.htm/#Galleries
Director: Mr. Bill Dooley
Admission: voluntary contribution.
Attendance: 10,000   *Established:* 1967
ADA Compliant: Y
Open: **During School Year**,
         Monday to Friday, 9am-4:30pm;
         Sunday, 2pm-5pm.
Facilities: **Gallery**.
Activities: **Films**; **Lectures**; **Temporary Exhibitions**; **Travelling Exhibitions**.
Publications: exhibition catalogues.

Garland Hall. Photograph courtesy of Sarah Moody Gallery of Art, University of Alabama, Tuscaloosa, Alabama.

The Gallery provides the local university community, residents of west Alabama and visitors with an opportunity to view the work of mid-career artists who enjoy regional as well as national recognition. The Moody Gallery maintains a permanent collection of works on paper, which it began in 1967 and continues to expand. Each year the collection is featured in the gallery, with particular emphasis given to new acquisitions. The collection includes works by Robert Rauschenberg, Manuel Neri, Carrie Mae Weems, Alexander Calder, Picasso, Vija Celmins, Ida Applebroog, Ansel Adams, Salvador Dali , and Judy Pfaff. Works are acquired through the support of the Farley Moody Galbraith Endowment Fund. Also of possible interest on campus is the Ferguson Center Gallery (open: Mon-Fri, 9am-4:30pm; Sun, 2pm-5pm).

Alaska

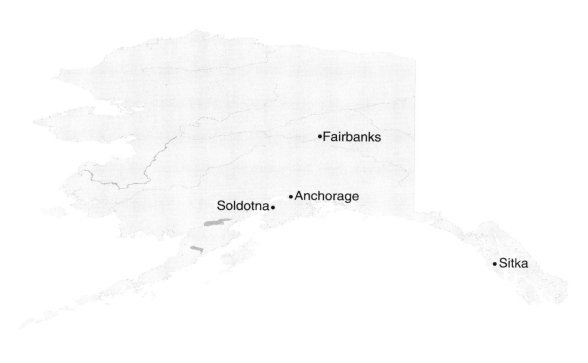

A number in parentheses following a city name indicates the number of museums/galleries in that municipality. If there is no number, one is understood. For example, in the text one listing would be found under each Alaskan city shown on map.

Alaska

Anchorage

University of Alaska, Anchorage - Galleries ⓒ⁴⁴

Kimura Art Gallery: Arts Building, 2nd Floor
3211 Providence Drive
Anchorage, AK   99508
Tel: (907) 786-1799
Internet Address: http://www.uaa.alaska.edu
Professor of Art History: Dr. Charles E. Licka
Admission: free.
Attendance: 5,000   *Established:* 1986
Membership: N   *ADA Compliant:* Y
Parking: free on site.
Open: Monday to Friday, 10am-5pm.
Facilities: **Exhibition Area** (1,200 square feet).
Activities: **Temporary Exhibitions**.
Publications: brochures (occasional); monographs (occasional).

Dennis Oppenheim, *Image Intervention*, 1984, Collection of University of Alaska Anchorage. Photograph courtesy of University of Alaska Anchorage, Anchorage, Alaska.

The Gallery focuses on contemporary art and presents a wide range of international, national, and Alaskan art. These exhibitions are independently curated and consist of solo. group, faculty, invitational, and BFA thesis exhibitions. The Gallery's express purpose is to serve as an educational space not only for the University, but also for the city of Anchorage and the state of Alaska. There is also site-specific sculpture at various campus locations. Also of possible interest on campus is the Campus Center Gallery (786-1219) located in Campus Center Room 229, 3211 Providence Drive (Open: Mon-Thurs, 10am-7pm; Fri, 10am-5pm).

Fairbanks

University of Alaska Museum

University of Alaska-Fairbanks, 907 Yukon Drive
Fairbanks, AK   99775-6960
Tel: (907) 474-7505
Fax: (907) 474-5469
Internet Address: http://www.uaf.alaska.edu
Director: Ms. Aldona Jonaitis
Admission: fee-$5.00.
Attendance: 124,000   *Established:* 1929   *Membership:* Y   *ADA Compliant:* Y
Open: **September to May**, Daily, 9am-5pm.
          June to August, Daily, 9am-7pm.
Closed: New Year's Day, Thanksgiving Day, Christmas Day.
Facilities: **Museum Store**.
Activities: **Guided Tours**; **Temporary Exhibitions**; **Traveling Exhibitions**.
Publications: brochures; exhibition catalogues; newspaper (annual).

There are over a million objects in the Museum's cultural and natural history collections. The fine arts collection constitutes an invaluable record of Alaska's cultural richness and aesthetic diversity and includes nearly 3,000 works of art. The major focus of the collection is Alaskan regional art, historic through contemporary, and includes all major media of visual expression. To make full use of the art collection's potential, the Museum offers a multitude of exhibitions, educational programs, and public events. The collection serves as an important tool for scholarly research in the art history of Alaska and for classroom support in the study of drawing, painting, photography, printmaking, and sculpture.

Sitka

Sheldon Jackson College - Sheldon Jackson Museum

104 College Drive, Sitka, AK   99835-7657

Tel: (907) 747-8981

Fax: (907) 747-3004

Internet Address: http://www.sheldonjackson.edu

Admission: fee: adult-$3.00, child-free, student-free.

Established: 1888

Open: **mid-May - mid-Sept**,
   Monday to Friday, 9am-6pm; Saturday to Sunday, 10am-6pm.
   mid-Sept - mid-May,
   Tuesday to Saturday, 10am-4pm.

Facilities: **Architecture** (National Register building, 1895); **Exhibition Area**.

Activities: **Demonstrations** (summer); **Education Programs**; **Travelling Exhibitions**.

Located in the oldest concrete building in Alaska, the Museum houses a collection of Alaskan ethnographic material, including objects from the Eskimo, Aleut, Athabaskan, Tlingit, Haida. and Tsimshan cultures. Since 1984 it has been one of the Alaska State Museums.

Soldotna

Kenai Peninsula College - Campus Art Gallery

University of Alaska, Anchorage, 34820 College Drive

Soldotna, AK   99669

Tel: (907) 262-0370

Fax: (907) 262-0358

Internet Address: http://www.uaa.alaska.edu/kenai/AboutKPC/ArtGallery.html

Director: Mr. Gary Freeburg

Admission: free.

Attendance: 6,000   *Established:* 1985   *Membership:* N   *ADA Compliant:* Y

Parking: free on site.

Open: Monday to Daily, 8am-8pm.

Facilities: **Exhibition Area** (66 linear feet).

Activities: **Temporary Exhibitions** (change monthly).

The Gallery presents in monthly exhibitions works by local and regional artists in a wide rage of media and expressions.

Arizona

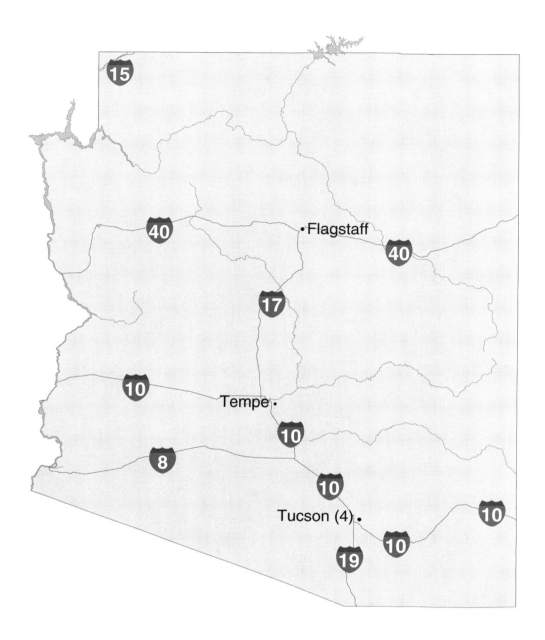

The number in parentheses following the city name indicates the number of museums/galleries in that municipality. If there is no number, one is understood. For example, in the text four listings would be found under Tucson and one listing under Tempe.

Arizona

Flagstaff

Northern Arizona University Art Museum and Galleries ⓒᴬ

Old Main Building, North Campus
Knoles Drive and McMullen Circle, Flagstaff, AZ   86011
Tel: (520) 523-3471   *Fax:* (520) 523-1424
Internet Address: http://www.nau.edu/~art_museum-p/
Director: Dr. Joel S. Eide
Admission: voluntary contribution.
Established: 1961   *Membership:* N
Open: **Old Main Art Museum**, Monday to Friday, 8am-5pm; Sunday, 1pm-4pm.
         Beasley Art Museum, Monday to Friday, 8am-5pm.
         Summer, call for hours.
Closed: Legal Holidays, Academic Holidays.
Facilities: **Museum Store**.
Activities: **Arts Festival**; **Films**; **Gallery Talks**; **Guided Tours**; **Lectures**; **Temporary Exhibitions**; **Traveling Exhibitions**.
Publications: exhibition catalogues.

Located in the historic Old Main building on Northern Arizona University's north campus in Flagstaff, the Old Main Art Museum features contemporary art exhibitions by local, state, national, and international artists. The NAU Art Museum and Galleries also include the Charles E. Beasley Art Museum and Gallery, which features 30-day exhibits of contemporary art as well as a permanent display of selected works by Mr. Beasley. Works by NAU students are also highlighted, including annual juried exhibits and biannual BFA exhibits. (The Richard E. Beasley Art Museum and Gallery is located on the second floor of the Creative and Communication Arts building on central campus. The closest cross streets are Knoles and Riordan.)

Tempe

Arizona State University Art Museum ⓒᴬ

Nelson Fine Arts Center: 10th St. & Mill Ave.
Matthews Center: Campus Center
Tempe, AZ   85287-2911
Tel: (602) 965-2787
Fax: (602) 965-5254
Internet Address: http://www.asuam.fa.asu.edu
Director: Ms. Marilyn Zeitlin
Admission: free.
Attendance: 52,000   *Established:* 1950
Membership: Y   *ADA Compliant:* Y
Open: **Matthews Center**,
              Tuesday to Saturday, 10am-5pm.
         Nelson Fine Arts Center,
              Tuesday, 10am-9pm;
              Wednesday to Saturday, 10am-5pm;
              Sunday, 1pm-5pm.
Closed: Legal Holidays.
Facilities: **Architecture** Nelson Fine Arts Center (Post-Modern building, 1989 design by Antoine Predock); **Exhibition Area** Matthews Center (4 galleries, permanent collection & experimental gallery), Nelson Fine Arts Center (5 galleries, changing exhibitions); **Library** (500 volumes); **Print Study Room**; **Reading Room**; **Sculpture Terraces and Court**; **Shop**.

Exterior View of Arizona State University Art Museum, Nelson Fine Arts Center (1989), designed by Antoine Predock. Photograph courtesy of Arizona State University Art Museum, Tempe, Arizona.

Arizona State University Art Museum, cont.

Activities: **Education Programs**; **Film and Video Festival**; **Gallery Talks**; **Guided Tours**; **Lectures**; **Performances**; **Temporary Exhibitions**; **Traveling Exhibitions**.

Publications: exhibition catalogues.

The Museum is housed in two facilities: the Nelson Fine Arts Center and the Matthews Center . The Nelson Fine Arts Center, an elegant post modern building located on the edge of the campus, serves as the primary museum exhibition space. The Matthews Center, formerly the ASU library and located in the center of the campus, houses the University's permanent collection, the College of Fine Arts student-run galleries (Harry Wood, Northlight, and Step), and other exhibitions more relevant to the students. With a collection of over 8,500 objects, the Museum focuses on contemporary art (new media and innovative presentations), crafts (American ceramics and wood turned objects), prints (historic and contemporary - American and European), art from the Southwest with emphasis on Latino artists, and Latin American Art.

Tucson

The University of Arizona - Center for Creative Photography (CCP) ⓒᴬᴬ

1030 N. Olive
Tucson, AZ   85721-0103
Tel: (520) 621-7968
Fax: (520) 621-9444
Internet Address: http://www.ccp.arizona.edu/ccp.html
Director: Mr. Terence R. Pitts
Admission: free.
Attendance: 70,000   *Established:* 1975
Membership: Y   *ADA Compliant:* Y
Parking: pay in the visitors' section of Park Ave. garage.
Open: Monday to Friday, 11am-5pm;
         Sunday, noon-5pm.
Closed: Legal Holidays.
Facilities: **Gallery**; **Library** (15,000 volumes); **Photo Archives** (use by appointment with archivist); **Print Viewing Area** (available to public in afternoon, reserve in advance); **Shop** (books, cards, jewelry, posters & videos).
Activities: **Gallery Talks**; **Guided Tours** (groups reserve in advance with Curator of Education); **Lectures**; **Temporary Exhibitions** (approximately every 6 weeks); **Traveling Exhibitions**.
Publications: books; exhibition catalogues; serial publication, "The Archive".

Edward Weston, *Charis Wilson, 1935*, Center for Creative Photography. Photograph courtesy of Center for Creative Photography, The University of Arizona, Tucson, Arizona. Copyright 1989 Center for Creative Photography, Arizona Board of Regents.

Located on the campus of the University of Arizona, the Center for Creative Photography is a research institution and museum housing a collection of more than 60,000 fine prints, over 40 photographers' archives, galleries, a library and research facilities. Over 2,000 photographers are represented in the Center's extensive fine print collection. Included are works by Ansel Adams, Edward Weston, Louise Dahl-Wolfe, Richard Avedon, Lola Alvarez Bravo, W. Eugene Smith, and Diane Arbus.

The University of Arizona - Joseph Gross Gallery ⓒᴬᴬ

Fine Arts Complex,Speedway and Park
Tucson, AZ   85721
Tel: (520) 626-4215
Fax: (320) 621-6930
Internet Address: http://www.arts.arizona.edu/galleries
Curator: Ms. Julie Sasse
Admission: free.
Established: 1978

The University of Arizona - Joseph Gross Gallery, cont.

Parking: parking at visitor's garage.
Open: Monday to Friday, 10am-5pm.
Closed: September to April, 1pm-4pm.
Facilities: **Galleries** (2).
Activities: **Temporary Exhibitions**.

The Joseph Gross Gallery, located in the Fine Arts Complex, presents the work of students, faculty, and professional artists.

Laurie Lundquist, *The Fisherman's Wife*, 1997, mixed media, 10 x 6 x 4 feet, "Surface Tension" mixed media installation, Joseph Gross Gallery. Photograph courtesy of The University of Arizona, Tucson, Arizona.

The University of Arizona Museum of Art (UAMA)

Park and Speedway, Tucson, AZ   85721
Tel: (520) 621-7567   *Fax:* (520) 621-8770
Internet Address: http://www.artmuseum.arizona.edu
Director and Chief Curator: Dr. Peter Bermingham
Admission: free.
Attendance: 30,000   *Established:* 1955   *Membership:* Y   *ADA Compliant:* Y
Parking: garage on Park Ave. at corner with Speedway Blvd..
Open: **September to mid-May**,
        Monday to Friday, 9am-5pm; Sunday, noon-4pm.
        May 15 to Labor Day,
        Monday to Friday, 10am-3:30pm; Sunday, noon-4pm.
Closed: University Holidays.
Facilities: **Galleries** (2 floors, 14,000 square feet); **Library**; **Shop** (books, catalogues, posters).
Activities: **Guided Tours** (1st and last Wed in month, 12:15pm); **Lectures**; **Permanent Exhibits**;
        Temporary Exhibitions; **Traveling Exhibitions**.
Publications: collection catalogue; exhibition catalogues.

With more than 3,000 paintings, sculptures, drawings and prints, UAMA presents one of the most comprehensive university collections of Renaissance and later European and American Art in the Southwest. The permanent collection is complemented by a continuous series of temporary exhibitions, including crafts, graphics, painting and sculpture. Of particular note are the Samuel H. Kress Collection of 14th through early 19th-century European paintings, including 26 panels of a 15th-century Spanish altarpiece from the Cathedral of Ciudad Rodrigo and a permanent exhibit of 61 clay and plaster models and sketches by 20th-century sculptor Jacques Lipchitz. Other strengths of the collection include a concentration in American paintings and prints of the 1930's, modernist paintings from 1920-1970, more than 2,000 prints from the last five centuries, and more than 60 works on paper by Maynard Dixon and Paul Landacre, two important Southwestern artists from earlier in this century.

University of Arizona Student Union Galleries

University of Arizona, Student Union Building
Tucson, AZ   85721
Tel: (520) 621-8046   *Fax:* (520) 621-6930
Internet Address: http://www.arts.arizona.edu/galleries
Gallery Curator: Ms. Julie Sasse
Admission: free.
Attendance: 32,000   *Established:* 1971   *Membership:* N   *ADA Compliant:* Y
Parking: pay parking at 2nd and Mountain Ave..
Open: Monday to Friday, 10am-4pm.
Closed: Legal Holidays, Installation Days.
Facilities: **Food Services** Restaurant; **Gallery**.

University of Arizona Student Union Galleries, cont.

Activities: **Guided Tours** (upon request); **Temporary Exhibitions** (approximately 35/year); **Travelling Exhibitions**.

The three Union Galleries (Union, Rotunda and Arizona) function as an integral part of the Memorial Student Union offering approximately 35 exhibitions annually. The galleries display original art by regional and national artists. Works in a variety of media are shown, including painting, sculpture, graphics, ceramics, fiber-work, and new genres. Past exhibits include alumni art invitationals, juried student art competitions, student and faculty shows, and traveling and curated exhibitions.

View of Union Gallery during "Tucson Connection: Annual Alumni Invitational", November 1997. Photograph courtesy of University of Arizona Union Galleries, Tucson, Arizona.

Arkansas

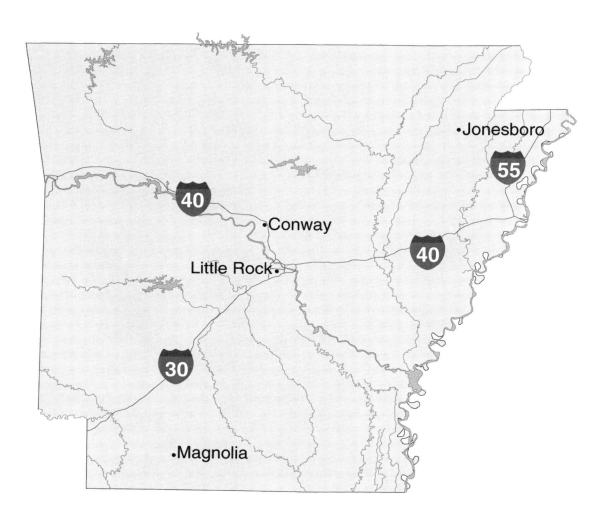

The number in parentheses following the city name indicates the number of museums/galleries in that municipality. If there is no number, one is understood. For example, in the text one listing would be found under each Arkansan municipality shown on the map.

Arkansas

Conway

University of Central Arkansas - Baum Gallery of Fine Art ⒸⒶ

University of Central Arkansas
Conway, AR   72035
Tel: (501) 450-5793
Fax: (501) 450-5958
Internet Address:
   http://www.uca.edu/art/baumhome/index.htm
Gallery Director: Mr. Garlan Jenkens
Admission: free.
Attendance: 15,000   *Established:* 1994
Membership: Y   *ADA Compliant:* Y
Parking: free, in blue zones in front of gallery.
Open: Monday, 10am-4pm; Tuesday, 10am-8pm;
         Wednesday to Saturday, 10am-4pm.
Closed: Academic Holidays.
Facilities: **Galleries** (5).
Activities: **Guided Tours**; **Temporary Exhibitions**.
Publications: brochures; exhibition catalogues.

Marshall Arisman, *El Salvadore aka Priest
589*, 1995, oil on paper, 30.5 x 38 inches.
Baum Gallery of Fine Art. Photograph courtesy of Baum Gallery of Fine Art, University
of Central Arkansas, Conway, Arkansas.

The Gallery presents approximately forty temporary exhibitions per year including major traveling exhibitions and changing shows drawn from its permanent collection. There are annual BFA and BA senior student expositions. The permanent collection includes works by Marshall Arisman, Roger Bowman, Dr. Andrew Cohen, Warren Criswell, Don Netzer. Laura Phillips, Julian Stanczak, and Larry Zox.

Jonesboro

Arkansas State University Art Gallery ⒸⒶ

Caraway Road, Jonesboro, AR   72467
Tel: (870) 972-3050
Fax: (870) 972-3932
Internet Address: http://www.astate.edu/docs/acad/cfa/art
Chairman, Dept. of Art: Mr. Curtis Steele
Admission: free.
Attendance: 3,600   *Established:* 1967   *Membership:* N   *ADA Compliant:* Y
Parking: Free, with visitor's pass.
Open: Monday to Friday, 10am-4pm.
Closed: Legal Holidays.
Facilities: **Auditorium**; **Gallery** (1,600 square feet).
Activities: **Education Programs**; **Temporary Exhibitions** (4-6/year); **Traveling Exhibitions**;
      Visiting Artist Program.
Publications: calendar.

The Gallery exhibits the work of contemporary American and international artists in 4-6 shows during the academic year. In addition, there are an annual juried student exhibition, graduate thesis exhibitions, and an annual holiday sale. During the summer months selections from the university's permanent collection are exhibited. In the fall, the annual Delta National Small Prints Exhibition, a national juried competition, is on display.

Little Rock

University of Arkansas at Little Rock Art Galleries (UALR Art Galleries)

Department of Art
2801 S. University
Little Rock, AR   72204-1099
Tel: (501) 569-3182
Fax: (501) 569-8775
Internet Address:
   http://www.ualr.edu/~artdept/gallery.html
Gallery Curator:
   Ms. Shannon Dillard Mitchell
Admission: free.
Attendance: 7,500   *Established:* 1972
Membership: N   *ADA Compliant:* Y
Open: **Academic Year**,
      Monday to Friday, 9am-5pm;
      Sunday, 2pm-5pm.
Closed: Legal Holidays, Christmas Week,
      Academic Holidays.

UALR Gallery during a faculty exhibition. Photograph courtesy of University of Arkansas at Little Rock, Department of Art, Little Rock, Arkansas.

Facilities: **Galleries** (3, total 4,100 square feet).
Activities: **Education Programs** (tours and workshops for k-12 students); **Gallery Talks** (with visiting artists); **Lectures** (usually in evening with guest lecturers or visiting artists); **Temporary Exhibitions**; **Traveling Exhibitions**.
Publications: calendar (biennial); exhibition catalogues.

UALR presents temporary and traveling exhibitions in three galleries.

Magnolia

Southern Arkansas University - Art Gallery

Brinson Fine Arts Building, State Route 355, Magnolia, AR   71753
Tel: (870) 235-4242   *Fax:* (870) 235-5005
Internet Address: http://www.saumag.edu
Admission: free.
Open: **Call for hours.**
Facilities: **Exhibition Area.**
Activities: **Temporary Exhibitions.**

The Gallery exhibits work by artists of national and international reputation, faculty, and students. There are also periodic visits by artists and other art professionals each semester.

California

The number in parentheses following the city name indicates the number of museums/galleries in that municipality. If there is no number, one is understood. For example, in the text two listings would be found under La Jolla and one listing under San Diego. Cities within the greater Los Angeles and San Francisco metropolitan areas will be found on the respective maps on the facing page.

Greater Los Angeles Metropolitan Area

(including Carson, Claremont, Fullerton, Irvine, Long Beach, Los Angeles, Malibu, Monterey Park, Northridge, Orange, Pasadena, Pomona, Rancho Cucamonga, Santa Ana, Santa Monica, Torrance, and Walnut.)

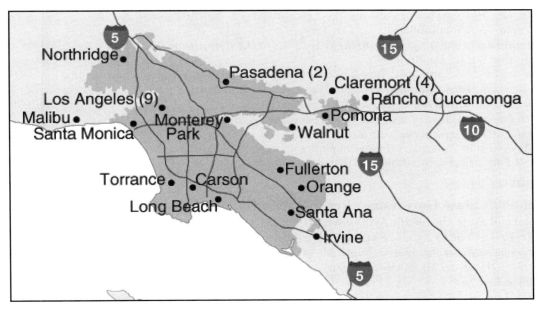

Greater San Francisco Metropolitan Area

(including Belmont, Berkeley, Cupertino, Hayward, Moraga, Oakland, San Francisco, San Jose, Santa Clara, and Stanford.)

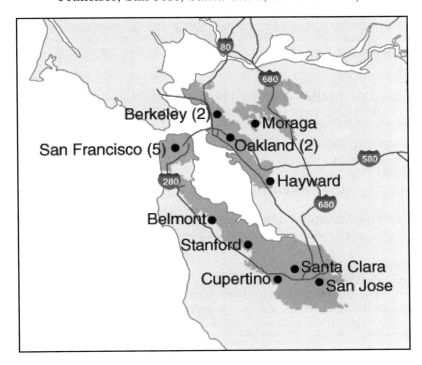

California

Aptos

Cabrillo College Art Gallery Ⓒⁱᵃ
Room 1002, 6500 Soquel Drive, Aptos, CA 95003
Tel: (831) 479-6308   *Fax:* (831) 479-5045
Internet Address: http://www.cabrillo.cc.ca.us/divisions/vapa/artgallery/
Director: Mr. Tobin Keller
Attendance: 10,000   *Established:* 1972   *ADA Compliant:* Y
Parking: metered parking.
Open: Monday, 9am-4pm; Tuesday, 9am-4pm and 7pm-10pm; Wednesday, 9am-4pm;
     Thursday, 9am-4pm and 7pm-10pm; Friday, 9am-4pm.
Facilities: **Exhibition Area** (1,300 square feet).
Activities: **Temporary Exhibitions**; **Travelling Exhibitions**.
Publications: announcements (occasional).
The Cabrillo College Art Gallery mounts temporary and traveling exhibitions consisting of the work of nationally- and internationally-recognized artists in a diversity of media.

Arcata

Humboldt State University - Reese Bullen Gallery Ⓒⁱᵃ
Humboldt State University, Art Building 101, 1 Harpst street, Arcata, CA 95521
Tel: (707) 826-5818   *Fax:* (707) 826-3628
Internet Address: http://www.humboldt.edu/~artrbg/
Gallery Director: Mr. Martin Morgan
Admission: free.
Attendance: 5,000   *Established:* 1970   *Membership:* N   *ADA Compliant:* Y
Open: **September to May**, Monday to Friday, 11am-4pm.
Closed: Academic Holidays.
Facilities: **Gallery** (1,500 square feet).
Activities: **Education Programs**; **Guided Tours**; **Loan Exhibitions**; **Temporary Exhibitions**.
Publications: exhibition catalogues.
The gallery features changing exhibitions including shows by outside artists and faculty. There are annual juried student and senior student exhibitions. A second, smaller facility, the Foyer Gallery, is also on campus.

Bakersfield

California State University, Bakersfield - Todd Madigan Gallery Ⓒⁱᵃ
9001 Stockdale Highway (adjacent to the Dore Theatre), Bakersfield, CA 93301
Tel: (805) 664-2238   *Fax:* (805) 665-6901
Internet Address: http://academic.csubak.edu/home/acadpro/departments.art/Toad.htm
Director: Ms. Margaret Nowling
Admission: free.
Established: 1981   *ADA Compliant:* Y
Parking: limited.
Open: **mid-September to mid-June**, Tuesday to Thursday, noon-4pm; Saturday, 1pm-4pm.
Closed: mid-June to mid-September, University Holidays.
Facilities: **Gallery**.
Activities: **Temporary Exhibitions**.
The Madigan Gallery presents temporary exhibitions of works of professional artists, the CSUB faculty, and students. Previous exhibits have featured the works of Henri Matisse, John Altoon, Cézanne, Goya, Rembrandt, Titian, and Mary Kelley, as well as many others. A listing of Gallery events and exhibits is published quarterly and may be obtained by contacting the Fine Arts Office at (805) 664-3093.

Belmont

College of Notre Dame - The Wiegand Gallery

College of Notre Dame, Madison Art Center
1500 Ralston Ave.
Belmont, CA   94002-1997
Tel: (415) 508-3595
Fax: (415) 637-0493
Internet Address: http://www.cnd.edu
Director: Mr. Charles Strong
Admission: voluntary contribution.
Attendance: 3,600   *Established:* 1970
Membership: Y   *ADA Compliant:* Y
Parking: free on site.
Open: Tuesday to Saturday, noon-4pm.
Closed: Between Exhibitions, Major Holidays.
Facilities: **Gallery**; **Theatre** (40 seats).
Activities: **Gallery Talks**; **Lectures** (artist talks); **Traveling Exhibitions** (4/year).

Exterior, Wiegand Gallery - Madison Art Center. Photograph courtesy of Wiegand Gallery, Belmont, California.

Publications: exhibition catalogues.

The Gallery is housed in the Madison Art Center, a stone building that was originally built as a carriage house on the site of the country estate of 19th-century financier William Chapman Ralston. The exhibition space, with its porthole windows and skylights, is an unusually warm, inviting environment in which to experience art. The Gallery is dedicated to changing exhibitions that exemplify a broad range of artistic expression. As a venue for California and Bay Area 20th-century art, the Gallery has promoted the work of emerging younger artists, mid-career artists, and unusual or rarely seen work by such established artists as Elmer Bischoff, Joan Brown, Richard Diebenkorn, Paul Kos, James Melchert, Manuel Neri, Katherine Porter, Hassel Smith, and Wayne Thiebaud.

Berkeley

University of California, Berkeley Art Museum and Pacific Film Archive ⒸⒶⒶ
(BAM/PFA)

University of California
2626 Bancroft Way
Berkeley, CA   94704
Tel: (510) 642-0808
Fax: (510) 642-4889
TDDY: (510) 642-8734
Internet Address:
   http://www.bampfa.berkeley.edu
Director: Mr. Kevin E. Consey
Admission: fee: adult-$6.00, child-$4.00,
   student-$4.00, senior-$4.00.
Attendance: 260,000   *Established:* 1965
Membership: Y   *ADA Compliant:* Y
Parking: metered on street and nearby public
   lots.
Open: Wednesday to Sunday, 11am-5pm;
   Thursday, 11am-9pm.
Closed: Academic Holidays.

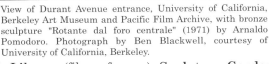

View of Durant Avenue entrance, University of California, Berkeley Art Museum and Pacific Film Archive, with bronze sculpture "Rotante dal foro centrale" (1971) by Arnaldo Pomodoro. Photograph by Ben Blackwell, courtesy of University of California, Berkeley.

Facilities: **Food Services** (Mon-Sun, 11am-4pm); **Library** (film reference); **Sculpture Garden**; **Shop**; **Theatre** (234 seat).
Activities: **Films**; **Gallery Talks**; **Lectures**; **Temporary Exhibitions**.
Publications: brochures; calendar (bi-monthly); exhibition catalogues.

University of California, Berkeley Art Museum and Pacific Film Archive, cont.

The University of California, Berkeley Art Museum and Pacific Film Archive is the university's principal visual arts center and one of the largest university art museums in the United States. Its distinctive building, designed by Mario Ciampi & Associates (San Francisco) and completed in 1970, arranges fan-shaped galleries in overlapping terraces that provide views of artwork from different perspectives. International in scope, the museum's permanent collection of over 10,000 objects comprises a full range of art. Selections from the collection are on view year-round, together with special and traveling exhibitions. Its cutting-edge MATRIX program explores contemporary art in a series of exhibitions that form a continuous survey. Each spring, the museum mounts an exhibition of work by Master of Fine Arts students. The Pacific Film Archive offers one of the nation's most comprehensive academic film programs. PFA's daily exhibition program emphasizes excellence and diversity. It highlights challenging works of independent film and video, and rare archival prints of classic cinema, and premiers, retrospectives, and rediscoveries from world cinema. A complementary education program of guided tours, lectures, symposia, and other special events is an important facet of the museum's outreach to the Berkeley campus and to the entire Bay Area. PFA Information (24-hours): (510) 642-1124. The U.C. Berkeley Art Museum has developed an impressive art collection of paintings, sculptures, and works on paper. The collection contains works by old masters such as Peter Paul Rubens, Giovanni Savoldo, and Giovanni Caracciolo; important collections of American primitive painting and early California landscapes; and a significant collection of European and American prints and drawings. Early 20th-century masters such as Fernand Leger, Rene Magritte, Aristide Maillol, and Joan Miró are represented. Of particular note is its collection of late twentieth-century art, including works by Alexander Calder, Mark Rothko, Helen Frankenthaler, Hans Hoffman, Theresa Kyung Cha, Nancy Spero, David Ireland, and Nayland Blake. The Museum also houses an outstanding Asian art collection of paintings, drawings, woodblock prints, sculpture, and ceramics, primarily from China, Japan and India. The Pacific Film Archive maintains a collection of 7,000 titles, with strengths in Soviet, American avant-garde, and Japanese cinema.

Carson

California State University, Dominguez Hills - University Art Gallery ⓒ⁴⁴

1000 E. Victoria St., Carson, CA 90747
Tel: (310) 243-3334
Fax: (310) 217-6967
Internet Address: http://www.csudh.edu
Director: Ms. Kathy Zimmerer
Admission: free.
Attendance: 10,000   *Established:* 1978   *Membership:* Y   *ADA Compliant:* Y
Parking: permit parking all CSU lots - $1.50.
Open: **September to May**, Monday to Thursday, 9:30am-4:30pm.
Closed: Academic Holidays.
Facilities: **Gallery** (2,150 square feet).
Activities: **Education Programs**; **Guided Tours** (upon request); **Lectures**; **Temporary Exhibitions** (6/year).
Publications: exhibition catalogues (3/year); newsletter, "Art Department Newsletter" (annual).

The University Art Gallery is considered to be one of the major exhibition spaces of the South Bay area. The gallery supports and enhances the Art Department instructional program while giving students from other disciplines and interested community members a valuable opportunity to explore and experience contemporary and historical works of art. The gallery, with over 2,000 square feet of floor space and 18 foot high ceilings, accommodates large-scale paintings and sculptures by artists of local and national reputation. There are five exhibitions per year with an emphasis on multi-cultural art and artists and an annual art exhibition of work by BA graduates. In conjunction with the exhibitions program, the Art Gallery publishes three exhibition catalogues per year and sponsors a related guest lecture series. The Gallery is also often used as a forum for student art critique classes, discussions with artists, and university and community events, and provides tours to the community and schools. The Gallery does not maintain a permanent collection.

Chico

California State University, Chico - Janet Turner Print Collection & Gallery ^{ⓒᴬᴬ}
(JTPG)

California State University, Chico
Laxson Auditorium, 1st and Salem Sts.
Chico, CA   95929
Tel: (530) 898-4476
Fax: (530) 898-4082
Internet Address: http://www.csuchico.edu/hfa/hfa/Janet/html
Curator: Ms. Catherine Sullivan Sturgeon
Admission: free.
Attendance: 5,000   *Established:* 1981
Membership: Y   *ADA Compliant:* Y
Parking: municipal lot near site.
Open: Monday to Friday, 11am-4pm; during auditorium
        events.
Facilities: **Auditorium**; **Gallery**; **Library** (150 volumes).
Activities: **Gallery Talks**; **Lectures**.

Kitagawa Utamaro, *Woman with Child*, Japanese color relief wood cut. Turner Print Collection & Gallery. Photograph courtesy of Turner Print Collection & Gallery, California State University, Chico, California.

Located on the campus of California State University, Chico in the mezzanine of Laxson Auditorium, the Gallery presents temporary exhibitions,   including   an   annual   "Student Printmakers   Invitational   and   Collection   Acquisition Competition" each spring. Prints from the collection are also displayed in cases on the first floor of Ayres Hall, where most CSU, Chico art classes are held. The collection consists of approximately 2,700 original prints representing a spectrum of printmaking techniques from over forty countries and spanning six centuries.

Claremont

Claremont Graduate School - East and West Galleries ^{ⓒᴬᴬ}

251 East 10th St., Claremont, CA   91711
Tel: (909) 621-8071
Internet Address: http://www.cgu.edu/arts/art/calendar.html
Director: Mr. Dean DeCocker
Open: Call for hours.
Facilities: **Exhibition Area**.
Activities: **Lectures**; **Temporary Exhibitions**.

The Claremont Graduate School presents temporary exhibitions of the work of professional artists, faculty and students in two galleries, Peggy Phelps Gallery (West Gallery) and East Gallery.

Pomona College - Montgomery Gallery ^{ⓒᴬᴬ}

330 N. College Ave.
Claremont, CA   91711-6344
Tel: (909) 621-8283
Fax: (909) 621-8989
Internet Address:
    http://www.pomona.edu/montgomery
Director: Ms. Marjorie L. Harth
Admission: free.

From the exhibition "Rich Traditions Continue: The Arts of Native American Woman", Montgomery Gallery, 11/9-12/14/97, works from the Pomona College permanent collection. Photograph courtesy of Montgomery Gallery - Pomona College, Claremont, California.

Pomona College - Montgomery Gallery, cont.

Attendance: 9,000   *Established:* 1958   *Membership:* N   *ADA Compliant:* Y
Parking: on street.
Open: Tuesday to Friday, noon-5pm; Saturday to Sunday, 1pm-5pm.
Closed: Academic Holidays, Legal Holidays, Summer.
Facilities: **Gallery.**
Activities: **Gallery Talks; Guided Tours; Lectures; Temporary Exhibitions; Traveling Exhibitions.**
Publications: "Collaboration/Transformation: Lithographs from the Hamilton Press" (annual); exhibition catalogues.

Montgomery Gallery displays the permanent collections of Pomona College, presents a schedule of temporary exhibitions during the academic year, trains students in museum practice, and participates actively in the teaching mission of the College. The Pomona College collections number approximately 8,000 objects. Important holdings include the Kress Collection of 15th- and 16th-century Italian panel paintings; over 5,000 examples of pre-Columbian to 20th-century Native American art and artifacts (ceramics, baskets, and beadwork); a large collection of American and European prints, drawings and photographs; and contemporary painting and sculpture.

Scripps College - Clark Humanities Museum - Study ⓒ⁴ᴬ

Humanities Building, Scripps College, 1030 Columbia Avenue, Claremont, CA   91711
Tel: (909) 607-3606   *Fax:* (909) 621-8323
Internet Address: http://www.scrippscol.edu
Chairman, Museum Committee: Dr. Eric T. Haskell
Admission: free.
Established: 1970   *Membership:* N
Open: Monday to Friday, 9am-noon & 1pm-5pm.
Closed: Academic Holidays.
Facilities: **Gallery; Library.**
Activities: **Education Programs; Temporary Exhibitions.**
Publications: exhibition catalogues.

The Museum's collection includes American paintings, Japanese prints, and African Sculpture.

Scripps College - Ruth Chandler Williamson Gallery ⓒ⁴ᴬ

Millard Sheets Art Center
9th and Columbia Ave.
Claremont, CA   91711-3948
Tel: (909) 607-3517
Fax: (909) 621-8323
Internet Address: http://www.scrippscol.edu/
   ~dept/ gallery/wrwgallery/GalleryHome.html
Director: Ms. Mary Davis MacNaughton
Admission: free.
Attendance: 7,700   *Established:* 1993
Membership: N   *ADA Compliant:* Y
Open: Wednesday to Sunday, 1pm-5pm.
Closed: Legal Holidays, December 17 to January
     2, June 1 to August 30.
Facilities: **Gallery** (3,000 square feet, designed by
     Anshen and Allen).

Jun Kaneko, *Plate*, 1971, stoneware, raku fired, partially glazed, Scripps College, Marer Collection. Photograph by Susan Einstein, courtesy of Ruth Chandler Williamson Gallery, Scripps College, Claremont, California.

Scripps College - Ruth Chandler Williamson Gallery, cont.

Activities: **Education Programs**; **Films**; **Gallery Talks**; **Lectures**; **Temporary Exhibitions**; **Travelling Exhibitions.**

Publications: "Revolutions in Clay: The Marer Collection of Contemporary Ceramics"; exhibition catalogues.

The Ruth Chandler Williamson Gallery presents both historical and contemporary exhibitions in a variety of media. Each year, the Gallery presents the Scripps Ceramic Annual, which is the best known and longest running exhibition of contemporary ceramics in the United States. In conjunction with this exhibition, the Gallery presents an artist panel discussion. Other activities include exhibition-related lectures, symposia, films, gallery talks, and a large Clay Day and Music Festival. The gallery presents loan exhibitions and participates in inter-museum loans. Juried student and senior studio art major exhibitions are held annually in the spring. The permanent collection consists of the General Edward Clinton Collection of American paintings and works on paper; the Dr. and Mrs. William E. Ballard Collection of Japanese prints; the Fred and Estelle Marer Collection of Japanese prints and contemporary American, British, Korean, Mexican, and Japanese ceramics; the Mary Wig and James Johnson Collections of Japanese prints; the Dorothy Adler Routh Collection of cloisonné; the Wagner Collection of African sculpture; and American prints, drawings and photographs.

Cupertino

De Anza College - Euphrat Museum of Art

De Anza College, 21250 Stevens Creek Blvd., Cupertino, CA 95014

Tel: (408) 864-8836 *Fax:* (408) 864-8738

Internet Address: http://wwwdeanza.fhda.edu/Euphrat

Director: Jan Rindfleisch

Admission: voluntary contribution.

Attendance: 10,000 *Established:* 1971 *Membership:* Y *ADA Compliant:* Y

Open: **Late Sept. to Mid-June**, Tuesday to Thursday, 11am-4pm; Wednesday, 11am-4pm and 6pm-8pm; Saturday, 11am-2pm.

Facilities: **Gallery**; **Library** (300 volumes).

Activities: **Education Programs**; **Guided Tours** (groups by appointment); **Lectures**; **Temporary Exhibitions**; **Traveling Exhibitions.**

Publications: booklets (annual).

The Museum houses a collection of contemporary art in a variety of media and presents traveling and community exhibitions.

Davis

University of California, Davis - Richard L. Nelson Gallery & Fine Arts Collection

University of California, Davis, 124-125 Art Bldg., 1 Shields Ave., Davis, CA 95616 CAA

Tel: (916) 752-8500 *Fax:* (916) 754-9112

Internet Address: http://idea.ucdavis.edu/art/nelson/

Director: Mr. Price Amerson

Admission: voluntary contribution.

Attendance: 13,400 *Established:* 1976 *Membership:* Y *ADA Compliant:* Y

Open: **September to July**, Monday to Friday, noon-5pm; Sunday, 2pm-5pm.

Closed: Legal Holidays, Academic Holidays.

Facilities: **Gallery**; **Library** (550 volumes); **Shop.**

Activities: **Education Programs**; **Guided Tours**; **Lectures**; **Temporary Exhibitions**; **Traveling Exhibitions.**

Publications: exhibition catalogues (annual).

The Gallery focuses on contemporary and historical American and Northern California art. Also of possible interest on campus are the Design Gallery located in 145 Walker Hall (open: Mon-Fri, noon-5pm; Sun, 2pm-5-pm) and the Memorial Union Gallery located on the 2nd Floor of the Memorial Union Building (Mon-Fri, 9am-5pm).

El Cajon

Grossmont College - Hyde Gallery

8800 Grossmont College Drive, El Cajon, CA 92020
Tel: (619) 465-1700   *Fax:* (619) 644-7922
Internet Address: http://grossmont.gcccd.cc.ca.us/home
Art Director: Mr. Roger Churley
Admission: voluntary contribution.
Established: 1961   *Membership:* Y   *ADA Compliant:* Y
Open: By appointment.
Closed: Academic Holidays.
Facilities: **Gallery**.
Activities: **Concerts**; **Films**; **Gallery Talks**; **Temporary Exhibitions**; **Traveling Exhibitions**.
Publications: exhibit announcements.

The Gallery's collection consists of prints, photographs, and ceramics. It also mounts temporary exhibitions.

Fresno

California State University, Fresno - Phebe Conley Art Gallery ⓒ

5241 Maple Drive, Fresno, CA 93740
Tel: (559) 278-2516   *Fax:* (559) 278-4706
Internet Address: http://www.csufresno.edu
Open: Weekdays, 8am-noon and 1pm-5pm.
Facilities: **Exhibition Area**.
Activities: **Temporary Exhibitions**.

The Gallery presents temporary exhibitions including an annual student exhibition in the spring. Also of possible interest on campus are the President's Gallery located in the Thomas Administration Building (open: weekdays, 8am-5pm) and the Dean's Gallery located in Room 186 of the Music Building (open: weekdays, 8am-noon and 1pm-5pm).

Fullerton

California State University, Fullerton - Art Galleries ⓒ

800 N. State College Blvd., Visual Arts Center, Fullerton, CA 92634-9480
Tel: (714) 773-3262   *Fax:* (714) 773-3005
Internet Address: http://www.art.fullerton.edu/
Gallery Director: Prof. Mike McGee
Admission: suggested contribution-$3.00.
Established: 1967   *Membership:* Y   *ADA Compliant:* Y
Open: Monday to Tuesday, noon-4pm; Wednesday, 3pm-7pm; Thursday, noon-4pm;
          Sunday, 3pm-5pm.
Closed: Legal Holidays.
Facilities: **Auditorium** (150 seats); **Food Services** Cafeteria; **Galleries** (4; Main Gallery, 2,500
    square feet); **Library** (1,500 volumes); **Shop**; **Theatre**.
Activities: **Arts Festival**; **Education Programs**; **Films**; **Gallery Talks**; **Guided Tours**;
    Lectures; **Temporary Exhibitions**; **Traveling Exhibitions**.
Publications: exhibition catalogues (quarterly).

In all, there are four galleries at CSU Fullerton. The Main Art Gallery in the Visual Arts Center often features presentations of work of emerging and recognized contemporary artists. Since its opening in 1970, 137 exhibitions have been presented with the publication of some 60 catalogues. Integral to the program is the ability to provide space and physical assistance for artists to install environmental and ephemeral and transitory works. The mission of the gallery program is to bring carefully developed exhibitions to the campus. Three galleries exhibit student work. The East and West Galleries are scheduled to showcase the current work of graduate students.   The range of work is as broad as

California State University, Fullerton - Art Galleries, cont.

the varied disciplines represented in the graduate program. Exhibitions are changed each week in these galleries during the academic year. The Exit Gallery, under the supervision of a committee of undergraduates, showcases the individual and collaborative work of undergraduate students and also is changed on a weekly basis in order to give students the opportunity to show their current work.

Hayward

California State University, Hayward - Art Gallery *(CA)*

Art and Education Building, 25800 Carlos Bee Blvd, Hayward, CA   94542
Tel: (510) 881-3299
Internet Address: http://www.csuhayward.edu/UA/artgallery2.html
Director: Lew Carson
Admission: free.
Open: Monday to Tuesday, 11am-3pm; Wednesday to Thursday, 1pm-7pm.
Facilities: **Exhibition Area**.
Activities: **Temporary Exhibitions**.

The Gallery presents a series of temporary exhibitions by students, faculty and outside artists, including an annual juried student show.

Irvine

University of California, Irvine - The Art Gallery *(CA)*

University of California, Irvine, W. Peltason Road, Irvine, CA   92717-2771
Tel: (714) 824-8251   *Fax:* (714) 824-5297
Internet Address: http://www.arts.uci.edu/studioart/html/galleryinfo.html
Director: Mr.. Brad Spence
Admission: free.
Attendance: 10,000   *Established:* 1965   *Membership:* Y   *ADA Compliant:* Y
Open: **October to mid-June**, Monday to Saturday, noon-5pm.
Closed: New Year's Day, Easter, Christmas Eve to Christmas, Academic Holidays.
Facilities: **Gallery**; **Shop**.
Activities: **Guided Tours**; **Lectures**; **Traveling Exhibitions**.
Publications: exhibition catalogues.

The Gallery is devoted temporary exhibitions, including MFA student thesis exhibitions. Events include talks by faculty and visiting lecturers.

La Jolla

University of California, San Diego - Stuart Collection *(CA)*

University of California, San Diego, 406 University Center, La Jolla, CA   92093-0010
Tel: (619) 534-2117
Fax: (619) 534-9713
Internet Address: http://govt.uscd.edu/sj/sthome.html
Director: Ms. Mary L. Beebe
Admission: voluntary contribution.
Established: 1981
Membership: N   *ADA Compliant:* Y
Parking: parking permit required; obtain at campus entrance.
Open: Daily, 24 hours.
Facilities: **Sculpture throughout Campus** (obtain brochure and map from kiosk at campus entrance).
Activities: **Guided Tours** (group tours by appointment); **Lectures**; **Temporary Exhibitions**.
Publications: brochures.

The Stuart Collection of Sculpture at the University of California, San Diego seeks to enrich the cultural, intellectual, and scholarly life of the UCSD campus and of the San Diego community by

La Jolla, California

University of California, San Diego - Stuart Collection, cont.

building and maintaining a unique collection of site-specific works by leading artists of our time. The entire 1,200-acre campus, situated on a dramatic mesa above the Pacific Ocean, may be considered as sites for commissioned sculpture. The Collection is further distinguished from a traditional sculpture garden by integration of some of the projects with university buildings. Throughout the proposal, design and construction processes, artists select and tailor their work to a specific UCSD site. A significant number of the artists represented have been better known for their work in other media before creating their first permanent outdoor sculptures for the Stuart Collection. The collection includes works by Terry Allen, Michael Asher, Jackie Ferrara, Ian Hamilton Finlay, Richard Fleischner, Jenny Holzer, Robert Irwin, Bruce Nauman, Nam June Paik, Niki de Saint Phalle, Alexis Smith and William Wegman.

Alexis Smith, *Snake Path*, 1992, Stuart Collection, University of California, San Diego. Photograph courtesy of Stuart Collection, University of California, San Diego, California.

University of California, San Diego - University Art Gallery ©

Mandeville Center Building, 9500 Gilman Drive, La Jolla, CA   92093-0327
Tel: (619) 534-2864   *Fax:* (619) 534-0668
Internet Address: http://orpheus.ucsd.edu/gallery/info.html
Director: Ms. Kathleen Stoughton
Admission: free.
Attendance: 25,000   *Established:* 1974   *Membership:* Y   *ADA Compliant:* Y
Open: **September to June**, Tuesday to Saturday, 11am-4pm.
Closed: Legal Holidays.
Facilities: **Architecture** (designed by Quincy Jones, FAIA); **Exhibit Space** (2,800 square feet).
Activities: **Guided Tours**; **Lectures**; **Symposia**; **Temporary Exhibitions** (5-6/year).
Publications: exhibition catalogues (1-2/year).

The mission of the University Art Gallery is to exhibit, research, and interpret the art of contemporary artists of diverse ethnic backgrounds.

Lancaster

Antelope Valley College Gallery

3041 W. Avenue K, Lancaster, CA   93536
Tel: (805) 722-6395   *Fax:* (805) 722-3102
Internet Address: http://avc.edu/ArtGalry/index.html
Director: Ms. Patrica Hinds
Admission: free.
Open: Monday to Thursday, 9am-3pm and 7pm-9pm.
Facilities: **Gallery**.
Activities: **Temporary Exhibitions**.

The Gallery displays traditional and contemporary work by visiting professional artists, local artists, faculty, and students.

Long Beach

California State University, Long Beach - University Art Museum ©

1250 Bellflower Blvd., Long Beach, CA   90840-1901
Tel: (562) 985-5761   *Fax:* (562) 985-7602
Internet Address: http://www.csulb.edu/~uam
Director: Ms. Constance W. Glenn

California State University, Long Beach - University Art Museum, cont.

Admission: voluntary contribution.

Attendance: 55,000   *Established:* 1949

Membership: Y   *ADA Compliant:* Y

Parking: metered Parking Lot A or with reservation, Parking Lot 11.

Open: **Fall to Spring,**
Tuesday to Thursday, noon-8pm;
Friday to Sunday, noon-5pm.
Summer,
Call for hours.

Closed: Academic Holidays.

Facilities: **Auditorium**; **Food Services** Food Court on campus (many selections); **Library** (main campus library); **Outdoor Sculpture** (throughout campus, 21 works); **Theatre** (nearby university performing arts center).

View of Gallery, University Art Museum, during exhibit of "The Great American Pop Art Store: Multiples of the Sixties". Photograph courtesy of University Art Museum - California State University, Long Beach, California.

Activities: **Education Programs** (adults and students); **Films**; **Gallery Talks** (regularly scheduled; call for information); **Guided Tours** (on request; call for information); **Temporary Exhibitions**; **Traveling Exhibitions**.

Publications: brochures; exhibition catalogues (biennial); newsletter (biennial).

Centrally located on the CSULB campus, near the Richard and Karen Carpenter Performing Arts Center and the Pyramid Events Center, the UAM occupies a ground-level facility with ample parking. In addition to the 10,000 square-foot indoor space, the new museum extends outdoors, with attractive sites for sculpture and installations. The UAM presents diverse and imaginative exhibitions devoted to the work of contemporary artists. It offers artists a place to experiment, innovate, and present new work. The site-specific outdoor sculpture collection of twenty-one works sited across the 322-acre CSULB campus may be toured with a map available at the UAM. In addition to featuring the finest in contemporary art, the UAM introduces the accomplishments of the design community to West Coast audiences. The Museum's collections of site-specific outdoor sculpture and works of art on paper feature examples of the work of important contemporary masters. Presented as major exhibitions, offered for examination by students and scholars, and circulated to national institutions, the UAM collections are a permanent, regional visual arts resource and archive of contemporary culture.

Los Angeles

California State University, Los Angeles - Luckman Fine Arts Gallery ⒸⒶⒶ

Luckman Fine Arts Complex
5151 State University Drive
Los Angeles, CA 90032-8116

Tel: (213) 343-6604

Fax: (213) 343-6423

Internet Address: www.calstatela.edu/

Exec. Director: Dr. Clifford Harper

Admission: free.

Established: 1994

Parking: free on site.

Open: Monday to Thursday, noon-5pm;
Saturday, noon-5pm.

Facilities: **Gallery** (7000 square feet).

Activities: **Temporary Exhibitions**.

The Gallery features temporary exhibitions of the work of nationally recognized artists.

Exterior view of Luckman Fine Arts Complex, site of Luckman Fine Arts Gallery. Photograph courtesy of Luckman Fine Arts Gallery, Los Angeles, California.

Los Angeles City College - Da Vinci Art Gallery

Da Vinci Hall, 855 N. Vermont Ave., Los Angeles, CA 90029
Tel: (213) 953-4118
Internet Address: http://www.lacc.cc.ca.us
Director: Mr. Raoul De la Sota
Admission: free.
Attendance: 5,000   *Established:* 1963   *ADA Compliant:* Y
Parking: on street.
Open: Monday to Thursday, 10am-3pm and 6pm-8pm; Friday, 10am-2pm; Saturday, 10am-1pm.
Facilities: **Exhibition Area** (412 square feet, 802 square feet hanging space).
Activities: **Temporary Exhibitions** (6/year).

The Gallery mounts exhibitions of the work of professional artists, faculty, and students.

Loyola Marymount University - Laband Art Gallery ⓒ⁴⁴

7900 Loyola Blvd. (just north of LA International Airport), Los Angeles, CA 90045-8346
Tel: (310) 338-2880   *Fax:* (310) 338-6024
Internet Address: http://www.lmv.edu/colleges/cfa/art/laband
Director: Mr. Gordon Fuglie
Admission: voluntary contribution.
Attendance: 6,500   *Established:* 1985   *Membership:* N   *ADA Compliant:* Y
Parking: free parking.
Open: **Mid-August to May**, Wednesday to Friday, 11am-4pm; Saturday, noon-4pm.
Closed: Summer, Major Holidays.
Facilities: **Auditorium** (212 seats); **Gallery** (2,300 square feet).
Activities: **Arts Festival**; **Concerts**; **Dance Recitals**; **Education Programs**; **Films**; **Gallery Talks**; **Guided Tours**; **Lectures**.
Publications: brochures (occasional); exhibition catalogues (3/year).

A part of the LMU campus on bluffs overlooking Marina del Rey and the Pacific Ocean, the Laband is located in the Fritz B. Burns Fine Arts Center. Its exhibitions are defined by three concepts: (1) thematic projects featuring traditional and non-traditional spirituality; (2) the exploration of social and political issues; and (3) ethnological and/or anthropological displays. On occasion, an exhibition will encompass two or all three of these concerns. In addition, the gallery hosts the National Biennial Exhibition of the Los Angeles Printmaking Society, the only ongoing survey of recent American graphic art in Southern California. The adjacent Murphy Concert Hall is used for slide lectures or conferences related to the gallery's programs.

Mount St. Mary's College - José Drudis-Biada Gallery ⓒ⁴⁴

12001 Chalon Road, Los Angeles, CA 90049
Tel: (310) 954-4362
Internet Address: http://www.msmc.la.edu
Director: Jody Baral
Admission: free.
Established: 1974
Parking: free on site.
Open: **Academic Year**, Tuesday to Saturday, noon-5pm.
Closed: Academic Holidays.
Facilities: **Exhibition Area** (2000 square feet).
Activities: **Temporary Exhibitions**.

The Gallery presents temporary exhibitions of the work of Los Angeles artists.

Occidental College - Weingart and Arthur G. Coons Galleries ⓒ⁴⁴

1600 Campus Road, Los Angeles, CA 90041
Tel: (213) 259-2749   *Fax:* (213) 259-2930

Occidental College - Weingart and Arthur G. Coons Galleries, cont.

Internet Address: http://www.oxy.edu
Director: Ms. Linda Lyke
Open: Tuesday to Friday, 1pm-4:30pm.
Facilities: **Exhibition Area**.
Activities: **Temporary Exhibitions**.

The College presents temporary exhibitions of contemporary art in two galleries: The Arthur G. Coons Lower Gallery and Weingart Gallery.

Otis College of Art and Design - Galleries

Otis College of Art and Design., 9045 Lincoln Blvd., Los Angeles, CA   90045-3550
Tel: (310) 665-6905
Internet Address: http://www.otisart.edu
Director: Dr. Anne Ayres
Admission: free.
Attendance: 5,000   *Established:* 1940   *Membership:* Y   *ADA Compliant:* Y
Open: Tuesday to Saturday, 10am-5pm.
Closed: New Year's Eve to New Year's Day, Memorial Day, Christmas Eve to Christmas Day.
Facilities: **Galleries** (2).
Activities: **Temporary Exhibitions**; **Traveling Exhibitions**.
Publications: exhibition catalogues.

The College maintains two galleries. The Otis Gallery, located on the ground floor of the Goldsmith Campus, showcases national and international art and design. The Bolsky Gallery, a student-run facility, features the work of students.

UCLA at the Armand Hammer Museum of Art and Cultural Center ⓒ

10899 Wilshire Blvd. at Westwood Blvd. (Westwood Village)
Los Angeles, CA   90024-4201
Tel: (310) 443-7000
Fax: (310) 443-7099
TDDY: (310) 443-7094
Internet Address:
  http://www.arts.ucla.edu/hammer/main.html
Director: Mr. Henry Hopkins
Admission: fee: adult-$4.50, child-free, student-$3.00, senior-$3.00.
Attendance: 120,000   *Established:* 1994
Membership: Y   *ADA Compliant:* Y
Parking: pay, under museum, $2.75 for 1st 3 hours.
Open: Tuesday to Wednesday, 11am-7pm;
    Thursday, 11am-9pm;
    Friday to Saturday, 11am-7pm;
    Sunday, 11am-5pm.
Closed: Independence Day, Thanksgiving Day,
    Christmas Day.

View from the courtyard of UCLA at the Armand Hammer Museum of Art and Cultural Center. Photograph by Tim Strett-Porter, courtesy of UCLA at the Armand Hammer Museum of Art and Cultural Center, Los Angeles, California.

Facilities: **Architecture** (1990, designed by Edward Larrabee Barnes); **Exhibition Area** (14,000 square feet); **Food Services** Courtyard Café (food cart serving light refreshments, Tues-Sun, 11am-5pm); **Library** (55,000 volumes); **Rental/Sales Gallery** (Tues-Sat, 11am-4pm; Sun, noon-4pm); **Sculpture Garden**; **Shop** (books, jewelry, prints, posters, and gifts).
Activities: **Children's Programs**; **Gallery Talks**; **Guided Tours** (Tues-Sun, 1pm; groups 20+, reserve in advance, $3/person); **Lectures**; **Readings**; **Temporary Exhibitions**; **Traveling Exhibitions**.
Publications: collection catalogue; exhibition catalogues; newsletter.

UCLA at the Armand Hammer Museum of Art and Cultural Center, cont.

Located in the heart of Westwood Village, UCLA at the Armand Hammer Museum of Art and Cultural Center serves as a meeting place and showcase for the arts. Throughout the year, visitors can enjoy a variety of arts programs organized by UCLA or major national and international institutions. In addition to offering a diverse schedule of historical and contemporary art exhibitions, the Museum presents music, dance, poetry, video, gallery talks, symposia, and docent tours for people of all ages. The Armand Hammer Collection features primarily Impressionist and Post-Impressionist paintings by such artists as Mary Cassatt, Claude Monet, Camille Pissarro, John Singer Sargent, and Vincent van Gogh. Paintings by John Constable, Pablo Picasso and others from UCLA's collections are also on view. Exhibitions drawn from the Armand Hammer Daumier and Contemporaries Collection are also shown on a rotating basis and include the painting, sculpture and lithography of 19th-century French artist Honoré Daumier and his contemporaries. The Museum also displays exhibitions drawn from the extensive collection of the UCLA Grunwald Center for the Graphic Arts (see separate listing), one of the finest university collections of graphic arts in the country. The Museum staff also administers the Franklin D. Murphy Sculpture Garden, one of the most distinguished outdoor sculpture collections in the country. Spanning more than five acres on UCLA's North Campus, the Sculpture Garden features over 70 works by such artists as Jean Arp, Alexander Calder, Claire Falkenstein, Barbara Hepworth, Gaston Lachaise, Jacques Lipchitz, Henri Matisse, Henry Moore, Isamu Noguchi, Auguste Rodin, David Smith and Francisco Zuñiga.

UCLA - Grunwald Center for the Graphic Arts at the Armand Hammer Museum of Art and Cultural Center (C44)

10899 Wilshire Blvd. at Westwood Blvd.
(3rd Floor, Gallery Level)
Los Angeles, CA 90024-4201
Tel: (310) 443-7076
Fax: (310) 443-7099
TDDY: (310) 443-7094
Internet Address:
   http://www.ucla.edu/museums/hammer_frame.html
Director: Mr. David Rodes
Admission: free.
Attendance: 76,000   *Established:* 1956
Membership: Y   *ADA Compliant:* Y
Parking: underground garage - $2.75 for 3 hours.
Open: Monday to Friday, 10am-4pm, by appointment only.
Facilities: **Library** (55,000 volumes); **Print Study Room** (by
   appointment, (310) 443-7078).
Publications: books; exhibition catalogues.

Located on the third floor (gallery level) of the Armand Hammer Museum of Art and Cultural Center at UCLA, the Grunwald Center is one of the finest university collections of graphic arts in the nation. The Center's holdings consist of more than 35,000 prints, drawings, photographs and artists'

George Cruikshank, *Snuffing Our Boney*, 1814, etching with hand coloring. Grunwald Center for the Graphic Arts at UCLA. Reproduction courtesy of Grunwald Center for the Graphic Arts at UCLA, Los Angeles, California.

books dating from the Renaissance to the present. A primary resource for teaching and research, the Center serves UCLA students, faculty, and the public. Independently and in association with major museums and libraries around the world, the Center organizes exhibitions and publishes catalogues. The Center provides a valuable resource for artists, art historians and museum professionals and is open by appointment only. Among the 5,000 pre-19th-century prints and drawings held by the Center are works by Canaletto, Dürer, Mantegna, Rembrandt, and Tiepolo. A comprehensive collection of 19th- and 20th-century art includes works by Cézanne, Toulouse-Lautrec, Kirchner, Kollwitz, Nolde, Matisse, and Picasso, as well as by contemporary artists such as Carlos Almaraz, Richard Diebenkorn, Jasper Johns, Barbara Morgan, Joyce Treiman, and June Wayne. The Richard Vogler George Cruikshank archives contain over 3,000 prints, drawings, and illustrations by the English caricaturist. Additionally, the Center is the repository for the complete archives of Corita Kent and the Tamarind Lithography Workshop. Japanese works on

UCLA - Grunwald Center for the Graphic Arts at Armand Hammer Museum, cont.

paper are also represented with a sizeable archive. The Center's holdings are highlighted by a collection of 20th-century artists' books and also include a considerable number of 20th-century American photographs.

University of Southern California - Fisher Gallery ⓒ

823 Exposition Blvd., Harris Hall (between Figueroa and Watt Way)
Los Angeles, CA   90089-0292
Tel: (213) 740-4561
Fax: (213) 740-7676
Internet Address: http://www.usc.edu/dept/Fischer_Gallery
Director: Dr. Selma Holo
Admission: free.
Attendance: 11,000   *Established:* 1939   *Membership:* N   *ADA Compliant:* Y
Parking: on campus ($6) or metered on Exposition Blvd. & Vermont Ave.
Open: **September to June**, Tuesday to Friday, noon-5pm.
          During Exhibitions, Saturday, 11am-3pm.
          Summer, call for hours.
Facilities: **Galleries**.
Activities: **Films**; **Gallery Talks**; **Guided Tours** (during exhibition, Tues, 1pm); **Lectures**;
    Permanent Exhibits; **Temporary Exhibitions**; **Traveling Exhibitions**.
Publications: exhibition catalogues.

Fisher Gallery, the accredited art museum of the University of Southern California, offers exhibitions ranging from antiquities and Old Master artists through contemporary works by artists with local, national and international reputations. In addition to showing the permanent collection, the Gallery presents traveling exhibitions and organizes its own exhibitions. The exhibition schedule includes regular year-long exhibitions of the permanent collection in the Walter and Hertha Klinger Gallery in the Quinn Wing and changing exhibitions (of about 12 weeks duration) in the main galleries. Between the two facilities is a reading room where catalogs and other relevant materials are placed to encourage reflection by Museum audiences. Small focus exhibitions or orientation materials are also placed in the reading room. Klinger Gallery, Quinn Wing, the museum's permanent collection exhibition space, is open during the academic year and by appointment during the summer months. Permanent collections include groups of 19th-century American landscapes; 18th- and 19th-century Northern European paintings; 18th-century British portraiture; 19th-century Barbizon paintings; and 20th-century works on paper, paintings, and sculpture.

Malibu

Pepperdine University - Frederick R. Weisman Museum of Art ⓒ

Pepperdine Universit
24255 Pacific Coast Hwy.
Malibu, CA   90263
Tel: (310) 456-4851
Fax: (310) 456-4556
Internet Address: http://www.pepperdine.edu
Director: Mr. Michael Zakian
Admission: free.
Attendance: 20,000   *Established:* 1992
Membership: Y   *ADA Compliant:* Y
Parking: free.
Open: Tuesday to Sunday, 11am-5pm.
Closed: Memorial Day, Independence Day,
          Labor Day, Thanksgiving Day,
          Christmas Day to New Year's Week.
Facilities: **Exhibition Area** (3,000 square feet).

Exterior view of Frederick R. Weisman Museum of Art. Photograph courtesy of Frederick R. Weisman Museum of Art, Pepperdine University, Malibu, California.

Malibu, California

Pepperdine University - Frederick R. Weisman Museum of Art, cont.
Activities: Temporary Exhibitions.

The Museum hosts a new temporary exhibition of historic or contemporary art every two months as well as senior student exhibitions. Selections from the Frederick R. Weisman Art Foundation are usually on view in the mezzanine gallery. The permanent collection focuses primarily on 20th-century American and contemporary California art. For theatre guests, the Museum is open one hour prior to evening performances through first intermission.

Mission Viejo

Saddleback College Art Gallery ☺

Fine Arts Complex, 28000 Marguerite Parkway, Mission Viejo, CA   92692
Tel: (714) 582-4924   **Fax:** (714) 347-0580
Internet Address: http://iserver.saddleback.cc.ca.us/div/fac/artexhibit.html
Gallery Director: Ms. Karen Collins-McGuire
Open: September to May, Mon to Weds, noon-4pm; Thurs, 5pm-8pm; Fri, 10am-2pm.
Facilities: Gallery.
Activities: Temporary Exhibitions.

The Art Gallery presents temporary exhibitions featuring the work of locally, regionally and nationally recognized artists. Shows are chosen for "their ability to provoke thought and to challenge assumptions and pre-conceived ideas, as well as their social, political and cultural focus". There is a juried student exhibition in May of each year.

Monterey Park

East Los Angeles College - Vincent Price Gallery

Building 5, 1301 Avenida Cesar Chavez, Monterey Park, CA   91754
Tel: (213) 265-8841
Internet Address: http://members.aol.com/vpgallery/PriceGallery.html
Director: Mr. Thomas Silliman
Admission: free.
Parking: on street in front of campus.
Open: Monday, noon-3pm; Tuesday, noon-3pm and 6pm-9pm;Wednesday to Friday, noon-3pm.
Facilities: Gallery.
Activities: Guided Tours.

It was in 1951 that Price first visited the campus of East Los Angeles College. Invited to lecture on the "Aesthetic Responsibilities of the Citizen," Price arrived to find he was (in his words) "speaking in a Quonset hut on a mud flat." Struck by the spirit of the students and the community's need for the opportunity to experience original art works first hand, Price donated some ninety pieces to establish the first "teaching art collection" owned by a community college in the United States. Over the decades, Price and other patrons donated to the collection with the goal of illustrating diverse periods, styles, media, and techniques. Facilities consist of the main gallery, a smaller permanent gallery, and an exhibit preparation workshop. Assembled with works from private and public art collections, the Gallery's own collection, and student art work, the exhibits produced by the Gallery are curated, prepared and installed by students as part of an educational program. Meant to be a hands-on teaching tool, the collection of over 2,000 works features a variety of artistic techniques: wood carving from Africa, New Guinea, and Pre-Columbian Mexico; ceramics from ancient Peru, Mexico and Etruria; Aztec and ancient Egyptian sculpture; watercolor painting by William Bryce; oil and acrylic painting by Hans Burckhardt and Rafael Coronel; ink drawing by Frank Romero and Joseph Giasco; pastel drawing by John Paul Jones and Howard Warshaw; pencil drawing by William Wiley, Aristide Maillol and Eugene Delacroix; lithography by Jose Luis Cuevas, Fritz Scholder and Roy Lichtenstein; etchings by Peter Winslow Milton and Francisco Goya; serigraphy by Friedenrich Hundertwasser and Victor Vasarely; woodcut printmaking by Ito Shinsui and Albrecht Dürer; and gouache painting by Paul Vurlin and Jesus "Chucho" Reyes. Other important artists represented include Bonnard, Daumier, Dali, Diebenkorn, Goya, Hiroshige I, Hockney, Manet, Piranesi, Picasso, Redon, Rothko, Rouault, Siqueiros, Tamayo, and Utrillo.

Moraga

St. Mary's College - Hearst Art Gallery

1928 St. Mary's Road (opposite Soda Activity Center)
Moraga, CA 94575
Tel: (510) 631-4379   *Fax:* (510) 376-5128
Internet Address:
    http://gaelnet.stmarys-ca.edu/ gallery/intro.html
Dean for Academic Resources:
    Ms. Stephanie Banquet
Admission: suggested contribution-$1.00.
Attendance: 16,000   *Established:* 1977
Membership: Y   *ADA Compliant:* Y
Parking: free on site.
Open: Wednesday to Sunday, 11am-4:30pm.
Closed: Legal Holidays, Between Exhibits.

William Keith, *Gray Rain Clouds; Cattle in Meadow*, late 1880's. Hearst Art Gallery. Photograph courtesy of Hearst Art Gallery, Saint Mary's College, Moraga, California.

Facilities: **Food Services** (campus coffee shop); **Galleries** (2); **Picnic Area**; **Shop**.
Activities: **Guided Tours** (groups, arrangements in advance); **Lectures**; **Temporary Exhibitions**
    (5/year); **Traveling Exhibitions**.
Publications: exhibition catalogues; leaflets.

The Hearst Art Gallery was built with the aid of a grant from the William Randolph Hearst Foundation. It opened in 1977, replacing a smaller William Keith Gallery originally established in 1934. The College had already been collecting and exhibiting art for several decades, including many works by William Keith (1838-1911), a key figure in the history of California art. The William Keith Collection continues as a special feature of the Gallery, with a selection of Keith's paintings always on view. The Gallery actively collects and exhibits 19th- and 20th-century California landscapes by other artists and in other media as well. Christian imagery in art is another focus of the collection and of occasional exhibitions. From German 15th-century carved-wood Madonnas, to Russian and Greek icons, to contemporary artists' responses to traditional Christian themes, the Gallery examines the religious tradition that has inspired so much of Western art. Each year a student show of work by art majors and other undergraduates is organized and installed by a student committee in consultation with the gallery curator. Saint Mary's College has a collection of about 2,200 art objects. Some highlights include 150 paintings by William Keith (1838-1911); 150 other American paintings, primarily by late 19th- to early 20th-century artists, including Albert Bierstadt, Norton Bush, William Coulter, Armin Hansen, George Inness, Maurice Logan and J. Francis Murphy; 21 drawings and watercolors by Morris Graves; 32 etchings by renowned California printmaker Roi Partridge; 20 drawings and prints and one oil painting by California artist Frank Van Sloun; 577 photographs of California landscapes by Stanley Truman; and large scale color prints by modern masters Manuel Neri, Nathan Oliveira and Wayne Thiebaud.

Northridge

California State University, Northridge - Art Galleries

Art Dome, Music Lawn 236, 18111 Nordhoff Street, Northridge, CA 91330-8299
Tel: (818) 677-2226   *Fax:* (818) 677-5910
Internet Address: http://www.csun.edu/~hfart009/
Director: Ms. Louise Lewis
Admission: free.
Attendance: 36,000   *Established:* 1972   *Membership:* Y   *ADA Compliant:* Y
Parking: $1.75 in student lots; free on weekends.
Open: **September to May**,
        Monday to Saturday, noon-4pm; Tuesday to Friday, 10am-4pm, during exhibitions.
Closed: June to August, University Holidays.
Facilities: **Food Services** (on campus); **Gallery**; **Shop** (art books, cards, gift items, ethnic artifacts).
Activities: **Concerts**; **Dance Recitals**; **Education Programs**; **Gallery Talks**; **Guided Tours**
    (docent tours for groups, reserve in advance); **Lectures**; **Temporary Exhibitions** (4-5/year).

California State University, Northridge - Art Galleries, cont.

Publications: exhibition catalogues (4-5/year).

The Art Gallery conducts an art program from international and multicultural perspectives. Historical and contemporary, thematic and media-oriented exhibitions are presented, to reflect the broad spectrum of art in today's global society and to accommodate an equally broad audience. Special events such as lectures, performances, video and film presentations, symposia, and tours have also become an integral part of the Gallery program. CSU Northridge Galleries are located in temporary space as a result of the earthquake in 1994; a new building is scheduled to open in the spring of 2000. CSU Northridge Art Galleries do not maintain a permanent collection. Temporary exhibitions are displayed in the Performing Arts Center Lobby, USU (hours: Mon-Fri, noon-2pm and one hour before performances); and changing exhibitions of works by students, faculty and Master's Degree candidates are featured in the North Gallery at Halsted Houses 1102 (hours vary; call (818) 677-2156).

Oakland

California College of Arts and Crafts - Steven H. Oliver Art Center ©

5212 Broadway at College Ave., Oakland, CA 94618

Tel: (510) 594-3650   *Fax:* (510) 428-1346

Internet Address: http://www.ccac-art.edu

C.E.O.: Mr. Lorne Buckman

Admission: free.

Attendance: 32,000   *Established:* 1907   *Membership:* Y   *ADA Compliant:* Y

Open: Monday to Friday, 10am-4pm; Saturday, noon-4pm.

Closed: Legal Holidays.

Facilities: **Gallery**.

Activities: **Education Programs**; **Gallery Talks**; **Guided Tours** (for organized groups); **Lecture Series**; **Temporary Exhibitions**.

Publications: exhibition catalogues.

Founded at the height of the Arts and Crafts movement, CCAC offers programs of study in drawing, painting, printmaking, ceramics, glass, jewelry/metals arts, sculpture, textiles, wood/furniture, photography, film/video/performance, fashion design, graphic design, industrial design, illustration, architecture and interior architecture. The Oliver Center presents temporary exhibitions and programs in the fields of art, architecture, and design. CCAC has two campuses. The Oliver Art Center is located on the Oakland campus (please see separate listing for the galleries at the San Francisco campus).

Mills College Art Gallery ©

5000 MacArthur Blvd., Oakland, CA 94613

Tel: (510) 430-2164   *Fax:* (510) 430-3168

Internet Address: http://www.mills.edu

Director: Dr. Katherine B. Crum

Admission: voluntary contribution.

Attendance: 9,000   *Established:* 1925   *Membership:* Y   *ADA Compliant:* Y

Open: **September to May**, Tuesday to Saturday, 11am-4pm; Sunday, noon-4pm.

Facilities: **Galleries** (2).

Activities: **Lecture Series**; **Temporary Exhibitions**.

Publications: brochures; newsletter; posters.

Mills College presents temporary exhibitions of both historical and contemporary art by nationally and internationally known artists. Work by undergraduate art majors and graduate degree candidates is also exhibited each year. The Mills art collection has a national reputation, and works are constantly on loan to museums around the country. The collection consists of more than 6,000 works on paper, paintings, ceramics, textiles, objects, and antiquities and includes works by artists such as Dürer, Rembrandt, Delacroix, Cézanne, Nolde, Leger, Picasso and Braque, as well as a strong group of German expressionist prints, Asian textiles and ceramics, and works by contemporary California artists.

Orange

Chapman University - Guggenheim Gallery ⓒ⁴⁴

333 N. Glassell St., Orange, CA   92666
Tel: (714) 997-6729
Internet Address: http://www.chapman.edu/comm/art/c_gall.htm
Director: Ms. Maggi Owens
Admission: free.
Open: call for hours.
Facilities: **Gallery**.
Activities: **Temporary Exhibitions**.

The Gallery provides a venue for artists and exhibitions that question aesthetic conventions and the role of the arts in society, addressing artistic and social issues that are often timely and provocative. The gallery encourages programming that crosses cultural boundaries and offers exhibition opportunities for emerging under-recognized and minority artists. The Guggenheim Gallery sponsors an annual schedule of exhibitions that includes four major shows of works by local, national and internationally known artists, two department-wide student shows, one at the end of each semester, as well as small group and solo shows for junior art majors and graduating seniors. The departmental show at the end of each semester is a student production from the initial call for entries, through the hanging, opening reception to the final de-installation. Junior-year art majors exhibit their work in small group shows and seniors have individual exhibitions of their work. When the schedule allows, some of the department's more ambitious students will mount shows of their most recent work.

Pasadena

Art Center College of Design - Alyce de Roulet Williamson Gallery ⓒ⁴⁴

1700 Lida St., Pasadena, CA   91103
Tel: (818) 396-2244   *Fax:* (818) 405-9104
Internet Address: http://www.artcenter.edu/exhibit/williamson.html
Director: Mr. Stephen Nowlin
Admission: free.
Established: 1991
Parking: free on site.
Open: Tuesday to Wednesday, noon-5pm; Thursday, noon-9pm; Friday to Sunday, noon-5pm.
Facilities: **Gallery** (4,600 square feet); **Sculpture Garden**.
Activities: **Temporary Exhibitions**.

The Alyce de Roulet Williamson Gallery is located in the center of the college's landmark steel-and-glass International Style building, the gallery features temporary exhibitions of work by both established and emerging fine artists and designers. Works by students are exhibited year-round in a separate gallery.

Pasadena City College Art Gallery and Boone Sculpture Garden

1570 E. Colorado Blvd., Pasadena, CA   91150
Tel: (626) 585-7412
Internet Address: http://www.paccd.cc.ca.us
Parking: parking lots, east side of campus.
Open: Call for hours.
Facilities: **Gallery**; **Sculpture Garden** (1996 design by Jody Pinto).
Activities: **Permanent Exhibits**; **Temporary Exhibitions** (8/academic year).
Publications: exhibition catalogues; posters.

The Art Division mounts temporary exhibitions of professional work during the academic year including a guest-curated show, a group faculty show, and an artist-in-residence exhibit. There are additionally a juried student show, a scholarship exhibition, and a summer group series featuring student independent studies. The Division is also closely involved in the development of a permanent contemporary art collection on exhibition in the Shatford Library and in support of the Boone Sculpture Garden.

Pomona

California State Polytechnic University - The W. Keith and Jean Kellogg Art Gallery ⒸⒶ

Student Union Building, 3801 W. Temple Ave, Pomona, CA   91768
Tel: (909) 869-4302   *Fax:* (909) 869-4939
Internet Address: http://www.csupomona.edu/art/Gallery.html
Gallery Director: Mr. Patrick Merrill
Admission: free.
Open: Tuesday to Friday, 11am-4pm; Saturday, noon-4pm.
Facilities: **Galleries** (2; 2,000 square feet).
Activities: **Readings**; **Temporary Exhibitions** (5/year).

Located at the front of the Student Union building, the Kellogg Art Gallery holds five exhibitions throughout the fall, winter, and spring quarters. In January, the gallery presents the annual Ink and Clay Juried Exhibition featuring the finest print and ceramic art from the Southern California region. At the end of the spring quarter the best of Cal Poly's graduating art students present their Senior Projects.

Rancho Cucamonga

Chaffey College - Wignall Museum/Gallery

Chaffey College, 5885 N. Haven Ave., Rancho Cucamonga, CA   91737-3002
Tel: (909) 941-2703   *Fax:* (909) 941-2783
Administrative Director: Ms. Virginia M. Eaton
Admission: voluntary contribution.
Attendance: 30,000   *Established:* 1972   *Membership:* Y   *ADA Compliant:* Y
Parking: on campus, Lot #5.
Open: **August to May**, Monday to Friday, 10am-4pm; Sunday, noon-4pm.
Closed: Major Holidays, Academic Holidays.
Facilities: **Gallery**.
Activities: **Arts Festival**; **Concerts**); **Education Programs**; **Guided Tours** (groups, reservations in advance); **Lectures**; **Performances**; **Temporary Exhibitions**; **Traveling Exhibitions**.
Publications: exhibition catalogues.

The Gallery features temporary exhibits of work by college faculty and students, and occasional displays of artwork by local artists or on loan from local collectors. The Gallery also presents a schedule of cultural activities, including concerts, lectures, artist receptions, and readings.

Riverside

La Sierra University - Brandstater Gallery

4700 Pierce St.
Riverside, CA   92515
Tel: (909) 785-2959
Fax: (909) 785-2901
Internet Address: http://www.lasierra.edu/art
Director: Ms. Susan Patt
Admission: free.
Parking: free on site.
Open: Monday to Thursday,
         10am-noon and 1:30pm-4pm;
         Sunday, 2pm-5pm.
Closed: University Holidays.
Facilities: **Gallery** (1200 square feet).
Activities: **Temporary Exhibitions**.
Publications: exhibition catalogues (occasional).

Exterior view of La Sierra University Visual Art Center, site of Brandstater Gallery. Photograph courtesy of Brandstater Gallery, Riverside California.

La Sierra University - Brandstater Gallery. cont.

The Gallery features regularly scheduled temporary exhibitions of the work of students, alumni, and regionally and nationally recognized artists.

UCR/California Museum of Photography ⒸⒶ

Exterior view of UCR/California Museum of Photography. Photograph courtesy of UCR/California Museum of Photography, Riverside, California.

3824 Main Street (Main St. Pedestrian Mall & University Ave.)
Riverside, CA 92501
Tel: (909) 784-3686   *Fax:* (909) 787-4797
Internet Address: http://www.cmp.ucr.edu
Director: Prof. Jonathan Green
Admission: fee: adult-$2, child-free, student-$1, senior-$1.
Attendance: 35,000   *Established:* 1973
Membership: Y   *ADA Compliant:* Y
Open: Wednesday to Saturday, 11am-5pm;
    Sunday, noon-5pm.
Closed: Easter, Thanksgiving Day, Christmas Day,
    New Year's Eve to New Year's Day.
Facilities: **Galleries**; **Shop**.
Activities: **Guided Tours**; **Lectures**; **Temporary Exhibitions**;
    Traveling Exhibitions.
Publications: exhibition catalogues.

UCR/California Museum of Photography, a facility of the University of California, Riverside, is dedicated to promoting the understanding of photography and related media through collection, research, exhibition, and instruction. UCR/CMP showcases photography and related imaging technologies and the apparatuses that support these visual forms. UCR/CMP is housed in an acclaimed four-story facility on Riverside's popular pedestrian mall. Renovated by architect Stanley Saitowitz, this one-time dime store now portrays a machine in the service of art. Saitowitz's design treats the building as a metaphor of the camera. Such elements as a third-floor, walk-in camera obscura built into the building's outer facade, dark rubber floors, and exposed air ducts produce an environment in which the people inside may be seen as the camera's film, absorbing light and information, becoming vehicles for transmission of the museum experience. Across from the Museum's admissions desk is the Net Gallery, where the public can explore UCR/CMP's World Wide Web site, as well as "visit" the collections of other museums from around the world. Many items from the permanent collections and archives can be seen in the museum's main-level. In addition to the museum's permanent gallery installation, UCR/CMP presents changing exhibitions that address visual culture as fine art, as social commentary, and as history. UCR/CMP's permanent collections include the Keystone-Mast archive of 350,000 stereographs dating from 1870 to 1940, the Bingham Technology Collection of 10,000 cameras and viewing devices, and the University Print Collection, which features work by well-known artists such as Ansel Adams, Lewis Baltz, Francis Bedford, Manuel Alvarez Bravo, Larry Clark, Elliot Erwitt, Walker Evans, Francis Frith, William Klein, Barbara Morgan, Albert Renger-Patzch, Adam Vroman, Carlton Watkins, and Edward Weston.

University of California, Riverside - Sweeney Art Gallery ⒸⒶ

Watkins House, 1701 Canyon Crest Drive, Riverside, CA 92521
Tel: (909) 787-3755   *Fax:* (909) 787-3798
Internet Address: http://www.sweeney.ucr.edu
Director: Ms. Katherine V. Warren
Admission: voluntary contribution.
Attendance: 7,500   *Established:* 1963   *Membership:* Y   *ADA Compliant:* Y
Open: Tuesday to Friday, 11am-4pm; Saturday to Sunday, noon-4pm.
Closed: Legal Holidays.
Facilities: **Gallery**; **Library** (500 volumes).
Activities: **Lectures**; **Temporary Exhibitions** (12/year); **Traveling Exhibitions**.
Publications: exhibition catalogues; newsletter (quarterly).

University of California, Riverside - Sweeney Art Gallery, cont.

The Gallery, located in Watkins House across from the main campus of the University of California, Riverside presents temporary exhibitions and holds a small, but growing, permanent collection. The Gallery's exhibitions are integrated with the University curriculum when possible. The Gallery will be moving to the new Sweeney/Rubin Alumni and Visitor's Center at the entrance to the campus upon its completion. The building's design is by Mehrdad Yazdani of Dworsky Associates, Los Angeles.

Rohnert Park

Sonoma State University - University Art Gallery ⓒᴬᴬ

1801 E. Cotati Ave., Rohnert Park, CA 94928
Tel: (707) 664-2295   *Fax:* (707) 664-2505
Internet Address: http://www.sonoma.edu/ArtGallery/
Director: Mr. Michael Schwager
Admission: free.
Established: 1978   *Membership:* Y   *ADA Compliant:* Y
Open: **September to May**, Tuesday to Friday, 11am-4pm.
          October to May, Saturday to Sunday, noon-4pm.
Facilities: **Exhibition Area** (2 galleries, 2,500 square feet); **Shop**.
Activities: **Art Auction**; **Education Programs**; **Lectures**; **Temporary Exhibitions**.
Publications: exhibition catalogues; posters.

The University Art Gallery is devoted to changing exhibitions of works of art from important private and public collections as well as new work directly from the artists' studios. The Gallery presents exhibitions in two adjoining galleries, public lectures, and educational outreach programs and also publishes catalogues and brochures on contemporary artists of regional, national, and international significance. A brief list of artists whose work has been exhibited includes Terry Allen, Jennifer Bartlett, Enrique Chagoya, Chuck Close, Sue Coe, Viola Frey, Mineko Grimmer, The Guerrilla Girls, Mildred Howard, Mike Kelly, Maya Lin, James Luna, Manuel Ocampo, Judy Pfaff, John Roloff, Joan Snyder, Bill Viola, William Wegman, and Terry Winters. In addition to programs devoted to artists from outside the University, the Art Gallery presents several exhibitions featuring the work of faculty and students. Annual exhibitions by graduating BFA students and the Juried Student Show are presented each spring. Work by the Sonoma State University Art Department faculty is shown in the Gallery every other year. The Art Gallery also hosts a variety of events, including the annual Art from the Heart fundraising art auction, which features donated works of art by emerging and nationally recognized artists from around the country.

Sacramento

California State University, Sacramento - Art Galleries ⓒᴬᴬ

Fine Arts Building, Sinclair (off State University Drive), Sacramento, CA 95819
Tel: (916) 278-6166
Internet Address: http://www.asn.csus.edu/art/
Admission: free.
Open: **Academic Year**, Daily, noon-5pm.
Facilities: **Galleries** (2).
Activities: **Temporary Exhibitions**.

The University boasts two galleries, both located in the Fine Arts Building. The Robert Else Gallery and the Witt Gallery mounts temporary exhibitions throughout the academic year of work by professional artists, undergraduates and graduate students, including annual juried shows.

San Bernardino

California State University, San Bernardino - Robert V. Fullerton Art Museum

Visual Arts Center, 5500 University Parkway, San Bernardino, CA 92324
Tel: (909) 880-7373   *Fax:* (909) 880-7068
Internet Address: http://www.csusb.edu
Director of Operations: Ms. Eva Kirsch

California State University, San Bernardino - R.V. Fullerton Art Museum, cont.

Admission: voluntary contribution.

Attendance: 12,000   *Established:* 1972   *Membership:* Y   *ADA Compliant:* Y

Parking: pay on site - $1.50.

Open: **Fall to Spring**,
   Tuesday to Wednesday, 11am-5pm;
   Thursday, 1pm-7pm;
   Friday, 10am-4pm;
   Saturday to Sunday, noon-5pm.
   Summer, call for hours.

Closed: Legal Holidays.

Facilities: **Gallery** (6,500 square feet).

Activities: **Education Programs; Temporary Exhibitions; Traveling Exhibitions.**

Publications: collection catalogue; exhibition catalogues (annual).

In addition to presenting loan exhibitions, the museum displays objects from its permanent collection, including Asian and Etruscan ceramics, Huichol paintings, African sculpture, Egyptian antiquities, prints, and drawings.

Shawabti figure, c.1303-1200 B.C., New Kingdom, Dynasty XIX, height 9 3/8 inches, painted wood. Harer Family Trust Collection, Robert V. Fullerton Art Museum. Photograph courtesy of California State University, San Bernardino, California.

San Diego

San Diego State University - University Art Gallery ⓒᴬᴬ

5500 Campanile Drive, San Diego, CA   92182-4805

Tel: (619) 594-4941

Fax: (619) 594-1217

Internet Address: http://psfa/sdsu.edu/school_of_art/maingallery/maingallery.html

Director: Ms. Tina Yapelli

Admission: voluntary contribution.

Membership: Y   *ADA Compliant:* Y

Open: **September to May**, Monday to Thursday, noon-4pm; Saturday, noon-4pm.

Closed: Legal Holidays.

Facilities: **Gallery.**

Activities: **Education Programs; Lectures; Temporary Exhibitions; Traveling Exhibitions.**

Publications: brochures (triennial); exhibition catalogues (triennial).

The University Art Gallery features major exhibitions by nationally and internationally known contemporary artists. There are two additional galleries on campus. Graduate thesis exhibitions and select group shows are held in The Everett Gee Jackson Gallery, and undergraduate exhibits are primarily mounted in The Flor y Canto Gallery.

San Francisco

Academy of Art College Galleries ⓒᴬᴬ

410 Bush St., San Francisco, CA   94108

Tel: (415) 274-2204   *Fax:* (415) 274-8672

Internet Address: http://www.academyart.edu

Vice President: Ms. Ann Lawrence

Open: Monday to Saturday, 10am-5pm.

Facilities: **Galleries** (3).

Activities: **Temporary Exhibitions.**

The College also maintains galleries at 180 New Montgomery Street (415-788-6044) and 551 Sutter Street (415-274-8600). Call for hours. The galleries display temporary exhibitions of the work of students, faculty, and professional artists.

San Francisco, California

California College of Arts and Crafts - Tecoah and Thomas Bruce Galleries ⒸⒶⒶ

San Francisco Campus, 450 Irwin St. at 16th and Wisconsin, San Francisco, CA   94107
Tel: (417) 703-9540
Internet Address: http://www.ccac-art.edu
Dir, Inst for Exhibitions & Pub Prgms: Mr. Lawrence M. Rinder
Admission: free.
Established: 1907
Open: Monday to Friday, 9am-4pm; Saturday to Sunday, noon-4pm.
Facilities: **Galleries**.
Activities: **Temporary Exhibitions**.

Founded at the height of the Arts and Crafts movement, CCAC offers programs of study in drawing, painting, printmaking, ceramics, glass, jewelry/metals arts, sculpture, textiles, wood/furniture, photography, film/video/performance, fashion design, graphic design, industrial design, illustration, architecture and interior architecture. The Bruce Galleries present temporary exhibitions and programs in the fields of art, architecture, and design. CCAC has two campuses. The Tecoah and Thomas Bruce Galleries are located on the San Francisco campus (please see separate listing for the Oliver Art Center at the Oakland campus). CCAC is developing a new primary program and exhibition site on the San Francisco campus, the Kent and Vicki Logan Center at CCAC. Scheduled to open in January 1999, the 12,000 square foot Logan Center will include a grand entry courtyard and reception area, a public exhibition gallery, a second floor graduate student gallery, a café, and other public services.

San Francisco Art Institute Galleries ⒸⒶⒶ

800 Chestnut Street, San Francisco, CA   94133
Tel: (415) 749-4564   *Fax:* (415) 749-1036
Internet Address: http://www.sfai.edu/
Director: Ms. Jean-Edith Weiffenbach
Admission: free.
Attendance: 18,000   *Established:* 1871   *Membership:* Y   *ADA Compliant:* Y
Open: Tues to Weds, 10am-5pm; Thurs, 10am-8pm; Fri to Sat, 10am-5pm; Sun, noon-5pm.
Closed: Legal Holidays.
Facilities: **Auditorium** (250 seats); **Gallery**; **Library** (27,000 volumes).
Activities: **Performances**; **Temporary Exhibitions**.
Publications: exhibition catalogues.

The Walter/McBean Gallery features temporary exhibitions. Project Space, upstairs at the Walter/McBean, features small-scale solo exhibitions of new work primarily by California artists who are at the edge of artistic invention. Student work is exhibited weekly in the Diego Rivera Gallery with a reception on every Thursday evening, 5:30pm-7:30pm. One of Diego Rivera's first fresco commissions outside of Mexico, "The Making of a Fresco Showing the Building of a City" (1930), is at the Institute.

San Francisco State University - Art Department Gallery ⒸⒶⒶ

College of Creative Arts, 1600 Holloway Ave (Arts & Industry Bldg. Add), San Francisco, CA   94132
Tel: (415) 338-6535
Internet Address: http://www.sfsu.edu/~artdept/artgallery.html
Gallery Manager: Ms. Sharon Spain
Admission: free.
Open: Call for hours.
Facilities: **Gallery** (3,800 square feet).
Activities: **Temporary Exhibitions**.

The Art Department Gallery is a teaching facility that presents both professional and student-oriented exhibitions each semester. Professional exhibitions are organized to features the range and diversity of both contemporary and historical art. Student exhibitions include the Stillwell Show (juried exhibition) and the Annual MFA Thesis Exhibition.

University of San Francisco - Mary and Carter Thacher Gallery ⓒⓐ

Gleeson Library/Geshke Center, 2130 Fulton Street, San Francisco, CA 94117-1080
Tel: (415) 422-5555
Internet Address: http://www.usfca.edu
Director: Thomas M. Lucas, S.J., Ph.D.
Admission: free.
Open: Library Hours.
Facilities: **Exhibition Area**.
Activities: **Temporary Exhibitions**.
The Gallery presents temporary exhibitions.

San Jacinto

Mount San Jacinto College - Fine Arts Gallery

1499 N. State St., San Jacinto, CA 92583
Tel: (909) 487-6752 *Ext:* 1531   *Fax:* (909) 654-6236
Internet Address: http://www.msjc.cc.ca.us
Director: Ms. Lucinda Luvaas
Open: Monday, 10am-4pm; Tuesday, 10am-4pm and 7pm-9pm; Wednesday to Friday, 10am-4pm;
        Saturday, 1pm-4pm.
Facilities: **Gallery**.
Activities: **Temporary Exhibitions**.
The Gallery features temporary exhibitions of the work of locally, regionally, and nationally recognized artists.

San Jose

San Jose State University Art Galleries ⓒⓐ

Art Dept., One Washington Square, San Jose State University, San Jose, CA 95192-0089
Tel: (408) 924-4328   *Fax:* (408) 924-4326
Internet Address: http://www.sjsu.edu/depts/art_design/events/galleries.html
Director: Ms. Ann Ostheimer
Admission: free.
Attendance: 14,000   *Established:* 1959   *ADA Compliant:* Y
Parking: Call for parking pass.
Open: **September to May**, Tuesday, 11am-4pm and 6pm-8pm; Wednesday to Friday, 11am-4pm.
Facilities: **Gallery** (new exhibition every 6 weeks during academic year).
Activities: **Education Program** (students); **Guided Tours**; **Lecture Series** (during academic year,
        Tues, 5pm); **Temporary/Traveling Exhibitions** (new exhibit every six weeks).
Publications: brochures; exhibition catalogues.
The main gallery, The Natalie and James Thompson Art Gallery, presents six exhibits annually of work by professional artists. Each year there are exhibits of contemporary design and history of art, a collaborative exhibition with other art institutions in the Bay Area, and a special exhibition and residency. In addition to the Thompson Gallery there are eight small student galleries. Included in this matrix is a special installation/performance space and small design gallery. There are additional exhibition spaces in cases throughout the Art Building. In most of the galleries, exhibits of student art work change weekly, resulting in over 160 exhibitions annually.

San Luis Obispo

California Polytechnic State University - University Gallery ⓒⓐ

171 Dexter Bldg., University Drive and Poly Vue (adjacent of Kennedy Library)
San Luis Obispo, CA 93407
Tel: (805) 756-1148   *Fax:* (805) 756-6321
Internet Address: http://artdesign.libart.calpoly.edu/webpages/html/gallery.html

California Polytechnic State University - University Gallery, cont.

Director: Ms. Crissa Hewitt

Admission: free.

Open: Monday to Tuesday, 11am-4pm; Wednesday, 11am-4pm and 7pm-9pm;
Thursday to Sunday, 11am-4pm.

Facilities: **Exhibition Area**.

Activities: **Temporary Exhibitions** (6/year).

The University Gallery presents exhibitions of work in a wide variety media by nationally and internationally recognized artists, as well as artwork by students, alumni and faculty. art work. Exhibitions are supplemented by other on-site programs. Also of possible interest on campus, the Galerie (756-1182) located in Room 221 of the University Union presents exhibitions featuring contemporary and historical works of art in a variety of media.

Cuesta College Art Gallery

Library, Highway 1, San Luis Obispo, CA   93403

Tel: (805) 546-3202

Internet Address: http://www.cuesta.cc.ca.us/finearts/gallery.htm

Director: Ms. Marta Peluso

Open: **Fall to Spring**, Monday to Thursday, 7:30am-9pm; Friday, 7:30am-4pm; Sunday, noon-6pm.
Summer, Monday to Thursday, 7:30am-4pm; Friday, 7:30am-1pm.

Facilities: **Exhibition Area**.

Activities: **Lectures**; **Temporary Exhibitions**.

The Gallery presents temporary exhibitions of contemporary work by locally, regionally, and nationally recognized artists.

San Marcos

Palomar College - Boehm Gallery

1140 Mission Road, Palomar College, San Marcos, CA   92069-1487

Tel: (760) 744-1150 *Ext:* 2304   *Fax:* (760) 744-8123

Internet Address: http://www.palomar.edu

Director: Mr. Harry Bliss

Admission: voluntary contribution.

Attendance: 65,000   *Established:* 1964   *ADA Compliant:* Y

Open: **September to June**,
Tuesday, 10am-4pm; Wednesday to Thursday, 10am-7pm; Friday to Saturday, 10am-2pm.

Closed: Academic Holidays.

Facilities: **Galleries** (2000 square feet); **Library** (8,500 volumes); **Reading Room**.

Activities: **Gallery Talks**; **Lectures**; **Temporary Exhibitions**.

Publications: exhibition catalogues.

The permanent collection of the Boehm Gallery numbers approximately two hundred works, dating from the 15th through 20th centuries, in a variety of media. The Gallery features six exhibitions per year, including student and faculty work, as well as that of nationally recognized professional artists.

Santa Ana

Santa Ana College - SAC Main Gallery (SAC)

17th at Bristol Streets, 1530 W. 17th St., Santa Ana, CA   92706

Tel: (714) 564-5615   *Fax:* (714) 564-6379

Internet Address: http://www.rancho.cc.ca.us/rsccd/sac/sac_home.htm

Director: Ms. Mayde Herberg

Admission: free.

Attendance: 9,000   *Established:* 1970   *Membership:* N   *ADA Compliant:* Y

Parking: metered lots.

Santa Ana College - SAC Main Gallery, cont.
Open: Monday, 10am-2pm; Tuesday to Wednesday, 10am-2pm and 6:30pm-8:30pm; Thursday, 10am-2pm.
Closed: Academic Holidays, Legal Holidays.
Facilities: **Galleries** (1,100 square feet); **Library** (exhibition catalogues).
Activities: **Education Programs**; **Guided Tours** (by appointment); **Lectures Series** (Mon, 12:30pm).
Publications: exhibition catalogues (3/year).

The SAC Main Gallery was established on campus to provide an educational site for art. An additional gallery, the RSC Arts Gallery, was opened in 1996 in Santa Ana's new 'Artists Village', downtown (207 N. Broadway; Wed-Sat, noon-4pm; tel. 564-5605). This gallery annex doubles the display area available for the study of art and exhibition design. Both galleries are devoted to the display of current work by professional artists as well as that of faculty and students. The College does not maintain a permanent collection.

Santa Barbara

University of California, Santa Barbara - University Art Museum ⓒ (UAM)
University of California, El Colegio Road, Santa Barbara, CA 93106-7130
Tel: (805) 893-2951   *Fax:* (805) 893-3013
Internet Address: http://www.uam.ucsb.edu
Director: Ms. Marla C. Berns
Admission: voluntary contribution.
Attendance: 20,000   *Established:* 1959   *Membership:* Y   *ADA Compliant:* Y
Parking: park in Lot #23.
Open: Tuesday to Saturday, 10am-4pm; Sunday, 1pm-5pm.
          Holidays, 1pm-5pm.
Closed: New Year's Day, Easter, Thanksgiving Day, Christmas Day.
Facilities: **Galleries**; **Library** (arts library in Music Building); **Shop**.
Activities: **Education Programs**; **Films**; **Gallery Talks**; **Guided Tours**; **Lectures**; **Temporary Exhibitions**; **Traveling Exhibitions**.
Publications: brochures; exhibition catalogues; newsletter.

The Museum presents permanent, temporary, and traveling exhibitions. Permanent collections include the Morgenroth Collection of Renaissance Medals and Plaquettes; the Sedgwick Collection of old master paintings; and works on paper including drawings, and photographs. A collection of over 350,000 architectural drawings, mostly the work of California architects, is housed separately (1332 Arts Building - (805) 893-2724). The Museum is undergoing a major renovation, scheduled for completion in September, 1999. The reconstruction will create a new entrance with an adjoining plaza and five exhibition spaces (three galleries devoted to the display of works from the permanent collection and two to temporary exhibitions). The renovation will allow for the permanent collection galleries to remain open during the installation of temporary exhibits. During the renovation period the Museum will be closed to visitors.

Santa Clara

Santa Clara University - de Saisset Museum ⓒ
Santa Clara University, 500 El Camino Real, Santa Clara, CA 95053-0550
Tel: (408) 554-4528
Fax: (408) 554-7840
TDDY: (800) 735-2929
Internet Address: http://www.scu.edu/SCU/Departments/deSaisset/information
Director: Ms. Rebecca M. Schapp
Admission: voluntary contribution.
Attendance: 30,000   *Established:* 1955
Membership: Y
Parking: obtain free visitor's parking pass at campus entrance.

Santa Clara University - de Saisset Museum, cont.

Open: Tuesday to Sunday, 11am-4pm.
Closed: Legal Holidays, Good Friday,
   M. L. King Birthday.
Facilities: **Auditorium** (200 seats); **Building** (17,000 square feet); **Library** (1,200 volumes); **Shop**.
Activities: **Guided Tours**; **Temporary Exhibitions**; **Traveling Exhibitions**.
Publications: exhibition catalogues; newsletter, "California Artist Profiles".

Thomas Moran, *East Hampton, Long Island*, 19th-century. de Saisset Museum, gift of Robert M. Husband. Photograph courtesy of de Saisset Museum, Santa Clara University, Santa Clara, California.

The de Saisset Museum, located adjacent to Mission Santa Clara de Asís in the heart of the Santa Clara University campus, is the University's museum of art and history. The Museum's permanent collection contains a wide range of artworks in a variety of media. While the collection is rich in contemporary prints and photographs, it possesses historical old-world flavor with Renaissance prints, works by Albrecht Dürer, and the acclaimed sculpture "Othello" by 19th-century Italian artist Gian-Pietro Calvi. The Museum presents temporary exhibitions of contemporary and historically important art, ranging from local artists to touring national exhibits, often on ethical and moral themes. In addition, there are lectures, concerts, and films for the educational and cultural benefits of the University community, local residents, and visitors. The de Saisset Museum is also the caretaker of the University's California History Collection, which includes historical and ethnographic artifacts from the Native American period through the founding of the Mission and College. These are displayed in three galleries focusing on the Ohlone Indian, Mission, and early College periods. The Museum's art collection includes paintings, prints, and sculptures by European and American artists from the 16th century to the present; European and Asian decorative art; and African tribal art. Among the many contemporary works in the collection is the largest public collection of the influential and historically important early 20th-century artist Henrietta Shore. In addition the collection contains works by Arnold G. Mountfort, Sam Francis, Bruce Conner, and many other artists of national and international renown. Also of note are works from the Depression-era New Deal art program; film documentation of experimental performance art in the early 1970s; the Helen Johnston Collection of photographs by artists such as Ansel Adams, Ruth Bernhard, Wynn Bullock, Imogen Cunningham, Judy Dater, Annie Leibovitz, Les Krims, Lisette Model, and Edward Weston; and archival prints from the Palo Alto fine arts press, Smith Andersen Editions, by Stanley Boxer, David Gilhooly, Joseph Goldyne, Frank Lobdell, Marguerite M. Saegesser, Inez Storer, and others. Wheelchair accessibility is limited to the galleries located on the main floor.

Santa Cruz

University of California, Santa Cruz - Mary Porter Sesnon Art Gallery ⒸⒶ

Porter College, University of California, Santa Cruz,
1156 High Street, Santa Cruz, CA 95064
Tel: (831) 459-3606
Internet Address: http://arts.ucsc.edu/sesnon
Director: Ms. Pamela Bailey
Admission: free.
ADA Compliant: Y
Open: **Fall to Spring**, Tuesday to Saturday, noon-5pm.
Closed: Academic Holidays, Summer.
Facilities: **Exhibition Area**.
Activities: **Temporary Exhibitions**.

University of California, Santa Cruz - Mary Porter Sesnon Art Gallery, cont.

The Sesnon Gallery operates a museum-oriented program for educational purposes. The Gallery organizes an annual schedule of temporary exhibitions that represents a broad range of methods, media, and cultures in a local/regional/national context with a focus on contemporary practice.

Santa Monica

Santa Monica College Art Gallery

Santa Monica Community College District, 1900 Pico Blvd., Santa Monica, CA   90405
Tel: (310) 452-9231
Internet Address: http://www.smc.edu
Parking: Free at Airport Parking Lot.
Open: Tuesday to Thursday, 11am-3pm and 5:30pm-8:30pm; Friday, 11am-3pm; Saturday, 11am-4pm.
Facilities: Gallery.
Activities: Temporary Exhibitions.

The Gallery presents temporary exhibitions of the work of both students and professional artists.

Santa Rosa

Santa Rosa Junior College - Jesse Peter Native American Art Museum Ⓒᴬᴬ

Santa Rosa Junior College, 1501 Mendocino Ave., Santa Rosa, CA   95401
Tel: (707) 527-4479   *Fax:* (707) 527-4816
Internet Address: http://www.santarosa.edu
Director: Mr. Foley C. Benson
Admission: voluntary contribution.
Attendance: 17,000   *Established:* 1932   *Membership:* N   *ADA Compliant:* Y
Parking: parking available; fee charged.
Open: September to June, Monday to Friday, noon-4pm.
Closed: Academic Holidays.
Facilities: Exhibition Area.
Activities: Guided Tours; Lectures.
Publications: monographs (occasional).

The Museum presents exhibitions of traditional and contemporary Native American art and artifacts. Also of possible interest, the Art Gallery presents a schedule of exhibitions of the work in diverse media with an emphasis on artists not generally exhibited locally. Located in the former museum building near the center of the campus, the Gallery is open Sunday and Tuesday through Friday, noon to 4pm.

Stanford

Stanford University - Iris & B. Gerald Cantor Center for Visual Arts Ⓒᴬᴬ

Lomita Drive and Museum Way, Stanford, CA   94305-5060
Tel: (415) 725-0462   *Fax:* (415) 725-0464
Internet Address: http://www.leland.stanford.edu/dept/SUMA
Director: Mr. Thomas K. Seligman
Admission: free.
Established: 1885   *Membership:* Y
Facilities: Auditorium; Library; Shop.
Activities: Concerts; Gallery Talks; Guided Tours; Lectures; Temporary Exhibitions; Traveling Exhibitions.
Publications: exhibition catalogues; journal.

Closed after the 1989 earthquake, the Stanford Museum reopened as the Iris & B. Gerald Cantor Center for Visual Arts in January of 1999. The facility, totaling approximately 120,000 square feet, includes the historic museum building, the B. Gerald Cantor Rodin Sculpture Garden, new sculpture

Stanford University - Iris & B. Gerald Cantor Center for Visual Arts, cont.

garden areas, and a new wing. The latter includes galleries for the display of special exhibitions and the permanent collection of contemporary art, a café, a bookshop, and a lecture/performance room. Stanford University has significant collections of outdoor art. In addition to the Museum's sculpture gardens, works by such artists as Josef Albers, Alexander Calder, Joan Miró, Henry Moore, James Rosati, George Segal, and Kenneth Snelson are installed throughout the campus. A Papua New Guinea Sculpture Garden is located near the intersection of Lomita Drive and Santa Teresa Street. Stanford maintains extensive permanent collections in virtually all areas. The European Painting Collection includes examples dating from the Renaissance through the end of the 19th-century with particular focus on British and French works from the later 18th- and early 19th-centuries. Seventeenth-century Holland and Italy are represented by smaller groups of paintings. The Museum's collection of European sculpture spans the fifteenth through nineteenth centuries. A highlight of the collection is a group of over 200 works by the French sculptor Auguste Rodin, many of which are on permanent display in the Iris and B. Gerald Cantor Rodin Sculpture Garden. The American Painting Collection ranges from the early 19th-century into the 20th-twentieth century, with particular strengths in later 19th-century landscapes, including important paintings from the 1870's by the California painter William Keith. The museum holds many works by William Trost Richards, Rex Slinkard, and Theodore Wores. The Modern and Contemporary Collections include in the collection are significant works by painters affiliated with Stanford such as Richard Diebenkorn, Nathan Oliveira and Frank Lobdell, as well as works by Bay Area artists such as Paul Wonner, Theophilus Brown and Wayne Thiebaud. The Print and Drawing Collections include more than 3,500 prints and 1,500 drawings, mainly from the 18th- and 19th-centuries. In the drawing collection, areas of particular interest include images of artists, academic studies, and caricatures, as well as works by Fragonard, G.B. and G.D. Tiepolo, J. R. Cozens, Turner, Delacroix, Gericault, Menzel, Prendergast, Gwen John, Mark Tobey, and de Kooning. The strength of the print collection lies in early 19th-century French lithographs, including a fine selection by Theodore Gericault, Richard P. Bonington's complete oeuvre, as well as many caricatures. The Photography Collection spans the history of the medium from prints by Eadweard Muybridge and William Henry Fox Talbot to work by the most important contemporaries. The Art of the Americas spans the Western Hemisphere in ancient and modem times. The pre-Columbian period concentrates on the ceramic traditions in Peru, Mexico, and the Southwestern United States. The 19th- and 20th- century collections deal in greater detail with North America, especially California. The Ancient Collection includes two thousand examples of ancient Cypriot terracotta, Greek and Roman works, sculpture from kingdom of Palmyra, and Egyptian artifacts. The African Collection concentrates on traditional sculpture of sub-Saharan Africa dating from the 19th- and 20th-centuries.The Museum also has substantial collections of Asian and Pacific art. Also of possible interest on campus is the T. W. Stanford Art Gallery (Tues-Fri, 10-5; Sat-Sun, 1-5).

Torrance

El Camino College Art Gallery

16007 Crenshaw Blvd., Torrance, CA 90506
Tel: (310) 660-3010   *Fax:* (310) 660-3798
Internet Address: http://www.elcamino.cc.ca.us/cmart.htm
Art Gallery Curator: Ms. Susanna Meiers
Admission: free.
Open: Monday to Tuesday, 10am-3pm; Wednesday to Thursday, 10am-8pm; Friday, 10am-2pm.
Facilities: **Exhibition Area**.
Activities: **Temporary Exhibitions**.

The gallery presents exhibitions of works by professional artists, faculty, and students.

Ventura

Ventura College - Art Galleries

4667 Telegraph Road, Ventura, CA 93003
Tel: (805) 648-8974   *Fax:* (805) 654-6466
Internet Address: http://www.ventura.cc.ca.us

Ventura College - Art Galleries, cont.

Director: Ms. Deborah McKillop
Open: Call for hours.
Facilities: **Galleries**.
Activities: **Temporary Exhibitions**.

The Ventura College art galleries, Gallery2 and New Media Gallery, present faculty and student work, as well as artwork by professional artist from throughout the United States. Exhibitions have featured among others the work of Carlos Almaraz, Don Bachardy, Billy Al Bengston, Gary F. Brown, Robert Frame, Louise Nevelson, and Julian Schnabel. The College permanent art collection includes works by Goya, Dali, and Chagall, which may be seen in the campus library.

Visalia

College of the Sequoias - COS Gallery ⓒᴬ

915 S. Mooney Blvd., Room 214A (opposite the Administration Bldg.), Visalia, CA 93277
Tel: (559) 737-4861
Internet Address: http://infinity.sequoias.cc.ca.us/art/division/gallery.htm
Director: Mr. Richard Lee Peterson
Admission: free.
Open: Monday to Friday, noon-5pm.
Facilities: **Exhibition Area**.
Activities: **Lectures** (sponsored by the Visalia Art League); **Temporary Exhibitions**.

The Gallery presents a schedule of temporary exhibitions.

Walnut

Mount San Antonio College Art Gallery

1100 N. Grand Ave., Walnut, CA 91789
Tel: (909) 594-5611 *Ext:* 4328
Fax: (909) 468-3954
Internet Address: www.mtsac.edu
Director: Ms. Fatemeh Burnes
Admission: free.
Established: 1946
Parking: free on site.
Open: Tuesday, 11am-2pm and 5pm-8pm;
Wednesday to Thursday, 11am-2pm.
Facilities: **Gallery** (2,000 square feet).
Activities: **Temporary Exhibitions**.

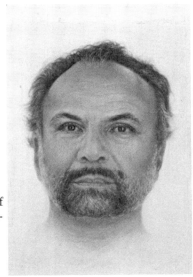

The Gallery presents temporary exhibitions of the work of emerging artists as well as those with national and international reputations.

Craig Attebery, *Richard*, 1998, (detail), oil on paper, 23.25 x 15.5 inches. Exhibited in temporary exhibition at Mt. San Antonio Gallery, 1999. Photograph courtesy of Lizard/ Harp Gallery, Los Angeles, California.

Colorado

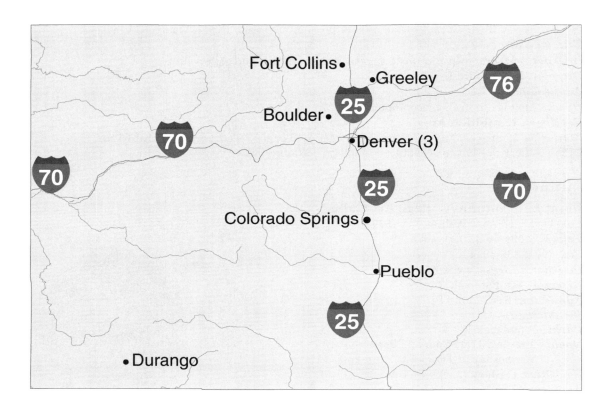

The number in parentheses following the city name indicates the number of museums/galleries in that municipality. If there is no number, one is understood. For example, in the text three listings would be found under Denver and one listing under Boulder.

Colorado

Boulder

University of Colorado - CU Art Galleries (CAA)

University of Colorado
Boulder, CO   80309
Tel: (303) 492-8300
Fax: (303) 492-4886
Internet Address: http://www.colorado.edu
Director: Ms. Susan Krane
Admission: voluntary contribution: adult-$2.00,
   student-free.
Attendance: 30,000   *Established:* 1978
Membership: N   *ADA Compliant:* Y
Parking: public parking lot.
Open: Monday, 8am-5pm;
      Tuesday, 8am-8pm;
      Wednesday to Friday, 8am-5pm;
      Saturday, noon-4pm.
Closed: New Year's Eve, New Year's Day,
      Independence Day, Christmas Vacation.
Facilities: **Exhibition Area** (3 galleries; total
   6,000 square feet).
Activities: **Gallery Dialogues; Lectures;
   Permanent Collection Exhibits;
   Temporary Exhibitions; Traveling
   Exhibitions.**

George Grosz, *Street Scene*, (detail), 19 x 24½ inches, c. 1928,
drawing - pen and ink on paper. CU Art Galleries. Photograph
courtesy of CU Art Galleries, University of Colorado, Boulder
Campus, Boulder, Colorado.

Publications: exhibition catalogues.

The CU Art Galleries of the University of Colorado at Boulder are committed to enhancing public understanding of the visual arts and to advocating interdisciplinary approaches to the social, cultural, technological, and historical contexts of art. The Galleries present exhibitions of regional, national, and international significance and related educational events. Student exhibitions of work by MFA and BFA candidates are also scheduled. Its activities serve the academic community of the University, the metropolitan area, and statewide populations. The Art Galleries are stewards of the Colorado Collection, a permanent study and teaching resource for the citizens of the State. They promote the preservation, interpretation and exhibition of the Colorado Collection, and its use for scholarly endeavors and outreach efforts.

Colorado Springs

University of Colorado, Colorado Springs - Gallery of Contemporary Art (CAA)

1420 Austin Bluffs Parkway
Colorado Springs, CO   80933-7150
Tel: (719) 262-3567   *Fax:* (719) 262-3183   *TDDY:* (719) 262-3621
Internet Address: http://harpy.uccs.edu/gallery/framesgallery.html
Director: Asst. Prof Gerry Riggs
Admission: fee: adult-$1.00, child-free, student-$0.50, senior-$0.50.
Attendance: 24,000   *Established:* 1981   *Membership:* Y   *ADA Compliant:* Y
Open: Monday to Friday, 10am-4pm; Saturday, 1pm-4pm.
Closed: Legal Holidays.
Facilities: **Galleries.**
Activities: **Concerts; Education Programs; Guided Tours; Lectures; Temporary Exhibitions;
   Traveling Exhibitions.**

The goal of the Gallery of Contemporary Art is to organize and host exhibitions of acclaimed regional, national, and international artists.

Denver

Metropolitan State College of Denver - Center for the Visual Arts ⓒᴬᴬ
1734 Wazee St., Denver, CO 80202-1231
Tel: (303) 294-5207 *Fax:* (303) 294-5210
Internet Address: http://www.mcsd.edu./~metroart
Director: Ms. Sally L. Perisho
Admission: voluntary contribution.
Attendance: 25,000 *Established:* 1991 *Membership:* Y *ADA Compliant:* Y
Parking: metered parking.
Open: Tuesday to Friday, 10am-5pm; Saturday, 11am-4pm.
Closed: Legal Holidays.
Facilities: **Architecture** (historic warehouse); **Galleries**.
Activities: **Education Programs**.
Publications: newsletter (quarterly).
The Metro Center hosts exhibitions of culturally diverse artists and offers lectures, workshops and tours.

Rocky Mountain College of Art & Design - Philip J. Steele Gallery ⓒᴬᴬ
6875 E. Evans Ave., Denver, CO 80224
Tel: (303) 753-6046 *Fax:* (303) 759-4970
Internet Address: http://www.rmcad.edu
Gallery Director: Ms. Lisa Spivak
Admission: free.
Established: 1963 *Membership:* N
Open: Monday to Friday, 8am-6pm; Saturday, 9am-4pm.
Closed: New Year's Day, Memorial Day, Independence Day, Labor Day, Thanksgiving Day, Christmas Day.
Facilities: **Galleries**; **Library**; **Shop**.
Activities: **Education Programs**; **Lectures**.
The Gallery presents temporary exhibitions of contemporary art.

University of Denver - School of Art and Art History Gallery ⓒᴬᴬ
2121 East Asbury Ave., Shwayder Art Building, Denver, CO 80210
Tel: (303) 871-2846 *Fax:* (303) 871-4112
Internet Address: http://www.du.edu
Admission: free.
Established: 1940 *Membership:* N *ADA Compliant:* Y
Open: Monday to Friday, 9am-4pm;
Saturday to Sunday, noon-4pm (during exhibits).
Closed: July to August, December.
Facilities: **Galleries**.
Activities: **Lectures**.
Located on the University of Denver campus, the Gallery presents temporary exhibitions including the work of students.

Durango

Fort Lewis College - Art Gallery ⓒᴬᴬ
101 Art Building (off the Main Lobby), 1000 Rim Drive, Durango, CO 81301
Tel: (970) 247-7167 *Fax:* (970) 247-7520
Internet Address: http://www.fortlewis.edu/acad-aff/arts-sci/art/artpages/gallery.html
Gallery Director: Ms. Mary E. Tso
Admission: free.

Fort Lewis College - Art Gallery, cont.

Open: Monday to Friday, 10am-4pm, or by appointment.

Facilities: **Exhibition Area** (130 linear running feet).

Activities: **Lectures; Temporary Exhibitions; Workshops.**

The Gallery offers exhibitions of historical, mainstream, and avant garde work in both traveling and special artist exhibitions. In addition, exhibitions of student and faculty work complement the art gallery's calendar with solo and group shows, including the Senior Art Major and Juried Student Exhibitions each spring. Also of possible interest, student work is often on display in the Adjunct Gallery, located in the Student Lounge.

Fort Collins

Colorado State University - Hatton Gallery ©

Visual Arts Building
Fort Collins, CO   80523
Tel: (970) 491-6774
Fax: (970) 491-0505
Internet Address: http://www.colostate.edu
Director: Ms. Linda Frickman
Admission: voluntary contribution.
Attendance: 7,000   *Established:* 1970
Membership: N   *ADA Compliant:* Y
Parking: free on site.
Open: **Fall & Spring Semesters**
          Monday to Friday, 8:30am-4:30pm,
          Saturday, 1pm-4pm;
          Summer,
          Monday to Friday, 8:30am-4:30pm

Installation in Hatton Gallery: Tenth Colorado International Invitational Poster Exhibition, 1997, various artists. Photograph courtesy of Hatton Gallery, Colorado State University, Fort Collins, Colorado.

Closed: New Year's Day, Independence Day, Thanksgiving Day, Christmas Day.

Facilities: **Galleries.**

Activities: **Education Programs; Lectures; Temporary Exhibitions; Traveling Exhibitions.**

Publications: exhibition catalogues; posters.

The Hatton Gallery has a small permanent collection of posters and Japanese prints. It also presents frequent temporary exhibitions of the work of students and professional artists.

Greeley

University of Northern Colorado - Mariani Gallery ©

8th Ave. & 18th St., Guggenheim Hall
Greeley, CO   80639
Tel: (970) 351-2184
Fax: (970) 351-2299
Internet Address: http://arts.unco.edu/visarts/visarts/galleries
Chairman: Ms. Trista Lynch
Admission: voluntary contribution.
Attendance: 110,000   *Established:* 1972   *Membership:* N   *ADA Compliant:* Y
Parking: metered parking.
Open: Monday, 9am-4pm and 7pm-9pm; Tuesday 9am-4pm; Wednesday, 9am-4pm and 7pm-9pm;
         Thursday to Friday, 9am-4pm.
Closed: Summer.
Facilities: **Galleries** (2, total 1500 square feet).

The Mariani Gallery presents temporary exhibitions. Also of possible interest on campus, the Oak Room Gallery in Crabbe Hall presents the work of student, alumni, and other artists.

Pueblo

University of Southern Colorado Fine Art Gallery ⒸⒶ

2200 Bonforte Blvd, Pueblo, CO   81001-4901
Tel: (877) 872-9653
Internet Address: http://www.uscolo.edu/art/aboutart/.html
Director: Mr. Dennis Dalton
ADA Compliant: Y
Parking: free on site.
Open: Monday to Friday, 8am-5pm.
Facilities: **Gallery**.
Activities: **Lectures**; **Temporary Exhibitions**.

The Fine Art Gallery presents bi-monthly exhibits of the work of professional artists. There are also exhibits of student work.

Connecticut

The number in parentheses following the city name indicates the number of museums/galleries in that municipality. If there is no number, one is understood. For example, in the text two listings would be found under New Haven and one listing under Middletown.

Connecticut

Bridgeport

Housatonic Community College - Housatonic Museum of Art

900 Lafayette Blvd.
Bridgeport, CT   06604
Tel: (203) 332-5203
Fax: (203) 332-5123
Internet Address:
   http://www.hctc.commnet.edu/ artmuseum/index.html
Director: Ms. Robbin Zella
Admission: free.
Attendance: 7,500   *Established:* 1967
Membership: N   *ADA Compliant:* Y
Parking: free parking in student lot across street.
Open: **During academic year**.
Closed: Academic Holidays.
Facilities: **Food Services** Restaurant; **Galleries** (2 - total of 2000 square feet); **Library** (2,000 volumes); **Sculpture Garden**.
Activities: **Films**; **Gallery Talks**; **Guided Tours**; **Lectures**; **Temporary Exhibitions** (6 per year); **Traveling Exhibitions**.
Publications: exhibition catalogues.

Hugo Schieber, *Head of a Woman*, 1920, gouache on board, 29 x 23 3/4 inches, gift of Dr. Lee Goldstein, Housatonic Museum of Art. Photograph courtesy of Housatonic Museum of Art, Bridgeport, Connecticut.

Housatonic Museum of Art is part of Housatonic Community College, within walking distance of the train station, in downtown Bridgeport. The Museum has an important permanent collection and also presents temporary exhibitions. The collection consists chiefly of 20th-century American art and significant ethnographic holdings, featuring African sculpture. It includes works by Archipenko, Chagall, Christo, Elaine de Kooning, Lichtenstein, Marsh, Miró, Moore, Oldenberg, Ossorio, Picasso, Rauschenberg, Renoir, Rivers, Schieber, and Shinn, among many others.

University of Bridgeport - The University Gallery

Bernhard Arts & Humanities Center
84 Iranistan Ave.
Bridgeport, CT   06601-2449
Tel: (203) 576-4402
Fax: (203) 576-4051
Internet Address: http://www. bridgeport.edu
Director: Mr. Thomas Juliusberger
Admission: free.
Attendance: 3,000   *Established:* 1972
Membership: N   *ADA Compliant:* Y
Parking: free on site.
Open: **Mid-Jan. to Mid-May** and **September to Mid- Dec.**;
         Tuesday to Saturday, 1pm-4pm;
         Tuesday/Thursday, 5pm-7pm.
Facilities: **Galleries** (3,500 square feet).
Activities: **Gallery Talks**; **Lectures**; **Temporary Exhibitions**; **Traveling Exhibitions**.
Publications: exhibition catalogues.

Red Grooms, *Woman in Man's Arms*, 1973, Lithograph, 34/250. University Gallery. Photograph courtesy of University Gallery, University of Bridgeport, Bridgeport, Connecticut.

University of Bridgeport - The University Gallery, cont.

The University Gallery maintains a permanent collection and presents exhibitions focusing primarily on modern and contemporary art. The permanent collection of the Gallery includes works by Josef Albers, Ellsworth Kelly, Romare Bearden, Louise Nevelson, Red Grooms, and James Rosenquist.

Fairfield

Fairfield University - Thomas J. Walsh Art Gallery ⓒᴬᴬ

Regina A. Quick Center for the Arts, N. Benson Road
Fairfield, CT   06430
Tel: (203) 254-4242   **Fax:** (203) 254-4113
Internet Address: http://www.fairfield.edu
Communications: Dr. Philip Eliasoph
Admission: free.
Attendance: 10,000   **Established:** 1990   **Membership:** N   **ADA Compliant:** Y
Open: Tuesday to Saturday, 11am-5pm; Saturday, noon-4pm.
Closed: Memorial Day, Legal Holidays, Thanksgiving Day, Christmas Day.
Facilities: Galleries.
Activities: Arts Festival; Concerts; Education Programs; Films; Lectures; Performances; Temporary Exhibitions; Traveling Exhibitions.
Publications: collection catalogue.

The Walsh Art Gallery hosts six temporary exhibitions per year.

Hartford

Trinity College - Widener Gallery ⓒᴬᴬ

Austin Arts Center, 300 Summit St, Hartford, CT   06106
Tel: (860) 297-2133   **Fax:** (860) 297-5349
Internet Address: http://www.trincoll.edu
Curator: Felice Caivano
Admission: free.
Established: 1964   **Membership:** N   **ADA Compliant:** N
Open: Weekdays, 1pm-5pm.
Closed: Academic Holidays.
Facilities: Galleries; Theatre.
Activities: Education Programs.

The Gallery sponsors three exhibitions per year of the work of professional artists from outside the Trinity community. In addition, there are two student shows and one faculty show each year. The permanent collection is spread around the campus.

Middletown

Wesleyan University - Davison Art Center ⓒᴬᴬ (DAC)

301 High St., Middletown, CT   06459-0487
Tel: (860) 685-2500   **Fax:** (860) 685-2501
Internet Address: http://www.wesleyan.edu/dac/homehtml
Curator: Ms. Stephanie Wiles
Admission: voluntary contribution.
Attendance: 6,000   **Established:** 1952   **Membership:** Y   **ADA Compliant:** N
Parking: nearby on-street parking.
Open: **September to Early June**, Tuesday to Friday, noon-4pm; Saturday to Sunday, 2pm-5pm.
Closed: Academic Holidays, Legal Holidays.
Facilities: Architecture (1838-1840 Alsop House); **Library** (3,000 volumes); **Reading Room.**
Activities: Gallery Talks; Lectures.

Wesleyan University - Davison Art Center, cont.

Publications: exhibition catalogues.

The Davison Art Center of Wesleyan University maintains an impressive, high-quality collection of artworks, chiefly on paper. The collection is augmented frequently, with works that contribute to the educational mission of the Center. The Center's print collection includes work by Dürer, Rembrandt, Italian Renaissance artists, Goya, Manet, Millet, and modern and contemporary American artists, especially Jim Dine, along with a substantial collection of Japanese woodcuts. The photography collection ranges from the 1840's to the present and includes works by Muybridge, Atget, Steichen, Bourke-White, Mark, and Trager. The drawings in the Center's collection include works by many important French and American artists, such as Lalanne, Sargent, and Whistler. The painting collection is small, but also of high quality (e.g., Charles Sheeler). There is also a sculpture collection. Also of possible interest on campus is the Ezra and Cecile Zilkha Gallery, dedicated to temporary exhibitions of contemporary art in all media. Its exhibition program consists of 4-5 shows per year. The Zilkha Gallery (685-2684) is open Tues-Fri, noon-4pm, and Sat-Sun, 2pm-5pm.

New Britain

Central Connecticut State University Museum ©

Samuel T. Chen Arts Center, Maloney Hall, 1615 Stanley St.
New Britain, CT   06050
Tel: (860) 832-2633
Fax: (860) 832-2634
Internet Address: http://wwwas.ccsu.ctstateu.edu/depts/ART/GALLERY.html
Director: Mr. Ron Todd
Admission: free.
Attendance: 3,000   *Established:* 1965   *Membership:* N   *ADA Compliant:* Y
Open: **During Exhibitions**,
         Tuesday to Wednesday, 1pm-4pm; Thursday, 1pm-7pm; Friday, 1pm-4pm.
Facilities: **Exhibition Area** (200 linear feet); **Library**.
Activities: **Education Programs**.

The University Gallery presents six major exhibitions of contemporary art during each academic year. It also houses a small permanent collection.

New Haven

Yale Center for British Art ©

1080 Chapel Street
New Haven, CT   06520-8280
Tel: (203) 432-2800
Fax: (203) 432-9695
Internet Address: http://www.yale.edu/ycba
Director: Mr. Patrick McCaughy
Admission: voluntary contribution.
Attendance: 85,000   *Established:* 1977
Membership: Y   *ADA Compliant:* Y
Parking: lot behind building.
Open: Monday to Friday, 10am-4:30pm.
Closed: New Year's Eve, New Year's Day,
         Independence Day, Thanksgiving Day,
         Christmas Eve, Christmas Day.

Exterior view of Yale Center for British Art (1977), designed by Louis Kahn. Photograph by Richard Caspole, courtesy of Yale Center for British Art, New Haven, Connecticut.

Facilities: **Architecture** (1977, final building designed by Louis I. Kahn); **Auditorium** (200 seats); **Library** (20,000 volumes); **Shop** (Mon-Sat, 10am-5pm).
Activities: **Films**; **Gallery Talks**; **Guided Tours**; **Lectures**; **Temporary Exhibitions**.
Publications: exhibition catalogues.

The Yale Center for British Art contains masterpieces by the leading artists who have worked in Britain from the 16th century to the present, including paintings by Hogarth, Gainsborough,

New Haven, Connecticut

Yale Center for British Art, cont.

Reynolds, Stubbs, Constable, Turner, and Bonington. British sporting art, the Pre-Raphaelite Brotherhood, the Camden Town School, and the Bloomsbury Group are well represented, together with more recent 20th-century British art. Extensive collections of watercolors, drawings, prints, and rare books are available for public consultation. The Center mounts a regular program of changing exhibitions throughout the year and offers films, concerts, lectures, gallery talks, docent tours, and special programs for children - all free and open to the public. Given to Yale University by Paul Mellon, the Center was designed by Louis Kahn and opened in 1977. It stands across from Kahn's first museum commission, the Yale University Art Gallery(see below).

Yale University Art Gallery ⓒ (YUAG)

1111 Chapel Street, New Haven, CT   06520
Tel: (202) 432-0600   *Fax:* (204) 432-7159
Internet Address: http://www.yale.edu/artgallery
Director: Mr. Jock Reynolds
Admission: voluntary contribution.
Attendance: 103,000   *Established:* 1832   *Membership:* Y   *ADA Compliant:* Y
Parking: metered on street and commercial garage at 150 York Street.
Open: Tuesday to Saturday, 10am-5pm; Sunday, 1pm-6pm.
Closed: New Year's Day, Independence Day, August, Thanksgiving Day, Christmas Day.
Facilities: **Architecture** Original Building (Italian Gothic-style 1928, designed by Edgerton Swartout), Second Building (1953, designed by Louis I. Kahn); **Auditorium** (400 seats); **Sculpture Garden**; **Shop** (books, jewelry, accessories, museum publications).
Activities: **Concerts**; **Films**; **Gallery Talks** (Art à la Carte, selected Wednesdays, 12:20pm); **Guided Tours** (Sat, 11am and Sun, 3pm); **Lectures**; **Temporary Exhibitions**.
Publications: booklets (occasional); calendar (quarterly); exhibition catalogues (occasional).

Since its founding in 1832, the Yale University Art Gallery's collections have grown to number over 80,000 objects from around the world, dating from ancient Egypt to the present day. Among the highlights are masterpieces by Van Gogh, Manet, Monet, Picasso, Hopper, Homer, Eakins, and many contemporary artists, as well as notable collections of Etruscan and Greek vases, early Italian paintings, and African and Asian art. The Art Gallery's American paintings and decorative arts collections are among the finest in the world. The Art Gallery maintains a rigorous schedule of special exhibitions, educational programs, gallery talks, lectures, and symposia. It is used extensively for scholarly research in the history of art and museum training for graduate and undergraduate students. An entrance for persons using wheelchairs is at 201 York Street, with an unmetered parking space nearby. For further information on accessibility for the disabled call 432-0601 or 432-0620.

New London

Connecticut College - Lyman Allyn Art Museum ⓒ

625 Williams Street, New London, CT   06320
Tel: (860) 443-3433   *Fax:* (860) 442-1280
Internet Address: http://www.conncoll.edu/CAT/LymanAllyn/general.html
Exec. Director: Mr. Charles A. Shepard, III
Admission: fee: adult-$3.00, child-free, student-$2.00, senior-$2.00.
Attendance: 20,000   *Established:* 1930
Membership: Y   *ADA Compliant:* Y
Parking: free on site.
Open: Tuesday to Saturday, 10am-5pm; Sunday, 1pm-5pm.
Closed: Legal Holidays.

Exterior view of west entrance, Lyman Allyn Art Museum. Photograph courtesy of Lyman Allyn Art Museum, New London, Connecticut.

Connecticut College - Lyman Allyn Art Museum, cont.

Facilities: **Architecture** (Whaling mansion); **Auditorium** (100 seats); **Downtown Artspace**; **Library** (10,000 volumes); **Sculpture Garden**; **Shop**.

Activities: **Education Programs**; **Gallery Talks**; **Guided Tours**; **Lectures**; **Temporary Exhibitions**; **Traveling Exhibitions**.

Publications: collection catalogue; newsletter, "Columns" (quarterly).

Situated near Connecticut College and overlooking the U.S. Coast Guard Academy, the Lyman Allyn Art Museum is the principal comprehensive art museum serving southeastern Connecticut. With an impressive collection of more than 15,000 objects spanning 5,000 years and five continents, the Museum displays contemporary, modern, and primitive fine arts; 18th- and 19th-century American decorative arts; Connecticut Impressionist paintings; and three-dimensional art in its sculpture garden. The Museum also mounts temporary exhibitions. It is housed in a Neo-Classical building designed by Charles A. Platt, who also designed The Freer Gallery of Art and several buildings on the Connecticut College campus, with which the Museum has recently affiliated.

Old Lyme

Lyme Academy of Fine Arts - Galleries Ⓒᴬᴬ

84 Lyme St., Old Lyme, CT   06371

Tel: (860) 434-5232

Internet Address: http://www.lymeacademy.edu/general.htm

Admission: free.

Open: Tuesday to Saturday, 10am-4pm; Sunday, 1pm-4pm.

Facilities: **Exhibition Area**.

Activities: **Temporary Exhibitions**.

The Lyme Academy emphasizes traditional figurative instruction in its courses. Exhibitions include the work of professional artists, students, and alumni.

Storrs

University of Connecticut - The William Benton Museum of Art Ⓒᴬᴬ

University of Connecticut, 245 Glenbrook Road U-140, Storrs, CT   06269-2140

Tel: (860) 486-4520   *Fax:* (860) 486-0234

Internet Address: http://www.benton.uconn.edu

Acting Director: Mr. Sal Scolora

Admission: voluntary contribution.

Attendance: 20,000   *Established:* 1966   *Membership:* Y   *ADA Compliant:* Y

Open: **September to July**, Tuesday to Friday, 10am-4:30pm; Saturday to Sunday, 1pm-4:30pm.

Closed: Legal Holidays, Between Exhibitions.

Facilities: **Galleries**; **Shop**.

Activities: **Films** (related to exhibitions); **Gallery Talks**; **Lectures**; **Temporary Exhibitions**.

Publications: exhibition catalogues.

Housed in a National Register building (a converted dining hall), the Museum traces its roots to the donation to the University of his art collection by former University President Beach. His bequest included works by Hassam, Ranger, Lawson, and Wiggins. Since then, the collection has grown to include works by Cassatt, Benton, Bellows, Marsh, Rembrandt Peale, Braque, and Burne-Jones, now totaling some 4,000 objects.

West Hartford

Saint Joseph College - Art Study Gallery Ⓒᴬᴬ

Mercy Hall, 1678 Asylum Ave., West Hartford, CT   06117

Tel: (860) 232-4571   *Fax:* (860) 233-5695

Internet Address: http://www.sjc.edu

Director: Ms. Vicenza Uccello

Admission: free.

Saint Joseph College - Art Study Gallery, cont.

Attendance: 500   *Established:* 1932   *Membership:* N   *ADA Compliant:* Y

Open: Monday to Friday, 10am-4pm.

Closed: Legal Holidays.

Facilities: **Galleries**; **Library**.

Activities: **Education Programs**; **Temporary Exhibitions**.

Publications: brochures.

The Art Study Gallery presents temporary exhibitions and works from its permanent collection. In 1998 the College broke ground for a new arts complex, which will contain two exhibition galleries.

University of Hartford - Joseloff Gallery, Hartford Art School ⊕

Harry Jack Gray Center, 200 Bloomfield Ave.

West Hartford, CT   06117

Tel: (860) 768-4090

Fax: (860) 768-5159

Internet Address: http://www.uhavax.hartford.edu/~artschool/joseloffgallery.html

Director: Ms. Zina Davis

Admission: voluntary contribution.

Attendance: 10,000   *Established:* 1970   *Membership:* Y

Open: Tuesday to Friday, 11am-4pm; Saturday to Sunday, noon-4pm.

Closed: Academic Holidays, Legal Holidays.

Facilities: **Auditorium**; **Exhibition Area** (3,500 square feet).

Activities: **Education Programs**; **Temporary Exhibitions**.

Publications: brochures; calendar (annual); exhibition catalogues.

The Gallery presents temporary exhibitions including an annual faculty exhibit. There are also weekly shows of student work in the Student Gallery.

Delaware

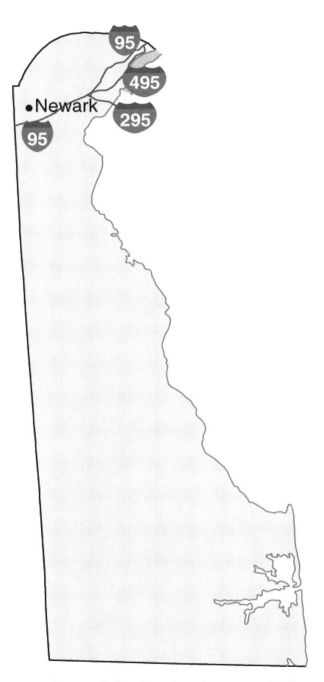

The number in parentheses following the city name indicates the number of museums/galleries in that municipality. If there is no number, one is understood. For example, in the text one listing would be found under Newark.

Delaware

Newark

University of Delaware - University Gallery Ⓒᴬᴬ

Main Street at N. College Ave., Newark, DE   19716
Tel: (302) 831-8242   *Fax:* (302) 831-4330
Internet Address: http://www.Seurat.art.udel.edu
Director: Ms. Belena S. Chapp
Admission: voluntary contribution.
Attendance: 15,000   *Established:* 1978   *Membership:* N   *ADA Compliant:* Y
Open: Monday to Friday, 11am-5pm; Saturday, 1pm-5pm.
Closed: Academic Holidays.
Facilities: **Architecture** (1832 Greek Revival building); **Exhibition Area**; **Gallery**.
Activities: **Education Programs**; **Temporary Exhibitions**.
Publications: exhibition catalogues.

The University Gallery presents exhibitions of regional and national significance. The Gallery houses over 6,000 art objects and ethnographic artifacts spanning the ancient period through the present. Its holdings include large collections of photographs by Kasebier, paintings by Walkowitz, WPA graphics, pre-Columbian ceramics, Russian icons, and works by Maillol, Rodin, Cassatt, and Moholy-Nagy, among others.

District of Columbia

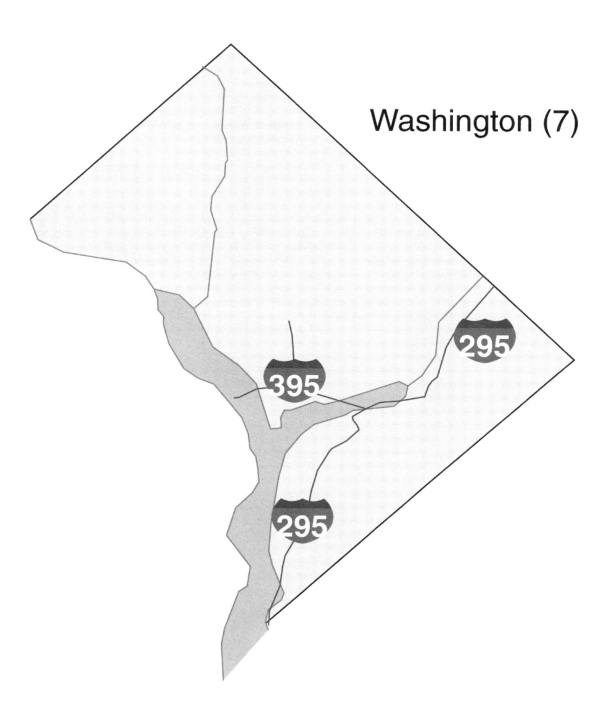

The number in parentheses following the city name indicates the number of museums/galleries in the District.

District of Columbia

Washington

American University - Watkins Gallery ⓒᴬᴬ

American University, 4400 Massachusetts Ave., N.W., Washington, DC   20016-8004
Tel: (202) 885-1064
Fax: (202) 885-1132
Internet Address: http://www.american.edu/academic.depts/cas/art/general/watkins.html
Director: Mr. Ron Haynie
Admission: free.
Established: 1945
Membership: N   *ADA Compliant:* Y
Parking: metered on street - limited.
Open: Monday to Friday, 10am-noon and 1pm-5pm.
Facilities: **Exhibition Area** (700 square feet).
Activities: **Lectures**; **Temporary Exhibitions** (16/year).

Karl Appel, title unknown, 27½ x 21½ inches. Gift of Muriel Miller Pear, Watkins Collection, American University. Photograph courtesy of the Watkins Gallery, American University, District of Columbia.

In addition to the various student exhibitions, which are part of American University's graduate and undergraduate studio art programs, the Gallery hosts five changing exhibitions each year, one of which is curated from the 4,000 piece Watkins Collection. The Watkins Collection began with the gift of a group of paintings by artist friends as a memorial to C. Law Watkins after his death in 1945. It has grown to include more than 450 paintings, and thousands of prints and drawings, with a focus primarily on 20th-century American art. Holdings include works by Karel Appel, Milton Avery, Pierre Bonnard, Marc Chagall, Giorgio de Chirico, Arthur Dove, Elaine de Kooning, Adolphe Gottlieb, Francisco Goya, Grace Hartigan, Marsden Hartley, Earl Kerkam, Paul Klee, Karl Knaths, Fernand Leger, John Marin, Reginald Marsh, Henri Matisse, Robert Rauschenberg, Kurt Schwitters, John Sloan, Jack Tworkov, and Edouard Vuillard, among others.

Catholic University of America - Salve Regina Art Gallery ⓒᴬᴬ

Salve Regina Hall, First Floor (at ground floor entrance to Dept. of Art)
Washington, DC   20064
Tel: (202) 319-5282
Internet Address: http://www.acad.cua.edu
Director: Mr. John Figura
Admission: free.
Open: Monday to Friday, 9am-5pm; Saturday, 1pm-5pm.
Facilities: **Exhibition Area**.
Activities: **Temporary Exhibitions** (7/academic year).

The Gallery presents exhibitions of work by students, faculty, and professional artists of local and national prominence. A juried exhibition of student work concludes the year's schedule each April.

Corcoran School of Art - Hemicycle Gallery ⓒᴬᴬ

17th St. and New York Ave., N.W.
Washington, DC   20006-9484
Tel: (202) 639-1800
Fax: (202) 639-1802
Internet Address: http://www.corcoran.edu/csa/gallery/hemicy.htm
Director of School Exhibitions: Mr. Paul W. Brewer
Admission: free.
Established: 1890

Corcoran School of Art - Hemicycle Gallery, cont,

ADA Compliant: Y

Parking: metered on street.

Open: Wednesday, 10am-5pm;
Thursday, 10am-9pm;
Friday to Monday, 10am-5pm.

Facilities: **Exhibition Area.**

Activities: **Temporary Exhibitions** (10/year).

The Hemicycle Gallery, considered by many to be the Corcoran Museum of Art's most beautiful gallery, was restored in 1991 as an exhibition center for the Corcoran School of Art, a private college offering a four-year program of study leading to a BFA degree. The Gallery features the work of Corcoran senior students, alumni, and faculty, as well as contemporary artists from the region and beyond. March through May is reserved for thesis exhibitions of work by graduating seniors.

Interior view, Hemicycle Gallery, Corcoran School of Art. Photograph courtesy of Corcoran School of Art, Washington, D.C.

George Washington University - Dimock Gallery ©

Lower Lisner Auditorium, 730 21st St., N.W., Washington, DC   20052

Tel: (202) 994-1525   *Fax:* (202) 994-1632

Internet Address: http://www.gwu.edu/~dimock

Curator: Ms. Lenore D. Miller

Admission: free.

Attendance: 3,500   *Established:* 1964   *Membership:* N

Parking: metered on street.

Open: Tuesday to Friday, 10am-5pm.

Closed: Legal Holidays.

Facilities: **Gallery.**

Activities: **Lectures**; **Temporary Exhibitions** (8-10/year).

Publications: exhibition catalogues.

Located on the lower level of Lisner Auditorium, the Dimock Gallery is the professional showcase for art within The George Washington University. Six to eight exhibitions are featured each year and include University-related shows, such as student, faculty, alumni, and permanent collection exhibitions, as well as shows of historical and contemporary importance, often with a focus on the Washington, DC area.

Georgetown University Art Gallery ©

Walsh Building 191, 1221 36th St., N.W., Washington, DC   20057

Tel: (202) 687-7010   *Fax:* (202) 687-3048

Internet Address: http://www.georgetown.edu/departments/AMT/gallery.html

Coordinator: Mr. John Morrell

Admission: free.

Established: 1789

Open: call for hours.

Facilities: **Exhibition Area.**

Activities: **Temporary Exhibitions.**

Publications: collection catalogue.

Located off the Walsh Building's main lobby on the ground floor, the art department's gallery presents regular exhibitions of work by faculty, visiting artists and students. Also of possible interest on campus, University memorabilia, decorative art, and works by European and American masters from the Georgetown University Antique and Art Collection are displayed in the Carroll Parlor, a period room located at 37th and O Streets (call for hours, 687-4406).

Howard University Gallery of Art

2455 6th St., N.W., Washington, DC   20059
Tel: (202) 806-6405   *Fax:* (202) 806-6503
Internet Address: http://www.founders.howard.edu/finearts/FineArts/GALLERy_FINAL/Gallery
Director: Dr. Tritobia H. Benjamin
Admission: free.
Established: 1928   *ADA Compliant:* Y
Parking: metered on street.
Open: **Academic Year**, Monday to Friday, 9:30am-5:30pm; Sunday, 1pm-4pm.
Closed: Legal Holidays.
Facilities: **Gallery**; **Print Study Room**.
Activities: **Permanent Exhibits**; **Temporary Exhibitions**; **Traveling Exhibitions**.
Publications: catalogues.

Serving as a study and research facility for the University and scholarly communities, the Gallery offers temporary exhibitions drawn from its permanent collections and from the work of nationally and internationally recognized artists. The Gallery's African American Collection, including paintings, sculpture, drawings, and prints, is one of the most extensive collections of black artists extant. Its African Art Collection includes traditional artifacts from the 18th through early 20th centuries. Other collections include Far Eastern and Decorative Arts, the Kress Study Collection (12 Renaissance and Baroque paintings), the Irving Gumbel Print Collection (European works from the 15th to 19th centuries), and the Twentieth Century Fine Art Collection (prints, paintings and tapestry, including a set of 14 wall hangings designed by Alexander Calder).

Florida

The number in parentheses following the city name indicates the number of museums/galleries in that municipality. If there is no number, one is understood. For example, in the text five listings would be found under Miami and one entry under Miami Beach.

Florida

Boca Raton

Florida Atlantic University - University Galleries Ⓒᴬᴬ

77 Glades Road, Boca Raton, FL   33431-0991
Tel: (561) 367-2966   *Fax:* (561) 367-2166
Internet Address: http://www.fau.edu/divdept/artshum/art_gal/htm
Admission: free.
Open: Tuesday to Friday, 11am-4pm; Saturday, noon-4pm.
Facilities: **Galleries** (2).
Activities: **Temporary Exhibitions**.

The University maintains two galleries, which serve to present and interpret a wide range of visual arts and other humanities disciplines through exhibitions and exhibition-related public programs such as lectures, performances, and films. The Schmidt Center Gallery, located in the Dorothy F. Schmidt Center for the Performing Arts, features six to eight presentations each year of contemporary visual art by regionally, nationally, and internationally recognized artists. As a more formal and publicly accessible space than the Ritter Art Gallery, The Schmidt Center Gallery seeks to present exhibition programs of interest to both university and public audiences in the South Florida region. The gallery will occasionally also present anthropology, history, and other humanities-based exhibitions, supporting the wider mission of the Schmidt College of Arts and Humanities, in collaboration with its faculty and selected outside scholars. The Ritter Gallery, located on the upper level of the Breezeway east of the Wimberly Library, presents six to eight exhibitions each year, many of which provide FAU art students with their initial experiences in public presentation of their work. The gallery is also available to students and college professors representing other humanities disciplines that can be interpreted through exhibiting historic or contemporary material culture. Finally, the gallery seeks to present non-traditional or experimental visual art and other presentations that may benefit from the informal nature of this gallery space.

Coral Gables

University of Miami - Lowe Art Museum Ⓒᴬᴬ

1301 Stanford Drive, Coral Gables, FL   33124-6310
Tel: (305) 284-3535   *Fax:* (305) 284-2024
Internet Address: http://www.lowemuseum.org
Director: Mr. Brian A. Dursum
Admission: fee: adult-$5.00, child-free, student-$3.00, senior-$3.00.
Attendance: 106,000   *Established:* 1950   *Membership:* Y   *ADA Compliant:* Y
Parking: pay on site.
Open: Tuesday to Wednesday, 10am-5pm; Thursday, noon-7pm; Friday to Saturday, 10am-5pm;
        Sunday, noon-5pm.
Closed: Legal Holidays.
Facilities: **Classrooms**; **Galleries**; **Library** (5,000 volumes, non-circulating); **Sculpture Garden**;
    Shop.
Activities: **Arts Festival**; **Concerts**; **Education Programs** (children); **Films**; **Gallery Talks**;
    Lectures; **Permanent Exhibits**; **Temporary Exhibitions**; **Traveling Exhibitions**.
Publications: catalogues; newsletter (quarterly).

The Lowe Art Museum houses an extensive collection of art from around the world, including Egyptian, Greek, and Roman antiquities; the Samuel H. Kress Collection of Renaissance and Baroque Art (works by Cranach the Elder, Guardi, della Robbia, and Tintoretto); European art (works by Dandini, Gainsborough, Monet, Gauguin, and Picasso); American art (works by Allston, Rembrandt Peale, Bierstadt, Inness, Henri, Sloan, Lichtenstein, Stella, Botero, Grooms, Nevelson, Warhol, and Lam); Native American art (particular strength in both North and South American textiles); Pre-Columbian art (art in all media representing diverse cultures from Mexico to Chile); African art (objects from various sub-Saharan cultures of West Africa); and Asian art (objects from China, Korea, Japan, and South Asia, including Chinese ceramics from the Neolithic Period to the 20th century, Indian stone sculpture, and Tibetan and Nepalese bronze miniatures).

Davie

Broward Community College Fine Arts Gallery ⓒᴬᴬ

3501 SW Davie Road, Davie, FL 33314
Tel: (954) 475-6517
Internet Address: http://fs.broward.cc.fl.us/central/art/gallery.html
Admission: free.
Open: Monday to Friday, 9am-2pm; Saturday, 10am-3pm.
Facilities: **Exhibition Area**.
Activities: **Juried Exhibit** (annual); **Temporary Exhibitions**.

The Gallery presents exhibitions of work in a variety of media by students and professional artists.

Daytona Beach

Daytona Beach Community College - Southeast Museum of Photography

Daytona Beach Community College, Building 37
1200 W. International Speedway Blvd.
Daytona Beach, FL 32114
Tel: (904) 254-4469
Fax: (904) 254-4487
TDDY: (904) 254-3023
Internet Address:
   http://www.dbcc.cc.fl.us/dbcc/htm/smp/smphome.htm
Director: Ms. Alison Devine Nordstrom
Admission: voluntary contribution.
Attendance: 40,000   *Established:* 1979
Membership: Y   *ADA Compliant:* Y
Parking: on campus.
Open: Tuesday, 10am-7pm;
        Wednesday to Friday, 10am-4pm;
        Saturday to Sunday, noon-4pm.
Closed: Legal Holidays.
Facilities: **Auditorium** (500 seats); **Exhibition Area** (8,000 square feet); **Library** (500 volumes).
Activities: **Education Programs** (undergraduate college students); **Films**; **Guided Tours**; **Lectures**.
Publications: catalogues (occasional); newsletter (quarterly).

Eli Reed, *Million Man March*, 1995, exhibited 1998 at Southeast Museum of Photography. Photograph copyright Eli Reed, courtesy of Southeast Museum of Photography, Daytona Beach, Florida.

The Southeast Museum of Photography presents solo and group temporary exhibitions of contemporary photography.

De Land

Stetson University - The Duncan Gallery of Art ⓒᴬᴬ

Stetson University, Sampson Hall
De Land, FL 32720-3756
Tel: (904) 822-7266   *Fax:* (904) 822-7268
Internet Address: http://www.edu/departments/art
Gallery Director: Mr. Dan Gunderson
Admission: free.
Attendance: 10,000   *Established:* 1965   *Membership:* Y   *ADA Compliant:* Y
Parking: free on site.
Open: Monday to Friday, 10am-4pm; Saturday to Sunday, 1pm-4pm.
Closed: Academic Holidays, Legal Holidays.
Facilities: **Gallery** (2,200 square feet).

Stetson University - The Duncan Gallery of Art, cont.

Activities: **Demonstrations**; **Education Programs** (undergraduate college students); **Gallery Talks**; **Lectures**; **Traveling Exhibitions**; **Workshops**.

Publications: exhibition catalogues.

The Duncan Gallery mounts temporary exhibitions on a monthly basis.

Fort Myers

Edison Community College Gallery of Fine Art

Barbara B. Mann Performing Arts Hall
8099 College Pkwy., S.W.
Fort Myers, FL   33919
Tel: (941) 489-9314
Fax: (941) 489-9482
Internet Address: http://www.edison.edu/scheduledevents/index.html
Curator: Ms. Marta Mieras
Admission: free.
Attendance: 20,000   *Established:* 1979   *Membership:* Y   *ADA Compliant:* Y
Open: Tuesday to Friday, 10am-4pm; Saturday, 11am-3pm; Sunday, 1pm-5pm.
Facilities: **Auditorium** (194 seats); **Classrooms**; **Exhibition Area**; **Food Services** Cafeteria; **Galleries** (2); **Library**.
Activities: **Films**; **Guided Tours**.
Publications: exhibition catalogues.

The Gallery of Fine Arts presents temporary exhibitions centering on art from various historical periods, in various media, and from Western and non-Western cultures. These exhibitions consist of works from the Edison Community College permanent collection as well as works from other sources.

Gainesville

Santa Fe Community College - Santa Fe Gallery

Santa Fe Community College
3000 NW 83rd St., Bldg. P, Room 201
Gainesville, FL   32606
Tel: (352) 395-5621
Fax: (352) 395-5281
Internet Address: http://www.santafe.cc.fl.us
Director: Ms. Mallory O'Connor
Admission: free.
Attendance: 10,000   *Established:* 1978
Membership: Y   *ADA Compliant:* Y
Parking: free on site.
Open: Monday, 10am-3pm;
Tuesday, 10am-3pm and 6pm-8pm;
Wednesday to Friday, 10am-3pm.
Closed: Academic Holidays.
Facilities: **Exhibition Area** (1,800 square feet).

Jim Atyeo, *The Great Alachua Savanna*, 1997, installation in Santa Fe Gallery. Photograph courtesy of Santa Fe Gallery, Santa Fe Community College, Gainesville, Florida.

Activities: **Education Programs** (undergraduate and graduate college students); **Guided Tours** (on request); **Lectures**; **Participatory Exhibits**.
Publications: exhibition brochures.

Focusing on contemporary art, the Santa Fe Gallery holds eight exhibitions per year, including one faculty show and two student shows.

University of Florida - Samuel P. Harn Museum of Art

University of Florida, S.W. 34th Street and Hull Road, Gainesville, FL   32611

Tel: (352) 392-9826   *Fax:* (352) 392-3892

Internet Address: http://www.arts.ufl.edu/harn

Director: Mr. Budd Harris Bishop

Admission: voluntary contribution.

Attendance: 65,000   *Established:* 1981

Membership: Y   *ADA Compliant:* Y

Parking: metered on site.

Open: Tuesday to Friday, 11am-5pm;
Saturday, 10am-5pm;
Sunday, 1pm-5pm.

Closed: New Year's Day, ML King Day, Memorial Day,
Independence Day, Labor Day, Veterans Day,
Thanksgiving Day to Thanksgiving Friday,
Christmas Day.

Facilities: **Auditorium** (250 seats); **Exhibition Area** (22,000
square feet); **Library**; **Object Study Room**; **Shop**; **Study
Center** (800 square feet).

Activities: **Concerts**; **Education Programs** (adults, undergradu-
ate/graduate students, and children); **Films**; **Gallery Talks**;
Guided Tours (Wed, 12:30pm; Sat-Sun, 2pm; family 2nd Sun
in month, 1;15pm); **Lectures**; **Performances**; **Temporary
Exhibitions**; **Traveling Exhibitions**.

Exterior view of the entrance and east face of the Harn Museum of Art. Photograph courtesy of Harn Museum of Art, University of Florida, Gainesville, Florida.

Publications: exhibition catalogues; newsletter (monthly); newsletter, "Collection Exchange"; report (biennial).

The Harn Museum of Art offers approximately fifteen changing exhibitions per year, consisting of both historical and contemporary art, from its own collection as well as from other major institutions and collections. The Harn's own collection of more than 5,500 paintings, prints, and sculptures dates to the pre-Columbian era. The American collection features early 20th-century artists, including Bellows, Marin, Soyer, Kent, and Avery, along with work by contemporary artists. The Asian collection includes selections from China, Korea, Southeast Asia, and India. There are also African and Oceanic collections.

University of Florida - University Gallery

University of Florida, Fine Arts Building B, Gainesville, FL   32611-5803

Tel: (352) 392-0201 *Ext:* 230   *Fax:* (352) 846-0266

Internet Address: http://www.arts.ufl.edu/galleries.html

Director: Mr. James Wyman

Admission: voluntary contribution.

Attendance: 3,500   *Established:* 1965   *Membership:* Y   *ADA Compliant:* Y

Parking: By permit only; call for instructions.

Open: Tuesday, 10am-8pm; Wednesday to Friday, 10am-5pm; Saturday, 1pm-5pm.

Closed: Legal Holidays.

Facilities: **Exhibition Area** (features student work); **Library** (30,000 volumes).

Activities: **Gallery Talks**; **Lectures**; **Temporary Exhibitions** (approximately 6/year); **Traveling
Exhibitions**.

Publications: exhibition catalogues (occasional).

Located at the east end of the Fine Arts Campus Complex, the University Gallery presents exhibitions of contemporary art in a variety of media, as well as student and faculty shows. Also of possible interest on campus are the Focus Gallery (located in Fine Arts Building C; open Monday-Friday, 8am-11:45pm and 1pm-4:45pm), displaying the work of students or emerging artists; and the Grinter Gallery (located in Grinter Hall; open Monday-Friday, 10am-4pm), specializing in international artwork. For information on the University's Samuel P. Harn Museum of Art, see separate listing.

Jacksonville

Jacksonville University - The Alexander Brest Museum and Gallery ⓒⒶⒶ

Jacksonville University
2800 University Blvd., North
Jacksonville, FL   32211
Tel: (904) 744-3950   *Ext:* 7371
Fax: (904) 745-7375
Internet Address:
   http://www.junix.ju.edu/ju/abmg.htm
Curator: Mr. David Lauderdale
Admission: free.
Attendance: 21,000   *Established:* 1977
Membership: Y   *ADA Compliant:* Y
Open: Monday to Friday, 9am-4:30pm;
      Saturday, noon-5pm.
Closed: Memorial Day, Independence Day,
      Labor Day, Veterans Day, Thanksgiving Day,
      Christmas Day.
Facilities: **Exhibition Area** (4,250 square feet).
Activities: **Concerts**; **Guided Tours**; **Lectures**;
      Temporary Exhibitions.
Publications: "A Guide to the Collection: The
      Alexander Brest Museum and Gallery".

Cluster lamp with pond Favrile lily design, c. 1903-1906, Tiffany, bronze. Alexander Brest Museum collection. Photograph by Richard Sowell, courtesy of Alexander Brest Museum, Jacksonville University, Jacksonville, Florida.

The Museum presents temporary exhibitions of the work of faculty, students, and local, regional, national, and international artists. It also displays objects from its permanent collection, which includes 17th-through 19th-century European and Oriental ivory, pre-Columbian artifacts, Steuben glass, Chinese porcelain and cloisonné, Tiffany glass, and Boehm porcelain.

University of North Florida - University Gallery ⓒⒶⒶ

4567 St. Johns Bluff Road, Jacksonville, FL   32216
Tel: (904) 620-2534   *Fax:* (904) 646-2505
Internet Address: http://www.unf.edu/dept/gallery
Director: Mr. Paul C. Karabinis
Admission: free.
Open: Monday/Wednesday/Friday, 9am-3pm; Tuesday/Thursday, 9am-5pm.
Closed: Legal Holidays.
Facilities: **Exhibition Area** (900 square feet).
Activities: **Lectures**; **Performances** (concert series); **Temporary Exhibitions**.

The gallery presents a variety of exhibitions featuring regionally and nationally recognized artists, as well as the annual Visual Arts Faculty Art Show, Graduating Senior Show, and Juried Student Art Show.

Lake Worth

Palm Beach Community College - Museum of Contemporary Art (MCA)

Palm Beach Community College, 601 Lake Ave.
Lake Worth, FL   33460
Tel: (407) 582-0006   *Fax:* (407) 582-0504
Internet Address: http://www.mcapbcc.qpg.com
Director: Mr. Jim Peele
Admission: fee-$2.00.
Attendance: 11,000   *Established:* 1989

Lake Worth, Florida

Palm Beach Community College - Museum of Contemporary Art, cont.

Membership: Y   *ADA Compliant:* Y
Parking: public lot and street parking.
Open: Tuesday to Sunday, noon-5pm.
    also, Friday, noon-9pm.
Closed: Christmas Day, New Year's Day,
    ML King Day, Independence Day,
    Thanksgiving Day.
Facilities: **Architecture** (Art Deco former
    movie theatre, 1939); **Exhibition Area**
    (10,000 square feet); **Library** (300 volumes).
Activities: **Concerts**; **Education Programs**
    (adults and children); **Films**; **Permanent
    Exhibits**; **Traveling Exhibitions**.

The Museum is housed in a converted 1939 Art Deco theatre and is dedicated to the exhibition of the work of contemporary artists, both from its permanent collection and in temporary exhibitions of works on loan. The permanent collection consists chiefly of art glass, ceramics, and sculpture, including kinetic sculpture.

Drawing of Museum of Contemporary Art. Courtesy of Museum of Contemporary Art, Lake Worth, Florida.

Lakeland

Florida Southern College - Melvin Gallery ©

111 Lake Hollingsworth Drive
Lakeland, FL   33801
Tel: (941) 680-4111
Internet Address: http://www.flsouthern.edu/art/gallery.html
Department Chairman: Mr. Downing Barnitz
Admission: free.
Open: Call for hours.
Facilities: **Exhibition Area**.
Activities: **Temporary Exhibitions**.

The gallery presents temporary exhibitions, including annual faculty, juried student, and juried Lakeland Art Guild shows.

Madison

North Florida Community College Art Gallery

Turner Davis Drive, Madison, FL   32340
Tel: (850) 973-2288
Fax: (850) 973-9288
Internet Address: http://www.nflcc.cc.fl.us
Director: Mr. William F. Gardner, Jr.
Admission: free.
Established: 1975   *ADA Compliant:* Y
Parking: free on site.
Open: Monday to Friday, 8am-3pm.
Facilities: **Classrooms**; **Gallery**; **Theatre**.
Activities: **Arts Festival**; **Education Programs** (adults, undergraduate college students, and children); **Films**; **Gallery Talks**; **Guided Tours**; **Lectures**; **Permanent Exhibits**.

The Art Gallery presents a wide variety of art in temporary exhibitions and also maintains a small permanent collection.

Miami

Florida International University - The Art Museum

University Park, PC110
Miami, FL 33199
Tel: (305) 348-2890
Fax: (305) 348-2762
Internet Address:
  http://www.fiu.edu/museum.html
Director: Ms. Dahlia Morgan
Admission: free.
Attendance: 76,000   *Established:* 1977
Membership: Y   *ADA Compliant:* Y
Parking: metered in PC lot.
Open: Monday, 10am-9pm;
    Tuesday to Friday, 10am-5pm;
    Saturday, noon-4pm.
Closed: Academic Holidays.

Jonathan Borofsky, *The Hammering Man at 2,938,405*, 1977-1985, Cor-Ten steel, motorized, height 24 feet. Margulies Family Collection, The Art Museum at Florida International University. Photograph courtesy of The Art Museum at Florida International University, Miami, Florida.

Facilities: **Auditorium**; **Galleries**; **Library** (non-circulating); **Sculpture Park**.
Activities: **Education Programs** (adults and children); **Gallery Talks**; **Temporary Exhibitions**; **Traveling Exhibitions**.
Publications: exhibition catalogues.

The Art Museum at Florida International University in an important cultural resource. It mounts approximately ten temporary exhibitions per year, showing student and faculty work as well as major traveling exhibitions. The most notable aspect of the permanent collection at the Museum is its outdoor sculpture. The collection of 57 pieces includes works by Dubuffet, Miró, Nevelson, Calder, Noguchi, and Serra. The general collection consists of works on paper (works by Gottlieb, Kelly, Oldenburg, Motherwell, Rosenquist, Rauschenburg, and Indiana); photographs (by Abbott, Hassam, and Eggleston); pre-Columbian art from numerous cultures; and painting, especially Haitian and Brazilian folk art. The Metropolitan Museum and Art Center Collection includes paintings (by Hoffmann, Tamayo, Glackens, Chase, and Bermudez); prints (Warhol, Lichtenstein, Indiana, and Hockney); Asian art (Japanese netsuke, Benin bronzes); sculpture (pieces by Rodin and Lipchitz); and photographs (works by Muybridge). Finally, the Oscar B. Cintas Fellowship Foundation Collection is comprised of works by artists of Cuban descent who have received Cintas Fellowships and includes paintings, prints, and drawings. The Museum is in the process of constructing a 40,000-square-foot facility to house its collection and to serve as a more suitable venue for exhibitions.

Miami-Dade Community College - Kendall Campus Art Gallery

11011 Southwest 104th St.
Miami, FL 33176-3393
Tel: (305) 237-2322
Fax: (305) 237-2901
TDDY: (800) 955-8771
Internet Address: http://www.kendall.mcdd.edu/art/gallery.htm
Director: Mr. Robert J. Sindelir
Admission: free.
Attendance: 7,000   *Established:* 1970   *ADA Compliant:* Y
Parking: free in student lots.
Open: **September to May**,
      Monday, 8am-4pm; Tuesday to Wednesday, noon-7:30pm; Thursday to Friday, 8am-4pm.
    June to early-August,
      Monday, 8am-4pm; Tuesday to Wednesday, noon-7:30pm; Thursday, 8am-4pm.
Closed: Legal Holidays.
Facilities: **Auditorium** (300 seats); **Exhibition Area** (3,000 square feet); **Food Services** Restaurant (300 seats).

Miami, Florida

Miami-Dade Community College - Kendall Campus Art Gallery, cont.

Activities: **Education Programs** (college students); **Films; Guided Tours; Lectures; Temporary Exhibitions; Traveling Exhibitions.**

Publications: exhibition catalogues.

The Art Gallery mounts temporary exhibitions of student work as well as that of professional artists.

Miami-Dade Community College, North Campus - Gallery North Ⓒ

Leroy Collins Campus Center, Room 4207-1
11380 Northwest 27th Ave.
Miami, FL 33167
Tel: (305) 237-1532   *Fax:* (305) 237-1850   *TDDY:* (800) 955-8771
Internet Address: http://www.mdcc.edu/north/nrthgal.htm
Gallery Director: Ms. April Dolkar
Admission: free.
Open: Monday to Thursday, 10am-4pm.
Facilities: **Exhibition Area.**
Activities: **Temporary Exhibitions.**

The Gallery mounts temporary exhibitions.

Miami-Dade Community College - Wolfson Campus Galleries Ⓒ

300 Northeast 2nd Ave., 5th, #1365
Miami, FL 33132-2297
Tel: (305) 237-3278   *Fax:* (305) 237-3645
Internet Address: http://www.mdcc.edu/wolfson/cultural/caffcal.html
Admission: free.
Open: Monday to Friday, 9am-5pm.
Facilities: **Exhibition Area.**
Activities: **Temporary Exhibitions.**

There are three galleries on the M-DCC's Wolfson Campus. The Centre Gallery features exhibitions of experimental works as well as national and international collections. The Interamerican Art Gallery, located at 627 S.W. 27th Ave., highlights the work of local and international artists. The Francis Wolfson Art Gallery features works by faculty, students, and Florida artists.

New World School of the Arts - New World Gallery

25 Northeast 2nd St.
Miami, FL 33132
Tel: (305) 237-3620
Fax: (305) 237-3794
Internet Address: www.mdcc.edu/nwsa/
Dean of Visual Arts: Dr. Mel Alexenberg
Admission: free.
Attendance: 2,500   *Established:* 1987
Membership: N   *ADA Compliant:* Y
Parking: municipal garage.
Open: Monday to Friday, 9am-5pm.
Facilities: **Exhibition Area.**
Activities: **Temporary Exhibitions.**

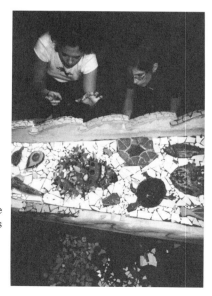

The New World Gallery exhibits contemporary art and the work of its students and faculty in approximately six shows per year.

Mel Alexanberg and Miriam Benjanin, *Art Throne*, 1998, mixed-media 20-foot sculpted seat, created through intergenerational and multicultural collaboration. Photograph courtesy of New World Gallery, Miami, Florida.

Miami Beach

Florida International University - The Wolfsonian

1001 Washington Ave.
Miami Beach, FL   33139
Tel: (305) 531-1001
Fax: (305) 531-2133
Internet Address: http://www.fiu.edu/~wolfson/
Director: Ms. Cathy Leff
Admission: fee: adult-$5.00, child-$3.50, student-$3.50,
   senior-$3.50.
Attendance: 26,000   *Established:* 1986
Membership: Y   *ADA Compliant:* Y
Parking: valet, municipal lots, and metered on-street parking.
Open: Tuesday to Wednesday, 11am-6pm;
          Thursday, 11am-9pm;
          Friday to Saturday, 11am-6pm;
          Sunday, noon-5pm.
Facilities: **Exhibition Area** (15,000 square feet); **Library**
   (35,000 volumes); **Shop** (prints, books, cards, jewelry, publica-
   tions).
Activities: **Concerts**; **Education Programs** (adults); **Guided
   Tours** (groups, reserve in advance); **Lectures**; **Permanent
   Exhibitions**; **Temporary Exhibitions**; **Traveling
   Exhibitions**.

Exterior view of The Wolfsonian.
Photograph courtesy of The Wolfsonian -
Florida International University, Miami
Beach, Florida.

Publications: "The Wolfsonian Bulletin"; books; catalogues.

Located in the heart of Miami Beach's Art Deco District, the Wolfsonian-FIU was founded in 1986
to promote the collection, preservation, and understanding of art and design from the period 1885-
1945. In 1997 it joined the state's public education system as a division of Florida International
University. Permanent, temporary, and traveling shows address broad themes of the 19th and 20th
centuries, such as nationalism, political persuasion, industrialization, architecture and urbanism, con-
sumerism and advertising, transportation, and world's fairs. Although drawing primarily on its own
holdings, the Wolfsonian also features exhibitions and objects on loan from other institutions. The
Wolfsonian holds more then 70,000 objects predominantly from North American and Europe, providing rich evidence of the cultural, political, and technological changes that swept the globe in the century preceding World War II. The collection features furniture, decorative arts, industrial design,
paintings, sculpture, architectural models, works on paper, books, and ephemera. Notable among
these are Depression-era prints and mural studies by WPA artists, items from the British Arts and
Crafts movement and the German Werkstäten and Werkbund, and artifacts of political propaganda.

Orlando

University of Central Florida Art Gallery

University of Central Florida
Main Campus, Visual Arts Building
Orlando, FL   32816
Tel: (407) 823-2676
Fax: (407) 823-6470
Internet Address: http://www.oir.ucf.edu/
Admission: free.
Open: Monday to Friday, 9am-4pm.
Facilities: **Exhibition Area**.
Activities: **Temporary Exhibitions**.

The Gallery features exhibitions of the works of established and emerging artists from Florida, the
region, and abroad.

Palm Harbor

St. Petersburg Junior College - Leepa-Rattner Museum of Fine Art ⓒ⒜

SPJC Tarpon Springs Center, 600 Klosterman Road
Palm Harbor, FL   34683-1299
Tel: (727) 712-5750
Internet Address: http://www.spjc.cc.fl.us/webcentral/welcome/museum.htm
Established: 2000
Parking: nearby college lots.
Facilities: **Exhibition Area**.
Activities: **Permanent Exhibits**; **Temporary Exhibitions**.

Scheduled to open in 2000, the Museum will serve as a repository and fine arts center for the permanent collection, a venue for traveling exhibitions, and an educational/research facility. The permanent collection includes artworks and personal items of Minotaure group member and Henry Miller associate, Abraham Rattner; a retrospective of the work of Allen Leepa; first-run posters from 20th-century Paris art exhibitions. Among the other artists represented in the permanent collection are Marc Chagall, Max Ernst, Hans Hofmann, Henry Moore, Pablo Picasso, and Georges Roualt.

Pensacola

Pensacola Junior College - Visual Arts Gallery

Pensacola Junior College, 1000 College Ave.
Pensacola, FL   32504
Tel: (904) 484-2563
Fax: (904) 484-1826
Internet Address: http://www.dept.pjc.cc.fl.us/art/events.html
Director: Mr. Allan Peterson
Admission: free.
Attendance: 28,000   *Established:* 1970   *ADA Compliant:* Y
Open: **September to May**, Monday to Thursday, 8am-9pm; Friday, 8am-3:30pm.
Closed: Holidays.
Facilities: **Exhibition Area**; **Studio Complex**.
Activities: **Education Programs** (college students); **Guided Tours**; **Temporary Exhibitions**.
Publications: announcements; brochures; catalogues; posters.

The Gallery presents a schedule of exhibitions during the school year, including faculty and student shows.

University of West Florida Art Gallery ⓒ⒜

11000 University Pkwy.
Pensacola, FL   32514
Tel: (904) 474-2045   *Ext:* 2696
Fax: (904) 474-3247
Internet Address: http://www.uwf.edu/~art
Director: Ms. Gail McKenney
Admission: voluntary contribution.
Attendance: 11,000   *Established:* 1970
Membership: Y   *ADA Compliant:* Y
Parking: free in lots adjacent to building.
Open: **mid-January to early December**,
          Monday to Thursday, 10am-5pm;
          Friday, 10am-4pm; Sunday, 1pm-4pm.
Closed: Easter Friday, Veterans Day,
          Thanksgiving Day.
Facilities: **Gallery** (1,650 square feet, plus
smaller exhibit space).

View of Gallery during Art Faculty Exhibition. Photograph courtesy of University of West Florida Art Gallery, Pensacola, Florida.

University of West Florida Art Gallery, cont.

Activities: **Films** (several/year); **Gallery Talks** (often during opening reception for exhibit); **Guided Tours** (call to arrange); **Lectures** (adjunct art faculty lecture series, plus other speakers); **Temporary Exhibitions**; **Traveling Exhibitions** (1/year).

Publications: catalogues; posters.

The Art Gallery's major exhibition emphasis is on Contemporary Art, but the Gallery also exhibits art from other historical periods and various cultures in accord with its educational mission. In addition, the Art Gallery has a small permanent collection of Modern and Contemporary works on paper, which are exhibited on a regular basis.

Sarasota

Ringling School of Art and Design - Selby Gallery ⓒ

Dr. Martin Luther King Jr. Way
(½ block east of US Rte. 41 Tamiami Trail)
Sarasota, FL   34234
Tel: (941) 359-7563   *Fax:* (941) 359-7517
Internet Address: http://www.rsad.edu
Director: Mr. Kevin Dean
Admission: voluntary contribution.
Attendance: 18,000   *Established:* 1986
Membership: Y   *ADA Compliant:* Y
Parking: free on site.
Open: **During Exhibitions**,
        Monday to Saturday, 10am-4pm.
Closed: Academic Holidays.
Facilities: **Auditorium** (125 seats); **Exhibition Area** (3,000 square feet).

Exterior view of Selby Gallery. Photograph courtesy of Selby Gallery, Ringling School of Art and Design, Sarasota, Florida.

Activities: **Concerts**; **Gallery Talks**; **Lectures**; **Readings**; **Temporary Exhibitions** (8+/year).
Publications: exhibition catalogues.

Located on the campus of the Ringling School of Art and Design, the Selby Gallery presents a season of art exhibitions by nationally and internationally known artists and designers. Although the Gallery focuses on contemporary art, photography, illustration, graphic design, interior design, and computer animation, exhibitions of historical importance are also presented. In addition, the Gallery highlights the work of faculty, staff, and students through annual exhibitions.

Tallahassee

Florida A&M University - Foster-Tanner Fine Arts Gallery

Foster-Tanner Building
Gamble Street and M.L. King Blvd.
Tallahassee, FL   32307
Tel: (850) 599-3161
Fax: (850) 599-8761
Internet Address: http://www.famu.edu
Director: Gylbert G. Coker
Admission: free.
Established: 1997
Parking: University garage.
Open: Monday to Friday, 9am-5pm.
Facilities: **Galleries** (2).
Activities: **Temporary   Exhibitions**;
     Travelling Exhibitions.
Publications: exhibition catalogues (occasional).

Interior view, Foster-Tanner Fine Arts Gallery. Photograph courtesy of Florida A&M University, Tallahassee, Florida.

The Gallery presents six exhibitions each season, including the work of students and local artists, as well as travelling exhibitions.

Tallahassee, Florida

Florida State University - Museum of Fine Arts ⒸⒶⒹ

Fine Arts Building, Copeland and W. Tennessee Sts.
Tallahassee, FL 32306
Tel: (904) 644-6836
Fax: (904) 644-7229
Internet Address: http://www.fsu.edu/~svad/FSUMuseum/index.html
Director: Ms. Allys Palladino-Craig
Admission: free.
Attendance: 44,000   *Established:* 1950
Membership: Y   *ADA Compliant:* Y
Parking: metered and pay lot parking on West Call St.
Open: **September to April**,
         Monday to Friday, 10am-4pm;
         Saturday to Sunday, 1pm-4pm.
         May to August,
         Monday to Friday, 10am-4pm.
Closed: Academic Holidays.
Facilities: **Galleries** (7); **Lecture Room**; **Sculpture Courtyard**.
Activities: **Education Programs**; **Gallery Talks**; **Guided Tours** (groups, 644-1299); **Lectures**; **Performances**; **Permanent Exhibits**; **Temporary Exhibitions**; **Traveling Exhibitions**.
Publications: art history journal, "Athanor"; brochures; curatorial publication, "Thematic"; exhibition catalogues.

Trevor Bell, *Gumbaranjon*, 1991, acrylic on shaped canvas, 7' 1" x 6' 9". From 1994 exhibition of contemporary painting, "Chroma", Museum of Fine Arts, Florida State University, Tallahassee, Florida. Photograph courtesy of Trevor Bell.

The Museum of Fine Arts, a division of the School of Visual Arts and Dance at Florida State University, is the largest art museum within two hours driving time of Tallahassee. At the time of its formation in 1950, it occupied one small room, operated without specific funding, and was administered by faculty on a volunteer basis. Spurred on particularly by the move in 1970 into a new facility of over 16,000 square feet and by the establishment of the School of Visual Arts in 1973, the growth of the Museum has been significant and steady. The Museum presents a balanced schedule of changing exhibitions based on available resources, categories of media, art historical periods and contemporary issues. The scope ranges from national impact exhibitions, often scholarly presentations of works never previously exhibited, to the work of regional artists or students. Lower level exhibitions run concurrently with upper gallery changing exhibitions.

Tampa

University of South Florida Contemporary Art Museum ⒸⒶⒹ (USF CAM)

W. Holley Drive (adjacent to the College of Fine Arts), Tampa, FL 33620
Tel: (813) 974-2849
Fax: (813) 974-5130
Internet Address: http://www.arts.usf.edu/museum
Director: Ms. Margaret A. Miller
Admission: free.
Attendance: 52,000   *Established:* 1968   *Membership:* Y   *ADA Compliant:* Y
Parking: free on site.
Open: Monday to Friday, 10am-5pm;
         Saturday, 1pm-4pm.
Closed: Academic Holidays.
Facilities: **Galleries** (4; 2 exhibition galleries, 2 apart from museum); **Shop**.

University of South Florida Contemporary Art Museum, cont.

Facilities: **Galleries** (4; 2 exhibition galleries, 2 apart from museum); **Shop**.

Activities: **Education Programs** (undergraduate and graduate college students); **Gallery Talks**; **Guided Tours** (groups, reserve two weeks in advance, 974-4133); **Lectures**; **Temporary Exhibitions**; **Traveling Exhibitions**.

Publications: calendar (biennial); exhibition catalogues; newsletter; posters.

Exterior view of University of South Florida Contemporary Art Museum. Photograph courtesy of University of South Florida Contemporary Art Museum, Tampa, Florida.

USF CAM presents changing exhibitions, designed to introduce students, faculty, and the community to current trends in contemporary fine art from Florida, the United States, and around the world. The Museum also maintains the University's art collection of over 3,500 artworks. Its primary strength is in contemporary graphics. Many of CAM's holdings have been produced at USF's Graphicstudio, an internationally recognized print atelier. CAM's holdings include works by such artists as Vito Acconci, Arakawa, Sandro Chia, Chuck Close, Jim Dine, David Hockney, Jasper Johns, Roy Lichtenstein, Robert Maplethorpe, Matt Mullican, Robert Rauschenberg, James Rosenquist, Richard Serra, and Andy Warhol. Additionally, site specific works have been placed throughout the USF campus under Florida's Art in State Buildings Program. Major public arts projects include works by Dale Eldred, Richard Fleischner, Doug Hollis, Nancy Holt, Tim Rollins and K.O.S., Ned Smyth, and Elyn Zimmerman.

University of Tampa - Lee Scarfone Gallery

401 W. Kennedy, Tampa, FL   33606

Tel: (813) 253-3333   *Fax:* (813) 258-7211

Internet Address: http://www.utampa.edu/acad/clas/art/gallery.htm

Director: Ms. Dorothy C. Cowden

Admission: voluntary contribution.

Attendance: 11,000   *Established:* 1977   *Membership:* Y   *ADA Compliant:* Y

Parking: parking lot near building.

Open: **August to May**, Tuesday to Friday, 10am-4pm; Saturday, 1pm-4pm.

Closed: June to July, Academic Holidays.

Facilities: **Architecture** (renovated WPA building, 1977 design by architect Lee Scarfone); **Exhibition Area** (2 galleries, 5,800 square feet); **Lecture Facility** (25 seats).

Activities: **Arts Festival**; **Concerts**; **Dance Recitals**; **Films**; **Guided Tours**; **Lectures**; **Performances**; **Temporary Exhibitions** (9-11/year).

Publications: brochures; exhibition catalogues.

The Lee Scarfone Gallery, the University of Tampa's teaching gallery, provides a venue for exhibitions of work by national, international, and regional artists, faculty, and students. Multimedia events including lectures, workshops, and performances complement the visual arts exhibitions. In the lecture hall, there is a continuing exhibit of monotypes created in the STUDIO-f guest artist program.

Winter Haven

Polk Community College Art Gallery

Winter Haven Campus, Fine Arts Complex, 999 Avenue H, N.E.

Winter Haven, FL   33881-4299

Tel: (941) 297-1050

Fax: (941) 297-1053

Internet Address: http://www.polk.cc.fl.us

Admission: free.

Winter Haven, Florida

Polk Community College Art Gallery, cont.

Open: **August to April**, Monday to Friday, 10am-2pm.

May to July, Monday to Thursday, 10am-3pm.

Facilities: **Gallery**.

Activities: **Temporary Exhibitions**.

The Gallery features temporary exhibitions of the work of local artists.

Winter Park

Rollins College - The George D. and Harriet W. Cornell Fine Arts Museum (C4A)

Rollins College
1000 Holt Ave. (at end)
Winter Park, FL 32789-4499

Tel: (407) 646-2526

Fax: (407) 646-2524

Internet Address: www// rollins.edu/cfam

Director: Arthur R. Blumenthal, Ph.D.

Admission: free.

Attendance: 23,000   *Established:* 1978

Membership: Y   *ADA Compliant:* Y

Parking: free in adjacent Rollins College Lot H.

Open: Tuesday to Friday, 10am-5pm;

Saturday to Sunday, 1pm-5pm.

Closed: Major Holidays.

Facilities: **Galleries**.

Activities: **Concert Series**; **Film Series** (Sunday); **Gallery Talks**; **Guided Tours** (groups, Mon-Fri, schedule in advance); **Lecture Series**; **Lectures**; **Permanent Exhibits**; **Temporary Exhibitions**; **Traveling Exhibitions**.

Publications: collection handbook; exhibition catalogues; posters.

Sir Thomas Lawrence, *Portrait of Harriet Gordon*, c. 1820, oil on canvas. Gift of Myers family in memory of John C. Myers, Sr., George D. and Harriet W. Cornell Fine Arts Museum. Photograph courtesy of George D. and Harriet W. Cornell Fine Arts Museum, Rollins College, Winter Park, Florida.

Located at the end of Holt Avenue on the Winter Park campus of Rollins College, the Cornell Fine Arts Museum organizes exhibitions based on its permanent collection. Temporary exhibitions also include an annual solo exhibition by a Florida (or Rollins alumnus) artist, faculty curated shows, and the annual Senior Art Show in May. The permanent collection consists of more than 6,000 works with strengths in American and European art.

Georgia

The number in parentheses following the city name indicates the number of museums/galleries in that municipality. If there is no number, one is understood. For example, in the text six listings would be found under Atlanta and one listing under Decatur.

Georgia

Athens

University of Georgia - Georgia Museum of Art

Performing & Visual Arts Complex
90 Carlton St., East Campus
Athens, GA   30602-1719
Tel: (706) 542-4662
Fax: (706) 542-1051
TDDY: (706) 542-1007
Internet Address:
   http://www.budgets.uga.edu/gma
Director: Mr. William U. Eiland
Admission: suggested contribution-$1.00.
Attendance: 61,000   *Established:* 1945
Membership: Y   *ADA Compliant:* Y
Parking: adjacent to building.
Open: Tuesday to Thursday, 10am-5pm;
        Friday, 10am-9pm;
        Saturday, 10am-5pm;
        Sunday, 1pm-5pm.
Closed: Legal Holidays.
Facilities: **Auditorium**; **Building** (52,000
   square feet); **Food Services** On Display Café
   (Mon-Fri, 10am-2pm); **Galleries** (10, of which
   4 reserved for permanent collection); **Library**
   (non-circulating); **Shop** (Tues-Sat, 11am-4pm;
   Sun, 1pm-4pm); **Study Room**; **Theater**.

Childe Hassam, *Bridge at Old Lyme*, 1908, oil on canvas, 24 x 27 inches, Eva Underhill Holbrook Memorial Collection of American Art, gift of Alfred H. Holbrook, Georgia Museum of Art. Photograph courtesy of Georgia Museum of Art, Athens, Georgia.

Activities: **Concerts** (classical and contemporary); **Education Programs** (adults, university students, children and families); **Film Series**; **Gallery Talks** (adults and children); **Guided Tours** (groups of 5+); **Lectures**; **Permanent Exhibits**; **Temporary/Traveling Exhibitions** (20/year).
Publications: bulletin, "Georgia Museum of Art Bulletin" (annual); exhibition catalogues; gallery guides; newsletter (quarterly).

Hosting a variety of culturally diverse exhibitions, the GMA draws both from its permanent collection and from other museums and private collections, representing all periods of art history. The Lamar Dodd Gallery, the Rachel Cosby Conway Gallery, the Alfred Heber Holbrook Gallery and the Samuel H. Kress Gallery in the C. L. Morehead Jr. Wing feature important American canvases in the permanent collection and Old Master works from the Kress collection. The George-Ann and Boone Knox Gallery of Prints and Drawings presents rotating exhibitions of works on paper from the Museum's extensive collection and from other private and public collections. The Virginia and Alfred Kennedy and Philip Henry Alston, Jr. Galleries feature temporary exhibitions from private and public collections. The museum's permanent collection of over 7,000 objects features 19th- and 20th-century American paintings, American and European prints and drawings dating from the 16th century to the present, Japanese prints, and the Samuel H. Kress Study Collection of Italian Renaissance Paintings. The West Foundation Collection is also incorporated into the exhibition of the permanent collection. The collection is on long-term loan to the museum and consists of British watercolors, 19th-century American paintings, and several 19th-century American Neo-classical sculptures.

Atlanta

The Atlanta College of Art Gallery

Atlanta College of Art, 1280 Peachtree St., N.E., Atlanta, GA   30309
Tel: (404) 733-5001   *Fax:* (404) 733-5201
Internet Address: http://www.aca.edu
Admission: voluntary contribution.
Attendance: 12,000   *Established:* 1928   *Membership:* Y   *ADA Compliant:* Y

The Atlanta College of Art Gallery, cont.

Open: Monday to Saturday, 10am-5pm.
Facilities: **Exhibition Area** (2 galleries).
Activities: **Temporary Exhibitions.**

The Atlanta College of Art Gallery mounts exhibitions of regional, national, and international importance in addition to showing student, faculty, and alumni work. It also sponsors a visiting artists lecture series. Also of possible interest is Gallery 100, a student-run gallery, hosting weekly student shows showcasing individual and group work.

Clark Atlanta University Art Gallery

Trevor Arnett Hall, 2nd Floor, James P. Brawley Drive at Fair St., Atlanta, GA   30314
Tel: (404) 880-6644
Internet Address: http://www.cau.edu/cau/collections.html
Director: Ms. Tina Dunkley
Admission: free.
Open: Call for hours.
Facilities: **Gallery.**
Activities: **Temporary Exhibitions.**

With approximately 500 works of art, the University's art collection's strength is an extensive collection of African American art including works by Catlett, Lawrence, Tanner, and Woodruff. Additional holdings include works by other representative American artists and a collection of African art and Africana. A portion of the collections is displayed regularly in the Catherine Waddell Gallery.

Emory University - Michael C. Carlos Museum ⓒᵃᵘ

571 S. Kilgo St.
Atlanta, GA   30322
Tel: (404) 727-4282
Fax: (404) 727-4292
TDDY: (404) 727-8017
Internet Address: http://www.cc.emory.edu/CARLOS
Director: Mr. Anthony G. Hirschel
Admission: suggested contribution-$3.00.
Attendance: 87,000   *Established:* 1920
Membership: Y   *ADA Compliant:* Y
Parking: free on campus and pay at B. Jones Bldg. or Fishburne Deck.
Open: Monday to Saturday, 10am-5pm;
Sunday, noon-5pm.

View of Egyptian Gallery, Michael C. Carlos Museum. Photograph by Steven Brooke, courtesy of Michael C. Carlos Museum, Emory University, Atlanta, Georgia.

Facilities: **Architecture** Beaux Arts building (1919), Renovation/Expansion (1993 designed by Michael Graves; total 45,000 square feet); **Exhibition Area** (29 permanent collection galleries, 8 special exhibition galleries); **Food Services** Café Antico (Mon-Fri, 8:30am-5pm; Sat & Sun, noon-5pm); **Shop** (books, gifts, jewelry).
Activities: **Films**; **Gallery Talks**; **Guided Tours** (call 727-2363); **Lectures**; **Permanent Exhibits**; **Temporary/Traveling Exhibitions**.
Publications: catalogue, "Surrealist Vision and Technique"; exhibition catalogues (occasional); handbook, "Michael C. Carlos Museum"; newsletter (quarterly).

Located on the historic quadrangle of the Emory University campus, the Michael C. Carlos Museum has a permanent collection of some 16,000 objects including art from ancient Egypt, Greece, Rome, the Near East, the Americas, Asia, Africa, Oceania, and artworks on paper ranging from the Middle Ages to the 20th century. The Museum also offers special exhibitions of all periods drawn from its own holdings and from other institutions, both national and international.

Georgia Institute of Technology - Richards and Westbrook Galleries ⓒᴬᴬ

Robert Ferst Center for the Arts (across from the Student Center)
Atlanta, GA 30332
Tel: (404) 894-9600
Internet Address: http://www.aux.gatech.edu/studentcenter/ ferstcenter/html/galleries.htm
Admission: free.
*Open:.*Call for hours.
Facilities: **Galleries** (2).
Activities: **Temporary Exhibitions**.

The Ferst Center includes two galleries presenting temporary exhibitions of work by professional artists, as well as an annual student art show each spring. The galleries also participate in the Georgia Tech's spring arts festival.

Georgia State University School of Art and Design Galleries ⓒᴬᴬ

University Plaza, Atlanta, GA 30303
Tel: (404) 651-0489   *Fax:* (404) 651-1779
Internet Address: http://www.gsu.edu
Director: Teri Williams
Admission: free.
Established: 1970
Membership: N   *ADA Compliant:* Y
Parking: pay on site.
Open: Monday to Friday, 10am-6pm.
Closed: New Year's Day, Independence Day, Labor Day,
          Thanksgiving Day, last week in Dec..
Facilities: **Auditorium** (400 seats); **Classrooms**; **Exhibition Area** (2 galleries); **Food Services** Cafeteria (400 seats); **Library** (3,000 volumes, use by special permission); **Reading Room**.
Activities: **Education Programs** (adults, undergraduate/graduate students and children); **Films**; **Gallery Talks**; **Lectures**; **Temporary Exhibitions**; **Traveling Exhibitions**.
Publications: exhibition catalogues.

View of student exhibition, School of Art and Design Galleries. Photograph courtesy of Georgia State University, Atlanta, Georgia.

While the School has no permanent collection, it presents temporary exhibitions of student and faculty work that are reflective of the School's curriculum, as well as individual and group shows of works by professional artists.

Oglethorpe University Museum

Oglethorpe University, 4484 Peachtree Road, N.E., Atlanta, GA   30319
Tel: (404) 364-8555
Fax: (404) 364-8556
Internet Address: http://www.oglethorpe.edu/museum
Director: Mr. Lloyd Nick
Admission: free.
Attendance: 8,000   *Established:* 1993   *Membership:* Y   *ADA Compliant:* Y
Parking: free on site.
Open: Tuesday to Wednesday, noon-5pm; Thursday, noon-7pm; Friday to Sunday, noon-5pm.
Closed: Legal Holidays, Christmas Day to New Year's Day.
Facilities: **Auditorium** (100 seats); **Exhibition Area** (3,500 square feet); **Shop**.
Activities: **Concerts**; **Films**; **Guided Tours**; **Lectures**; **Traveling Exhibitions**.
Publications: catalogues; newsletter.

The Museum presents exhibitions drawn from its permanent collection and temporary/traveling exhibitions from other collections focusing on figurative, representational and spiritual art.

Augusta, Georgia

Augusta

Augusta State University - Fine Arts Gallery ⓒ
2500 Walton Way, Augusta, GA   30904
Tel: (706) 737-1453   *Fax:* (706) 667-4937
Internet Address: http://www.aug.edu
Director: Prof. Jackson Cheatham
Admission: free.
Membership: N   *ADA Compliant:* Y
Parking: free on site.
Open: Monday to Friday, 8am-10pm.
Facilities: Exhibition Area.
Activities: Temporary Exhibitions.

The Gallery presents temporary exhibitions of student and faculty work, as well as the work of regional and national artists.

Columbus

Columbus State University - Gallery ⓒ
Fine Arts Hall, Columbus, GA   31907
Tel: (706) 568-2001
Internet Address: http://art.colstate.edu/
Open: Call for hours.
Facilities: Exhibition Area.
Activities: Temporary Exhibitions.

The University maintains two exhibition spaces for the display of work by nationally and internationally recognized artists. The are also numerous student and faculty exhibits, including an annual juried student art show.

Decatur

Agnes Scott College - Dalton Galleries ⓒ
Dana Fine Arts Building, 141 E. College Ave.
Decatur, GA   30030
Tel: (404) 471-6049
Internet Address: http://www.agnesscott.edu/aas/calendars/cal_info/visual_art.htm
Director: Dr. Donna Sadler
Admission: free.
Established: 1957   *ADA Compliant:* Y
Open: Academic Year, Monday to Friday, 10am-4:30pm; Sunday, 2pm-4:30pm.
Facilities: Gallery.
Activities: Temporary Exhibitions.

Located in the Dana Fine Arts Building, the Dalton Galleries present temporary visual arts exhibitions, including an annual student exhibition in the spring.

Gainesville

Brenau University - Brenau University Galleries
One Centennial Circle
Gainesville, GA   30501
Tel: (770) 534-6263
Fax: (770) 534-6114
TDDY: (770) 534-6200
Internet Address: http://www.brenau.edu/events/Arts/visualart.htm
Director: Ms. Jean Westmacott
Admission: voluntary contribution.

Brenau University - Brenau University Galleries, cont.

Attendance: 23,000   *Established:* 1983
Membership: N   *ADA Compliant:* Y
Parking: street parking.
Open: **Fall to Spring**,
      Monday to Friday, 10am-4pm;
      Sunday, 2pm-5pm.
      Summer,
      Monday to Thursday, 1pm-4pm.
Closed: Easter, Spring Break, Memorial Day,
      Independence Day, Labor Day, Thanksgiving Week.
Facilities: **Auditorium** (700 seats); **Galleries** (2); **Shop**; **Studios**.
Activities: **Arts Festival**; **Education Programs** (adults and graduate/undergraduate college students); **Guided Tours** (by appointment); **Lectures** (occasional); **Performances**; **Temporary Exhibitions** (7-9/year); **Traveling Exhibitions**; **Workshops** (1/year matched with exhibition for K-12 students).
Publications: brochure/catalogue.

In foreground is Simmons Visual Arts Center, home to Brenau Galleries. Photograph by Tommy Thompson, courtesy of Brenau Galleries, Brenau University, Gainesville, Georgia.

As an integral part of the Brenau University academic community, the Brenau University Galleries provide exhibitions and programs that identify and enhance artistic talent, respond to issues of special relevance to women, advance scholarship in the visual arts, and encourage understanding and appreciation of diverse cultures. The gallery program evolved from small annual showings of student and faculty work to more extensive exhibitions in the mid-1980s. In 1990-91, Brenau strengthened its support of Fine Arts and gallery programs by renovating the 1914 former library building to create the new Simmons Visual Arts Center. This renovation added a second gallery on the Brenau campus: the large Sellars Gallery on the main floor of the Simmons Visual Arts Center adjacent to the Presidents Gallery in the Pearce Auditorium Building.

Kennesaw

Kennesaw State University Art Galleries

1000 Chastain Road
Kennesaw, GA   30060
Tel: (770) 499-3223
Internet Address: http://www.kennesaw.edu/
    visual_arts/-Art_Gallery/GALLERY.html
Open: Monday to Friday, 10am-4pm.
Facilities: **Exhibition Area** (2 galleries).
Activities: **Lectures**; **Temporary Exhibitions**.
Publications: exhibition catalogues (occasional).

The Sturgis Library and Fine Arts galleries (the latter located in the Mac Wilson Building) present contemporary and traditional art through curated and traveling exhibitions. The galleries also present five senior student art exhibitions, a juried student show, and an alumni invitational exhibition annually. There are approximately fifteen shows each year. The permanent collection consists of 215 paintings and works on paper.

N.C. Wyeth, *Jonathan and David*, oil, 42 x 32 inches. Kenesaw State Universities Art Galleries collection, gift of Dr. Noah Meadows. Photograph courtesy of Kenesaw State University Art Galleries, Kennesaw, Georgia.

LaGrange

LaGrange College - Lamar Dodd Art Center

302 Forrest Ave.
LaGrange, GA 30240
Tel: (706) 812-7211
Fax: (404) 884-6567
Internet Address: http://www.lgc.peachnet.edu
Curator: Ms. Debra Quillen
Admission: free.
Attendance: 2,500   *Established:* 1982
ADA Compliant: Y
Parking: free on site.
Open: **Academic Year**,
    Monday to Friday, 9am-4pm;
    Saturday, 1pm-4pm.
Closed: Academic Holidays.

Exterior view of Lamar Dodd Art Center, LaGrange College. Photograph courtesy of Lamar Dodd Art Center, LaGrange College, LaGrange, Georgia.

Facilities: **Architecture** (1982, designed by Louis A Scarbrough); **Exhibition Area** (over 6,000 feet of gallery space).
Activities: **Guided Tours** (on request); **Juried Exhibits** (biennial exhibition, April-May, even years).
Publications: exhibition catalogues.

Named in honor of LaGrange native and nationally-known artist Dr. Lamar Dodd, the Center's galleries house a retrospective collection of paintings and drawings by Lamar Dodd, the College's art collection, and space devoted to temporary exhibitions of work by professional artists, faculty and students.

Mount Berry

Berry College - Moon Gallery ©

Moon Building
2277 Martha Berry Highway, N.W.
Mount Berry, GA 30149-5028
Tel: (706) 236-2219
Fax: (706) 238-7835
Internet Address:
 http://www.berry.edu/academic/hass/gallery.html
Director: Dr. Thomas J. Mew, III
Admission: free.
Attendance: 2,500   *Established:* 1971
ADA Compliant: Y
Parking: parking lot.
Open: Weekdays, 9am-4pm.
Facilities: **Exhibition Area** (1,600 square feet).
Activities: **Temporary Exhibitions** (7-8/year).
Publications: brochure, "Gallery Brochure with Description of Shows" (annual).

Tommy Mew, *Dolce, Dolce (Italia Series)*, 1995, mixed media drawing, 18 inches x 26 inches. Berry Coolege Permanent Collection. Photograph courtesy of Berry College, Mount Berry, Georgia.

The Gallery presents the work of professional artists in temporary exhibitions, usually of three weeks duration. Student shows include week-long Senior Thesis Exhibitions by art majors and a juried Senior Student Honors Show. The college's permanent collection is housed in both the Moon Building and the Martha Berry Museum.

Savannah

Savannah College of Art and Design - Galleries Ⓒᴬᴰ

340 Bull St., Savannah, GA 37401
Tel: (912) 525-4950
Internet Address: http://www.scad.edu
Open: Call for hours.

The Savannah College of Art and Design operates a number of galleries: Alexander Hall, 668 Indian Street (student work); Bergen Hall, 101 Martin Luther King Jr. Blvd. at Broughton Street (photography); Exhibit A Gallery, 340 Bull Street (temporary exhibitions of work by national and international artists); Eichberg Hall, 229 Martin Luther King Jr. Blvd. (student and professional work in temporary exhibits); Ex Libris, 228 Martin Luther King Jr. at Perry Street (traveling exhibitions, works from the permanent collection, and student and faculty work); Hamilton Hall, 522 Indian Street (video art by students, faculty, and professional artists); Pinnacle Gallery, 320 East Liberty street (celebrates multiculturalism through the arts); Rapid Transit Gallery, 342 Bull Street (graduate student thesis shows); and Savannah International Airport Gallery, 400 Airways Avenue (faculty, student, and alumni work).

Statesboro

Georgia Southern University - Gallery 303 Ⓒᴬᴰ

Foy Fine Arts Building, Third Floor, Statesboro, GA 30460
Tel: (912) 681-5358
Internet Address: http://www2.gasou.edu/art/gallery/gallery.html
Admission: free.
Open: Monday to Friday, 8am-5pm.
Facilities: **Exhibition Area.**
Activities: **Guided Tours** (by appointment); **Temporary Exhibitions** (8/year).
Publications: gallery calendar (annual).

The Gallery features temporary exhibitions of contemporary artwork by faculty and students. Also of possible interest on campus, the Betty Foy Sanders Art Collection, featuring the art and artists of Georgia, is housed in the Henderson Library.

Valdosta

Valdosta State University Fine Arts Gallery Ⓒᴬᴰ

Fine Arts Building, School of the Arts, Valdosta, GA 31698
Tel: (912) 333-5835   *Fax:* (912) 333-7408
Internet Address: http://www.valdosta.peachnet.edu/art/
Gallery Director: Ms. Karin G. Murray
Admission: voluntary contribution.
Attendance: 10,000   *Established:* 1906   *ADA Compliant:* Y
Open: Monday to Thursday, 10am-4pm; Friday, 10am-3pm.
Closed: Academic Holidays.
Facilities: **Gallery.**
Activities: **Education Programs** (undergraduate college students); **Gallery Talks**; **Guided Tours** (contact VSU public relations at 333-5980).
Publications: exhibition catalogues; posters.

Located on the first floor of the Fine Arts building, the Art Gallery presents traveling exhibitions, national competitive exhibits, invitational exhibits in a variety of media, and annual shows of faculty and student work.

Guam

A number in parentheses following a city name indicates the number of museums/galleries in that municipality. If there is no number, one is understood. For example, in the text one listing would be found under Mangilao.

Guam

Mangilao

University of Guam - Isla Center for the Arts

15 Dean's Circle, Mangilao, GU   96923

Tel: (671) 735-2965

Fax: (671) 735-2967

Internet Address: isla@uogq.edu

Director: Ms. Carrie Brewster

Admission: free.

Attendance: 18,000   *Established:* 1980

Membership: Y   *ADA Compliant:* Y

Parking: ample.

Open: Monday to Wednesday, 10am-5pm;
Thursday, 10am-9pm;
Friday, 10am-5pm;
Saturday, 10am-2pm.

Ngiraibuuch, storyboard relating myth of Chief Koror receiving a gift of stone money; Palauan. Isla Center for the Arts collection. Photograph courtesy of Isla Center for the Arts, Mangilao, Guam.

Closed: Legal Holidays.

Facilities: **Exhibition Area** (1,000 square feet); **Shop**.

Activities: **Films**; **Lectures**; **Temporary Exhibitions**; **Traveling Exhibitions**.

Publications: exhibition catalogues (quarterly).

The Isla Center for the Arts presents temporary exhibitions that are curated by Center staff or borrowed from international institutions. Its permanent collection of over 500 items is evidence of its dedication to cultural diversity. Highlighted in the collection are many Micronesian artifacts. While focusing mainly on the islands of the western Pacific, it also includes lithographs and prints from such European masters as Rembrandt, Goya, Daumier, Dürer, and Pissaro, as well as antique Japanese woodcuts, Ming Dynasty landscapes, and pre-Columbian pottery.

Hawaii

A number in parentheses following a city name indicates the number of museums/galleries in that municipality. If there is no number, one is understood. For example, in the text one listing would be found under each Hawaiian city shown on map.

Hawaii

Island of Oahu

Honolulu

University of Hawaii at Manoa - Art Gallery ⒸⒶ

2535 The Mall, Honolulu, HI   96822

Tel: (808) 956-6888   *Fax:* (808) 956-9043

Internet Address: http://www.hawaii.edu/artgallery

Director: Mr. Tom Klobe

Admission: voluntary contribution.

Attendance: 50,000   *Established:* 1976   *ADA Compliant:* Y

Parking: pay on site - $3.00.

Open: Monday to Friday, 10am-4pm; Sunday, noon-4pm.

Closed: Legal Holidays.

Facilities: **Auditorium** (300 seats); **Classrooms**; **Exhibition Area** (4,200 square feet).

Activities: **Arts Festival**; **Films**; **Gallery Talks**; **Guided Tours**; **Self-guided Tour of Art on Campus**; **Lectures**; **Traveling Exhibitions**).

Publications: exhibition catalogues.

The University of Hawaii Art Gallery presents temporary exhibitions of both historical and contemporary art. The Main Gallery features six major exhibitions per year, while the smaller Commons Gallery showcases student thesis exhibitions, the work of visiting artists, and on-going class work. Additionally, the Gallery has initiated and organized twelve traveling exhibitions, which have been presented at museums in the United States, Mexico, Canada, Japan, Taiwan, and Guam. Also of possible interest on campus are the East-West Center Gallery (944-7111), located in Burns Hall (corner of Dole Street and East-West Road) and the School of Architecture Gallery (956-7225), located at 2410 Campus Road.

University of Hawaii at Manoa-Outreach College - John Young Museum of Art

Krauss Hall, 2500 Dole St., Honolulu, HI   96822

Tel: (808) 956-3634

Internet Address: http://www.outreach.hawaii.edu/JYmuseum

Director: L.B. Nerio

Admission: free

Established: 1999

Parking: campus lots (lower campus suggested), $3.00.

Open: Tuesday, 10am-1pm; Friday, noon-3pm; Sunday, 1pm-4pm.

Facilities: **Architecture** (1931 design by Harry Simms Bent); **Reading Room**; **Exhibition Area**; **Water Garden** (design by Betsy Sakata).

Activities: **Group Visits** (by appointment, 956-8866)

Housed in the oldest wood frame building on the UHM campus, the Museum was endowed with a starter collection from the holdings of Hawaii painter John Young. The collection, emphasizing the University's special interest in Asia and the Pacific region, includes ancient artifacts and antiquities from Cambodia, China, India, Japan, Korea, Myanmar, the Pacific Islands, Sri Lanka, and Thailand. Of special note are several authentic Hawaiian koa wood chairs.

Kaneohe

Windward Community College - Gallery Iolani

45-720 Kea'ahala Road, Kaneohe, HI   96744

Tel: (808) 235-7346

Internet Address: http://www.wcc.hawaii.edu

Director: Toni Martin

Open: Tuesday to Saturday, 1pm-5pm.

Facilities: **Exhibition Area**.

The gallery presents temporary exhibitions.

Idaho

A number in parentheses following a city name indicates the number of museums/galleries in that municipality. If there is no number, one is understood. For example, in the text one listing would be found under each Idahoan city shown on map.

Idaho

Boise

Boise State University - Galleries Ⓒ⁴⁴

Gallery 1 - Liberal Arts Building, 1874 University Drive
Gallery 2 - Hemingway Center Building, 1819 University Drive
Boise, ID   83725
Tel: (208) 426-3576   *Fax:* (208) 426-3576
Internet Address: http://www.idbsu.edu/art/galsh99.html
Director: Mr. Richard A. Young
Admission: free.
Attendance: 500
Parking: parking permits available.
Open: Monday to Friday, 9am-6pm.
Closed: Academic Holidays.
Facilities: **Exhibition Area**.
Activities: **Temporary Exhibitions**.

The Art Department maintains two galleries. Gallery 1 is located in the Liberal Arts Building and Gallery 2 is located in the Hemingway Center Building. Exhibitions include work by professional artists, faculty, and students and include annual student BFA Thesis Exhibitions and a biennial national juried exhibition of realist and representational art.

Moscow

University of Idaho - Prichard Art Gallery Ⓒ⁴⁴

414/416 S. Main St., Moscow, ID   83843
Tel: (208) 885-3586   *Fax:* (208) 885-3622
Internet Address: http://www.uidaho.edu/art/info
Director: Ms. Gail Siegel
Admission: voluntary contribution.
Attendance: 15,000   *Established:* 1982   *Membership:* Y
Parking: free on site.
Open: **September to May**,
          Monday to Friday, 11am-8pm; Saturday, 10am-4pm.
          June to August,
          Tuesday to Friday, 1pm-7pm; Saturday, 9am-3pm.
Closed: during installations.
Facilities: **Exhibition Area**.
Activities: **Guided Tours** (elementary and secondary school students); **Lectures**; **Temporary Exhibitions** (7/year).

Located in downtown Moscow, the Prichard Art Gallery is an outreach facility of the University of Idaho College of Art and Architecture serving the community and the university with a year-round schedule of exhibitions. The Gallery hosts seven to nine exhibitions annually featuring the fine arts, architecture, and landscape architecture. Ceramics, photography, glass art, fine craft, computer art, folk art, and installation art are also exhibited, along with traditional arts, painting, and sculpture.

Pocatello

Idaho State University - John B. Davis Art Gallery Ⓒ⁴⁴

Fine Arts Building (Lower Level), Center St. and 6th Ave.,
Pocatello, ID   83209
Tel: (208) 236-2442   *Fax:* (208) 236-4610
Internet Address: http://www.isu.edu
Director: Mr. Doug Warnock
Admission: free.

Idaho State University - John B. Davis Art Gallery, cont.

Open: Monday/Wednesday/Friday, 10am-4pm;
Tuesday/Thursday, 10am-4pm and 7pm-9pm.

Facilities: **Exhibition Area.**

Activities: **Temporary Exhibitions.**

The Gallery offers temporary shows including graduate student MFA Thesis exhibitions. Also of possible interest on campus are the Transition Gallery and Mind's Eye Photo Gallery in the Earl Pond Student Union Building.

Twin Falls

The College of Southern Idaho - Herrett Center for Arts and Science

315 Falls Ave.

Twin Falls, ID 83303-1238

Tel: (208) 733-9554   *Ext:* 2655

Fax: (208) 736-4712

Internet Address: http://www.csi.cc.id.us/
support/museum/hcas_king.html

Gallery Manager: Mr. Russell Hepworth

Admission: free.

Parking: free on site.

Open: Tuesday, 9:30am-9pm;
Wednesday-Thursday, 9:30am-4:30pm;
Friday, 9:30am-9pm;
Saturday, 1pm-9pm.

Closed: Federal Holidays.

Facilities: **Galleries**; **Shop.**

Activities: **Permanent Exhibits**; **Temporary Exhibitions.**

Embroidery, Peruvian Central Coast, 1000 A.D.-1532 A.D. Permanent collection, Herrett Art Center. Photograph courtesy of Herrett Art Center, Twin Falls, Idaho.

Housed in an architecturally interesting post-modern building, Herrett Center collections are primarily focused on anthropology. Four galleries are dedicated to pre-Columbian America including an ancient art gallery featuring textiles. Additionally, the Jean B. King Gallery of Art, co-sponsored by the College of Southern Idaho Art Department and Associated Students of CSI, presents monthly exhibitions of contemporary art, including works by faculty and an annual juried student show.

Illinois

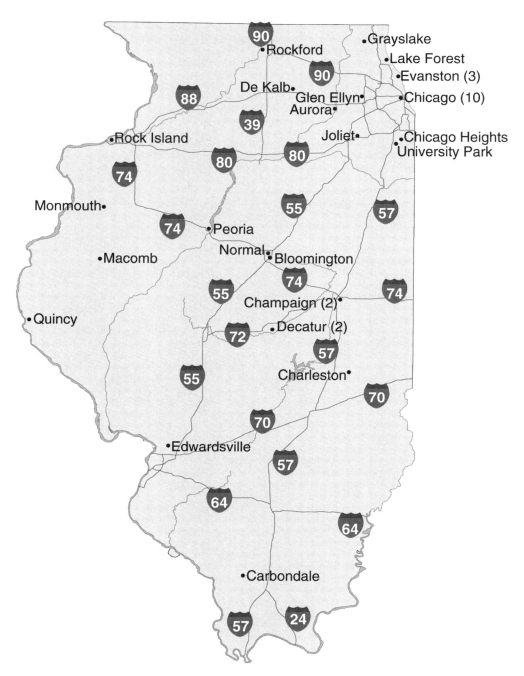

The number in parentheses following the city name indicates the number of museums/galleries in that municipality. If there is no number, one is understood. For example, in the text ten listings would be found under Chicago and one listing under University Park.

Illinois

Aurora

Aurora University - Schingoethe Center for Native American Cultures

Aurora University, Dunham Hall
347 S. Gladstone
Aurora, IL   60506-4892
Tel: (630) 844-5402
Fax: (630) 844-8884
Internet Address: http://www.aurora.edu
Director: Dr. Dona Bachman
Admission: voluntary contribution.
Attendance: 8,000   *Established:* 1990
Membership: Y   *ADA Compliant:* Y
Open: **February to December 15**,
      Tuesday, 10am-8pm;
      Wednesday to Friday, 10am-4pm;
      Sunday, 1pm-4pm.
Closed: Academic Holidays, August.
Facilities: **Exhibition Area**; **Library**.
Activities: **Arts   Festival**;   **Education
   Programs** (undergraduate/graduate college
   students   and   children);   **Guided   Tours**;
   Lectures; **Temporary Exhibitions**.

View of gallery. Photograph courtesy of Schingoethe Center for native American Cultures, Aurora, Illinois.

Publications: newsletter, "Spreading Wings" (monthly).

The Schingoethe Center preserves, interprets, and exhibits historical and contemporary Native American material culture and art.

Bloomington

Illinois Wesleyan University - Merwin and Wakeley Galleries ⒸⒶⒶ

Illinois Wesleyan University, School of Art, Graham street, Bloomington, IL   61702-2900
Tel: (309) 556-3077
Internet Address: http://titam.iwu.edu/~art/galler/htm
Director: Ms. Ann Murakishi
Admission: free.
Open: **September to May**,
      Monday, noon-4pm; Tuesday, noon-4pm and 7pm-9pm; Wednesday to Friday, noon-4pm;
      Saturday to Sunday, 1pm-4pm.
Facilities: **Exhibition Area** (2 galleries).
Activities: **Temporary Exhibitions**.

The Merwin and Wakeley Galleries present a schedule of temporary exhibitions that support the curriculum, the University community and the general public. Exhibitions include historical and contemporary exhibits and the work of visiting artists. Student shows include the Annual Juried School of Art Exhibition, the BFA Candidate Exhibition, and the BFA and BA Degree Exhibition.

Carbondale

Southern Illinois University, Carbondale - University Museum ⒸⒶⒶ

Southern Illinois University, Faner Hall (north end), Carbondale, IL   62901
Tel: (618) 453-5388   *Fax:* (618) 453-7409
Internet Address: http://www.museum.siu.edu
Director: Dr. John J. Whitlock
Admission: free.
Attendance: 42,000   *Established:* 1869   *Membership:* Y   *ADA Compliant:* Y
Parking: metered lot near student center and stadium.

Southern Illinois University, Carbondale - University Museum, cont.

Open: Tuesday to Saturday, 9am-3pm; Sunday, 1:30pm-4:30pm.

Closed: Academic Holidays, Legal Holidays.

Facilities: **Auditorium**; **Galleries** (eight; total of 5069 square feet); **Library**; **Sculpture Garden**; **Shop**.

Activities: **Artist Studio Tours**; **Concerts** (Wed. noon; April-October); **Films**; **Guided Tours** (groups schedule in advance); **Lectures**; **Temporary Exhibitions**; **Traveling Exhibitions**.

Publications: newsletter.

Exterior view of the Southern Illinois University Museum. Photograph courtesy of University Museum, Southern Illinois University, Carbondale, Illinois.

The University Museum houses over 52,000 objects in the arts, sciences, and humanities. The art collection consists of 2,500 objects, including European and American paintings, drawings, and prints; 19th- and 20th-century photography; 20th-century sculpture, metals, and ceramics; and musical instruments.

Champaign

Parkland College Art Gallery

2400 W. Bradley Ave., Champaign, IL   61821

Tel: (217) 351-2485

Fax: (217) 373-3899

Internet Address: http://www.parkland.cc.il.us/gallery

Director: Ms. Denise Seif

Admission: voluntary contribution.

Attendance: 15,000   *Established:* 1980

ADA Compliant: Y

Parking: free on site.

Open: **Fall to Spring**,
Mon to Thurs, 10am-3pm & 6pm-8pm;
Friday, 10am-3pm;
Saturday, 10am-noon.
Summer,
Monday, 10am-2pm;
Tues to Thurs, 10am-2pm & 6pm-8pm.

Closed: Academic Holidays, Legal Holidays.

Facilities: **Gallery**.

View of Parkland College Art Gallery. Photograph courtesy of Parkland College Art Gallery, Champaign, Illinois.

Activities: **Lectures**; **Temporary Exhibitions** (change monthly); **Traveling Exhibitions**.

The Parkland College Art Gallery offers temporary exhibitions intended to illustrate a wide range of traditional and innovative work, recognized and new talent, proven forms and fresh ones. There are faculty and juried student shows, and invitational watercolor and ceramics shows.

University of Illinois - Krannert Art Museum Ⓒ⁴⁴

University of Illinois, 500 E. Peabody Drive, Champaign, IL   61820

Tel: (217) 333-1861

Fax: (217) 333-0883

Internet Address: http://www.art.uiuc.edu/kam

Director: Mr. Maarten van de Guchte

Admission: voluntary contribution.

Attendance: 116,000   *Established:* 1961   *Membership:* Y   *ADA Compliant:* Y

Parking: metered on street.

114

University of Illinois - Krannert Art Museum, cont.

Open: Tuesday, 9am-4pm; Wednesday, 9am-8pm; Thursday to Friday, 9am-4pm;
Saturday, 10am-4pm; Sunday, 1pm-4pm.

Closed: Legal Holidays, Academic Holidays.

Facilities: **Auditorium**; **Food Services** Palette Café; **Galleries**.

Activities: **Education Programs** (adults, undergraduate/graduate students and children); **Gallery Talks**; **Guided Tours**; **Lectures**; **Permanent Exhibits**; **Temporary Exhibitions**; **Traveling Exhibitions**.

Publications: exhibition catalogues; magazine (semi-annual).

The Krannert Art Museum is a 48,000 square-foot facility with ten galleries and a collection of 9,000 works of art. Three of the galleries are devoted to temporary exhibitions, while the remainder display works from the permanent collection. The Museum's permanent collection consists of African art, with a special emphasis on objects from various West and Central African cultures; Asian art, from the cultures of China, Korea, Japan, India, and Thailand; Twentieth Century art, including paintings and sculptures by such artists as Muenter, Beckmann, Guston, Stella, and Warhol; European and American art from the 16th through the 19th centuries; ceramics, glass, and silver from the Renaissance to the present; ancient Mediterranean art from Egypt, Greece, and Italy; Medieval art, including painting, stained glass, and ivory; and pre-Columbian art from various Peruvian cultures.

Charleston

Eastern Illinois University - Tarble Arts Center ⓒ

South 9th St. at Cleveland Ave., Charleston, IL   61920

Tel: (217) 581-2787   *Fax:* (217) 581-2722

Internet Address: http://www.eiu.edu/~artdept/art.fac.1/artfac.tb.htm

Director: Mr. Michael Watts

Admission: voluntary contribution.

Attendance: 21,000   *Established:* 1982   *Membership:* Y   *ADA Compliant:* Y

Parking: free on site.

Open: **mid-August to mid-May**,
Tuesday to Friday, 10am-5pm; Saturday, 10am-4pm; Sunday, 1pm-4pm.
mid-May to mid-August,
Tuesday to Saturday, 10am-4pm; Sunday, 1pm-4pm.

Closed: Legal Holidays.

Facilities: **Classroom**; **Exhibition Area** (6,400 square feet); **Library**; **Sales/Rental Gallery**; **Sculpture Court**; **Shop**.

Activities: **Concerts**; **Education Programs**; **Temporary Exhibitions**; **Traveling Exhibitions**.

Publications: semester calendar; exhibition brochures; exhibition catalogues; newsletter (monthly).

The Tarble Arts Center presents a year-round schedule of changing visual arts exhibitions. It also has a permanent collection consisting of 1,000 pieces, including a 500-piece collection of 20th-century Illinois folk art; works on paper by contemporary Midwestern artists, including Jasper Johns and Claus Oldenberg: and prints by American Regionalists, such as Benton, Curry, Kent, Sample, Soyer, and Wood, along with the works of a number of "New Deal" artists.

Chicago

Columbia College Chicago - The Museum of Contemporary Photography ⓒ

Columbia College Chicago
600 S. Michigan Ave.
Chicago, IL   60605-1996

Tel: (312) 663-5554   *Fax:* (312) 360-1656

Internet Address: http://www.colum.edu/museum/index.html

Director: Ms. Denise Miller

Admission: free.

Established: 1976   *Membership:* Y   *ADA Compliant:* Y

Parking: public lot near site.

Columbia College Chicago - The Museum of Contemporary Photography, cont.

Open: **September to May,**
  Monday to Wednesday, 10am-5pm;
  Thursday, 10am-8pm;
  Friday, 10am-5pm;
  Saturday, noon-5pm.

  June to July,
  Monday to Friday, 10am-4pm;
  Saturday, noon-4pm.

Closed: August, New Year's Eve to New Year's
  Day, ML King Day, Memorial Day,
  Independence Day, Labor Day,
  Thanksgiving Weekend,
  Christmas Eve to Christmas Day.

Facilities: **Classrooms; Exhibition Area;
  Print Study Room.**

Activities: **Guided Tours; Lectures;
  Temporary Exhibitions; Traveling
  Exhibitions.**

Publications: exhibition catalogues (annual).

Interior view of Print Study Room, 2nd floor gallery, Museum of Contemporary Photography, Columbia College Chicago. Photograph courtesy of Columbia College Chicago, Chicago, Illinois.

The Museum of Contemporary Photography was founded by Columbia College Chicago to exhibit, collect, and promote contemporary photography. Each year the Museum presents a wide range of exhibitions in recognition of photography's many roles: as a medium of communication and artistic expression, as a documenter of life and the environment, as a commercial industry, and as a powerful tool in the service of science and technology. In addition, special projects in collaboration with other institutions combine photographic works with different forms of expression and investigate the medium's interaction with various arts, history, science and culture. The Museum fosters research and the appreciation of contemporary image making by ensuring that the photographs in the permanent collection and print study room are accessible to the public through exhibitions, publications, and private examination. The permanent collection focuses on American photography produced since 1959, the United States publication date of Robert Frank's seminal work "The Americans". Holdings are complemented by works from the Midwest Photographers Project, a program featuring works by regional photographers on loan to the print study room for a one-year period. Also of possible interest on the Columbia College Chicago campus are three additional galleries that exhibit the work of students, faculty and professional artists: the Center for the Book and Paper Arts Gallery (Open: Monday-Friday, 10am-5pm, 431-8612); the Art Gallery; and the Hokin Student Center Gallery.

DePaul University Art Gallery ⓒᴬᴬ

John T. Richardson Library
2350 N. Kenmore Ave. (at Fullerton)
Chicago, IL 60614-3214
Tel: (773) 325-7506
Fax: (773) 325-4506
Internet Address: http://www.edpaul.edu/~gallery
Director: Ms. Louise H. Lincoln
Admission: free.
Attendance: 4,000   *Established:* 1987   *Membership:* N   *ADA Compliant:* Y
Parking: university facility one block west at 3221 North Sheffield.
Open: **September to July,**
  Monday to Thursday, 11am-5pm; Friday, 11am-7pm; Saturday, 11am-5pm;
  Sunday, noon-5pm during exhibitions.
Closed: Academic Holidays.
Facilities: **Gallery.**
Activities: **Lectures; Permanent collection; Temporary Exhibitions; Traveling Exhibitions.**
Publications: exhibition catalogues; gallery notes.

DePaul University Art Gallery, cont.

The Gallery mounts diverse exhibitions throughout the academic year and also maintains the University's permanent collection of art, selections of which are exhibited on a rotating basis in the space adjacent to the temporary exhibition area. Spanning the 16th century to the present, University holdings consist mainly of paintings, prints, drawings, and photography and has a strong representation of religious imagery. Among the Artists represented are Jack Beal, William Blake, John Chamberlain, Chryssa, William Conger, Carlo Dolci, Jules Dupre, Gifford Dyer, Jacob Epstein, Thomas Hill, Thomas Lawrence, Gustave Loiseau, Charles Le Brun, Peter Lely, Edgar Payne, Seymour Rosofsky, Georges Roualt, William Schwartz, Julia Thecla, Louis Comfort Tiffany, Mark Tobey, Jules Verlet, and Gary Winograd.

Loyola University Museum of Medieval, Renaissance and Baroque Art - Martin D'Arcy Gallery of Art Ⓒᴬᴬ

Loyola University, Lake Shore Campus
6525 N. Sheridan Road
Chicago, IL   60626
Tel: (773) 508-2679
Fax: (508) 508-2993
Internet Address: http://www.luc.edu/depts/darcy
Director: Dr. Sally Metzler
Admission: free.
Attendance: 6,000   *Established:* 1969
Membership: Y   *ADA Compliant:* Y
Parking: pay parking on campus.
Open: **Fall to Spring**, Monday to Friday, noon-4pm.
Closed: Academic Holidays, Summer.
Facilities: **Gallery**; **Library** (10,000 volumes).
Activities: **Lecture Series** ("Kultur und Kaffee", most Weds, 3:30pm); **Temporary Exhibitions**.
Publications: exhibition catalogues.

Angel with Heraldic Shield, wood with polychrome and gilding, German, later 15th century. Collection of Martin D'Arcy Gallery. Photograph courtesy of Martin D'Arcy Gallery, Loyola University, Chicago, Illinois.

Located in the Cudahy Library on Loyola University Chicago's Lake Shore Campus, the Gallery provides an intimate setting housing over 300 Medieval, Renaissance and Baroque art objects. The Museum's focus is primarily on the permanent collection.

Northern Illinois University Art Gallery in Chicago Ⓒᴬᴬ (NIU Art Gallery)

215 W. Superior, 3rd Floor, Chicago, IL   60610
Tel: (312) 642-6010   *Fax:* (312) 642-9635
Internet Address: http://www.vpa.niu.edu/museum/chicago.htm
Admission: free.
Attendance: 1,867   *Established:* 1984   *Membership:* Y   *ADA Compliant:* Y
Parking: metered on street.
Open: **September to July**, Tuesday to Saturday, 11am-5pm.
Closed: August.
Facilities: **Exhibition Area** (2,000 square feet).
Activities: **Guided Tours**; **Lectures**; **Temporary Exhibitions** (7/year); **Traveling Exhibitions**.
Publications: exhibition catalogues.

A satellite gallery of the NIU Art Museum (De Kalb, Illinois), the Gallery was established to aid in the association and participation of the University in the Chicago art community and to help maintain relations with other Chicago art museums and galleries. Located in Chicago's River North gallery district, it presents temporary exhibitions, which change every six to eight weeks.

School of the Art Institute of Chicago - The Betty Rymer Gallery Ⓒᴬᴬ

280 South Columbus Drive, Chicago, IL   60603
Tel: (312) 443-3703   *Fax:* (312) 332-5859
Internet Address: http://www.artic.edu/~vartists/

School of the Art Institute of Chicago - The Betty Rymer Gallery, cont.

Gallery Director: Ms. Clair Broadfoot
Admission: free.
Attendance: 22,000   *Established:* 1988   *Membership:* N   *ADA Compliant:* Y
Parking: nearby public lots.
Open: Monday to Saturday, 10am-5pm; Thursday, 10am-8pm; Friday to Saturday, 10am-5pm.
Closed: Between Shows, Legal Holidays.
Facilities: **Gallery** (28,000 square feet).
Activities: **Temporary Exhibitions.**
Publications: brochure (annual); calendar (monthly); calendar, "Exhibitions and Events" (bi-monthly); exhibition catalogues (occasional).

The Betty Rymer Gallery showcases the strength and diversity of the School's programs, highlighting faculty and student work and mounting special exhibitions of the work of professional artists. Also of possible interest is the SAIC's Gallery 2 (563-5262) located at 847 W. Jackson Ave., Chicago, IL 60607 (open: Tues-Sat, 11am-6pm). Gallery 2 provides students with the opportunity to exhibit their work within a professional venue in close proximity to a number of other galleries. Students are selected to exhibit their work through an open proposal process. In addition, large theme-related juried shows are scheduled at least twice annually.

Spertus Institute of Jewish Studies - Spertus Museum

618 S. Michigan Ave., Chicago, IL   60605
Tel: (312) 922-9012   *Fax:* (312) 922-6406   *TDDY:* (312) 922-4950
Internet Address: http://www.spertus.edu/Museum.html
President: Mr. Howard A. Sulkin
Admission: fee: adult-$4.00, child-$2.00, student-$4.00, senior-$4.00.
Attendance: 70,000   *Established:* 1968   *Membership:* Y   *ADA Compliant:* Y
Open: Monday to Thursday, 10am-5pm; Friday, 10am-3pm; Sunday, 10am-5pm.
Closed: Jewish Holidays, Legal Holidays.
Facilities: **Archaeological Gallery** (children); **Auditorium**; **Classrooms**; **Galleries**; **Library** (1,000 volumes); **Shop** (traditional and contemporary design objects, books).
Activities: **Concerts**; **Education Programs** (graduate students); **Films**; **Gallery Talks**; **Guided Tours**; **Lectures**; **Permanent Exhibits**; **Temporary Exhibitions.**
Publications: calendar of events; exhibition catalogues; posters.

Through its changing and permanent collection exhibitions, Spertus Museum celebrates the creativity and diversity of Jewish culture. Selections from the permanent collection acquaint visitors with the beauty and customs of Jewish religion and culture from around the world.

University of Chicago - The David and Alfred Smart Museum of Art ⓒ

University of Chicago, 5550 S. Greenwood Ave., Chicago, IL   60637
Tel: (773) 702-0200   *Fax:* (773) 702-3121
Internet Address: http://csmaclab.-www.uchicago.edu/SmartMuseum
Director: Ms. Kimerly Rorschach
Admission: voluntary contribution.
Attendance: 30,000   *Established:* 1974
Membership: Y   *ADA Compliant:* Y
Parking: commercial adjacent to site; free evenings and weekends.
Open: Tuesday to Wednesday, 10am-4pm;
       Thursday, 10am-9pm;
       Friday, 10am-4pm;
       Saturday to Sunday, noon-6pm.
Closed: Legal Holidays.

Frank Lloyd Wright, *Dining Table*, 1908, Permanent collection, Smart Museum of Art. Photograph courtesy of Smart Museum of Art, University of Chicago, Chicago, Illinois.

University of Chicago - The David and Alfred Smart Museum of Art, cont.

Facilities: **Exhibition Area**; **Food Services** (Café); **Sculpture Garden**; **Shop**.

Activities: **Gallery Talks**; **Guided Tours**; **Lectures**; **Permanent Exhibits**; **Temporary Exhibitions**.

Publications: bulletin, "Smart Museum Bulletin" (annual); collection handbook; exhibition catalogues.

Designed by Edward Larrabee Barnes, the Smart Museum of Art and its adjacent Elden Sculpture Garden house over 7,000 works of art. From ancient Greek vases and Chinese bronzes to medieval sculpture and Old Master paintings; Frank Lloyd Wright furniture and Tiffany glass to modern sculpture by Degas, Matisse, and Rodin; and 20th-century paintings and sculpture by Rothko, Dove, Rivera, Moore, and Hunt, the collection spans 5,000 years of artistic creation. The collection is presented in a series of displays that integrate various media and emphasize art-historical context as well as content. The Museum also presents special temporary exhibitions.

University of Chicago - Oriental Institute Museum ⒸⒶⒶ

1155 East 58th St.

Chicago, IL 60637-1569

Tel: (773) 702-9520

Fax: (773) 702-9853

Internet Address: http://www.oi.uchicago.edu/ OI/mus/OI_museum.html

Museum Director: Karen L. Wilson, Ph.D.

Admission: no charge/donations accepted.

Attendance: 62,000   *Established:* 1894

Membership: Y   *ADA Compliant:* Y

Parking: metered on street and nearby metered lot on Woodlawn Ave.

Open: Tuesday to Sunday, call for hours.

Facilities: **Auditorium** (275 seats); **Classrooms**; **Galleries**; **Library** (25,000 volumes, available to members); **Shop** (Tues-Sat, 10am-4pm; Sun, noon-4pm).

Human-headed Winged Bull (lamassu); gypsum (?); neo-Assyrian period, c. 721-705 B.C., Khorsabad, northern Iraq. Oriental Institute Museum. This colossal sculpture was one of a pair that guarded the entrance to throne room of King Sargon II. Photograph courtesy of Oriental Institute Museum, University of Chicago, Chicago, Illinois.

Activities: **Education Programs** (adults, graduate/undergraduate students and children); **Films** (Sunday afternoon); **Guided Tours**; **Lectures**; **Permanent Exhibits**; **Temporary Exhibitions**.

Publications: annual report; brochure; exhibition catalogues; guide; newsletter, "News & Notes" (quarterly).

The Oriental Institute Museum is a showcase of the history, art, and archaeology of the ancient Near East. The Museum exhibits a major collection of antiquities from ancient Egypt, Mesopotamia, Syria/Palestine, Persia, and Anatolia. The Museum is currently closed for renovation, climate control, and expansion, Plans call for the reopening of the first gallery (the Egyptian Gallery) in late 1998. In the meantime, the gift shop and bookstore remain open, and the Education Office continues to offer a variety of programs.

University of Chicago - The Renaissance Society ⒸⒶⒶ

5811 S. Ellis Ave., Chicago, IL 60637

Tel: (312) 702-8670   *Fax:* (312) 702-9669

Internet Address: http;//www.renaissancesociety.org

Director: Ms. Susanne Ghez

Admission: free.

Attendance: 15,000   *Established:* 1915

Membership: Y   *ADA Compliant:* Y

Open: **October to June**,
Tuesday to Friday, 10am-5pm;
Saturday to Sunday, noon-5pm.

Closed: Legal Holidays.

View of gallery during exhibition. Photograph courtesy of Renaissance Society, University of Chicago, Chicago, Illinois.

University of Chicago - The Renaissance Society, cont.

Facilities: **Galleries.**

Activities: **Concerts; Films and Video Screenings; Gallery Talks; Lectures; Performances; Temporary Exhibitions.**

Publications: exhibition catalogues; newsletter (each exhibition).

Founded in 1915 at the University of Chicago to encourage a greater understanding of culture - in the broad, literal sense of the term "renaissance" - the Renaissance Society focuses on the forefront of contemporary art, mounting concept-based, group and solo exhibitions of challenging and provocative art. In the past, the Society first presented works by Arp, Brancusi, Calder, Chagall, Leger, Miró, Moholy-Nagy, Mondrian, Noguchi, and Picasso. Exhibitions in recent decades have introduced Chicago to the work of Louise Bourgeois, Phyllis Bramson, Mike Kelley, Joseph Kosuth, Bruce Nauman, Ed Paschke, and Julian Schnabel.

University of Illinois at Chicago - Gallery 400 ⓒ

400 S. Peoria St. (two blocks west of Halsted at Van Buren St.), Chicago, IL   60607-7034

Tel: (312) 996-6114   *Fax:* (312) 996-6115

Internet Address: http://www.uic.edu

Director: Ms. Karen Indeck

Admission: free.

Open: Monday to Friday, 9am-5pm; Saturday, noon-4pm.

Facilities: **Gallery.**

Activities: **Lecture Series** (visiting artists); **Temporary Exhibitions.**

The gallery presents temporary exhibitions of contemporary work in the fields of art, architecture and design.

Chicago Heights

Prairie State College - Christopher Art Gallery

202 S. Halsted St., Chicago Heights, IL   60411

Tel: (708) 709-3394   *Fax:* (708) 709-3774

Internet Address: http://www.prairie.cc.il.us

Gallery Manager: Jan Bonavia

Admission: free.

Established: 1996   *Membership:* N

Parking: Lot D, off Vollmer Road.

Open: Tuesday, 10am-2pm; Wednesday to Thursday, 10am-2pm and 5pm-7pm.

Closed: Academic Holidays.

Facilities: **Gallery** (1,300 square feet).

Activities: **Temporary Exhibitions.**

The Gallery offers six to eight exhibitions annually featuring student work as well as that of local and regional artists. The permanent collection, consisting chiefly of photographs, is also displayed on an occasional basis.

De Kalb

Northern Illinois University Art Museum ⓒ

Northern Illinois University, Altgeld Hall, Lincoln Highway (SR 38), De Kalb, IL   60115

Tel: (815) 753-1936   *Fax:* (815) 753-7897

Internet Address: http://www.vpa.niu.edu/museum

Director: Ms. Peggy Doherty

Admission: free.

Attendance: 18,000   *Established:* 1970   *Membership:* Y   *ADA Compliant:* Y

Parking: call for information.

Open: Monday to Wednesday, 10am-5pm; Thursday, 10am-7pm; Friday, 10am-5pm; Saturday, noon-4pm.

Closed: Legal Holidays.

Northern Illinois University Art Museum, cont.

Facilities: **Exhibition Area** (5,000 square feet).

Activities: **Education Programs** (undergraduate and graduate college students); **Gallery Talks**; **Guided Tours**; **Lectures**; **Temporary Exhibitions**; **Traveling Exhibitions**.

Publications: exhibition catalogues; newsletter, "Museum Notes".

Aseparate academic unit within the College of Visual and Performing Arts, the NIU Art Museum displays selections from its permanent collection and temporary exhibitions in three galleries. Its main gallery, located on the second floor of Altgeld Hall, presents five exhibitions annually. Also on the De Kalb campus, the Jack Olson Gallery, located on the 2nd floor of Jack Arends Hall in the School of Art, mounts four professional shows each year and provides a venue for MFA exhibitions, design, regional high school, and other outreach exhibitions. The third gallery is located in Chicago; for information on Northern Illinois University Art Gallery in Chicago, see listing under Chicago.

Decatur

Millikin University - Kirkland Fine Arts Center Galleries ⒸⒶⒶ

1184 W. Main St., Decatur, IL   62522

Tel: (217) 424-6227   *Fax:* (217) 424-3993

Internet Address: http;//www.millikin.edu

Curator: Mr. James Schietinger

Admission: voluntary contribution.

Attendance: 20,000   *Established:* 1969   *ADA Compliant:* Y

Open: Monday to Friday, noon-5pm.

Closed: Academic Holidays.

Facilities: **Auditorium** (2,000 seats); **Classrooms**; **Gallery**; **Theatre**.

Activities: **Arts Festival**; **Concerts**; **Dance Recitals**; **Education Programs** (undergraduate college students); **Performances**; **Temporary Exhibitions**.

Located in Kirkland Fine Arts Center, Perkinson, Studio, and Lower galleries feature a schedule of professional artists exhibits, invitational shows, Senior student B.F.A. exhibits, and an annual Spring Student Show.

Millikin University - The Birks Museum ⒸⒶⒶ

Millikin University, Gorin Hall, 2nd Floor, 1184 W. Main, Decatur, IL   62522

Tel: (217) 424-6214   *Fax:* (217) 424-3992

Internet Address: http://www.millikin.edu

Museum Director: Dr. Charles E. Hale

Admission: free.

Attendance: 1,700   *Established:* 1981

Open: **August 21 to May 20**,
>   Monday, 3:15pm-5pm; Tuesday, 1:15pm-5pm; Wednesday, 3:15pm-5pm;
>   Thursday, 1:15pm-5pm; Sunday, 2pm-4pm.

>   **May 28 to August 15**,
>   Monday, 2pm-4pm; Tuesday, 1pm-4pm; Wednesday, 2pm-4pm;
>   Thursday to Friday, 1pm-4pm; Sunday, 1pm-4pm.

Facilities: **Galleries**; **Library** (160 volumes, non-circulating).

Activities: **Education Programs** (adults, graduate/undergraduate students and children); **Guided Tours** (groups, reserve in advance); **Lectures**; **Temporary Exhibitions**; **Traveling Exhibitions**.

Publications: brochure, "The Birks Museum".

Located on the second floor of Gorin Hall, the Museum mounts special exhibitions featuring the Birks collection of decorative arts, as well as pieces on loan from collectors or other museums. The core of the Museum's permanent collection is over 1,000 pieces of European, oriental, and American ceramics and glassware. A select number of items date from the 15th and 16th centuries, with the majority dating in the 18th through 20th centuries. There is also some furniture and a selection of Chinese art objects.

Edwardsville, Illinois

Edwardsville

Southern Illinois University, Edwardsville - The University Museum ⓒᴬ⁴

Southern Illinois University at Edwardsville, SR 159, Edwardsville, IL 62026
Tel: (618) 692-2996
Fax: (618) 692-2995
Internet Address: http://www.siue.edu/ART/Museum.html
Director: Mr. Eric B. Barnett
Admission: free.
Attendance: 20,000   *Established:* 1959   *Membership:* Y   *ADA Compliant:* Y
Parking: pay on site.
Open: Monday to Friday, 8am-10pm.
Facilities: **Galleries**; **Sculpture Garden**.
Activities: **Education Programs** (undergraduate and graduate college students); **Guided Tours**;
     Permanent Exhibits; **Temporary Exhibitions**.
Publications: catalogue, "Louis H. Sullivan Architectural Ornament Collection".

Southern Illinois University, Edwardsville has adopted the "museum without walls" concept. Works from the University's collections are presented throughout the campus. In cooperation with the Department of Art and Design, the University Museum presents an annual series of art exhibitions. The University's holdings include a collection of architectural ornaments by architect Louis H. Sullivan.

Evanston

Kendall College - John M. and Betty Seabury Mitchell Museum of the American Indian ⓒᴬ⁴

2600 Central Park, Evanston, IL 60201
Tel: (847) 475-1030
Internet Address: http://www.kendall.edu
Director: Mr. Patrick Jennings
Admission: fee-$1.00.
Attendance: 10,000   *Established:* 1977   *Membership:* Y
Open: **September to July**, Tuesday to Friday, 10am-6pm; Saturday to Sunday, 11am-4pm.
Closed: August, Academic Holidays.
Facilities: **Auditorium** (100 seats); **Galleries**; **Library** (2,000 volumes); **Shop**.
Activities: **Education Programs** (undergraduate college students); **Films**; **Guided Tours** (reserve
     in advance); **Lectures**; **Permanent Exhibits**; **Temporary Exhibitions**.
Publications: brochure, "The Mitchell Museum"; newsletter.

A part of Kendall College since 1977, the Museum maintains a permanent collection representative of the native peoples of the United States and Canada. It presents permanent exhibits and mounts temporary thematic exhibitions focusing on the art (including contemporary art), artifacts and culture of Native Americans.

Northwestern University - Dittmar Gallery ⓒᴬ⁴

Norris University Center, 1999 S. Campus Drive, Evanston, IL 60208
Tel: (847) 491-7346
Internet Address: http://www.stuaff.nwu,edu/morris/dittmar.html
Contact: Mr. Ricardo Frazer
Admission: free.
Open: Daily, 10am-10pm.
Facilities: **Exhibition Area**.
Activities: **Temporary Exhibitions**.

Located in the Norris University Center, the Dittmar Memorial Gallery features exhibitions focusing on ethnic cultural art, work of emerging artists, art by or about women, and artwork by Northwestern University undergraduate and graduate art students.

Northwestern University - Mary and Leigh Block Museum of Art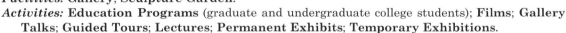

1967 South Campus Drive
Evanston, IL 60208-2410
Tel: (847) 491-4001
Fax: (847) 491-2261
Internet Address: http://www.nwu.edu/museum
Director: Mr. David Mickenberg
Admission: voluntary contribution.
Attendance: 30,000   *Established:* 1980
Membership: Y   *ADA Compliant:* Y
Parking: on site (free after 5pm and Sat-Sun).
Open: **Academic Year**,
          Tuesday to Wednesday, noon-5pm;
          Thursday to Sunday, noon-8pm.
     Summer,
          Tuesday to Saturday, noon-5pm.

Barbara Hepworth, *Two Forms (Divided Circle)*, 1969, bronze, Gift of Leigh Block, Mary and Leigh Block Museum of Art. Photograph courtesy of Mary and Leigh Block Museum of Art, Northwestern University, Evanston, Illinois.

Facilities: **Gallery**; **Sculpture Garden**.
Activities: **Education Programs** (graduate and undergraduate college students); **Films**; **Gallery Talks**; **Guided Tours**; **Lectures**; **Permanent Exhibits**; **Temporary Exhibitions**.
Publications: exhibition catalogues.

Located on the lakeshore campus of Northwestern University in Evanston, the Mary and Leigh Block Museum of Art has earned a worldwide reputation for its research, exhibitions, publications, and campus and community programs. The Museum's focus is on prints and drawings from many periods and large sculptures produced by 20th-century European and American artists. It currently numbers nearly 2,000 works on paper which range from the 13th century to the present by artists of diverse nationalities. The Block Museum's outdoor sculpture garden features 17 bronze sculptures by major European and American artists and is considered one of the most significant modernist groupings in the region. It features works by Jean Arp, Virginia Ferrari, Barbara Hepworth, Jean Ipousteguy, Jacques Lipchitz, Joan Miró, Henry Moore, Arnoldo Pomodoro, Antoine Poncet, and others. The Museum also hosts nationally-touring exhibits. Also of possible interest on campus is the Dittmar Memorial Gallery (see separate listing).

Glen Ellyn

College of DuPage - Gahlberg Gallery, Arts Center

425 22nd St. and Park Blvd.
Glen Ellyn, IL 60137-6599
Tel: (630) 942-2321   *Ext:* 2321
Fax: (630) 790-9806
Internet Address: http://www.cod.edu/artscntr
Director and Curator: Ms. Eileen Broido
Admission: free.
Attendance: 15,000   *Established:* 1986
Membership: N   *ADA Compliant:* Y
Parking: free on site.
Open: Monday to Wednesday, 11am-3pm;
          Thursday, 11am-3pm and 6pm-8pm;
          Saturday, 11am-3pm.
Facilities: **Gallery**.
Activities: **Lectures**; **Temporary Exhibitions**
     (8 - 10 per year).
Publications: brochures; exhibition catalogues.

Nicholas Sistler, *Still Life With Venus*, 1996, gouache on paper, 2.5 x 3.5 inches. Exhibited at Gahlberg Gallery Arts Center, 1997. Photograph courtesy of Gahlberg Gallery, College of DuPage, Glen Ellyn, Illinois.

The Gallery presents eight to ten changing exhibitions per year of both contemporary and historical art, arranged by both in-house and guest curators.

Grayslake

College of Lake County - Community Gallery of Art ⓒᴬᴬ

19351 W. Washington St., Grayslake, IL   60045
Tel: (847) 543-2240   *Fax:* (847) 223-7690
Internet Address: http://www.clc/cc.il.us
Director: Mr. Steve Jones
Admission: voluntary contribution.
Membership: Y   *ADA Compliant:* Y
Parking: free on site.
Open: Monday to Thursday, 8am-10pm;
       Friday, 8am-4:30pm;
       Saturday, 9am-4:30pm;
       Sunday, 1pm-5pm.

Henry J. Darger, *Untitled*, watercolor (two-sided), 19 x 47 inches. Shure Family Collection, exhibited at College of Lake County, Community Gallery of Art, 1998. Photograph by Bill Kniest, courtesy of College of Lake County, Community Gallery of Art, Grayslake, Illinois.

Facilities: **Gallery** (2500 square feet).
Activities: **Guided Tours**; **Temporary Exhibitions**.
Publications: brochures for exhibitions.

The Gallery mounts temporary exhibitions of student work as well as that of professional artists with regional, national, and international reputations.

Joliet

Joliet Junior College - Laura A. Sprague Art Gallery

1215 Houbolt Road, Joliet, IL   60431-8938
Tel: (815) 729-9020 *Ext:* 2423
Internet Address: http://www.jcc.cc.il.us
Director: Mr. Joe Milosevich
Open: Monday/Wednesday/Friday, 9am-2pm; Tuesday/Thursday, 9am-2pm and 6pm-8pm.
Facilities: **Exhibition Area**.
Activities: **Temporary Exhibitions**.

The Art Department's Laura A. Sprague Art Gallery features temporary exhibits of works by guest artists, faculty, and students.

Lake Forest

Lake Forest College - Sonnenschein Gallery ⓒᴬᴬ

555 Sheridan Road, Lake Forest, IL   60045
Tel: (847) 735-5194
Internet Address: http://www.lfc.edu/academics/art/gallery/art0001.htm
Director: Ms. Rebecca Goldberg
Open: Daily, 2:30pm-5pm.
Facilities: **Galleries**.

Located in the Durand Art Institute, the Sonnenschein Gallery mounts changing exhibitions throughout the academic year, displaying both student and faculty work as well as selections from the College's permanent collection and works lent by other collections. The adjacent Albright Room is used to display the College's collections of Pre-Columbian and African art. The permanent collection consists of European drawings and prints, contemporary American prints, Pre-Columbian art, African art, and prints, drawings, paintings, and photographs from various periods.

Macomb

Western Illinois University Art Gallery ⓒᴬᴬ

1 University Circle, (just north of Sherman Hall), Macomb, IL   61455
Tel: (309) 298-1587   *Fax:* (309) 298-2400
Internet Address: http://www.wiu.edu/users/miart/gallery.html
Curator of Exhibits: Mr. John R. Graham
Admission: free.

Western Illinois University Art Gallery, cont.

Attendance: 9,000   *Established:* 1899   *Membership:* N   *ADA Compliant:* Y
Parking: obtain temporary. permit   from WIU Office of Public Safety.

Open: **Academic Year**,
 Monday, 9am-4pm;
 Tuesday, 9am-4pm and 6pm-8pm;
 Wednesday to Friday, 9am-4pm.
Closed: Legal Holidays, School Vacations.
Facilities: **Galleries** (3).
Activities: **Gallery Talks; Lectures; Temporary Exhibitions; Traveling Exhibitions.**
Publications: exhibition catalogues.

The Gallery presents a schedule of temporary exhibitions of work drawn from its permanent collection, professional artists, faculty, and students. In addition to gallery exhibits, sculptures are sited throughout the campus. Holdings include Works Progress Administration graphics and paintings, contemporary graphics, paintings, sculpture, glass, and ceramics.

Archibald J. Motley, Jr., *The Jazz Singers*, c. 1937, oil on canvas, 32 x 42 inches, WPA. Permanent collection, Western Illinois University Art Gallery. Photograph courtesy of Western Illinois University, Macomb, Illinois.

Monmouth

Monmouth College - Len G. Everett Gallery

Hewes Library, Broadway, Monmouth, IL   61462
Tel: (309) 457-2364
Internet Address: http://www.monm.edu/academic/Art/gallery.html
Gallery Director: Ms. Cheryl Meeker
Admission: free.
Open: Call for hours.
Facilities: **Gallery.**
Activities: **Temporary Exhibitions.**

Located in the Hewes Library, the Everett Gallery offers temporary exhibitions of work by professional artists and students, including an annual student exhibition and competition each Spring.

Normal

Illinois State University Galleries ⒸⒶ

110 Center for the Visual Arts, Beaufort Street, Normal, IL   61790
Tel: (309) 438-5487   *Fax:* (309) 438-5161
Internet Address: http://www.orat.ilstu.edu/cfa/galleries
Director: Mr. Barry Binderman
Open: Monday, noon-4pm; Tuesday, 9:30am-9pm; Wednesday to Friday, 9:30am-4:30pm;
 Saturday to Sunday, noon-4pm.
Facilities: **Galleries.**
Activities: **Temporary Exhibitions.**

University Galleries is devoted to presenting a wide survey of contemporary art in its three galleries. The Galleries mount temporary exhibitions, both self-curated and traveling. A measure of its stature is that it has itself organized fourteen traveling exhibitions since 1990.

Peoria

Bradley University - Art Galleries ⒸⒶ

College of Communications and Fine Arts, 1501 West Bradley Avenue, Peoria, IL   61625
Tel: (309) 677-2989
Internet Address: http://gcc.bradley.edu/art/resrc.html

Bradley University - Art Galleries, cont.

Director: Mr. John Heintzman

Open: **Heuser Gallery**, Monday to Friday, 10am-4pm.

Hartmann Gallery, Monday to Friday, noon-4pm.

Facilities: **Exhibition Area**.

Activities: **Lectures**; **Permanent Exhibits**; **Temporary Exhibitions**.

The University offers exhibits in two galleries: the Heuser Art Center Gallery and the Hartmann Center for the Performing Arts Gallery. These two galleries provide Bradley with the opportunity to present exhibitions that focus upon artists who work in alternative styles or thematic shows that heighten awareness of contemporary issues in the art world. Bradley University sponsors and organizes the Bradley National Print and Drawing Exhibition, the oldest continuous competition of its kind in the United States. This event expanded its boundaries and included international artists for the first time in 1995. (Because of its size, the exhibition is hosted at four gallery sites in the community: Bradley University's Heuser Art Center Gallery, The Hartmann Center Gallery, The Peoria Art Guild and Lakeview Museum of Arts and Sciences.) Also included in the exhibition program is the annual Jacob and Lorrie Bunn Lectureship in Photography, which brings a fine arts photographer or photojournalist of national prominence to the campus. In addition, as part of the University's Visiting Artists Series, artists of national stature participate in the Master Print Program of Cradle Oak Press, Bradley's printmaking research studio. These visiting artists create limited editions of their work. The Galleries also host the thesis exhibitions of BFA, MA and MFA students. Faculty exhibitions and an undergraduate fine arts competition are held on a biennial basis. Also of possible interest on campus, exhibits in the Cullom-Davis Library often feature artworks.

Quincy

Quincy University - Gray Gallery

Brenner Library, 1800 College

Quincy, IL   62301

Tel: (217) 228-5371

Fax: (217) 228-5257

Internet Address: http://www.quincy.edu

Director: Mr. Robert Lee Mejer

Admission: free.

Attendance: 85,000   *Established:* 1968

ADA Compliant: Y

Parking: on site.

Open: Monday to Thursday, 8am-11pm;
Friday, 8am-8pm;
Saturday, 11am-5pm;
Sunday, 1pm-5pm.

View of the Gray Gallery during an exhibition of works on paper by Sarah Slavick, 1991. Photograph courtesy of Art Department, Quincy University, Quincy, Illinois.

Facilities: **Exhibition Area** (foyer and gallery, 2 rooms, 110 linear feet); **Library** (15,000 volumes on art).

Activities: **Temporary Exhibitions**.

Housed in the Brenner Library, the Gray Gallery presents an annual exhibition schedule, which includes exhibitions by nationally and regionally noted artists, alumni, art faculty, and students. The Art Faculty Exhibit, Juried Student Art Show and the Baccalaureate Senior Retrospective are held annually. Although not found in Gray Gallery, the sculpture "Windows to the Future" by Father Tom Brown, OFM, located on Penny Lane, may also be of interest.

Rock Island

Augustana College Art Gallery ⓒ

Centennial Hall, 7th Ave. and 38th St., Rock Island, IL   61201-2296

Tel: (309) 794-7231   *Fax:* (309) 794-7678

Internet Address: http://www.augustana.edu

Director: Ms. Sherry C. Maurer

Augustana College Art Gallery, cont.

Admission: free.
Attendance: 40,000   *Established:* 1983   *ADA Compliant:* Y
Parking: free, lot next to Centennial Hall.
Open: **September to May**, Tuesday to Saturday, noon-4pm.
Closed: Academic Holidays.
Facilities: **Exhibition Area** (3,310 square feet).
Activities: **Concerts**; **Education Programs** (adults and undergraduate college students); **Films**; **Guided Tours** (groups, by advance appointment); **Juried Exhibits**; **Lectures**; **Temporary Exhibitions**.
Publications: calendar (annual).

Located in the front of the Centennial Hall auditorium, the Augustana College Art Gallery serves the College and the community by presenting temporary visual arts exhibitions and interpretive programs to augment a liberal arts curriculum. Shows include the annual juried Rock Island Fine Arts Exhibition (open to artists residing within a 150-mile radius of the Quad Cities) and student shows.

Rockford

Rockford College Art Gallery ⓒⒶ

Clark Arts Center, 5050 E. State, Rockford, IL   61108
Tel: (815) 226-4034   *Fax:* (815) 226-4119
Internet Address: http://www.rockford.edu
Director: Ms. Maureen Gustafson
Admission: free.
Established: 1847   *Membership:* Y   *ADA Compliant:* Y
Parking: free nearby.
Open: **September to May**, Daily, 2pm-5pm.
Facilities: **Exhibition Area** (1,400 square feet).
Activities: **Education Programs**; **Guided Tours** (by appointment); **Lectures**; **Temporary Exhibitions** (7-8/year); **Traveling Exhibitions**.
Publications: exhibition catalogues.

The Gallery mounts seven to eight exhibits each academic year. The College's holdings include 20th century paintings, prints by modern and contemporary masters, photography, ceramics, drawings, installations, assemblages, and ethnographic art.

University Park

Governors State University - Nathan Manilow Sculpture Park ⓒⒶ

Wagner House, University Parkway, University Park, IL   60466
Tel: (708) 534-4105   *Fax:* (708) 534-8959   *TDDY:* (708) 534-8650
Internet Address: http://wwwgovst.edu/users/gscu/pt/park3
Director: Ms. Beverly Goldberg
Admission: voluntary contribution.
Attendance: 800   *Established:* 1969
Open: Daily, 24 hours.
Facilities: **Library**; **Sculpture Park** (over 20 works).
Activities: **Guided Tours**.
Publications: brochure; catalogue.

Placed throughout the University's 750 acre campus, art in the Nathan Manilow Sculpture Park comprises one of the largest collections of monumental sculpture in the country. Among the artists represented are Vito Acconci, John Chamberlain, Mark di Suvero, Ted Garner, Charles Ginnever, John Henry, Jene Highstein, Richard Hunt, Terrence Karpowicz, Clement Meadore, Mary Miss, Bruce Nauman, John Payne, Jerry Peart, Martin Puryear, Joel Shapiro, and Edvins Strautmanis.

Indiana

The number in parentheses following the city name indicates the number of museums/galleries in that municipality. If there is no number, one is understood. For example, in the text two listings would be found under Bloomington and one listing under Terre Haute.

Indiana

Bloomington

Indiana University Art Museum ⓒ (IUAM)

Indiana University, East 7th St.
Bloomington, IN   47405-5401
Tel: (812) 855-5445
Fax: (812) 855-1023
Internet Address:
   http://www.indiana.edu/~iuartmus/home.html
Director: Dr. Adelheid M. Gealt
Admission: free.
Attendance: 70,000   *Established:* 1941
Membership: N   *ADA Compliant:* Y
Parking: metered spaces behind Museum
   and in Main Library lot.
Open: Wednesday to Friday, 10am-5pm;
   Saturday to Sunday, noon-5pm.
Closed: New Year's Day, Memorial Day,
   Independence Day, Labor Day,
   Thanksgiving Day, Christmas Day.

Exterior view of Indiana University Art Museum (1982), designed by I.M. Pei and Partners. Photograph courtesy of Indiana University Art Museum, Bloomington, Indiana.

Facilities: **Architecture** (1982 design by I.M. Pei and Partners); **Galleries**; **Library**; **Sculpture Garden**.
Activities: **Gallery Talks** ("Noon Talks"); **Guided Tours** (arrange in advance, 855-1045.); **Performances** ("The Arts Connection", monthly concert series); **Permanent Exhibits**; **Temporary Exhibitions**; **Traveling Exhibitions**.
Publications: annual report; calendar (monthly); collection catalogue; exhibition catalogues.

Since its founding, the Museum has grown to include over 30,000 objects - paintings, prints, drawings, photographs, sculpture, ceramics, jewelry, textiles - representing nearly every art-producing culture throughout history. Three permanent collection galleries display the art of the Western world from Byzantine to modern times (1st floor), Ancient and Asian art (2nd floor), and the art of Africa, the Pacific, and pre-Columbian Americas (3rd floor). Temporary exhibitions (rotating, traveling, and School of Fine Arts student and faculty exhibitions) are mounted in the Special Exhibitions, Hexagon, Focalpoint, and Children's Corner galleries. Changing sculpture exhibitions are scheduled periodically in the Museum's outdoor Sculpture Terrace. Arrangements may be made by appointment in advance to view portions of the collections that are in storage.

Indiana University - School of Fine Arts Gallery ⓒ (SOFA Gallery)

Henry Radford Hope School of Fine Arts
Fine Arts Building 123, E. 7th Street
Bloomington, IN   47405
Tel: (812) 855-8490
Fax: (812) 855-7498
Internet Address: http://www.fa/indiana.edu/~sofa/index.html
Director: Ms Betsy Stirratt
Admission: voluntary contribution.
Attendance: 20,000   *Established:* 1987   *ADA Compliant:* Y
Open: Tuesday to Thursday, noon-4pm; Friday, noon-8pm; Saturday to Sunday, 1pm-4pm.
Closed: Spring Break, Summer Break, Thanksgiving Day, Christmas Day.
Facilities: **Exhibition Area**.
Activities: **Gallery Talks**; **Guided Tours**; **Lectures**; **Temporary Exhibitions**.

The SOFA Gallery presents contemporary art by significant regionally and nationally known artists, as well as by students within the school. Also in the School of Fine Arts is the Bomb Shelter, a small exhibition space showcasing a new artist or group of artists every one to three weeks.

Crawfordsville

Wabash College - Eric Dean Gallery ⓒᴬᴬ
Wabash College, Wabash Avenue, Crawfordsville, IN   47933
Tel: (765) 361-6364
Internet Address: http://www.wabash.edu
Open: Monday to Friday, 8am-noon and1pm-4:30pm.
Facilities: **Galleries.**
Activities: **Permanent Exhibits; Temporary Exhibitions.**

In addition to mounting displays of its extensive collection of contemporary art, the Gallery presents temporary exhibitions of the work of professional artists.

Greencastle

DePauw University - Emison Art Center Gallery ⓒᴬᴬ
309 S. College Ave., Greencastle, IN   46135
Tel: (765) 658-4336   *Fax:* (765) 658-4177
Internet Address: http://www,depauw.edu/art
Gallery Curator: Ms. Martha Opdahl
Admission: free.
Membership: N   *ADA Compliant:* Y
Parking: free on site.
Open: Monday to Friday, 9am-4pm; Saturday, 10am-4pm; Sunday, 1pm-5pm.
Closed: January, June to August, Academic Holidays.
Facilities: **Gallery.**
Activities: **Temporary Exhibitions.**
Publications: exhibition catalogues (occasional).

The Gallery presents from six to eight exhibitions during the academic year, which showcase work in a variety of media by contemporary artists of regional and national reputation, as well as mainstream and non-Western art. Student and faculty work is also displayed.

Huntington

Huntington College - Robert E. Wilson Gallery
Merillat Center for the Arts, 2303 College Avenue
Huntington, IN   46750
Tel: (219) 359-4260
Internet Address: http://www.huntcol.edu/mca/mca_gallery.html
Director: Ms. Margaret Roush
Open: Monday to Friday, 9am-5pm; before & after Center performances.
Facilities: **Exhibition Area.**
Activities: **Temporary Exhibitions.**

The Wilson Gallery presents a series of changing exhibits during the year. Exhibition by student, faculty, and professional artists feature a wide range of media and themes. The Gallery's permanent collection includes prints by Salvador Dali and paintings by many contemporary American and European artists.

Indianapolis

Herron School of Art - Herron Gallery ⓒᴬᴬ
1701 N. Pennsylvania St., Indianapolis, IN   46202
Tel: (317) 920-2423
Internet Address: http://www.herron.iupui.edu
Gallery Director: Mr. David Russick
Admission: free.
Attendance: 35,000   *Established:* 1979   *ADA Compliant:* Y

Herron School of Art - Herron Gallery, cont.
Open: Monday to Wednesday, 10am-5pm; Thursday, noon-8pm; Friday to Saturday, 10am-3pm; or by appointment (920-2420).
Facilities: **Exhibition Area.**
Activities: **Temporary Exhibitions** (6/year).

The Gallery presents contemporary art, focusing on the latest and often experimental areas in the visual arts. Exhibitions feature the work of locally, regionally, nationally, and internationally recognized artists and range in size from solo shows to theme exhibitions including twenty or more artists.

University of Indianapolis - Art Galleries ⓒ
1400 East Hanna Avenue
Indianapolis, IN   46227
Tel: (317) 788-3253
Internet Address: http://www.uindy.edu/~art/
Department Cahir: Mr. Dee E. Schaad
Admission: free.
Open: **Academic Year**, Monday to Friday, 9am-9pm.
Closed: Academic Holidays.
Facilities: **Galleries** (2).
Activities: **Temporary Exhibitions** (monthly, during academic year).

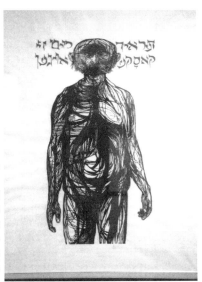

The Christel DeHaan Fine Arts Center contains a gallery used for temporary exhibits that complement the Art Department's teaching mission. Student, faculty, one person and group exhibits are held in the Leah Ransburgh Gallery located on campus in Good Hall. The University has an extensive permanent collection composed mostly of prints, but does include some painting and sculpture. Holdings include works by Jim Dine, Frank Gallo, Mauricio Lasansky, Louise Nevelson, Picasso, Robert Rauschenberg, and Rembrandt. On display in the hallway of the DeHaan Fine Arts Center and in public access areas of the Krannert Memorial Library, the permanent collection is open to the public daily.

Leonard Baskin, *Stravismic Jew*, University of Indianapolis Permanent Collection. Photograph courtesy of Christel DeHaan Fine Arts Center, University of Indianapolis, Indianapolis, Indiana.

Kokomo

Indiana University Kokomo - IUK Art Gallery ⓒ
Kelley Center Complex
2300 S. Washington St.
Kokomo, IN   46904
Tel: (765) 455-9523
Fax: (765) 455-9444
Internet Address: http://www.indiana.edu/
Director: Ms. Lynda L. Collins
Admission: free.
Established: 1995
Membership: Y   *ADA Compliant:* Y
Parking: free on site.
Open: Monday to Tuesday, noon-4pm;
Wednesday, noon-8pm;
Thursday, noon-4pm;
Sunday, 3pm-5pm.
Closed: Legal Holidays, Summer.
Facilities: **Exhibition Area** (2,000 square feet).

View of gallery, Indiana University Kokomo, during exhibition of work of Tom Hale, AWS, 1998. Photograph courtesy of Indiana University Kokomo, Kokomo, Indiana.

Indiana University Kokomo - IUK Art Gallery, cont.

Activities: **Guided Tours** (by appointment); **Lectures** (by appointment); **Temporary Exhibitions**.

The IUK Art Gallery is a new exhibition space in the Kelley Center Complex. It presents seven to nine exhibitions per year featuring the work of artists with regional and national reputations.

Muncie

Ball State University Museum of Art ⊕

2000 W. University Ave.
Muncie, IN   47306
Tel: (765) 285-5242
Fax: (765) 285-5275
Internet Address:
   http://panda.tierranet.com/MOA2/mainpage.htm
Director: Mr. Alain Joyaux
Admission: voluntary contribution.
Attendance: 32,000   *Established:* 1936
Membership: Y   *ADA Compliant:* Y
Parking: metered on street and nearby commercial lots.
Open: Tuesday to Friday, 9am-4:30pm;
          Saturday to Sunday, 1:30pm-4:30pm.
Closed: Legal Holidays, University Holidays.
Facilities: **Architecture** (Gothic Revival-style building, 1936 designed by George Schreiber); **Exhibition Area** (16,000 square feet); **Sculpture Garden**.
Activities: **Concerts**; **Gallery Talks** (occasional, Sunday, 2:30pm); **Guided Tours**; **Lectures**; **Permanent Exhibits**; **Temporary Exhibitions**; **Traveling Exhibitions**.
Publications: biennial report (biennial); exhibition catalogues.

Mademoiselle Befort, *A Young Woman From Thebes Tending Her Wounded Father*, 1809, Collection of and photograph courtesy of Ball State University Museum of Art , Muncie, Indiana.

The Museum presents permanent exhibitions plus special shows and events, including an annual student art show and a biennial exhibition of work by faculty members. The collection includes holdings in American 19th- and early 20th-century paintings, European 18th- and 19th-century paintings, 16th- through 20th-century drawings, and ethnographic, Oriental, and decorative arts.

Notre Dame

University of Notre Dame - The Snite Museum of Art ⊕

Moose Krause Circle, Notre Dame, IN   46556
Tel: (219) 631-5466
Fax: (219) 631-8501
Internet Address:
   http://www.nd.edu/~sniteart/97/main3.html
Director: Dr. Dean A. Porter
Admission: suggested contribution-$2.00.
Attendance: 102,000   *Established:* 1842
Membership: Y   *ADA Compliant:* Y
Parking: university visitors' lot.
Open: Tuesday to Wednesday, 10am-4pm
          Thursday to Saturday, 10am-5pm;
          Sunday, 1pm-4pm.
Closed: Legal Holidays.

David Hayes, *Griffon*, 1989, painted steel, height 324 inches. Humana Foundation Endowment for American Art. In background is view of Snite Museum of Art (1980), designed by Ambrose Richardson. Photograph courtesy of Snite Museum of Art, University of Notre Dame, South Bend, Indiana.

University of Notre Dame - The Snite Museum of Art, cont.

Facilities: **Architecture** (constructed 1980; designed by Ambrose Richardson); **Galleries**; **Library** (20,000 volumes); **Sculpture Garden**; **Shop**.

Activities: **Concerts**; **Education Programs** (adults and children); **Films**; **Gallery Talks**; **Guided Tours**; **Lectures**; **Permanent Exhibits**; **Temporary Exhibitions**; **Traveling Exhibitions**.

Publications: exhibition catalogues.

The Snite Museum of Art has a comprehensive collection of over 19,000 objects housed in its 70,000-square-foot building. It mounts temporary exhibitions in addition to displaying objects from the collection. The majority of the Museum's exhibit space is devoted to its permanent collection, which includes objects from antiquity to the 20th century, and features important works by Ghirlandaio, Claude, Bloemaert, Boucher, Eakins, Remington, O'Keeffe, Rickey, Joseph Stella, and Jim Dine. Notable collections housed in the Museum include The Kress Study Collection, the Feddersen collection of Rembrandt etchings, the Butkin bequest of 19th-century French paintings, the Reilly collection of Old Master drawings, the Janos Scholz collection of 19th-century European photographs, and the Leighton collection of pre-Classic figurines. The Museum maintains a separate gallery of sculpture and drawings by Ivan Mestrovic, which is the American study center for his art. The Print, Drawing, and Photography Gallery is designed for displaying collections of works on paper, as well as temporary exhibitions on loan from other institutions and private collectors. The Museum schedules a dozen exhibitions annually on subjects as diverse as Old Master drawings, contemporary prints, and pre-Columbian sculptures. The O'Shaughnessy Galleries host the annual student show and a biennial faculty show. On the lower level are the Museum's ethnographic collections, the John T. Higgins Gallery of American Art, and the museum reference library. Entrance to the Courtyard is at the north end of the atrium and leads to the outdoor sculpture display in the garden. Featured in the courtyard is a George Rickey kinetic sculpture. David Hayes, class of 1953, is the creator of Griffon, the 27-foot steel sculpture at the entrance to the Museum.

South Bend

Indiana University South Bend Ⓒᴬᴬ

1700 Mishawaka Ave., South Bend, IN 46634

Tel: (219) 237-4872

Internet Address: http://www.iusb.edu/~artevent/hytml/gallery.html

Admission: free.

Open: Monday to Friday, 8am-10pm; Saturday, 8am-noon; Sunday, 1pm-6pm.

Facilities: **Exhibition Area**.

Activities: **Gallery Talks**; **Temporary Exhibitions**.

The gallery offers temporary exhibitions.

Terre Haute

Indiana State University Art Gallery Ⓒᴬᴬ

Center for Performing & Fine Arts, 7th and Chestnut Sts.

Terre Haute, IN 47809

Tel: (812) 237-3720

Fax: (812) 237-4369

Internet Address: http://www.indstate.edu

Director: Mr. Craig Zollars

Admission: free.

Established: 1953   *ADA Compliant:* Y

Open: Monday to Wednesday, 11am-4pm; Thursday, 1pm-8pm; Friday, 11am-4pm.

Closed: Legal Holidays.

Facilities: **Gallery** (3,700 square feet).

Activities: **Education Programs** (undergraduate and graduate college students); **Lecture Series** (visiting artists); **Temporary Exhibitions** (regional and national contemporary artists).

Publications: exhibition catalogues (2/year).

Indiana State University Art Gallery, cont.

The Gallery presents temporary exhibitions of works from the permanent collections and by professional artists. The schedule includes semi-annual graduate thesis exhibitions and annual faculty, B.F.A. Senior, and juried student exhibitions. University holdings include nearly 2,000 paintings, sculptures, prints, drawings, and artifacts from various periods and cultures. The collection is particularly strong in 20th-century American art highlighted by 200 works from the Works Progress Administration's Federal Art Project and a collection of works from the 1970s (pop, op, and photo-realist art). While not on permanent exhibition at a central site, many works from the collection are displayed in public areas throughout the campus.

Valparaiso

Valparaiso University - Brauer Museum of Art (C,A)

Valparaiso University, Center for the Arts, Chapel Drive
Valparaiso, IN   46383-6349
Tel: (219) 464-5365
Fax: (219) 464-5244
Director: Ms. Rita McCarthy
Admission: free.
Established: 1953
Membership: Y   *ADA Compliant:* Y
Parking: free on site.
Open: **Academic Year**
            Tuesday, 10am-5pm;
            Thursday to Friday, 10am-5pm;
            Wednesday, 10am-8:30pm;
            Saturday to Sunday, noon-5pm.
        Academic Holidays/Summer,
            Tuesday to Sunday, noon-5pm.

Georgia O'Keeffe, *Red Rust Hills*, 1930, oil on canvas, 16 x 30 inches. Sloan Purchase Fund, Brauer Museum of Art. Photograph courtesy of Brauer Museum of Art, Valparaiso, Indiana.

Closed: Good Friday, Easter, Independence Day, Thanksgiving Day,
        Christmas Eve to Christmas Day, New Year's Eve to New Year's Day.
Facilities: **Galleries** (4); **Recital Hall**; **Shop**; **Theatre**.
Activities: **Gallery Talks**; **Guided Tours** (Sat & Sun, 2pm); **Lectures**; **Permanent Exhibits**;
        Temporary Exhibitions; **Traveling Exhibitions**.
Publications: exhibition guides; newsletter, "Friends Newsletter".

The Brauer Museum of Art holds a permanent collection of over 1,600 works, including examples by many leading American artists of the 19th and 20th centuries, such as Anderson, Burchfield, Bricher, Church, Glackens, Hassam, Johnson, Kensett, Marin, O'Keeffe, Sierra, Sloan, and Warhol. The Museum also maintains collections of European works, prints, photography, sculpture, and religious art. It displays special loan exhibitions in addition to its permanent collection and also sponsors juried competitions of student art.

West Lafayette

Purdue University Galleries (C,A)

Ralph G, Beelke Memorial Gallery: Creative Arts Building Two, Northwestern & Stadium Aves.
Krannert Drawing Room: Krannert Building, Main Floor, Grant and State Sts.
Stewart Center Gallery: Stewart Center, West Lobby, State St. and Memorial Mall
West Lafayette, IN   47907
Tel: (765) 494-3061
Fax: (765) 496-2817
Internet Address: http://www.purdue.edu
Director: Ms. Mona Berg
Admission: voluntary contribution.
Attendance: 68,000   *Established:* 1978   *Membership:* Y   *ADA Compliant:* Y
Parking: pay university lots and on street.

Purdue University Galleries, cont.

Open: **Beelke Gallery**,
Monday to Friday, 10am-5pm.
Krannert Gallery,
Monday to Thursday, 8am-5pm and 7pm-9pm;
Friday, 8am-5pm.
Stewart Center,
Monday to Thursday, 10am-5pm and 7pm-9pm;
Friday, 10am-5pm;
Sunday, 1pm-4pm.

Closed: Academic Holidays.

Facilities: **Galleries** (Beelke, 1200 square feet; Krannert, 5500 square feet;.Stewart, 1200 square feet).

Activities: **Concerts**; **Films** (occasional); **Guided Tours** (on request); **Lectures** (with exhibit openings and weekly noontime "Brown Bag" talks); **Temporary Exhibitions** (6-8 weeks in duration); **Traveling Exhibitions**.

Publications: brochure (quarterly); calendar (annual); catalogue (quarterly); newsletter (semi-annual).

Diego Rivera, *Cabeza de Tehuana: Tehuantepec*, 1930, oil on canvas, 22.25 x 18.25 inches. Purdue University collection, gift of Edward Stowe Akeley and Anna Akeley, 1995. Photograph courtesy of Purdue University, West Lafayette, Indiana.

The Purdue University gallery program maintains three separate galleries on campus: Ralphe G. Beelke memorial Gallery (494-9355), Krannert Drawing Room (494-9700), and Stewart Center Gallery (494-5687). The Galleries present an active schedule of exhibitions of works from the permanent collection and objects lent by private collectors or other institutions, as well as annual exhibitions of MFA and undergraduate students work. The permanent collection of more than 5,000 objects includes pre-Columbian textiles; Native American baskets; modern and contemporary Mexican paintings, drawings, and prints; Japanese woodblock prints; European and American paintings, prints, and sculpture from the 16th century to the present; and photographs from 1839 to the present. Purdue University Galleries will be consolidated in the new Center for the Visual and Performing Arts, scheduled for completion in 2002.

Iowa

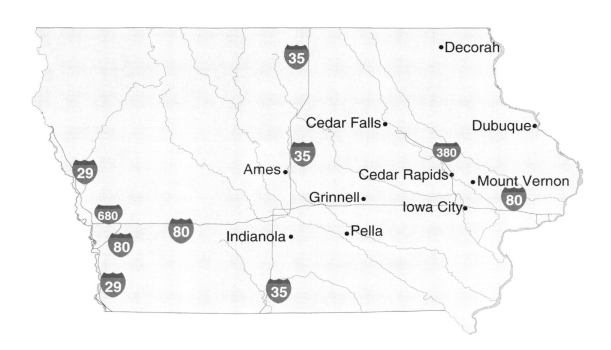

A number in parentheses following a city name indicates the number of museums/galleries in that municipality. If there is no number, one is understood. For example, in the text one listing would be found under each Iowan city shown on map.

Iowa

Ames

Iowa State University - Brunnier Art Museum (CAA)

290 Scheman Building, Ames, IA 50011
Tel: (515) 294-3342   *Fax:* (515) 294-7070
Internet Address: Http://www.museums.iastate.edu/
Director: Ms. Lynette Pohlman
Admission: voluntary contribution.
Attendance: 31,000   *Established:* 1975   *Membership:* Y   *ADA Compliant:* Y
Parking: lot north of building.
Open: Tuesday to Wednesday, 11am-4pm; Thursday, 11am-4pm and 5pm-9pm; Friday, 11am-4pm;
Saturday to Sunday, 1pm-4pm.
Closed: Easter, Memorial Day, Independence Day, Labor Day, Thanksgiving Day, Christmas Day.
Facilities: **Galleries**; **Library** (use on premises); **Reading Room**; **Shop**.
Activities: **Arts Festival**; **Demonstrations**; **Education Programs**; **Gallery Talks**; **Guided Tours** (groups, arrange in advance); **Lecture Series**; **Permanent Exhibits**; **Temporary Exhibitions**; **Traveling Exhibitions**; **Workshops**.
Publications: newsletter, "News from University Museums" (quarterly).

Located on the top floor of the Scheman Building, the Brunnier Art Museum has a permanent collection of decorative and fine arts spanning a variety of eras and artistic genres. The permanent collections are regularly on display in short- and long-term exhibits. Groupings of Oriental jades and snuff bottles, ceramics, Russian enamels, and ivory carvings often may be seen in rotating exhibitions. Additionally the Art on Campus Program continues a tradition of integrating buildings and art on the campus. Currently more than 200 major works of public art enhance Iowa State's buildings and landscapes from Christian Petersen statues and library murals designed by Grant Wood to contemporary art such as the G-Nome Project incorporated into the design of the Molecular Biology Building. University Museums offers a self-guiding brochure and a monthly Wednesday Walk tour of the Art on Campus Collection.

Cedar Falls

University of Northern Iowa - Gallery of Art (CAA)

Kamerick Art Building, First Floor, 1227 West 27th St., Cedar Falls, IA 50614-0362
Tel: (319) 273-2077   *Fax:* (319) 273-2731
Internet Address: http://www.uni.edu/artdept/gallery/index.html
Gallery Director: Mr. Shawn Holtz
Admission: free.
Attendance: 13,000   *Established:* 1978   *ADA Compliant:* Y
Open: **Academic Year**,
Monday to Thursday, 9am-9pm; Friday, 9am-5pm; Saturday to Sunday, 1pm-4pm.
Summer,
Monday to Friday, 10am-4pm; Saturday to Sunday, noon-4pm.
Closed: Legal Holidays.
Facilities: **Exhibition Area**.
Activities: **Education Programs** (undergraduate college students and children); **Films**; **Gallery Talks**; **Guided Tours**; **Lectures**; **Permanent Exhibits**; **Temporary Exhibitions** (6-8/year); **Traveling Exhibitions**.
Publications: exhibition catalogues.

Located on the first floor of the art building, the Gallery of Art present six to eight major exhibitions and a number of smaller shows each year, including annual shows by the art faculty in the fall and a competitive student show in the spring. The Gallery is also responsible for the University's permanent art collection, which includes works by such prominent artists as Berenice Abbott, Joseph Albers, Eugene Atget, Romare Bearden, George Grosz, Philip Guston, and Jerry Uelsmann. There are also sculptural works sited around the campus.

Cedar Rapids

Coe College - Galleries ⓒⒶ
Dows Fine Arts Center, First Ave. and 13th St.
Cedar Rapids, IA 52402
Tel: (319) 399-8000
Internet Address: http://www.public.coe.edu/departments/Art/galleries.html
Admission: free.
Open: Call for hours.
Facilities: Galleries.
Activities: Permanent Exhibits; Temporary Exhibitions.

The Dows Fine Arts Center, in addition to housing the college's permanent art collection, maintains two art galleries for monthly traveling exhibitions and student shows. With approximately 465 works, the Coe College Collection of Art, diverse in both scope and media, features twelve works by Grant Wood, 56 paintings by Coe graduate and art department founder Marvin Cone, and 45 paintings by another Coe graduate Conger Metcalf. Other artists represented include Karl Appel, Milton Avery, Leonard Baskin, Thomas Hart Benton, Ronald Bladen, Raoul Dufy, Mauricio Lasansky. Aristide Maillol, Henri Matisse, Thomas Nast, Francis Picabia, Pablo Picasso, Mark Rothko, and Henri Toulouse-Lautrec. The campus also features four major outdoor sculptures, as well as other sculptural works in the lobby of the Dow Fine Arts Center.

Decorah

Luther College - Fine Arts Collection ⓒⒶ
Luther College Library, 700 College Drive
Decorah, IA 52101-1042
Tel: (319) 387-1195
Fax: (319) 387-1657
Internet Address: http://www.luther.edu
Gallery Coordinator: Mr. David Kamm
Admission: free.
Attendance: 10,000
ADA Compliant: Y
Open: September to June,
      Monday to Friday, 8am-10pm;
      Saturday, 9am-5pm;
      Sunday, noon-10pm.
Closed: Academic Holidays.
Facilities: Exhibition Area (2,265 square feet).
Activities: Gallery Talks; Temporary Exhibitions; Traveling Exhibitions.
Publications: brochures; exhibition catalogues.

Gerhard Marcks, *Noah*, 1948, woodcut. Fine Arts Collection, Luther College. Photograph courtesy of Luther College, Decorah, Iowa.

The Fine Arts Collection exists to support the general mission of the college by promoting awareness and understanding of a broad spectrum of artistic expression through diversity in media, culture, and historical perspective. Nearly one-third of the collection is on circulating display throughout the campus. Over 1,100 items comprise the fine arts collection, anchored by extensive holdings of the works of Herbjørn Gausta, Marguerite Wildenhain, and Gerhard Marcks, The collection, housed in the Preus Library, also includes examples of pre-Columbian pottery and Inuit sculpture. Regional artists are well represented by paintings, prints, and ceramics, and examples of works by such international artists as Picasso, Vlaminck, and Whistler are also presented. Works in the collection include paintings, drawings, prints, photographs, sculpture, assemblages, textiles, ceramics, and utilitarian or ritual objects in any medium whose principal value resides in the their aesthetic merit.

Dubuque

Clarke College - Quigley Gallery
Wahlert Atrium, 1550 Clarke Drive, Dubuque, IA   52001
Tel: (319) 588-6356
Internet Address: http://keller.clarke.edu/~lkames/art_homepage/gallery.html
Director: Mr. Douglas Schlesier
Admission: free.
Open: Monday to Friday, noon-5pm; Saturday to Sunday, 1pm-5pm.
Facilities: **Exhibition Area**.
Activities: **Temporary Exhibitions**.

The Gallery presents temporary exhibitions including BA and BFA student exhibitions.

Grinnell

Grinnell College Print and Drawing Study Room ⓒ
Burling Library, 1111 6th Ave.
Grinnell, IA   50112-0811
Tel: (515) 269-3371
Fax: (515) 269-4283
Internet Address: http://www.grinnell.edu
Director: Ms. Kay Wilson-Jenkins
Admission: free.
Attendance: 4,500   *Established:* 1983   *ADA Compliant:* Y
Parking: lot at 6th Ave. & High St..
Open: **Academic Year**, Monday to Friday, 1pm-5pm; Sunday, 1pm-5pm.
Closed: Academic Holidays, Summer, Between Semesters.
Facilities: **Exhibition Area** (900 square feet); **Print Study Room**.
Activities: **Lectures**; **Temporary Exhibitions**.
Publications: exhibition catalogues.

Temporary exhibitions and selections from the College Permanent Art Collection are displayed in the Print and Drawing Study Room and Burling Gallery, located in the Burling Library. Intended primarily for use as a teaching collection, the permanent collection of paintings, sculpture, drawings and prints includes works by Calder, Chagall, Dürer, Picasso, Rauschenburg, Rembrandt, and Weber among other artists of national and international distinction. Also on campus, student artwork is displayed in the Scheaffer Gallery in the Fine Arts Center and the Terrace Gallery in the College Forum.

Indianola

Simpson College - Farnham Galleries ⓒ
701 North C St., Indianola, IA   50125
Tel: (515) 961-6251
Fax: (515) 961-1498
Internet Address: http://www.simpson.edu
Director: Dr. Janet Heinicke
Admission: voluntary contribution.
Attendance: 450   *Established:* 1982   *ADA Compliant:* Y
Open: Monday to Friday, 8:30am-4:30pm; Saturday to Sunday, by appointment.
Facilities: **Galleries**.
Activities: **Artist-in-Residence Program**; **Education Programs** (college students); **Gallery Talks**; **Temporary Exhibitions**.

Located in Mary Berry Hall, the Farnham Galleries present a schedule of temporary art exhibitions.

Iowa City

University of Iowa Museum of Art ⓒ

150 N. Riverside Drive, Iowa City, IA 52242-1789
Tel: (319) 335-1727   *Fax:* (319) 335-3677
Internet Address: http://www.uiowa.edu/~artmuseum
Director: Mr. Stephen Prokopoff
Admission: free.
Attendance: 35,000   *Established:* 1969   *Membership:* Y   *ADA Compliant:* Y
Parking: metered lots across Riverside Drive and north of the museum.
Open: Tuesday to Saturday, 10am-5pm; Sunday, noon-5pm.
Closed: New Year's Day, Thanksgiving Day, Christmas Day.
Facilities: **Galleries** (12); **Print Study Room**; **Sculpture Court**; **Teaching Gallery**.
Activities: **Concerts**; **Education Programs**; **Guided Tours** (reserve in advance); **Lectures**;
Permanent Exhibits; **Traveling Exhibitions**.
Publications: calendar; exhibition catalogues; newsletter.

Located in the Iowa Center for the Arts complex, the University of Iowa Museum of Art displays selections from its permanent collection and a program of varied temporary exhibitions, many organized by the Museum staff. The Museum strengths are in 20th-century American and European painting and sculpture, including works by Chagall, Gris, Leger, Matisse, and Picasso; Chinese jades; and African art, particularly sculpture. There are notable collections of pre-Columbian, Oceanic, Native American, and Near Eastern art; English and American silver; and contemporary American ceramics, prints, and photography. The Museum also houses the School of Art and Art History's Alternative Traditions in the Contemporary Arts (ATCA) collection of post World War II avant-garde art, including Neo-Dada, Fluxus, performance, and conceptual art and related material.

Mount Vernon

Cornell College - Armstrong Gallery ⓒ

Armstrong Hall of Fine Arts, 600 1st St., West
Mount Vernon, IA 52314-1098
Tel: (319) 895-4137   *Fax:* (319) 895-4492
Internet Address: http://www.cornell-iowa.edu
Department Chairman: Mr. Anthony Plaut
Admission: free.
Attendance: 5,000   *Established:* 1853
Open: **Academic Year**, Monday to Friday, 9am-4pm; Sunday, 2pm-4pm.
Closed: Academic Holidays.
Facilities: **Exhibition Area**.
Activities: **Education Programs** (undergraduate college students); **Lectures**; **Temporary Exhibitions**.

Located in Armstrong Hall of Fine Arts, the gallery presents monthly student and traveling exhibitions. Armstrong Hall houses the College's art collections, including the Whiting Glass Collection; nearly 200 prints from the collection of Dr. William K. Jacques; the Sonnenshein Collection of drawings by Michelangelo, the Carraci, Carlo Dolci, Gustave Doré, and others; a permanent collection of paintings, including works by Richard Anuskiewiscz, Karel Appel, Marc Chagall, Charles Demuth, Robert Motherwell, Robert Andrew Parker, Larry Rivers, and Max Weber; and a slide collection. Also of possible interest on campus is the Commons Gallery (open 8am to midnight), which mounts monthly exhibitions.

Pella

Central College - Mills Gallery ⓒ

Art and Behavioral Science Building (Lower Level), Pella, IA 50219
Tel: (515) 628-9000
Internet Address: http://www.central.edu/camplife/mills.html

Central College - Mills Gallery, cont.

Open: Monday to Friday, 9am-4pm.

Facilities: **Exhibition Area**.

Activities: **Temporary Exhibitions**.

The Gallery maintains a schedule of changing exhibitions including a senior art exhibition. (Each exhibition open on the first weekday of the month and concludes on the last weekday of the month.) The College's permanent collections focuses on contemporary American drawings and prints.

Kansas

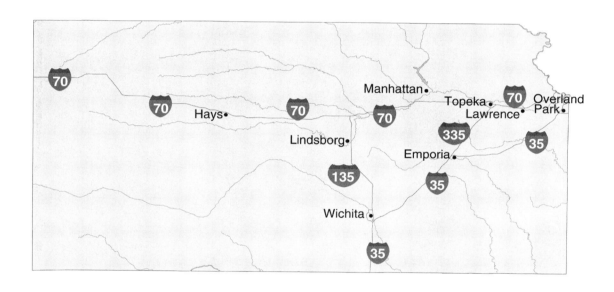

The number in parentheses following the city name indicates the number of museums/galleries in that municipality. If there is no number, one is understood. For example, in the text one listing would be found under each Kansan city.

Kansas

Emporia

Emporia State University - Norman R. Eppink Art Gallery ⓒ⁴⁹

King Hall, 13th and Market Sts., Emporia, KS 66801
Tel: (316) 341-5246   *Fax:* (316) 341-5681
Internet Address: http://www.emporia.edu/art/eppink.htm
Director: Mr. Donald Perry
Admission: voluntary contribution.
Attendance: 11,000   *Established:* 1939   *ADA Compliant:* Y
Open: Monday to Friday, 9am-4pm.
Closed: Academic Holidays.
Facilities: **Auditorium** (400 seats); **Classrooms**; **Food Services** Cafeteria; **Gallery**; **Library**; **Nature Center**; **Reading Room**; **Theatre**.
Activities: **Education Programs** (graduate and undergraduate college students); **Gallery Talks**; **Guided Tours**; **Lectures**; **Temporary Exhibitions**; **Traveling Exhibitions**.
Publications: catalogue, "Art Faculty Exhibition"; catalogue, "National Invitational Drawing Exhibition Catalogue".

The Gallery features temporary exhibitions. Across the hall from the Eppink Gallery is the Gilson Memorial Room, which also displays temporary exhibitions.

Hays

Fort Hays State University - Moss-Thorns Gallery of Art ⓒ⁴⁹

Department of Art, 600 Park St., Rarick Hall #102, Hays, KS 67601-4099
Tel: (642) 628-4247
Internet Address: http://www.fhsu.edu/htmlpages/arts/gallery.html
Director: Ms. Sondra Schwetman
Admission: free.
Open: **Academic Year**, Monday to Friday, 8:30am-4:30pm.
        Summer, Monday to Thursday, 8am-4:30pm; Friday, 8am-11am.
Facilities: **Exhibition Area**.
Activities: **Temporary Exhibitions**.

The Gallery presents temporary exhibitions including annual Faculty, Student Honors and Graduate Thesis Exhibitions.

Lawrence

University of Kansas - Spencer Museum of Art ⓒ⁴⁹

University of Kansas, 1301 Mississippi St., Lawrence, KS 66045-2136
Tel: (913) 864-4710   *Fax:* (913) 864-3112   *TDDY:* (800) 776-3777
Internet Address: http://www.ukans.edu/~sma
Director: Andrea S. Norris
Admission: voluntary contribution.
Attendance: 43,000   *Established:* 1928   *Membership:* Y   *ADA Compliant:* Y
Parking: metered lot north of museum.
Open: Tuesday to Wednesday, 10am-5pm; Thursday, 10am-9pm; Friday to Saturday, 10am-5pm; Sunday, noon-5pm.
Closed: New Year's Day, Independence Day, Thanksgiving Day to Thanksgiving Friday, Christmas Eve to Christmas Day.
Facilities: **Galleries**; **Library** (90,000 volumes); **Shop**.
Activities: **Concerts**; **Education Programs** (adults and children); **Films**; **Guided Tours**; **Lectures**; **Permanent Exhibits**; **Temporary Exhibitions**; **Traveling Exhibitions**.
Publications: collection catalogues; exhibition catalogues; journal, "The Register of the Spencer Museum of Art" (annual); newsletter (monthly).

University of Kansas - Spencer Museum of Art, cont.

The Museum displays works in seven galleries and has a comprehensive collection of over 17,000 objects that spans the history of European, North American, and East Asian art. Areas of special strength include medieval art; European and American paintings, sculpture and prints; photography; Japanese Edo-period paintings and prints; and 20th-century Chinese painting. There are also Western and Asian prints, drawings, and decorative arts, including a renowned quilt collection.

Lindsborg

Bethany College - Mingenback Art Center Gallery

421 N. 1st St., Lindsborg, KS   67456
Tel: (785) 227-3311 *Ext:* 8244
Internet Address: http://www.bethanylb.edu
Admission: free.
Open: **September to June**, Daily, 8am-5pm.
Facilities: **Exhibition Area.**
Activities: **Lecture Series**; **Temporary Exhibitions**.

Located on the southwest edge of the campus, the Mingenback Art Center Gallery mounts exhibitions year round of student and outside artists work. Also of possible interest, adjacent to the campus is the Birger Sandzen Memorial Gallery, dedicated to the works of the artist-teacher who dominated the art scene at Bethany and in Lindsborg during the first half of the twentieth century

Manhattan

Kansas State University - Marianna Kistler Beach Museum of Art ⓒ

Kansas State University, 701 Beach Lane
Manhattan, KS   66506
Tel: (785) 532-7718   *Fax:* (785) 532-7498
Internet Address: http://www.ksu.edu/bma/general_information
Admission: voluntary contribution.
Attendance: 20,000   *Established:* 1996
Membership: Y   *ADA Compliant:* Y
Parking: free on site.
Open: Tuesday to Wednesday, 10am-4:30pm;
          Thursday, 10am-8:30pm;
          Friday, 10am-4:30pm
          Saturday to Sunday, 1pm-4:30pm.
Closed: Major Holidays.
Facilities: **Food Services** Café; **Galleries**; **Shop.**
Activities: **Gallery Talks**; **Guided Tours** (by appointment); **Lecture Series** (1st Wednesday, noon); **Permanent Exhibits**; **Temporary Exhibitions**; **Visiting Artist Program.**
Publications: newsletter, "BMA Newsletter" (3 per yr).

View of entrance, Beach Museum of Art. Photograph by Douglas Kahn, courtesy of Beach Museum of Art, Kansas State University, Manhattan, Kansas.

The Beach Museum of Art houses Kansas State University's 20th-century American art collection. This collection, with its special emphasis on works by regional artists and American printmakers, includes works by John Steuart Curry, Birger Sandzen, and Dale Chihuly. The building , which opened in 1996, has 9,000 square feet of gallery space. The Museum also mounts temporary exhibitions of works from other major institutions, as well as solo and group shows of the work of contemporary artists.

Overland Park

Johnson County Community College Gallery of Art ⓒ

12345 College Blvd., Overland Park, KS   66210-1299
Tel: (913) 469-8500 *Ext:* 3972   *Fax:* (913) 469-2516   *TDDY:* (913) 469-3885
Internet Address: http://www.johnco.ks.us/

Johnson County Community College Gallery of Art, cont.

Director: Mr. Bruce Hartman
Admission: free.
Attendance: 200,000   *Established:* 1969
Membership: Y   *ADA Compliant:* Y
Parking: free on site.
Open: Monday, 10am-5pm;
      Tuesday to Wednesday, 10am-7pm;
      Thursday to Friday, 10am-5pm;
      Saturday to Sunday, 1pm-5pm.
Closed: Legal Holidays, Summer.
Facilities: **Auditoria** (1,400 seats and 400 seats); **Exhibition Area** (3,000 square feet); **Outdoor sculpture collection**; **Theatre** (150 seats).
Activities: **Concerts**; **Dance Recitals**; **Education Programs** (adults, undergraduate college students, and children); **Films**; **Guided Tours**; **Lectures**; **Performances**; **Temporary Exhibitions**; **Traveling Exhibitions**.
Publications: exhibition brochures (6 per yr).

Barry Flanagan, *Hare and Bell*, 1988, bronze; 138 x 72 x 108 inches. Oppenheimer-Stein Sculpture Collection. Gift of Jules and Doris Stein Foundation and H. Tony and Marti Oppenheimer. Photograph courtesy of Gallery of Art, Johnson County County Community College, Overland Park, Kansas.

With 3,000 square feet of exhibition space, the Gallery presents seven major exhibitions of contemporary art each year, drawing on artists, museums, galleries, and private collections, both nationally and internationally. The Gallery also houses a permanent collection of contemporary art. In addition, numerous large-scale and site-specific sculptures have been installed on the College grounds.

Topeka

Washburn University of Topeka - Mulvane Art Museum Ⓒ

Washburn University of Topeka, 17th and Jewell Sts., Topeka, KS   66621-1150
Tel: (913) 231-1010 *Ext:* 1324   *Fax:* (913) 234-2703
Internet Address: http://www.washburn.edu/cas/music/mulane.html
Director: Robert T. Soppelsa, Ph.D.
Admission: voluntary contribution.
Attendance: 12,000   *Established:* 1922   *Membership:* Y   *ADA Compliant:* Y
Parking: free across from museum.
Open: **September to mid-May**,
      Tuesday to Wednesday, 10am-7pm; Thursday to Friday, 10am-4pm;
      Saturday to Sunday, 1pm-4pm.
      mid-May to August,
      Tuesday to Friday, 10am-4pm; Saturday to Sunday, 1pm-4pm.
Closed: Academic Holidays, Exhibit Installation.
Facilities: **Fine Arts Library**; **Food Services** Café; **Print Study Room**; **Shop**.
Activities: **Art Classes** (K-adult); **Arts Festival**; **Concerts**; **Gallery Talks**; **Guided Tours**; **Lectures**; **Readings**.
Publications: brochures; exhibition catalogues; newsletter.

The Museum mounts ten to twelve temporary exhibitions per year and has a permanent collection of classical art, modern European art, Kansas-related art, and prints and drawings.

Wichita

Wichita State University - Edwin A. Ulrich Museum of Art Ⓒ

1845 Fairmont, Wichita, KS   67260-0046
Tel: (316) 578-3664   *Fax:* (316) 978-3898
Internet Address: http://www.twsu.edu/~ulrich

Wichita State University - Edwin A. Ulrich Museum of Art, cont.

Director: Mr. Donald E. Knaub

Admission: voluntary contribution.

Attendance: 10,000   *Established:* 1974

Membership: Y   *ADA Compliant:* Y

Parking: free on site.

Open: Daily, noon-5pm.

Closed: Legal Holidays.

Facilities: **Architecture** (mosaic by Joan Miro on museum façade); **Galleries**; **Sculpture Garden**.

Activities: **Artist-in-Residence Program**; **Education Programs** (undergraduate and graduate college students); **Gallery Talks**; **Guided Tours**; **Lectures**; **Permanent Exhibits**; **Temporary Exhibitions**; **Traveling Exhibitions**.

Publications: books; exhibition catalogues.

Left to right: Jesus Morales, "Weave Wall", granite (1995); Sophia Vari, "Danseuse Espagnole", bronze (1992); Joan Miro, "Personnages Oiseaux", Venetian glass and marble (1977-1978); façade of Museum in background. Photograph courtesy of Edwin A. Ulrich Museum of Art, Wichita State University, Wichita, Kansas.

The Edwin A. Ulrich Museum of Art houses a permanent collection of over 7,000 objects, with 19th- and 20th-century European and American paintings, drawings, sculpture, and prints forming the core of the collection. A major aspect of the collection is the 63-piece outdoor sculpture collection, including works by Rodin, Moore, Nevelson, Rickey, Chadwick, Jimenez, and Miró, among others. There is also an extensive collection of works by the American marine artist, Frederick Judd Waugh. Also of possible interest on campus is the Clayton Staples Gallery (open: Mon-Fri, 9am-5pm, 978-3555) on the second floor of the McKnight Art Center, which presents temporary exhibitions of the work of students and professional artists.

Kentucky

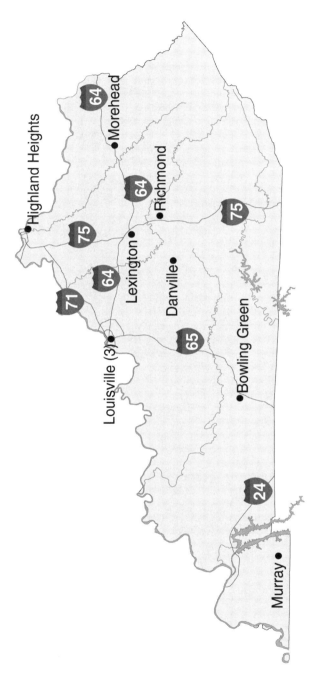

The number in parentheses following the city name indicates the number of museums/galleries in that municipality. If there is no number, one is understood. For example, in the text three listings would be found under Louisville and one listing under Lexington.

Kentucky

Bowling Green

Western Kentucky University - The Kentucky Museum ⒸⒶⒶ

Western Kentucky University, 1 Big Red Way
Bowling Green, KY   42101
Tel: (502) 745-6258
Fax: (502) 745-4878
Internet Address: http://www.wky.edu/library/museum
Administrator: Mr. Riley D. Handy
Admission: fee: adult-$2.00, child-$1.00, family-$5.00.
Attendance: 25,000   *Established:* 1931   *Membership:* Y   *ADA Compliant:* Y
Open: Tuesday to Saturday, 9:30am-4pm; Sunday, 1pm-4pm.
Closed: Academic Holidays.
Facilities: **Galleries**; **Library** (100,000 volumes, use on premises).
Activities: **Guided Tours**; **Lectures**; **Permanent Exhibits**; **Temporary Exhibitions**; **Workshops**.
Publications: brochures; exhibition catalogues; newsletter, "The Fanlight".

The Kentucky museum collects, preserves, and exhibits Kentucky artifacts. Its collections include archeology, art, clothing and textiles, furniture, glassware and ceramics, political memorabilia, quilts, and toys and games. The art collection includes works by Kentucky artists, such as Clement Reeves Edwards, Harlan Hubbard, Alphonse and Juliette Desport, Harvey Joiner, Sarah Gaines Peyton, and Matthew Harris Jouett. There are also prints by Bodmer, Catlin, Dine, Rosenquist, and Motherwell. Finally, there are collections of miniatures and folk art. Also of possible interest on campus, the University Gallery, located on the second floor of the Ivan Wilson Fine Arts Center, presents temporary exhibitions (Open: weekdays, 8:30am-3:30pm).

Danville

Centre College - Norton Center for the Arts ⒸⒶⒶ

600 W. Walnut St., Danville, KY   40422
Tel: (606) 236-4692
Internet Address: http://www.centre,edu/web/nortonctr/nortoncenter.html
Admission: free.
Open: call for hours.
Facilities: **Architecture** Norton Center (1974 design by William Wesley Peters); **Exhibition Area**.
Activities: **Education Programs**; **Temporary Exhibitions**.

The Norton Center is home to temporary exhibitions in its Grand Foyer, as well as housing the college's teaching collection of paintings and sculptures. Holdings are particularly strong in contemporary painting, 17th-century Dutch painting, and 19th-century French sculpture.

Highland Heights

Northern Kentucky University Art Galleries ⒸⒶⒶ (NKU)

NKU Fine Arts Center, Nunn Drive
Highland Heights, KY   41099
Tel: (606) 572-5148   *Fax:* (606) 572-5566
Internet Address: http://www.nku.edu/~art/gallery.html
Director: Mr. David J. Knight
Admission: voluntary contribution.
Attendance: 18,000   *Established:* 1968   *ADA Compliant:* Y
Open: **mid-January to mid-December**,
          Monday to Friday, 9am-9pm;   Saturday to Sunday, 1pm-5pm.
Closed: Legal Holidays, Spring Break, Between Terms.

Highland Heights, Kentucky

Northern Kentucky University Art Galleries, cont.

Facilities: **Exhibition Area** (2,700 square feet); **Library**.

Activities: **Lectures**; **Temporary Exhibitions** (12 per year); **Traveling Exhibitions**.

The Department of Art maintains two galleries: The Main Gallery and the Third Floor Gallery. The galleries offer monthly exhibitions of the work of professional artists, as well as weekly shows of student work. The University maintains a permanent collection of 1,000 pieces, most of which are on view around the campus.

View of main gallery during temporary exhibition. Photograph courtesy of Northern Kentucky University Art Galleries, Highland Heights, Kentucky.

Lexington

University of Kentucky Art Museum ⓒ

Rose St. and Euclid Ave., Lexington, KY   40506-0241

Tel: (606) 257-5716   *Fax:* (606) 323-1994

Internet Address: http://www.uky.edu

Director: Dr.. Harriet Fowler

Admission: free.

Attendance: 23,000   *Established:* 1979   *Membership:* Y   *ADA Compliant:* Y

Parking: Circle in front & University lots on Euclid Ave. & Rose St..

Open: Tuesday to Sunday, noon-5pm.

Closed: Academic Holidays.

Facilities: **Galleries** (2 levels).

Activities: **Guided Tours** (arrange in advance); **Temporary Exhibitions** (6/year).

Publications: calendar; exhibition catalogues; newsletter, "Educational Materials" (quarterly).

A component of the Otis A. Singletary Center for the Arts, the University of Kentucky Art Museum presents selections from its permanent collection, supplemented by an annual schedule of diverse exhibitions drawn from other museums, private collections, and exhibition services. The Museum also regularly assembles exhibitions of special regional interest and relevance, including retrospectives of work by contemporary Kentucky artists, as well as showings of outstanding local collections. Illustrated catalogues are frequently published to accompany these exhibitions. The Museum maintains a permanent collection of more than 3,000 European and American paintings, sculptures, prints, drawings, photographs, and decorative arts. There are also holdings in the art of the Americas, Africa, and Asia. Selections from the permanent collection are always on view and rotated regularly; works in storage are easily accessible by appointment. Also of possible interest are the Center for Contemporary Art, presenting MFA student thesis work and guest invitational exhibitions and the Downtown Gallery, a downtown Lexington exhibition space featuring the work of students, faculty, alumni, and guest artists.

Louisville

Spalding University - Huff Gallery ⓒ

853 Library Lane, Louisville, KY   40203

Tel: (502) 585-7122

Internet Address: http://www.spalding.edu/ugrad/art/huff.html

Contact: Mr. Robert Stagg

Admission: free.

Open: Monday to Thursday, 8am-9pm; Friday to Saturday, 8am-5pm; Sunday, 1pm-5pm.

Facilities: **Exhibition Area**.

Activities: **Temporary Exhibitions** (10/year).

Spalding University - Huff Gallery, cont.

The Gallery presents both solo and groups exhibitions of work in a variety of media by locally and regionally recognized artists. Student exhibitions, as well as shows by graduating seniors, are mounted at the end of each year.

University of Louisville - Allen R. Hite Art Institute Galleries

University of Louisville, Belknap Campus
3rd St. and Eastern Parkway
Louisville, KY 40292
Tel: (502) 852-6794
Fax: (502) 852-6791
Internet Address:
   http://www.louisville.edu/a-s/finearts
Director: Professor James Grubola
Admission: voluntary contribution.
Attendance: 15,000   *Established:* 1946
ADA Compliant: Y
Open: Monday to Friday, 8:30am-4:30pm;
   Weekends, by appointment.
Closed: Legal Holidays.
Facilities: Galleries (3); Library (75,000 volumes).
Activities: Demonstrations; Education Programs (undergraduate and graduate college students); Lectures; Temporary Exhibitions; Workshops.
Publications: exhibition catalogues; journal, "Parnassus".

Sam Gilliam, *Red Vase, Blue Element*, 1982, acrylic and mixed media on canvas, University of Louisville Art Collection. Photograph courtesy of Allen R. Hite Art Institute, University of Louisville, Louisville, Kentucky.

The Institute houses the Morris B. Belknap Jr. Gallery, the Dario A. Covi Gallery, and the Student Art League Gallery, as well as an art library, a visual resource center, and an art collection. The galleries feature rotating monthly exhibitions of the work of national and regional artists, craftspeople, and designers, in addition to student and faculty work. The Institute's art collection includes an extensive selection of prints and drawings from the 16th century to the present. The University of Louisville Photographic Archives, one of the largest and most thorough in the Southeast, is listed separately.

University of Louisville - Photographic Archives

Ekstrom Library, University of Louisville, Louisville, KY 40292
Tel: (502) 852-8730   *Fax:* (502) 852-8734
Internet Address: http://www.louisville.edu/library/ekstrom/special
Administrator: Mr. James C. Anderson
Admission: voluntary contribution.
Established: 1967   *ADA Compliant:* Y
Open: Monday to Wednesday, 10am-4:00pm; Thursday, 10am-8pm; Friday, 10am-4:00pm.
Facilities: Exhibition Gallery; Library (1,000 volumes); Reading Room.
Activities: Lectures; Temporary Exhibitions.

The Photographic Archives acquires significant documentary photograph collections, organizes them, and makes them available to both the researcher and the casual browser. Its gallery hosts changing exhibitions of prints from the Archives collections and from contemporary photographers. Housing over 1.2 million photographs, the permanent collection is composed of hundreds of discrete collections, including national documentary subjects, local history photographs, and a museum collection of fine prints. The fine art collection includes work by Ansel Adams, Stern J. Bramson, Paul Caponigro, Walker Evans, Arthur Fellig (Weegee), Phillipe Halsman, Dorothea Lange, Lisette Model, Edwin and Louise Rosskam, Arthur Rothstein, Ben Shahn, Edward Weston, Minor White, and Marion Post Wolcott.

Morehead

Morehead State University - Kentucky Folk Art Center ⓒᴬᴬ

102 West 1st Street
Morehead, KY 40351
Tel: (606) 783-2204
Fax: (606) 783-5034
Internet Address: http://www.morehead-st.edu/
  units/folkart/index.html
Director: Mr. Garry Barker
Admission: fee: adult-$3.00, senior-$2.00.
Attendance: 5,000   *Established:* 1985
Membership: Y
Parking: free on site.
Open: Monday to Saturday, 9am-5pm;
        Sunday, 1pm-5pm.

Exterior view of Kentucky Folk Art Center, a former whole-sale grocery warehouse (c. 1906). Photograph courtesy of Kentucky Folk Art Center, Morehead, Kentucky.

Facilities: **Auditorium**; **Exhibition Area** (10,000 square feet); **Library**; **Shop** (work from over 50 eastern Kentucky folk artists, books).
Activities: **Education Programs** (children); **Films**; **Lectures**; **Traveling Exhibitions**; **Workshops**.
Publications: newsletter, "KFAC News" (quarterly); video, "Local Visions".

Housed in a renovated brick grocery warehouse (c 1906), KFAC operates the Kentucky Folk Art Museum on the ground floor and a gallery on the second level. The Museum displays selections from Morehead State University's permanent collection of over 800 works of folk art; the rest of the collection is available for researchers and special exhibitions. The gallery features rotating exhibits.

Murray

Murray State University - University Art Galleries ⓒᴬᴬ

Price Doyle Fine Arts Center, 4th floor, 15th and Olive Sts.
Murray, KY 42071
Tel: (502) 762-3052   *Fax:* (502) 762-3920
Internet Address: http://www.mursuky.edu/qacd/cfac/art/gallery.htm
Director: Mr. Albert Sperath
Admission: free.
Attendance: 10,000   *Established:* 1971   *Membership:* N   *ADA Compliant:* Y
Parking: visitor parking free on campus.
Open: **Fall to Spring**, Monday/Wednesday/Friday, 9am-6pm; Tuesday/Thursday, 9am-7:30pm;
        Saturday, 10am-4pm; Sunday, 1pm-4pm.
        Summer, Monday to Friday, 9am-4pm.
Closed: Academic Holidays.
Facilities: **Galleries** (3, total 8,292 square feet of exhibition space and support areas); **Lecture Halls** (2).
Activities: **Education Programs** (adults, undergraduate/graduate students, and children); **Gallery Talks**; **Guided Tours**; **Lectures**; **Temporary Exhibitions**; **Traveling Exhibitions**.
Publications: exhibition catalogues.

The University has three galleries, the Main and Upper Level galleries at the Clara M. Eagle Art Gallery in the Doyle Fine Arts Center, and the Curris Center Gallery in the Student Center. The Main Gallery hosts exhibitions of contemporary art by artists working within a 500 mile radius. The Upper Level and Curris Center galleries present student shows and smaller shows of work by local artists. The University's permanent collection of 1,200 objects consists primarily of works on paper. A collection of 80 Works Progress Administration prints and the H.L. Jackson Print Collection are the most notable.

Richmond

Eastern Kentucky University - Fred P. Giles Gallery ☺

Jane F. Campbell Building, Richmond, KY 40475

Tel: (606) 622-1629

Internet Address: http://www.art.eku.edu/page2/htm

Open: **Fall to Spring**,
Monday, 11:45am-4:30pm; Tuesday, 1pm-4:30pm; Wednesday, 11:45am-4:30pm;
Thursday, 1pm-4:30pm; Friday, 11:45am-3:15pm.

Closed: Summer.

Facilities: **Exhibition Area**.

Activities: **Temporary Exhibitions**.

The Giles Gallery presents temporary exhibitions including the work of students.

Louisiana

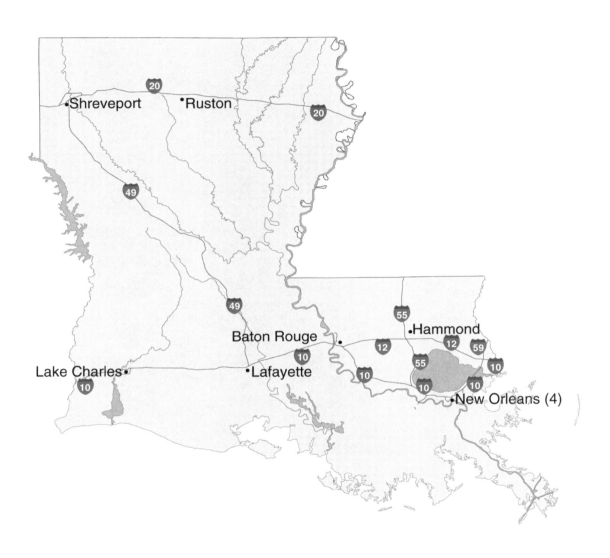

The number in parentheses following the city name indicates the number of museums/galleries in that municipality. If there is no number, one is understood. For example, in the text four listings would be found under New Orleans and one listing under Baton Rouge.

Louisiana

Baton Rouge

Louisiana State University Museum of Art ⒸⒶⒶ

Memorial Tower, Louisiana State University, Baton Rouge, LA   70803
Tel: (504) 388-4003
Internet Address: http://www.lsu.edu
Director and Curator: Mr. H. Parrott Bacot
Admission: voluntary contribution.
Attendance: 5,000   *Established:* 1959   *Membership:* Y
Open: Monday to Friday, 9am-4pm; Saturday, 10am-noon; Sunday, 1pm-4pm.
Closed: Academic Holidays.
Facilities: **Galleries**; **Library** (500 volumes, non-circulating).
Activities: **Films**; **Gallery Talks**; **Guided Tours**; **Lectures**; **Permanent Exhibits**; **Temporary Exhibitions**; **Traveling Exhibitions**.
Publications: exhibition catalogues.

Memorial Tower houses LSU's permanent art collection, which includes many Louisiana-related paintings, prints and drawings, and also mounts changing exhibitions. Also of possible interest on campus are the LSU Union Art Gallery (388-5188) at the corner of Raphael Semmes and Highland Road and the LSU School of Art Gallery (388-5143) in Foster Hall.

Hammond

Southeastern Louisiana University - Clark Hall Gallery ⒸⒶⒶ

N. Pine Street, Hammond, LA   70402
Tel: (504) 549-2193 *Ext:* 5080   *Fax:* (504) 549-5316
Internet Address: http://www.selu.edu/Academics/Depts/VizArts/ClarkHall/
Director: Mr. Don Marshall
Admission: free.
Attendance: 20,000   *Membership:* N   *ADA Compliant:* Y
Open: Monday to Friday, 8am-4:30pm.
Closed: Legal Holidays.
Facilities: **Exhibition Area**.
Activities: **Temporary Exhibitions** (8/year).

The gallery presents temporary exhibitions focusing on artworks in a wide variety of media by Louisiana artists, as well as student and faculty work.

Lafayette

University of Southwestern Louisiana - University Art Museum ⒸⒶⒶ

Univ. of SW Louisiana, Fletcher Hall
E. Lewis and Girard Park Drive
Lafayette, LA   70504
Tel: (318) 482-5326
Fax: (318) 482-5907
Director: Mr. Bryan Lafaye
Admission: free.
Attendance: 30,000   *Established:* 1968
Membership: Y   *ADA Compliant:* Y
Parking: free on site with ticket validation.
Open: Monday to Friday, 9am-4pm.
         Fletcher only, Saturday, 10am-4pm.
Closed: Academic Holidays.
Facilities: **Galleries** (2, Fletcher Hall and Permanent Collection Building).

Exterior view of Permanent Collection Building. Photograph by C.J. Franz, courtesy of University of Southwestern Louisiana, Lafayette, Louisiana.

Lafayette, Louisiana

University of Southwestern Louisiana - University Art Museum, cont.

Activities: **Concerts**; **Films**; **Gallery Talks**; **Guided Tours** (with reservation); **Lectures**; **Permanent Exhibits**; **Temporary Exhibitions** (3 per year); **Traveling Exhibitions** (3/year).

Publications: calendar; exhibition catalogues.

The University Art Museum offers visitors art exhibitions of regional, national, and international acclaim. The permanent collection is housed in an 18th-century-style plantation home and includes works by Le Sidaner, Marc, Kneller, Healy, and Rinck, among others. Touring exhibits can be seen in the Fletcher Hall Gallery located in the Art and Architecture Building.

Lake Charles

McNeese State University - Abercrombie Gallery ⊂ᴬᴬ

Shearman Fine Arts Center, Ryan and Sale Sts.
Lake Charles, LA   70609
Tel: (318) 475-5060
Fax: (318) 475-5927
Internet Address: http://www.mcneese.edu
Director: Mr. Bill Iles
Admission: free.
Attendance: 3,000   *Established:* 1983
Parking: free on site.
Open: Monday to Friday, 9am-4pm.
Facilities: **Exhibition Area** (110 running feet).
Activities: **Lecture Series**; **Temporary Exhibitions** (monthly).

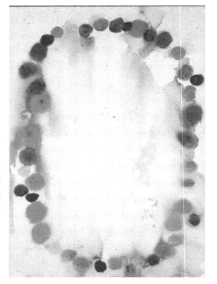

The Abercrombie Gallery presents monthly temporary exhibitions featuring works by students, faculty, and visiting artists. The Gallery also showcases the Annual McNeese National Works on Paper Exhibition, and the Biennial National Ceramics Invitational.

Mary Campbell, *Spectrum Oval*, 1996, watercolor, 20 x 14 inches. Best of Show Award, 10th Annual McNeese National Works on Paper Exhibition, 1997. Photograph courtesy of Abercrombie Gallery, McNeese State University, Lake Charles, Louisiana.

New Orleans

New Orleans Academy of Fine Arts - Academy Gallery

5256 Magazine St., New Orleans, LA   70115
Tel: (504) 899-8111
Director: Ms. Patsy Adams
Open: Monday to Friday, 9am-4pm; Saturday, 10am-4pm.
Facilities: **Exhibition Area**.
Activities: **Temporary Exhibitions**.

The Gallery functions as a teaching adjunct to the school, showing work of local, regional and national artists on a monthly basis.

Southern University at New Orleans - African Art Collection

Southern University Library, 6400 Press Drive
New Orleans, LA   70126
Tel: (504) 286-5207   *Fax:* (504) 286-5161
Internet Address: http://www.gnofn.org/~zaire/suno1.htm
Curator of CAAAS Collections: Dr. Sara Hollis
Parking: free on site.
Open: Call for hours.
Facilities: **Exhibition Area**.

Southern University at New Orleans - African Art Collection, cont.

The Center for African and African American Studies Art Collection at SUNO consists over 900 objects, most of them from Zaire.

Tulane University - Newcomb Arts Complex Ⓒ⁴²

Woldenberg Art Center, New Orleans, LA   70118-5698
Tel: (504) 865-5327   *Fax:* (504) 862-8710
Internet Address: http://www.tulane.edu
Acting Director: Ms. Sally Main
Admission: free.
Attendance: 1,200   *Established:* 1886   *ADA Compliant:* Y
Open: Monday to Friday, 9am-4:30pm.
Closed: New Year's Eve to New Year's Day, Mardi Gras, Thanksgiving Day, Christmas Day.
Facilities: **Gallery**; **Library**.
Activities: **Gallery Talks**.

The Complex contains a large gallery for student and faculty exhibitions and the Pace-Willson Glass Studio, a glassblowing facility. On display are Tiffany stained glass windows from the original Newcomb campus.

University of New Orleans - UNO Fine Arts Gallery Ⓒ⁴⁴

Fine Arts Complex, New Orleans, LA   70148
Tel: (504) 280-6493   *Fax:* (504) 280-7346
Internet Address: http://www.uno.edu/~finearts/gallery.html
Admission: free.
Open: Call for hours.
Facilities: **Exhibition Area** (2,100 square feet).
Activities: **Temporary Exhibitions**.

Located at the entrance to the Fine Arts Complex, the Gallery primarily displays exhibitions featuring graduate thesis work, undergraduate senior exit shows, and faculty work. Occasionally, the gallery director curates special exhibitions of work by noted regional artists.

Ruston

Louisiana Tech University Art Galleries Ⓒ⁴⁴

School of Art, Ruston, LA   71272
Tel: (318) 257-3909
Internet Address: http://www.art.latech.edu
Open: Call for hours.
Facilities: **Galleries** (2).
Activities: **Temporary Exhibitions**.

Two galleries, The Tech Art Gallery and The Belloq, present exhibitions of work by contemporary artists, focusing especially on that produced in the South and Midwest.

Shreveport

Centenary College - Meadows Museum of Art

2911 Centenary Blvd., Shreveport, LA   71104
Tel: (318) 869-5169   *Fax:* (318) 869-5730
Internet Address: http://www.centenary.edu
Director: Ms. Judy Godfrey
Admission: voluntary contribution.
Attendance: 19,000   *Established:* 1976   *Membership:* Y   *ADA Compliant:* Y
Parking: free behind building.
Open: Tuesday to Friday, noon-4pm; Saturday to Sunday, 1pm-4pm.
Closed: New Year's Day, Easter, 1st 2 weeks in Aug, Thanksgiving Day, Christmas Day.
Facilities: **Galleries** (8, total 8,500 square feet).

Centenary College - Meadows Museum of Art, cont.

Activities: **Concerts; Films; Gallery Talks; Guided Tours; Lectures; Permanent Exhibits; Temporary Exhibitions.**

Publications: booklet.

The Museum houses the Jean Despujols collection of paintings and drawings of Indochina. Consisting of over 360 oils, watercolors, and drawings, as well as over 1,000 photographs and complemented by the artist's diaries, the collection constitutes a remarkably comprehensive resource on the French colonial experience in Indochina.

Maine

The number in parentheses following the city name indicates the number of museums/galleries in that municipality. If there is no number, one is understood. For example, in the text two listings would be found under Portland and one listing under Gorham.

Maine

Brunswick

Bowdoin College Art Museum ⓒᴬᴬ

Walker Art Building, 9400 College Station
Brunswick, ME 04011
Tel: (207) 725-3275
Fax: (207) 725-3762
Internet Address: http://www.bowdoin.edu/cwis/acad/museums
Director: Dr. Katherine J. Watson
Admission: voluntary contribution.
Attendance: 25,000   *Established:* 1811   *ADA Compliant:* Y
Parking: free on Upper Park Row.
Open: Tuesday to Saturday, 10am-5pm; Sunday, 2pm-5pm.
Closed: Legal Holidays, Christmas Eve to January 2.
Facilities: **Architecture** (1894 designed by C.F. McKim; 1975 addition by E.L. Barnes); **Galleries** (Winslow Homer Gallery open only during summer); **Shop**.
Activities: **Education Programs** (adults and undergraduate college students); **Gallery Talks**; **Guided Tours** (reservations 2 weeks in advance); **Lectures**; **Permanent Exhibits**; **Temporary Exhibitions**; **Traveling Exhibitions**.
Publications: collection catalogue; exhibition catalogues.

The Bowdoin College Museum of Art numbers 13,000 objects in its collection. In the rotunda of the Museum building, designed by McKim, Meade & White, are murals of Athens, Rome, Florence, and Venice by John LaFarge, Elihu Vedder, Abbott Thayer, and Kenyon Cox. In addition to displaying its permanent collection, the Museum schedules an active program of temporary exhibitions of art lent by institutions and collectors throughout the United States. The Museum has a large collection of colonial and federal portraits, including works by Smibert, Feke, Blackburn, Copley, Stuart, Trumbull, and Sully; an ancient art collection containing sculpture, vases, terra cottas, bronzes, and glass, as well as five 9th-century B.C. Assyrian reliefs; a Samuel H. Kress Study Collection of twelve Renaissance paintings; Chinese and Korean ceramics; nineteen paintings by John Sloan; a significant collection of works by Winslow Homer; and other significant works by 19th- and 20th-century American artists, including Heade, Johnson, Inness, Eakins, Sargent, Glackens, Hartley, Gorky, Kline, Wyeth, and Katz.

Farmington

University of Maine at Farmington - UMF Art Gallery ⓒᴬᴬ

102 Main St. (Rear), Farmington, ME 04938
Tel: (207) 778-7001
Fax: (207) 778-7075
Internet Address: http://www.umf.maine.edu/gallery
Asst. Professor & Gallery Director: Ms. Sarah Radley Maline
Admission: free.
Established: 1983
Open: · Tuesday to Sunday, Noon-4pm.
Facilities: **Exhibition Area**.
Activities: **Lectures**; **Temporary Exhibitions** (6/year); **Workshops**.

Occupying a renovated large barn in the rear of 102 Main Street, the Gallery presents a schedule of exhibitions intended to demonstrate the diversity of style and media in contemporary art. Showings, complemented by related lectures and workshops, feature primarily artists who live in Maine. Permanent sculptures are installed on the lawn in front of the Gallery and artwork is also be displayed in Mantor Library, Einar Olsen Student Center, and in other buildings on campus.

Gorham

University of Southern Maine - Art Gallery ⓒ
Gorham Campus, College Ave., Gorham, ME   04106
Tel: (207) 780-5008
Internet Address: http://www.usm.maine.edu/~gallery
Director of Exhibitions and Programs: Ms. Carolyn Eyler
Admission: free.
Open: Tuesday to Friday, 11am-4pm; Saturday, 1pm-4pm.
Closed: Academic Holidays.
Facilities: **Exhibition Area**.
Activities: **Lectures**; **Temporary Exhibitions**.

The Gallery presents exhibitions of the work of professional artists and students, including an annual juried student show in the spring. USM also maintains a gallery on its Portland campus. See listing under Portland.

Lewiston

The Bates College Museum of Art ⓒ
Olin Arts Center
75 Russell St.
Lewiston, ME   04240-6044
Tel: (207) 786-6158
Fax: (207) 786-6123
Internet Address: www.bates.edu
Director: Dr.. Genetta McLean
Admission: free.
Attendance: 12,000   *Established:* 1986
Membership: Y   *ADA Compliant:* Y
Parking: free on street.
Open: Tuesday to Saturday, 10am-5pm;
          Sunday, 1pm-5pm.
Closed: Legal Holidays.
Facilities: **Galleries**.
Activities: **Gallery   Talks;   Permanent
    Exhibits;   Temporary   Exhibitions;
    Traveling Exhibitions**.
Publications: exhibition catalogues.

Marsden Hartley, *Georgetown Lighthouse Seascape.*, drawing. Bates College Museum of Art. Photograph by Melville McLean, courtesy of Bates College Museum of Art, Lewiston, Maine.

The Museum is home to one of the region's finest collections of masterworks on paper and is known nationally for its significant holdings of drawings by Marsden Hartley. It also houses prints, paintings, photographs, sculpture, and ceramics. The Museum hosts temporary exhibitions as well showings of the permanent collection throughout the year.

Orono

University of Maine Museum of Art ⓒ(UMMA)
109 Carnegie Hall, Orono, ME   04469-5712
Tel: (207) 581-3255   *Fax:* (207) 581-3083
Internet Address: http://umma.umecah.maine.edu/
Director: Mr. Wally Mason
Admission: free.
Attendance: 12,000   *Established:* 1946   *Membership:* Y
Parking: free with visitor permit.
Open: Monday to Saturday, 9am-4:30pm.
Facilities: **Exhibition Areas** (2 galleries in Carnegie Hall).

University of Maine Museum of Art , cont.

Activities: **Gallery Talks**; **Guided Tours** (upon request); **Temporary Exhibitions**; **Traveling Exhibitions**.

Publications: exhibition catalogues.

The Museum of Art is located in Carnegie Hall, donated by Andrew Carnegie and designed by Brainerd and Leeds in 1906, with renovations by Cooper Milliken (1947, 1966). The Museum mounts temporary exhibitions as well as displaying its permanent collection. The permanent collection includes works on paper by Audubon, Chagall, Goya, Hassam, Hopper, Tiepolo, and Whistler; paintings by Blakelock, Braque, Cassatt, Inness, Rivera, and Picasso; contemporary works by Beckmann, Dine, Lichtenstein, and Rauschenberg; and works by Maine artists, such as Abbott, Hartley, Homer, Marin, Sprinchorn, and Wyeth.

Portland

Maine College of Art - Institute of Contemporary Art ⓒ (ICA at MECA)

522 Congress St.
Portland, ME   04101
Tel: (207) 879-5742
Fax: (207) 772-5069
Internet Address: http://www.meca.edu
Director: Ms. Karen Kitchen
Admission: voluntary contribution.
Attendance: 6,000   *Established:* 1983
Membership: N   *ADA Compliant:* Y
Parking: on street.
Open: **September to May**,
          Tuesday to Wednesday, 11am-4pm;
          Thursday, 11am-9pm;
          Friday to Sunday, 11am-4pm.

          June to August,
          Wednesday to Saturday, 10am-4pm.

View of gallery during an exhibition. Photograph courtesy of Institute of Contemporary Art at the Maine College of Art, Portland, Maine.

Closed: Legal Holidays.

Facilities: **Exhibition Area** (2,100 square feet).

Activities: **Education Programs** (undergraduate and graduate college students); **Films**; **Guided Tours**; **Lectures**; **Traveling Exhibitions**.

Publications: exhibition catalogues.

A non-collecting institution, the ICA maintains an ongoing program of temporary exhibitions, focusing on regional, national, and international developments in contemporary art, and on the art of Maine College of Art students, faculty, and alumni/ae.

University of Southern Maine - Area Gallery ⓒ

Woodbury Campus Center, Bedford St., Portland, ME   04104
Tel: (207) 780-5008
Internet Address: http://www.usm.maine.edu/~gallery
Director of Exhibitions and Programs: Ms. Carolyn Eyler
Admission: free.
Parking: University parkings lots on both sides of street.
Open: Monday to Thursday, 8am-10pm; Friday, 8am-5pm; Saturday, 9am-5pm.
Closed: Academic Holidays.
Facilities: **Exhibition Area**.
Activities: **Lectures**; **Temporary Exhibitions**.

The Gallery presents exhibitions of the work of professional artists and students.

Waterville

Colby College Museum of Art Ⓒ⁴⁰

Bixler Art and Museum Center, 5600 Mayflower Hill Drive
Waterville, ME   04901
Tel: (207) 872-3228   *Fax:* (207) 872-3141
Internet Address: http://www.colby.edu/museum/geninfo.html
Director: Mr. Hugh J. Gourley, III
Admission: free.
Attendance: 10,000   *Established:* 1959   *Membership:* Y   *ADA Compliant:* Y
Parking: free in front of museum.
Open: Monday to Saturday, 10am-4:30pm; Sunday, 2pm-4:30pm.
Closed: Legal Holidays.
Facilities: **Galleries**; **Shop**.
Activities: **Arts Festival**; **Education Programs** (adults, undergraduate college students, and children); **Gallery Talks**; **Guided Tours** (on request); **Lectures**; **Permanent Exhibits**; **Temporary Exhibitions**; **Traveling Exhibitions**.
Publications: "Handbook of the Colby College Art Museum"; books; exhibition catalogues.

Located in the Bixler Art and Museum Center, the Museum has an outstanding permanent collection of 18th- through 20th-century American art and an active temporary exhibition program. The Paul Schupf Galleries for the Works of Alex Katz houses over 400 works donated by the artist. Colby's permanent collection also includes 18th-century American portrait artists such as Copley, Stuart, Peale; the Jette Collection of American Painters of the Impressionist Period, with works by 76 artists, the American Heritage Collection of primitive paintings, watercolors, and drawings; and The John Marin Collection of 26 paintings, watercolors, drawings and etchings; as well as works by Jennifer Bartlett, Chuck Close, Mark di Suvero, Carroll Dunham, Eric Fischl, Robert Henri, Sol LeWitt, Paul Manship, Louise Nevelson, Fairfield Porter, Joel Shapiro, Neil Welliver, Terry Winters, Andrew Wyeth, and many other 19th- and 20th-century artists who either lived or worked in Maine. Additionally, The Joan Whitney Payson Collection of French Impressionist and post-Impressionist Art, which includes works by Degas, Gauguin, Monet, Picasso, and Renoir, is resident at Colby for one semester every two years.

Maryland

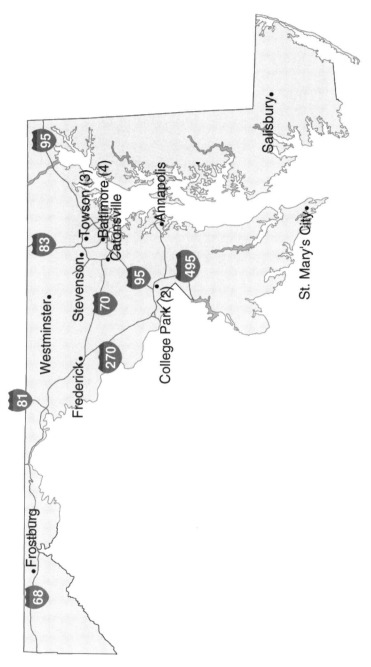

The number in parentheses following the city name indicates the number of museums/galleries in that municipality. If there is no number, one is understood. For example, in the text four listings would be found under Baltimore and one listing under Annapolis.

Maryland

Annapolis

St. John's College - Elizabeth Myers Mitchell Art Gallery Ⓒᴬᴬ

60 College Ave.
Annapolis, MD   21401
Tel: (410) 626-2556
Fax: (410) 263-4828
Internet Address:
   http://www.eidos.sjca.edu/events/gallery.phtml
Director: Ms. Hydee Schaller
Admission: voluntary contribution.
Attendance: 11,000   *Established:* 1989
Membership: Y   *ADA Compliant:* Y
Parking: limited, call in advance.
Open: **Academic Year**,
         Tuesday to Thursday, noon-5pm;
         Friday, noon-5pm and 7pm-8pm;
         Saturday to Sunday, noon-5pm.
Closed: Academic Holidays, between semesters.

Gallery talk by Jonathan Borofsky during his exhibition, "Prints and Multiples by Jonathan Borofsky, 1982-1991" at Mitchell Art Gallery. Photograph by Keith E. Harvey, courtesy of Elizabeth Myers Mitchell Art Gallery, St. John's College, Annapolis, Maryland.

Facilities: **Exhibition Area** (1,825 square feet); **Lecture Room**; **Studios**.
Activities: **Guided Tours** (Tues-Fri, groups 5+ schedule 3 weeks in advance); **Lectures**; **Studio Courses**; **Temporary Exhibitions**; **Traveling Exhibitions**.
Publications: exhibit brochures; exhibition catalogues (occasional); exhibition programs; newsletter, "Artline".

The primary purpose of the Mitchell Gallery is to establish possible connections between the visual arts and the liberal arts and to promote exhibits of unique historical and regional interest. Recently the Gallery's exhibition schedule has included such diverse shows as drawings by Old Masters and prints and multiples by Jonathan Borofsky. Further to explore the visual arts, the Gallery offers educational programs, lectures and discussions during the academic year in conjunction with each exhibition. The temporary exhibition schedule also includes the annual St. John's College Community Art Exhibition in the spring.

Baltimore

College of Notre Dame of Maryland - Gormley Gallery Ⓒᴬᴬ

Fourier Hall, 4701 N. Charles St., Baltimore, MD   21210-2404
Tel: (410) 532-5520
Fax: (410) 532-5795
Internet Address: http://www.ndm.edu
Department Chair: Domenico G. Firmani, Ph.D.
Admission: free.
Attendance: 1,000   *Membership:* N   *ADA Compliant:* Y
Parking: adjacent college lots.
Open: Monday to Friday, 8:30am-5:30pm.
Facilities: **Exhibition Area** (650 square feet).
Activities: **Temporary Exhibitions**.

The gallery presents exhibitions of student and faculty work and juried exhibitions.

The Johns Hopkins University - Evergreen House Ⓒᴬᴬ

4545 N. Charles St., Baltimore, MD   21210
Tel: (410) 516-0341   *Fax:* (410) 516-0864
Internet Address: http://www.jhu.edu/~evergreen/
Director: Ms. Lili R. Ott

Baltimore, Maryland

The Johns Hopkins University - Evergreen House, cont.

Admission: fee: adult-$6.00, student-$3.00, senior-$5.00.
Attendance: 5,300   *Established:* 1952
Membership: Y   *ADA Compliant:* Y
Parking: free on site.
Open: Monday to Friday, 10am-4pm;
          Saturday to Sunday, 1pm-4pm.
Facilities: **Architecture** (Italianate 19th century mansion); **Formal Gardens**; **Grounds** (26 acres); **Shop** (pottery and glass, museum jewelry, books).
Activities: **Concerts**; **Guided Tours** (required; groups reserve in advance); **Lectures**.
Publications: annual report; newsletter (quarterly).

View of Greek Revival portico on façade of Evergreen House. The house was built in 1850s and expanded after its purchase by the Garretts in 1878. Photograph courtesy of Johns Hopkins University, Baltimore, Maryland.

Listed on the National Register of Historic Places, Evergreen House is a magnificent Italianate home on 26 wooded and landscaped acres. Owned by Baltimore's Garrett family from 1878 to 1942, the mansion, carriage house and gardens underwent two generations of adaptations and renovations. The house has functioned as the Rare Book Library and Fine Arts Museum of The Johns Hopkins University since 1952. Highlights of the 48 room mansion include collections of post-Impressionist paintings; rare books; Chinese blue and white porcelain; Japanese netsuke, inro, and lacquer boxes; Tiffany glass; and Baltimore's only private theatre with colorful Russian designs by Leon Bakst. All the collections are seen in the context of the elegant style of life at Evergreen, displayed as they were enjoyed by the Garretts.

Loyola College - Art Gallery Ⓒᴬᴬ

DeChiaro College Center, 2nd Floor
4501 N. Charles St.
Baltimore, MD   21210
Tel: (410) 617-2799
Internet Address: http://www.loyola.edu/gallery/index.html
Admission: free.
Parking: college parking lot off Cold Spring Lane.
Open: Monday to Friday, 11am-5pm; Sunday, 1pm-4pm.
Closed: Academic Holidays.
Facilities: **Exhibition Area**.
Activities: **Temporary Exhibitions**.

Located on the second floor in the Julio Fine Arts Wing of the DeChiaro College Center, the Gallery presents temporary exhibits of the work of contemporary artists.

The Maryland Institute College of Art - Galleries Ⓒᴬᴬ

1300 Mt. Royal Ave., Baltimore, MD   21217
Tel: (410) 669-9200
Fax: (410) 669-9206
Internet Address: http://www.mica.edu/galleries/galleries_main.htm/
Exhibition Director: Mr. David J. Brown
Admission: free.
Established: 1826   *ADA Compliant:* Y
Open: Monday to Wednesday, 10am-5pm; Thursday to Friday, 10am-9pm; Saturday, 10am-5pm;
          Sunday, noon-5pm.
Facilities: **Auditorium**; **Classrooms**; **Galleries**; **Library** (39,000 volumes).
Activities: **Concerts**; **Lectures**; **Performances**; **Temporary Exhibitions** (90/year).
Publications: bulletins; exhibition catalogues; posters.

The Maryland Institute College of Art - Galleries, cont.

Each year over 90 public exhibitions are featured in MICA galleries. Exhibitions have featured a diverse group of major artists from various disciplines. Programming also includes exhibits of work by graduate and undergraduate students, faulty, and visiting artists. Galleries include two major spaces, the Decker Gallery in the former Mt. Royal Station (corner of Cathedral and Dolphin Sts.) and the Meyerhoff Gallery in the Fox Building (1341 Dickson St.), as well as the Graduate Thesis Gallery and several student galleries. A gallery is also planned for the newly acquired former AAA Building. The George A. Lucas Collection of 19th century art is on loan to the Baltimore Museum of Art and the Walters Art Gallery.

Catonsville

University of Maryland, Baltimore County - Albin O. Kuhn Library and Gallery ⓒ

University of Maryland-Baltimore County, 1000 Hilltop Circle, Catonsville, MD   21250
Tel: (410) 455-2270   *Fax:* (410) 455-1153
Internet Address: http://www.research.umbc.edu/aok/main
Chief Curator: Mr. Tom Beck
Admission: voluntary contribution.
Attendance: 15,000   *Established:* 1975   *Membership:* Y   *ADA Compliant:* Y
Open: Monday to Wednesday, noon-4:30pm; Thursday, noon-8pm; Friday, noon-4:30pm;
         Saturday, 1pm-5pm.
Closed: Legal Holidays, Academic Holidays.
Facilities: **Exhibition Area** (4,000 square feet, plus 420 square feet apart); **Library** (40,000 volumes); **Reading Room**.
Activities: **Education Programs** (college students); **Guided Tours**; **Temporary Exhibitions**; **Traveling Exhibitions**.
Publications: exhibition catalogues.

The Gallery displays items from the Library's Special Collections Department, as well as art and artifacts from all over the world. Traveling exhibitions are occasionally presented.

College Park

University of Maryland - Art Gallery ⓒ

1202 Art-Sociology Bldg., Univ. of Maryland (Campus Drive, adjacent to Tawes Theater)
College Park, MD   20742
Tel: (301) 405-2763   *Fax:* (302) 314-7774
Internet Address: http:www.inform.umd.edu/ArtGal
Director and Curator of collections: Terry Gips
Admission: free.
Attendance: 5,532   *Established:* 1966   *Membership:* Y   *ADA Compliant:* Y
Parking: metered & parking garage; free Saturdays in Parking Lot #1.
Open: **Fall to Spring**,
         Monday to Wednesday, 11am-4pm; Thursday, 11am-9pm; Friday, 11am-4pm;
         Saturday, 11am-5pm.
Closed: Summer, Legal Holidays, Academic Holidays, Between Exhibitions.
Facilities: **Exhibition Area** (4,000 square feet); **Library** (40,000 volumes).
Activities: **Gallery Talks**; **Lectures**; **Temporary Exhibitions** (5-8/year); **Traveling Exhibitions**.
Publications: exhibition catalogues.

The Gallery presents an exhibition program that complements the University's academic offerings and maintains a permanent art collection for study, research and exhibition. Five to eight exhibitions are produced each year, often accompanied by catalogues, lectures, gallery talks, and panel discussions. The permanent collection consists of traditional African sculpture; 20th-century prints, photographs and paintings by American and European artists; American social realist and regional prints, drawings, and paintings from the 1930s; Chinese ceramics; and mid-20th-century Japanese prints. The Gallery also holds on long-term loan from the National Museum of American Art an important collection of government-sponsored, 1930s mural studies for U.S. Post Offices. Also located in the Art

College Park, Maryland

University of Maryland - Art Gallery

Sociology Building is the student-run West Gallery, featuring the work of University of Maryland students (open: Mon-Fri, 8:30am-4:30pm). Additionally, the Parents' Association Art Gallery, located on the first floor of the Stamp Student Union features the work of local artists (open: Mon-Fri, 10am-6pm and Sat, 11am-5pm). Also of possible interest, the School of Architecture maintains a gallery space on the ground floor of the architecture building for the exhibition of architectural works by faculty, students, and professionals. Geographically adjacent to the College Park Campus, but administered separately is the Gallery at the Center for Adult Education, University of Maryland University College (see separate listing).

University of Maryland University College - Art Program Gallery

UMUC Inn and Conference Center, University Blvd. at Adelphi Road, College Park, MD   20747
Tel: (301) 985-7152   *Fax:* (301) 985-7678
Internet Address: http://www.umuc.edu
Director: Ms. Dena Crosson
Admission: free.
Established: 1978
Open: Daily, 8am-8pm.
Closed: Christmas Day to New Year's Day.
Facilities: **Exhibition Area**.
Activities: **Temporary Exhibitions**.

UMUC Arts Program maintains the Maryland Artists Collection of local artists, as well as the Mori Gallery and the International Collection, which feature artists from around the world. The Arts Program also sponsors an active temporary exhibition program, showcasing contemporary Maryland artists at three UMUC locations: the Inn and Conference Center in College Park, the Annapolis Center, and the St. Charles Center in Waldorf. The Arts Program permanent collection consists of the Maryland Artist Collection of more than 275 works by Maryland painters, printmakers, photographers, and sculptors; the Mori Collection; and the International Collection. Holdings also include the Herman Maril Collection, the largest number of works by that artist in any one collection. The Maril Collection is on display at UMUC's Inn and Conference Center on Sundays, 11am to 3pm, and during the week by appointment, (301) 985-7822. There are a number of other sites of possible interest on the University of Maryland campus; see separate listing for the Art Gallery of the University of Maryland for additional information.

Frederick

Hood College - Hodson Gallery ⓒ

Tatem Arts Center, 401 Rosemont Avenue, Frederick, MD   21701-8524
Tel: (301) 696-3456
Internet Address: http://www/hood.edu/artdept/gallery/gallery.html
Director: Ms. Joyce Michaud
Admission: free.
Open: **Academic Year**, Daily, 9am-7pm.
            Between Semesters, Weekdays, 10am-6pm.
Facilities: **Exhibition Area**.
Activities: **Temporary Exhibitions** (monthly).

The Gallery presents monthly exhibitions of work by professional artists, as well as an annual exhibit of student work. A full range of fine art media including painting, drawing, ceramics, prints, photography, sculpture, fiber, and computer-generated art is represented.

Frostburg

Frostburg State University - Stephanie Ann Roper Gallery ⓒ

Fine Arts Building, 101 Braddock Road, Frostburg, MD   21532
Tel: (301) 687-4797   *Fax:* (301) 687-3099
Internet Address: http://www.fsu.umd.edu/dept/art/gall.htm

Frostburg State University - Stephanie Ann Roper Gallery, cont.

Director: Mr. Dustin Davis

Admission: free.

ADA Compliant: Y

Parking: adjacent to facility.

Open: Sunday to Wednesday, noon-4pm.

Facilities: **Exhibition Area** (2,000 square feet).

Activities: **Performances**; **Temporary Exhibitions**.

A teaching gallery, the Roper Gallery displays the work of locally, regionally, and nationally recognized artists. Exhibitions include Baltimore Museum presentations, BFA senior student and juried student exhibitions, faculty shows, and cooperative performance exhibitions. Additional work may also be on display in the Library and Lane Center galleries.

Saint Mary's City

St. Mary's College of Maryland - Dwight Frederick Boyden Gallery ⒸⒶ

St. Mary's College of Maryland

Div. of Arts & Letters, 18952 E. Fisher Road

Saint Mary's City, MD   20686

Tel: (301) 862-0249

Fax: (301) 862-0958

Internet Address: http:www.smcm.edu/academics/gallery

Director: Mr. David Emerick

Admission: free.

Established: 1839

ADA Compliant: Y

Open: **Academic Term**,
　　　　Monday to Thursday, 11am-5pm;
　　　　Friday, 11am-4pm;
　　　　Saturday, noon-3pm.

Closed: Thanksgiving Week
　　　　mid-December to mid-January,
　　　　May to August.

Scott Noel, *Sympathy for the model*, 1996, Exhibited in the exhibition "Embodied Fictions", 1998 at the Boyden Gallery. Photograph courtesy of the Boyden Gallery, St. Mary's College of Maryland, St. Mary's City, Maryland.

Facilities: **Exhibition Area** (1,600 square feet).

Activities: **Lectures**; **Temporary Exhibitions**; **Traveling Exhibitions**.

Publications: exhibition catalogues.

The Gallery holds five exhibitions of regional artists, a student show, and senior shows during each academic year. Exhibitions represent a diverse approach to understanding art and its meaning in today's society. Visiting artist's workshops and lectures are often integrated with the exhibitions.

Salisbury

Salisbury State University Galleries ⒸⒶ

Salisbury State University, 1101 Camden Ave., Salisbury, MD   21801

Tel: (410) 543-6271   *Fax:* (410) 548-3002

Internet Address: http://www.ssu.umd.edu

Director: Mr. Kenneth Basile

Admission: voluntary contribution.

Attendance: 20,000   *Established:* 1962   *Membership:* Y   *ADA Compliant:* Y

Parking: visitor parking available.

Open: **During Exhibitions**, Tuesday to Friday, 10am-4pm; Saturday to Sunday, noon-4pm.

Closed: June to August, weekends, Legal Holidays.

Facilities: **Exhibition Area** (2 galleries); **Outside Sculpture** (campus-wide); **Shop**.

Activities: **Temporary Exhibitions**.

Publications: newsletter (quarterly).

Salisbury State University Galleries, cont.

The Salisbury State University Galleries sponsor a broad and varied program of art exhibitions including contemporary art by nationally recognized artists, and by emerging artists with significant regional reputations; materials of historical and scientific importance from different cultures and time periods; and the work of Art Department faculty and students. The main gallery, Fulton Hall Gallery is located in Fulton Hall; a second gallery, the Atrium Gallery, is located in Guerrieri University Center.

Exterior view of Fulton Hall, which houses the main gallery of University Galleries. Photograph courtesy of Salisbury State University Galleries, Salisbury, Maryland.

Stevenson

Villa Julie College Gallery

1525 Greenspring Valley Road
Stevenson, MD   21153-0641
Tel: (410) 602-7163   *Fax:* (410) 486-3552
Internet Address: http://www.vjc.edu/news_and_events/art_gallery/
Director: Ms. Diane DiSalvo
Established: 1997
Parking: free on site.
Open: Monday to Wednesday, 11am-5pm; Thursday, 11am-7pm; Friday, 11am-5pm;
       Saturday, 11am-4pm.
Facilities: **Exhibition Area.**
Activities: **Films; Lectures; Temporary Exhibitions.**

Villa Julie presents temporary exhibitions of historic and contemporary art in all media.

Towson

Goucher College - Rosenberg Gallery ⓒ

Kraushaar Auditorium Lobby, Merrick Hall
1021 Dulaney Valley Road
Towson, MD   21204-2794
Tel: (410) 337-6333
Fax: (410) 337-6405
Internet Address:
   http://www.goucher.edu/rosenberg
Exhibitions Director: Ms. Helen Glazer
Admission: free.
Attendance: 175,000   *Established:* 1885
Membership: N   *ADA Compliant:* Y
Parking: free on site.
Open: **September to May**,
       Monday to Friday, 9am-5pm.
Closed: Christmas Day to mid-January,
       Summer, Thanksgiving Weekend.

Interior of Rosenburg Gallery in lobby of Kraushaar Auditorium and Merrick Hall during a 1996 exhibition. On left are appliqué quilts by Mary Swann and on right mixed media works by Maria Barbosa. Photograph courtesy of Art Department, Goucher College, Towson, Maryland.

Facilities: **Auditoria** (2; 1,000 seats and 225 seats); **Exhibition Area** (144 running feet of wall space).
Activities: **Lectures** (evenings, 1-2/season); **Temporary Exhibitions** (6-8/year).
Publications: exhibition catalogues (quarterly).

Goucher College - Rosenberg Gallery, cont.

Operating under the auspices of Goucher's Art Department, the Gallery presents six to eight exhibitions of contemporary art each academic year. Most exhibits showcase work by regional artists in a wide variety of media; occasionally shows of works by other artists or traveling exhibitions sponsored by other institutions are scheduled. The Gallery has a special interest in providing opportunities for artists who are women, members of ethnic or racial minorities, or who live in rural areas of Maryland.

Towson University - Asian Arts and Culture Center ⓒ

Fine Arts Center, Towson University
(corner Cross Campus and Osler Drives)
Towson, MD   21252-0001
Tel: (410) 830-2807
Fax: (410) 830-4032
Internet Address: http://www.towson.edu/tu/asianarts
Director: Mrs. Suewhei Shieh
Admission: free.
Attendance: 6,000   *Established:* 1971
Membership: Y   *ADA Compliant:* Y
Parking: metered and on street.
Open: Monday to Friday, 11am-4pm.
Closed: Legal Holidays, Easter, Christmas Day.

View of section of permanent collection of Asian Arts and Culture Center. Photograph courtesy of Asian Arts and Culture Center, Towson University, Towson, Maryland.

Facilities: **Exhibition Area** (1,000 square feet); **Library** (100 volumes).
Activities: **Arts Festival**; **Concerts**; **Dance Recitals**; **Films**; **Lectures**; **Permanent Exhibits**; **Temporary Exhibitions**; **Traveling Exhibitions**; **Workshops**.

The Asian Arts and Culture Center at Towson University organizes art exhibitions and provides programming in traditional and innovative arts for the benefit of people of diverse cultural backgrounds. It also houses the University's collection of Asian art. The Center's emphasis is on providing the opportunity to meet, see, touch, feel, engage and truly experience the Asian lifestyle in an informal, accessible, and continuing forum.

Towson University - Holtzman Art Gallery ⓒ

Fine Arts Complex (corner of Cross Campus and Osler Drives), Towson, MD   21204
Tel: (410) 830-2333
Internet Address: http://www.towson.edu
Director: Mr. Christopher Bartlett
Admission: free.
Established: 1973
Open: Call for hours.
Facilities: Gallery.
Activities: **Temporary Exhibitions**.

Located in the Fine Arts Complex of Towson University, the Holtzman Art Gallery presents exhibitions of contemporary art in a broad range of media. Exhibits of well-known American and European artists, group shows, and theme shows are scheduled throughout the year.

Westminster

Western Maryland College - Rice Gallery ⓒ

2 College Hill, Westminster, MD   21157
Tel: (410) 857-2594
Internet Address: http://www.wmc.car.md.us
Director: Prof. Michael Losch
Facilities: Galleries.

The Rice Gallery exhibits works from the College's permanent collection and presents shows of the work of professional artists.

Massachusetts

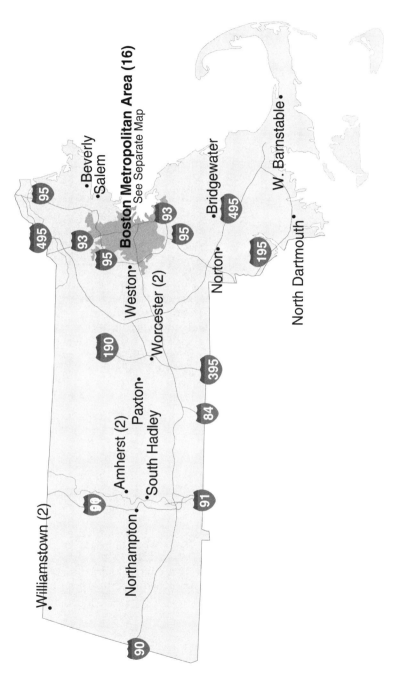

The number in parentheses following the city name indicates the number of museums/galleries in that municipality. If there is no number, one is understood. For example, in the text two listings would be found under Worcester and one listing under Norton. Cities within the greater Boston metropolitan area will be found on the map on the facing page.

Greater Boston Metropolitan Area

(including Boston, Cambridge, Chestnut Hill, Medford,
Waltham, and Wellesley.)

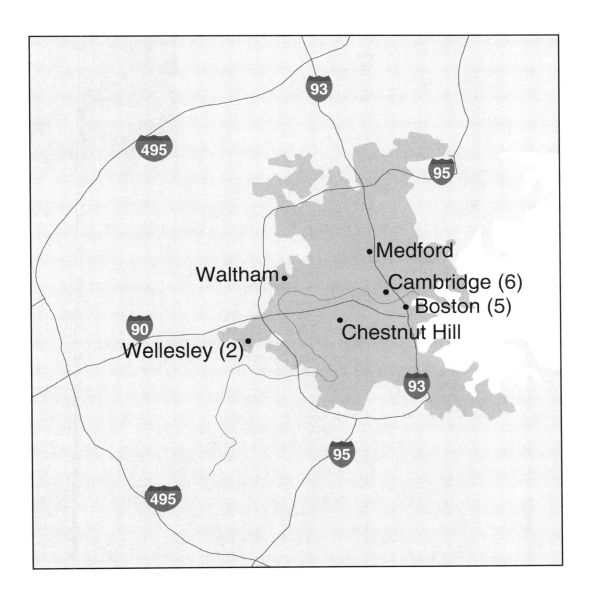

Massachusetts

Amherst

Amherst College - Mead Art Museum ⊂⁴⁴⊃

Amherst College, (corner of Routes 9 and 116)
Amherst, MA   01002-5000
Tel: (413) 542-2335   *Fax:* (413) 542-2117
Internet Address: http://www.amherst.edu/~mead
Acting Director: Dr. Jill Meredith
Admission: voluntary contribution.
Attendance: 16,000   *Established:* 1950
Membership: Y   *ADA Compliant:* Y
Parking: free on site.
Open: **September to May**,
           Monday to Wednesday, 10am-4:30pm;
      .. Thursday, 10am-9pm;
           Friday, 10am-4:30pm;
           Saturday to Sunday, 1pm-5pm.
         late-December to January,
           limited hours during interterm.
         June to August,
           Tuesday to Sunday, 1pm-4pm.

Adolphe Bouguereau, *Penelope (Le travail interrompu)*, oil on canvas, 63 x 39¼ inches. Museum Purchase, Mead Art Museum. Photograph courtesy of the Mead Art Museum, Amherst College, Amherst, Massachusetts.

Facilities: **Architecture** (1949, design by McKim, Mead, & White); **Classrooms**; **Galleries** (7); **Lecture Hall**; **Print Study Room** (6 exhibitions/year).
Activities: **Concerts**; **Film Series**; **Gallery Talks** (Tues, 12:15pm); **Guided Tours** (by appointment); **Lectures**; **Temporary Exhibitions** (10-12/year).
Publications: brochures; calendar (semi-annual); exhibition catalogues (occasional).

The Mead Art Museum exhibits and collects works of art from antiquity to the present. In addition to permanent displays, it offers ten to twelve exhibitions yearly, some drawn from the permanent collection, while others are loan exhibitions. The Collins Print Room displays six exhibitions yearly, selected from a collection of over 6,500 prints, drawings, and photographs, which span the 16th century to the present. Loan exhibitions and museum programs are open to the public and provide access to visual material, artists, and scholars from beyond the Amherst campus. The permanent collection of approximately 14,000 art objects is best known in the area of 18th- and 19th-century American art, but also includes important examples of European and Asian art that serve the needs of courses in the fine arts and humanities. The Mead holds Colonial and Federal portraits by John Singleton Copley, the Peale family, and Gilbert Stuart; landscapes by Thomas Cole, Frederic Church, and Asher B. Durand; figural studies by Winslow Homer, Thomas Eakins, and William Merritt Chase; and impressionist landscapes by Childe Hassam. Other American highlights include Robert Henri's "Salome", Ralston Crawford's "Nacelles Under Construction", and Pop portraiture by Andy Warhol. Sculptures range from portraits by Augustus Saint-Gaudens to monumental bronzes by Paul Manship to modernist constructions by Joseph Cornell and Frank Stella. European holdings include early Italian altarpieces and works by Edward Lear, Claude Monet, Joshua Reynolds, Peter Paul Rubens, and Franz Snyders. Holdings in Classical Antiquities are highlighted by four Assyrian monumental relief sculptures from the palace of Ashurnaisirpal II at Nimrud. Other holdings include sub-Saharan traditional tribal artifacts, pre-Columbian ceramics and textiles, Mexican folk art, Buddhist sculpture, Indian miniatures, Turkish and Persian textiles, Chinese ceramics, and a growing collection of Japanese art, including over 300 woodblock prints and a large group of 20th-century ceramics.

University of Massachusetts at Amherst - University Gallery ⊂⁴⁴⊃

Fine Arts Center, North Pleasant Street, University of Massachusetts, Amherst, MA   01003
Tel: (413) 545-3670   *Fax:* (413) 545-2018
Internet Address: http://www.umass.edu/fac/org/univgallery/index.html
Director: Ms. Betsy Siersma
Admission: free.

University of Massachusetts at Amherst - University Gallery, cont.

Attendance: 15,000   *Established:* 1975   *Membership:* Y   *ADA Compliant:* Y

Open: mid-September to early June,
  Tuesday to Friday, 11am-4:30pm; Saturday to Sunday, 2pm-5pm.

Closed: between terms.

Facilities: **Galleries** (4, total 6,533 square feet); **Sculpture Garden**.

Activities: **Education Programs** (undergraduate and graduate college students); **Films**; **Gallery Talks**; **Guided Tours**; **Lectures**; **Temporary Exhibitions**; **Traveling Exhibitions**.

Publications: exhibition catalogues.

Located on the lower level of the Fine Arts Center, the University Gallery offers an active exhibition schedule that features contemporary art in a range of media by emerging and established artists. The Gallery also houses and exhibits the University's permanent collection of 20th-century American works on paper, and its collection of public art. Additionally, the Hampden Gallery (located in the Southwest Residential Area; open Monday to Friday, 3pm-7pm and Sunday, 2pm-5pm), the Wheeler Gallery (located in the Central Residential Area; open Monday to Thursday, 4pm-8pm and Sunday 2pm-5pm), and the Herter Gallery (located on the main floor of Herter Hall, (413) 545-0976; open Monday to Friday,11am-4pm and Sunday, 2pm-5pm) showcase the work of students, faculty and emerging artists of local and regional importance, complemented by workshops, readings, and performance art. Also of possible interest on campus is the Augusta Savage Gallery (located at 101 New Africa House, (413) 545-5177; open Monday to Tuesday, 1pm-7pm, Wednesday to Friday, 1pm-5pm), a multicultural and multi-arts facility promoting the work of students and artists of color from diverse world cultures. Each year, the Savage Gallery presents five professional and four student exhibitions chosen on their aesthetic integrity and ability to enlighten the viewer about racial and cultural preconceptions. Its permanent collection contains traditional folk art and contemporary works by nationally renowned artists.

Beverly

Montserrat College of Art - Galleries ⓒ⁴⁴

23 Essex St., Beverly, MA 01915

Tel: (978) 922-8222   *Fax:* (978) 922-4268

Internet Address: http://www.montserrat.edu/events/events1.html

Director: Ms. Barbara O'Brien

Admission: free.

Established: 1970   *ADA Compliant:* Y

Parking: on street.

Open: **September to May,**
  Monday to Thursday, 11am-7pm; Friday, 11am-5pm; Saturday, noon-4pm.
  June to July,
  Monday to Friday, 9am-4pm.

Facilities: **Exhibition Area** (1,500 square feet).

Activities: **Gallery Talks**; **Symposia**; **Temporary Exhibitions** (monthly during academic year, one during June-July); **Visiting Artist Lectures**.

Publications: exhibition brochures.

The Montserrat Gallery features a year-round program of exhibitions of contemporary work by professional artists, usually presented in two-person or thematic exhibitions. In addition, the Alumni Gallery mounts exhibitions of faculty and alumni artwork. A third gallery, the Cabot Studio Building Gallery, focuses on the work of members of the Senior Seminar, as well as community outreach exhibitions.

Boston

The Art Institute of Boston Gallery ⓒ⁴⁴ (AIB Gallery)

700 Beacon St., Boston, MA 02215

Tel: (617) 262-1223 *Ext:* 308   *Fax:* (617) 437-1226

Internet Address: http://www.aiboston.edu

Boston, Massachusetts

The Art Institute of Boston Gallery, cont.

Director of Exhibitions: Prof. Bonnell Robinson
Admission: free.
Attendance: 6,000   *Membership:* N   *ADA Compliant:* Y
Parking: metered on street.
Open: Monday to Friday, 9am-5:30pm; Saturday, 9am-5pm; Sunday, noon-5pm.
Closed: Legal Holidays.
Facilities: **Gallery** (1,000 square feet).
Activities: **Lectures**; **Temporary Exhibitions** (6 per year).
Publications: catalogue (annual); posters.

The AIB Gallery mounts temporary exhibitions of the work of major national and international artists and presents group shows, including student and faculty work.

Boston University Art Gallery Ⓒᴬᴬ

855 Commonwealth Ave., Boston, MA 02215
Tel: (617) 353-4672
Fax: (617) 353-4509
Internet Address: http://www.bu.edu/ART/home.html
Director: Kim Sichel
Admission: free.
Attendance: 6,000   *Established:* 1960   *ADA Compliant:* Y
Parking: metered on street and nearby commercial lots.
Open: **mid-September to mid-May**,
        Tuesday to Friday, 10am-5pm; Saturday to Sunday, 1pm-5pm.
Closed: Between Semesters, Legal Holidays.
Facilities: **Architecture** (former Buick dealership); **Gallery**.
Activities: **Concerts**; **Education Programs** (undergraduate and graduate college students); **Gallery Talks**; **Lectures**; **Traveling Exhibitions**.
Publications: exhibition catalogues.

The Gallery maintains an ongoing program of four to five temporary exhibitions annually. Exhibitions focus on international, national, and regional art developments, chiefly in the 20th century. The gallery has a particular commitment to offer a culturally inclusive view of art, one that expands the boundaries of museum exhibitions and showcases alternatives to New York-oriented trends. It also has a long-term interest in showing 20th-century figurative art, complementing the traditional focus of the School of the Arts curriculum. Each spring, its season closes with a series of student exhibitions; the MFA candidates in painting, sculpture, and graphic design present their work, as do undergraduates in the School of the Arts. The Gallery does not maintain a permanent collection.

Massachusetts College of Art - Galleries Ⓒᴬᴬ

621 Huntington Ave., Boston, MA 02115
Tel: (617) 232-1555
Internet Address: http://www.massart.edu/campus/events/ex_ev.html
Admission: free.
Open: Monday to Friday, 10am-6pm; Saturday, 11am-5pm.
Facilities: **Galleries**.
Activities: **Temporary Exhibitions**.

The Sandra and David Bakalar Gallery and Huntington Gallery present temporary exhibitions. Additionally, there are three spaces for the exhibition of student work. Student shows run for approximately two weeks. The Student Life Gallery, located on the second floor of the Kennedy Building adjacent to the Student Center, can accommodate large scale installations and free-standing work. The Tower Gallery, on the second floor of the Tower Building, presents group student shows. Installation Station is used primarily for solo, large multimedia, interactive, or installation exhibitions.

School of Museum of Fine Arts-Boston - Barbara & Steven Grossman Gallery ⓒᴬ⁴

230 The Fenway, Boston, MA   02115
Tel: (617) 369-3718   *Fax:* (617) 424-6271
Internet Address: http://www.smfa.edu/offices/exhibitions/
Asst. Director: Ms. Lisa Tung
Admission: free.
Open: **Fall to Spring**,
          Tuesday, 10am-5pm; Wednesday to Thursday, 10am-8pm; Friday to Saturday, 10am-5pm;
          Sunday, 1pm-5pm.
          Summer,
          Monday to Friday, 10am-5pm.
Closed: Holidays.
Facilities: **Gallery**.
Activities: **Temporary Exhibitions**.
The Grossman Gallery presents temporary exhibitions, including shows of work by professional artists, faculty, staff, students, and alumni.

Simmons College - Trustman Art Gallery ⓒᴬ⁴

Main College Building, Fourth Floor, 300 The Fenway, Boston, MA   02115-5898
Tel: (617) 521-2268
Internet Address: http://www/simmons.edu/resources/trustman/trustman.html
Director: Mr. Robert Oppenheim
Admission: free.
Established: 1982
Open: **September to May**, Monday to Friday, 10am-4:30pm.
Facilities: **Exhibition Area**.
Activities: **Temporary Exhibitions**.
The Gallery presents exhibitions of work by professional artists, as well as an annual exhibition of student work.

Bridgewater

Bridgewater State College - Wallace L. Anderson Art Gallery ⓒᴬ⁴

The Art Center (Main Floor), Park Avenue, West Campus, Bridgewater, MA   02325
Tel: (508) 697-1359
Internet Address: http://www.bridgew.edu/DEPTS/ART
Admission: free.
Open: Monday to Friday, 8am-4pm.
Closed: Legal Holidays.
Facilities: **Exhibition Area**.
Activities: **Temporary Exhibitions**.
Located in the oldest existing campus structure, the Gallery offers changing exhibitions throughout the academic year, including an annual student show. A continuing exhibition of works from the College's permanent collection are on view in an adjacent gallery.

Cambridge

Harvard University Art Museums ⓒᴬ⁴

32 Quincy St. at Broadway, Cambridge, MA   02138
Tel: (617) 495-9400 *Ext:* 0   *Fax:* (617) 495-9936
Internet Address: http://www.artmuseums.harvard.edu
Director: Dr. James Cuno
Admission: fee: adult-$5.00, child-free, student-$3.00, senior-$4.00.
Attendance: 173,000   *Membership:* Y   *ADA Compliant:* Y
Parking: 3 hours/valet parking at Harvard Inn, 1201 Mass. Ave.

Harvard University Art Museums, cont.

Open: Monday to Saturday, 10am-5pm; Sunday, 1pm-5pm.
Closed: Legal Holidays.
Facilities: **Museums** (3).
Activities: **Concerts**; **Education Programs** (graduate and undergraduate college students); **Films**; **Lectures**.
Publications: "Bulletin" (3/year); "Review" (semi-annual); annual report; calendar (quarterly).

The Harvard University Art Museums make up one of the few university museums to have collections ranking with the best art museums anywhere. The approximately 150,000 objects in the Art Museums' collections range from antiquity to the present and come from Europe, North America, North Africa, the Middle East, India, Southeast Asia, and East Asia. The museums consist of three institutions, each with its own focus: Busch-Reisinger Museum, Fogg Art Museum, and The Arthur M. Sackler Museum. General information, applying to all three institutions, is found in this entry. More specific information on a particular institution may be found under its entry.

Harvard University - The Arthur M. Sackler Museum ♿

485 Broadway (across from the Fogg Art Museum), Cambridge, MA   02138
Tel: (617) 495-9400   *Fax:* (617) 495-9936
Internet Address:
   http://www.artmuseums.harvard.edu
Curator: Mr. Robert Mowry
Admission: fee (for all 3 museums): adult-$5.00, child-free, student-$3.00, senior-$4.00.
Established: 1985
Membership: Y
Parking: valet parking at Harvard Inn, 1201 Mass. Ave.
Open: Monday to Saturday, 10am-5pm; Sunday, 1pm-5pm.
Closed: Legal Holidays.
Facilities: **Architecture** (1985 design by British architect James Stirling); **Galleries** (3 floors).
Activities: **Gallery Talks** (dependent on exhibition; Sat, am; Sun, pm); **Guided Tours** (weekdays, 2pm; groups, reserve 3 weeks in advance, 496-8576); **Temporary Exhibitions**.

Interior view of Arthur M. Sackler Museum. Photograph courtesy of Harvard University Art Museums, Cambridge, Massachusetts.

Publications: collection catalogues; exhibition catalogues.

The Sackler, houses collections of ancient, Asian, Islamic, and later Indian art. Among its collections are an extensive collection of Chinese jades; Korean ceramics; Chinese cave temple painting and sculpture; a significant collection of Japanese woodblock prints; one of America's most important collections of Chinese bronzes; and Greek and Roman sculpture, vases, and coins. The Sackler Museum building also contains the Harvard University Art Museums' largest special exhibition gallery, an auditorium, the offices of Harvard's Department of Fine Arts, and the Rübel Library, a research center for Asian art.

Harvard University - Busch-Reisinger Museum ♿

32 Quincy St. at Broadway, Cambridge, MA   02138
Tel: (617) 495-2317   *Fax:* (617) 495-9936
Internet Address: http://www.artmuseums.harvard.edu
Curator: Mr. Peter Nisbit
Admission: fee (for all 3 museums): adult-$5.00, child-free, student-$3.00, senior-$4.00.
Established: 1902
Membership: Y   *ADA Compliant:* Y

Harvard University - Busch-Reisinger Museum, cont.

Parking: valet parking at Harvard Inn, 1201 Mass. Ave.

Open: Monday to Saturday, 10am-5pm; Sunday, 1pm-5pm.

Closed: Legal Holidays.

Facilities: **Architecture** (Werner Otto Hall, 1991 design by Gwathmey, Siegel, and Associates); **Galleries**; **Study Room** (Tues-Fri, 2pm-4:45pm).

Activities: **Gallery Talks** (vary with each exhibition); **Guided Tours** (weekdays, 1pm; groups, reserve 3 weeks in advance, 496-8576); **Temporary Exhibitions**; **Traveling Exhibitions**.

Publications: collection catalogues; exhibition catalogues.

Interior view of Busch-Reisinger Museum. Photograph courtesy of Harvard University Museums, Cambridge, Massachusetts.

The Busch-Reisinger Museum is devoted to the art of German-speaking countries and related cultures of central and northern Europe. Its collections of German expressionism, Vienna Secession art, and 1920s abstraction rank with the finest in the United States and include works by Beckmann, Beuys, Feininger, Kandinsky, Klee, Kirchner, Kokoschka, Klimt, Kollwitz, Moholy-Nagy, Marc, and Munch. Founded in 1902 as the "Germanic Museum" with a collection exclusively of reproductions, since 1930 the Busch-Reisinger has actively acquired original works of art, in particular, modern art considered "degenerate" by the Nazis. The collections have also been enriched by gifts from artists and designers associated with the famous Bauhaus, including the archives of the celebrated architect Walter Gropius. The Busch-Reisinger Museum also has important collections of late medieval, Renaissance, and baroque sculpture, 16th-century painting, and porcelain. The Busch-Reisinger Museum's permanent display of modern works of art and design is housed in the galleries of its new building, Werner Otto Hall (opened in 1991). Pre-1880 works are presented in appropriate galleries of the Fogg Art Museum. Works that are not normally on view, especially drawings, prints, and photographs, can be viewed in the study room of the Busch-Reisinger or in the special exhibitions gallery. Werner Otto Hall also houses Harvard's Fine Arts Library.

Harvard University - Fogg Art Museum ⒸⒶⒶ

32 Quincy St. at Broadway, Cambridge, MA 02138

Tel: (617) 495-9400 *Fax:* (617) 495-9936

Internet Address:
http://www.artmuseums.harvard.edu

Director: Dr. James Cuno

Admission: fee (for all 3 museums): adult-$5.00, child-free, student-$3.00, senior-$4.00.

Established: 1895

Membership: Y *ADA Compliant:* Y

Parking: valet parking at Harvard Inn, 1201 Mass. Ave.

Open: Monday to Saturday, 10am-5pm; Sunday, 1pm-5pm.

Closed: Legal Holidays.

Facilities: **Architecture** (Neo-Georgian exterior, 1927 design by Coolidge Bullfinch & Abbott); **Galleries** (2 floors); **Print Study Room** Agnes Mongan Center (Tues-Fri, 2pm-4:45pm; during academic year, Sat, 10am-12:45pm); **Shop** (books, catalogues, reproductions).

View of courtyard, Fogg Art Museum. Photograph courtesy of Harvard University Museums, Cambridge, Massachusetts.

Harvard University - Fogg Art Museum, cont.

Activities: **Gallery Talks** (dependent on exhibition; Sat, am; Sun, pm); **Guided Tours** (weekdays, 11am; groups, reserve 3 weeks in advance, 496-8576); **Temporary Exhibitions**; **Traveling Exhibitions**.

Publications: collection catalogues; exhibition catalogues.

The Fogg Art Museum is Harvard's oldest art museum. Around its Italian Renaissance courtyard, based on a 16th-century façade in Montepulciano, Italy, are galleries illustrating the history of Western art from the Middle Ages to the present, with particular strengths in Italian early Renaissance, British Pre-Raphaelite, and 19th-century French art. The Wertheim Collection, housed on the second floor of the Fogg, is one of America's finest collections of Impressionist and post-Impressionist work, and contains many famous masterworks. The Boston area's most important collection of Picasso's work is also found at the Fogg. The Agnes Mongan Center houses the collections, study room, and curatorial offices of the Fogg Art Museum's departments of prints, photographs, and drawings. The collections comprise approximately 60,000 prints, 12,000 drawings, and 8,000 photographs by European and American artists from the 14th-century to the present.

Harvard University Semitic Museum ⓒ⒜

6 Divinity Ave., Cambridge, MA   02138
Tel: (617) 495-4631
Fax: (617) 496-8904
Internet Address: http://www.fas.harvard.edu/~semitic/
Assistant Director: Mr. Joe Greene
Admission: voluntary contribution.
Attendance: 5,000   *Established:* 1889
Membership: Y   *ADA Compliant:* N
Open: Monday to Friday, 10am-4pm; Sunday, 1pm-4pm.
Closed: Academic Holidays.
Facilities: **Galleries**; **Shop**.
Activities: **Guided Tours**; **Lectures**; **Permanent Exhibits**; **Temporary Exhibitions**; **Traveling Exhibitions**.
Publications: books, "Harvard Semitic Series"; exhibition catalogues; newsletter.

The Museum, which shares its building with Harvard's Department of Near Eastern Languages and Civilizations, is dedicated to the use of its collections for the investigation and teaching of Near Eastern archaeology, history and culture. Through the collaborative efforts of departmental faculty, curators, museum curatorial staff, and students, the Museum mounts educational exhibits, sometimes in conjunction with courses, that not only serve the needs of the University, but also attract the general public and promote greater understanding of the civilizations of the Near East and its great cultural legacy.

Offering stand in shape of a house (14th century BC) from Harvard's excavations at Nuzi, Iraq, 1927-1931. Photograph courtesy of Harvard University Semitic Museum, Cambridge, Massachusetts.

MIT-List Visual Arts Center ⓒ⒜ (LVAC)

Weisner Building (MIT Bldg. E-15), 20 Ames St.
Cambridge, MA   02142-1308
Tel: (617) 253-4680
Fax: (617) 258-7265
Internet Address: http://web.mit.edu/lvac/www
Director: Ms. Katy Kline
Admission: voluntary contribution.
Attendance: 12,000   *Established:* 1950
ADA Compliant: Y
Parking: corner Main & Ames Sts., in campus lots evenings & weekends.

MIT-List Visual Arts Center, cont.

Open: **September to June**,
> Tuesday to Thursday, noon-6pm;
> Friday, noon-8pm;
> Saturday to Sunday, noon-6pm.

Closed: Legal Holidays.

Facilities: **Architecture** (Wiesner Building, 1985 design by I.M. Pei); **Galleries** (3); **Sculpture Collection** (throughout campus).

Activities: **Temporary Exhibitions** (3 exhibition periods/year with 1-3 exhibitions/period).

Publications: brochure, "The MIT List Visual Arts Center"; exhibition catalogues; gallery guides; guide, "Art and Architecture at MIT".

Exterior view of Wiesner Building, MIT. Photograph by Steve Rosenthal, courtesy of MIT List Visual Arts Center, Cambridge, Massachusetts.

Occupying three galleries on the main floor of the Wiesner Building, the List Visual Arts Center mounts approximately twelve exhibitions between September and June each year of current art making in all media: painting, sculpture, photography, video, installations, and experimental works that resist easy classification. Some exhibition examine one artist's work in depth; others bring together a variety of artists to provide different perspectives on a common theme. MIT's permanent collection of 20th-century art, which is particularly noted for major works of outdoor sculpture, is on view at all times throughout the campus.

Chestnut Hill

Boston College - Charles and Isabela V. McMullen Museum of Art ⓒᴀᴬ

Devlin Hall, 140 Commonwealth Ave., Chestnut Hill, MA   02167

Tel: (617) 552-8100
Fax: (617) 552-8577
Internet Address:
   http://www.bc.edu/bc_org/avp/cas/artmuseum
Director: Dr. Nancy Netzer
Admission: free.
Attendance: 30,000   *Established:* 1976
Membership: Y   *ADA Compliant:* Y
Parking: two free parking garages.
Open: **September to May**,
> Monday to Friday, 11am-4pm;
> Saturday to Sunday, noon-5pm.

> **June to August**,
> Monday to Thursday, 11am-3pm.

Closed: New Year's Day, ML King Day, Washington's B'day, Good Friday, Memorial Day, Christmas Day.

Facilities: **Architecture** (neo-Gothic, 1924 design by Charles D. Maginnis); **Auditorium** (350 seats); **Galleries** (2).

Activities: **Education Programs** (undergraduate and graduate college students); **Guided Tours** (Fri., 12:30pm; on request for groups); **Lectures; Temporary Exhibitions; Traveling Exhibitions.**

Michele di Ridolfo del Ghirlandaio, *Madonna and Child with Saint John the Baptist*, c. 1560, oil on canvas. Gift of Julie Shaw, McMullen Museum of Art. Photograph courtesy of McMullen Museum of Art, Boston College, Chestnut Hill, Massachusetts.

Publications: exhibition catalogues (3/year); newsletter, "Friends Newsletter" (3/year).

Boston College - Charles and Isabela V. McMullen Museum of Art, cont.

Occupying two floors of Devlin Hall, the Museum presents a notable permanent collection and temporary exhibitions from around the world. The permanent collection is displayed on a rotating basis in the Museum's ground floor galleries, while most temporary or traveling exhibitions are displayed in the special exhibition space on the first floor, and smaller thematic exhibitions are mounted in a gallery on the ground level. Begun in the 19th century, the University's permanent collection contains works that span the history of art from Europe, Asia and the Americas. Outstanding among them are Gothic and Baroque tapestries, Italian paintings of the 16th and 17th centuries, American landscape paintings of the 19th and early 20th centuries, and Japanese prints. For visitors who wish to find out more about the collection, the Museum provides the Micro Gallery, an interactive computer displaying information and images on works in the permanent collection, as well as photographs of related works.

Medford

Tufts University Gallery Ⓒᴬ

Tufts University, Aidekman Arts Center, Talbot Ave., Medford, MA   02155
Tel: (617) 627-3518   *Fax:* (617) 627-3121
Internet Address: http://www.tufts.edu
Gallery Director: Ms. Susan Masuoka
Admission: free.
Attendance: 16,000   *Established:* 1955   *ADA Compliant:* Y
Parking: free in front of the Arts Center.
Open: **September to mid-May**, Wednesday to Saturday, noon-8pm; Sunday, noon-5pm.
Closed: Thanksgiving Holiday, Between Semesters.
Facilities: **Exhibition Area** (5,700 square feet); **Sculpture Court.**
Activities: **Lectures**; **Temporary Exhibitions**; **Traveling Exhibitions**.
Publications: exhibition catalogues.

Located in the Aidekman Arts Center, the art gallery and sculpture court house permanently installed sculpture as well as rotating shows, including graduate students' work and professional shows, throughout the year.

North Dartmouth

University of Massachusetts Dartmouth - University Art Gallery Ⓒᴬ

University of Massachusetts Dartmouth, 285 Old Westport Road, North Dartmouth, MA   02747
Tel: (508) 999-8555   *Fax:* (508) 999-8901
Internet Address: http://www.umassd.edu
Director: Mr. Lasse B. Antonsen
Admission: free.
Established: 1987   *ADA Compliant:* Y
Open: **September to May**, Monday to Saturday, 1pm-5pm.
Facilities: **Auditorium** (350 seats); **Exhibition Area** (2,600 square feet).
Activities: **Art Auction** (annual); **Arts Festival**; **Concerts**; **Education Programs** (undergraduate and graduate college students); **Films**; **Guided Tours**; **Lectures**; **Traveling Exhibitions**.

UMass Dartmouth is home to several gallery spaces on both the main and the auxiliary campus that feature student and professional works throughout the year. The main gallery features exhibits of national and international artists and also exhibits student work in a juried show and a senior show.

Northampton

Smith College Museum of Art Ⓒᴬ

Elm St. at Bedford Terrace, Northampton, MA   01063
Tel: (413) 585-2760   *Fax:* (413) 585-2782   *TDDY:* (413) 585-2786
Internet Address: http://www.smith.edu/artmuseum
Director: Ms. Suzannah Fabing

Smith College Museum of Art, cont.

Admission: voluntary contribution.

Attendance: 32,000   *Established:* 1920   *Membership:* Y   *ADA Compliant:* Y

Open: The Museum is currently entirely closed. It is scheduled to reopen in the fall of 2002.

Facilities: **Galleries**; **Print Study Room** (Sept-May, Tues-Fri, 1pm-4pm); **Shop**.

Activities: **Concerts**; **Education Programs** (undergraduate and graduate college students); **Films**; **Gallery Talks**; **Guided Tours**; **Lectures**; **Temporary Exhibitions**; **Traveling Exhibitions**.

Publications: collection catalogue, "A Guide to the Collections"; exhibition catalogues.

The Smith College Museum of Art has a permanent collection numbering approximately 24,000 objects from a variety of cultures ranging in date from 2500 B.C. to the present. The primary emphasis of the collection, however, is on artists of Europe and America since the French Revolution. The scope of its collection is such that it frequently lends works for exhibitions in major museums. The Museum also has an active exhibition program of works of international importance, both contemporary and historical. American painting at Smith includes works by Copley, Eakins, the Hudson River School, Bierstadt, Sargent, Homer, Whistler, Sheeler, Stella, Motherwell, and Rothko. The print collection contains works by Dürer, Piranesi, Delacroix, Goya, Daumier, Munch, Picasso, Matisse, Hiroshige, and Hokusai. Drawings include examples by numerous Old Masters, as well as Matisse, Cézanne, Prendergast, Audubon, Seurat, Mondrian, and Klee. The Museum's holdings in photography span the history of the medium, from works by Fox and Muybridge to examples by Mapplethorpe. There are also smaller collections of ancient, Asian, African, Oceanic, and Native American art.

Norton

Wheaton College - Watson Gallery ⓒ

Wheaton College, E. Main St., Norton, MA   02766

Tel: (508) 286-3578

Fax: (508) 286-3565

Internet Address: http://www.wheatonma.edu

Director: Ms. Ann H. Murray

Admission: free.

Attendance: 4,500   *Established:* 1960

Membership: Y   *ADA Compliant:* Y

Parking: lot across street.

Open: **Fall to Spring**,
        Monday to Saturday, 12:30pm-4:30pm.

Closed: Spring Break, Summer, Columbus Day Weekend,
        Thanksgiving Break, Christmas Break,
        Academic Holidays.

Facilities: **Exhibition Area** (1,568 square feet).

Activities: **Temporary Exhibitions**.

Publications: exhibition catalogues (semi-annual).

Works from permanent collection, Watson Gallery. Photograph by Jonathan Hoover, courtesy of Watson Gallery, Wheaton College, Norton, Massachusetts.

The Watson Gallery features contemporary art in all media and presents thematic exhibitions based on works from the permanent collection, or borrowed from other institutions and private collections. The holdings of the Gallery range from antiquities to contemporary art, emphasizing prints (16th- to 20th-century); drawings (16th- to 20th-century); paintings (19th- and 20th-century); decorative arts; textiles; Native American baskets; and sculpture (antiquities, 19th- and 20th- centuries).

Paxton

Anna Maria College - The St. Luke's Gallery, Moll Art Center

50 Sunset Lane, Paxton, MA   01612-1198

Tel: (508) 849-3300   *Ext:* 442

Internet Address: http://www.annamaria.edu

Gallery Director: Ms. Elizabeth Killoran

Anna Maria College - The St. Luke's Gallery, Moll Art Center, cont.

Admission: free.

Attendance: 600   *Established:* 1972   *Membership:* N   *ADA Compliant:* Y

Parking: free on site.

Open: **September to June**,
         Monday to Wednesday, 9am-4pm.;
         Thursday, 9am-7pm;
         Friday, 9am-4pm
         Sunday, 2pm-4pm.

Closed: Legal Holidays.

Facilities: **Classrooms**; **Exhibition Area** (2,468 square feet); **Lecture Hall**; **Rental Gallery**; **Studios**.

Activities: **Education Programs** (college students); **Student Exhibits**; **Temporary Exhibitions** (local and regional artists).

The Gallery offers changing exhibits of original art in all media by local and regional artists.

Annie Sullivan, *Moon Boy Dream*, Work displayed in temporary exhibition at St. Luke's Gallery, September, 1997. Photograph courtesy of Moll Art Center, Anna Maria College, Paxton, Massachusetts.

Salem

Salem State College - Winfisky Gallery ⓒ

Ellison Campus Center, North Campus, Salem, MA 01970

Tel: (978) 542-6440

Internet Address: http://www.salem.mas.edu/ccpa/artsview_winfisky.htm

Admission: free.

Open: Monday to Friday, 10am-6pm; Saturday to Sunday, by appointment.

Facilities: **Exhibition Area**.

Activities: **Lecture Series**; **Temporary Exhibitions**.

Located in the lobby of the Ellison Campus Center, the Gallery presents a series of art exhibitions by regionally and nationally recognized artists and the annual Student Awards and Student Honors Exhibitions. The Department also hosts an artists lecture series based on topics of current interest.

South Hadley

Mount Holyoke College Art Museum ⓒ

Lower Lake Road, South Hadley, MA 01075-1499

Tel: (413) 538-2245   *Fax:* (413) 538-2144

Internet Address:
http://www.mtholyoke.edu/acad/resources/artmuse.shtml

Director: Ms. Marianne Dozema

Admission: voluntary contribution.

Established: 1875   *Membership:* Y

ADA Compliant: Y

Parking: free on site.

Open: Tuesday to Friday, 10am-5pm;
         Saturday to Sunday, 1pm-5pm.

Closed: Legal Holidays, Academic Holidays.

Dancing Ganesha, Indian, 10th century, sandstone. Mount Holyoke College Art Museum purchase, Belle and Hy Baier Fund, 1996. Photograph courtesy of Mount Holyoke College Art Museum, South Hadley, Massachusetts.

Mount Holyoke College Art Museum, cont.

Facilities: **Galleries**; **Library** (20,000 volumes); **Sculpture Garden**; **Shop**.

Activities: **Concerts**; **Education Programs**; **Films**; **Gallery Talks**; **Guided Tours**; **Lectures**; **Permanent Exhibitions**; **Temporary Exhibitions**; **Traveling Exhibitions**.

Publications: exhibition catalogues; newsletter; semester calendar.

The Mount Holyoke College Art Museum, one of the oldest collegiate art museums in the country, maintains a comprehensive collection of approximately 13,000 objects that range from pre-dynastic Egyptian artifacts to contemporary paintings, sculpture, and works of art on paper. Primary strengths include Asian art, 19th- and 20th-century European and American painting and sculpture, Egyptian, Greek, and Roman art, Medieval sculpture, early Renaissance painting, and an extensive collection of prints, drawings, and photographs. In addition to displaying a portion of its permanent collection, the Museum mounts several loan exhibitions each year.

Waltham

Brandeis University - Rose Art Museum Ⓒ⁴⁴

Brandeis University, 415 South St.
Waltham, MA 02254
Tel: (617) 736-3434
Fax: (617) 736-3439
TDDY: (617) 736-8516
Internet Address: http://www.brandeis.edu/rose
Director: Dr. Carl I. Belz
Admission: voluntary contribution.
Attendance: 7,000   *Established:* 1961
Membership: Y   *ADA Compliant:* Y
Parking: visitor parking on campus.
Open: Tuesday to Wednesday, noon-5pm;
   Thursday, noon-9pm;
   Friday to Sunday, noon-5pm.
Closed: Holidays.
Facilities: **Exhibition Area**.
Activities: **Guided Tours**; **Lectures**; **Permanent Exhibits**; **Temporary Exhibitions**.
Publications: exhibition catalogues; newsletter.

Willem de Kooning, *Untitled*, 1961, oil on canvas, 80 x 78 inches. Gift of Julian J. and Joachim Jean Aberbach, 1964, Rose Art Museum. Photograph courtesy of Rose Art Museum, Brandeis University, Waltham, Massachusetts.

In the field of contemporary American art, the Rose Art Museum's collections, exhibitions, and publications rank it among the most distinguished academic art museums in the United States. The Museum's collection is particularly strong in the field of American art of the 1960's and 1970's and numbers over 8,000 objects, including works by de Kooning, Johns, Lichtenstein, Louis, and Warhol. Recent Museum acquisitions include works by Ferrara, Frankenthaler, Pfaff, Rothenberg, and Serra.

Wellesley

Babson College - Horn Gallery

Horn Library, Room 100, Forest Street, Wellesley, MA 02157
Tel: (781) 239-4570   *Fax:* (781) 239-5226
Internet Address: http://www.babson.edu/archives/index.html
Curator: Ms. Deborah Bates
Open: Monday to Friday, noon-4pm.
Facilities: **Gallery**.
Activities: **Temporary Exhibitions**.

Located off the foyer of Horn Library, the Horn Gallery mounts temporary exhibits of artistic, cultural, or historical interest. At least one exhibit each year is devoted to artwork created by students, faculty, and staff.

Wellesley College - Davis Museum and Cultural Center ⓒᴬᴬ

Wellesley College, 106 Central St., Wellesley, MA   02181-8257

Tel: (617) 283-2051   *Fax:* (617) 283-2064

Internet Address: http://www.wellesleyu.edu/DavisMuseum

Director: Ms. Susan M. Taylor

Admission: free.

Attendance: 30,000   *Established:* 1889   *Membership:* Y   *ADA Compliant:* Y

Open: **August 16 to June 14,**
Tuesday, 11am-5pm; Wednesday to Thursday, 11am-8pm; Friday to Saturday, 11am-5pm Sunday, 1pm-5pm.
   June 15 to August 15,
Tuesday to Saturday, 11am-5pm; Sunday, 1pm-5pm.

Facilities: **Cinema** (167 seats); **Food Services** Collins Café (Mon-Fri, 8:30am-4pm); **Galleries** (17,250 square feet); **Print/Drawing/Photo Study Room**; **Seminar Room**; **Study Gallery**.

Activities: **Education Programs** (undergraduate college students); **Guided Tours** (groups, reserve two weeks in advance); **Lectures**; **Permanent Exhibits**; **Temporary Exhibitions**.

Publications: exhibition catalogues; exhibition handbook.

The permanent collection at the Davis Museum covers the history of art from prehistoric times through the present in Europe, North and South America, Africa, and Asia. Highlights are a small but outstanding African collection, Old Master drawings, modern photographs, and contemporary art. There is a special focus on Western woman artists of all periods. The collection includes works by Degas, Inness, Monet, Cézanne, de Kooning, Leger, Angelica Kaufman, and Sonia Delauney. Also of possible interest are the Jewett Arts Center Gallery, the Jewett Corridor Gallery, and the upstairs Sculpture Court Gallery, three distinct spaces primarily devoted to the exhibition of student work and shows generated by Art Department Students. Exhibitions by professional artists are also presented when the work relates to the educational goals and concerns of the Art Department.

West Barnstable

Cape Cod Community College - The Higgins Art Gallery

2240 Lyanough Road, West Barnstable, MA   02668

Tel: (508) 375-4044

Internet Address: http://www.vsa,cape.com/~neilr/home.htm

Director: Ms. Sara Ringler

Admission: free.

Open: Monday to Tuesday, 10am-4pm; Wednesday, 10am-7pm; Thursday to Friday, 10am-4pm.

Facilities: **Exhibition Area**.

Activities: **Temporary Exhibitions**.

The Higgins Art Gallery present temporary exhibitions.

Weston

Regis College - Carney Gallery

Fine Arts Center, 235 Wellesley St., Weston, MA   02193-1571

Tel: (781) 768-7000

Internet Address: http://www.regiscollege.edu/fac/Gallery.html

Dir, Fine Arts Center & Gallery Curator: Ms. Rosemary Noon

Admission: free.

Established: 1994

Open: Monday to Friday, 1pm-4pm; Saturday to Sunday, by appointment.

Facilities: **Exhibition Area** (1,000 square feet).

Activities: **Temporary Exhibitions**.

The Carney Gallery displays contemporary art in a variety of styles and media, mainly produced by women.

Williamstown

Williams College - Chapin Library of Rare Books ⓒᴬᴬ

Williams College, Stetson Hall, Main Street, Williamstown, MA 01267

Tel: (413) 597-2462

Fax: (413) 597-2929

Internet Address: http://www.williams.edu/library

Custodian: Mr. Robert G. Volz

Admission: free.

Attendance: 2,500   *Established:* 1923

Parking: free on site.

Open: Monday to Friday,
              10am-noon and 1pm-5pm.

Closed: Most Legal Holidays,
              except Independence Day.

Facilities: Exhibition Area.

Activities: **Lectures**; **Permanent Exhibits**; **Temporary Exhibitions**; **Tours** (by appointment).

Exterior view of Stetson Hall (1923), designed by Cram and Ferguson), the site of the Chapin Library of Rare Books. Wood-engraving by John DePol, courtesy of Williams College, Williamstown, Massachusetts.

Publications: collection catalogues (occasional).

The Chapin Library was formed to document civilization through rare books, manuscripts, and other original materials, and thereby to support the liberal arts curriculum of the College. The Library houses some 50,000 volumes as well as 100,000 manuscripts, letters, prints, maps, book-plates, photographs, stereo views, and other ephemera. The collection ranges from the early 9th to the 20th century and covers most of the interests and accomplishments of humanity. Its strengths include literature, Americana, the history of science, Bibles and liturgical books, the age of discovery and exploration in the Western Hemisphere, women's studies, African-American history, and the graphic and performing arts. Though American and British materials predominate, the Library also contains 40 medieval and Renaissance manuscripts, 550 incunabula (15th-century printed books), and 3,500 early continental imprints. Besides its general collections and ancillary reference books, the Chapin Library collects material by and about individual authors and historical figures, including Walt Whitman (1819-1892), Joseph Conrad (1857-1924), E.A. Robinson (1869-1935), Sir Winston Churchill (1874-1965), T.S. Eliot (1888-1965), William Faulkner (1897-1962), illustrator C.B. Falls (1874-1960), and architect and designer Herman Rosse (1887-1965). Three or four exhibitions are mounted from the Library's collections each year, often with a handlist or illustrated catalogue. Library holdings occasionally appear also in exhibitions at the Williams College Museum of Art and the Sterling and Francine Clark Art Institute (see separate entries). On permanent display in the Library's gallery are the Four Founding Documents of the United States - original printings of the Declaration of Independence, the Articles of Confederation, the Constitution, and the Bill of Rights - together with George Washington's autographed copy of the Federalist Papers. Every 4th of July, the Library sponsors an open house for viewing of the Four Founding Documents and readings by actors from the Williamstown Theatre Festival.

Williams College Museum of Art ⓒᴬᴬ

Main St., Williamstown, MA 01267-2566

Tel: (413) 597-2429   *Fax:* (413) 458-9017

Internet Address: http://www.williams.edu/WCMA

Director: Ms. Linda Shearer

Admission: free.

Attendance: 65,000   *Established:* 1926   *Membership:* Y   *ADA Compliant:* Y

Parking: free on site.

Open: Tuesday to Saturday, 10am-5pm; Sunday, 1pm-5pm.

Facilities: **Architecture** (classical octagon bldg., 1846, by Thomas Tefft); **Auditorium**; **Galleries**; **Print Study Room**.

Williams College Museum of Art, cont.

Activities: **Concerts**; **Education Programs** (undergraduate college students); **Gallery Talks**; **Guided Tours** (July-August: Wed & Sun, 2pm); **Lectures**; **Permanent Exhibits**; **Temporary Exhibitions**; **Traveling Exhibitions**.

Publications: exhibition catalogues (2-4/year).

The Williams College Museum of Art houses some 11,000 works that span the history of art. The collection emphasizes modern and contemporary art, American art from the late 18th century to the present, and non-Western art. In addition to displaying works from the permanent collection, the Museum mounts loan exhibitions of works from other collections. The Museum is housed in an 1846 two-story, brick, octagonal, neoclassical structure designed by Thomas Tefft. Extensive additions designed by Charles Moore were completed in the 1980's. The permanent collection consists of art in the following general categories: Ancient and Non-Western (Indian art, including Rajput and Mughal paintings; Chinese painting and calligraphy; and African art and artifacts); European and Medieval (special strengths in Medieval devotional art, Spanish and Northern Baroque painting, and graphic arts from Dürer to Picasso); American (18th- and 19th-century painting, including works by Copley, Eakins, Harnett, Hunt, Inness, Kensett, LaFarge, and West; and late 19th-century and early modern works by artists such as Avery, Burchfield, Demuth, Feininger, Hartley, Homer, Marin, O'Keeffe, Stella, and Wood); and Contemporary (works by de Kooning, Dine, Guston, LeWitt, Nevelson, Rauschenberg, Ringgold, Rivers, and Warhol; photographs by Arbus, Evans, Hine, Ray, Stieglitz, and Weems).

Worcester

Clark University - University Gallery ⓒ₄₄

Goddard Library Plaza, Downing St., Worcester, MA 01610

Tel: (508) 793-7113

Internet Address: http://www.clarku.edu/clarkarts/university-gallery.html

Open: **Academic Year**, Wednesday to Sunday, noon-5pm.

Closed: Academic Holidays.

Facilities: **Gallery**.

Activities: **Temporary Exhibitions** (3-5/year).

The Gallery mounts solo and group shows of nationally recognized, up-and-coming artists. The final show of each year is the Senior Thesis Show, a group exhibition of the best student senior thesis work. Student work is exhibited throughout the academic year in Little Center, the Abrahms Gallery, and in the student pub, Grind Central.

College of the Holy Cross - Iris and B. Gerald Cantor Art Gallery ⓒ₄₄

1 College St., Worcester, MA 01610

Tel: (508) 793-3356   *Fax:* (508) 793-3030

Internet Address: http://webster.holycross.edu/departments/cantor/website

Director: Ms. Ellen Lawrence

Admission: free.

Attendance: 1,000   *Established:* 1971   *ADA Compliant:* Y

Parking: free on site.

Open: Monday to Friday, 11am-4pm; Saturday to Sunday, 2pm-5pm.

Closed: Academic Holidays.

Facilities: **Classrooms**; **Exhibition Area** (2,000 square feet).

Activities: **Education Programs** (college students); **Juried Student Show**; **Temporary Exhibitions** (5-7/year); **Traveling Exhibitions**.

Publications: exhibition catalogues.

The Gallery offers temporary exhibitions of the work of students and professional artists.

Michigan

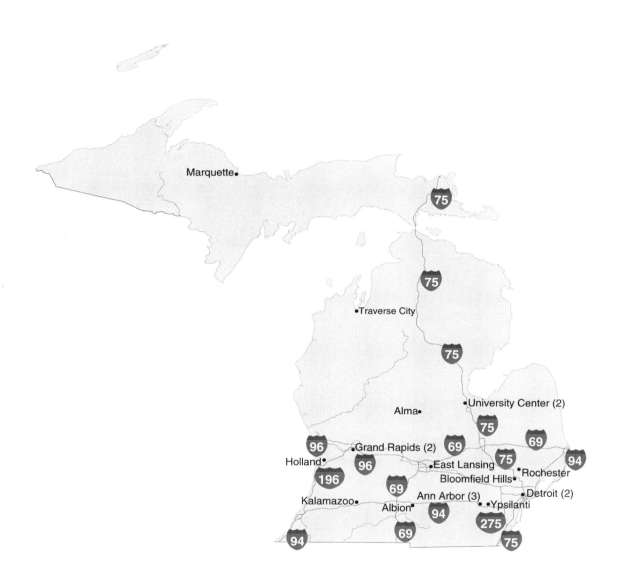

The number in parentheses following the city name indicates the number of museums/galleries in that municipality. If there is no number, one is understood. For example, in the text three listings would be found under Ann Arbor and one listing under Alma.

Michigan

Albion

Albion College Art Collection Ⓒᴬᴬ
Albion College, Dept. of Visual Arts
611 E. Porter, Albion, MI   49224
Tel: (517) 629-1000
Internet Address: http://www.albion.edu
Chairman, Department of Visual Arts: Ms. Lynne Chytilo
Admission: free.
Open: **September to May,**
        Monday to Friday, 9am-4:45pm; Saturday, 10am-4pm; Sunday, 2pm-4pm.
Closed: Academic Holidays, School Vacations.
Facilities: **Exhibition Area**; **Library** (4,500 volumes).
Activities: **Arts Festival**; **Education Programs** (undergraduate college students); **Gallery Talks**; **Guided Tours**; **Lectures**; **Permanent Exhibits**; **Temporary Exhibitions**; **Traveling Exhibitions**.

The Visual Arts Department of the College conducts a continuous exhibition program during the academic year. Art from collectors, artists, and regional museums is exhibited, augmented with selections from the permanent collection and the work of faculty and students. The College has a permanent collection of over 4,000 pieces, over half of which comprise the print collection, which includes works by Dürer, Rembrandt, Brueghel, Goya, Cassatt, Cézanne, Toulouse-Lautrec, Matisse, Chagall, and Picasso, as well as the work of contemporary printmakers. The collection also contains American and European paintings, ancient and modern glass and ceramics, and African and Native American objects.

Alma

Alma College - Flora Kirsch Beck Gallery Ⓒᴬᴬ
614 W. Superior St., Alma, MI   48801
Tel: (517) 463-7220
Internet Address: http://www.alma.edu/ACInfo/GalleryPage/F98Gallery.html
Admission: free.
Open: **Academic Year**, Monday to Friday, 9am-5pm; Saturday, 10am-2pm.
Facilities: **Exhibition Area**.
Activities: **Temporary Exhibitions** (7/year).

The Gallery presents temporary exhibitions of work by regional artists, faculty, and students, including an annual statewide print show, an annual juried student show in the fall term, and annual senior show in the spring.

Ann Arbor

University of Michigan - Kelsey Museum of Archaeology Ⓒᴬᴬ
434 S. State St. (opposite Angell Hall)
Ann Arbor, MI   48109-1390
Tel: (734) 764-9304
Fax: (734) 763-8976
Internet Address: http://www.umich.edu/~kelseydb/Home.html
Director: Ms. Sharon Herbert
Admission: free.
Attendance: 25,000   *Established:* 1928   *Membership:* Y
Open: Tuesday to Friday, 9am-4pm; Saturday to Sunday, 1pm-4pm.
Closed: Academic Holidays.
Facilities: **Galleries**; **Library** (5,000 volumes, by appointment).

University of Michigan - Kelsey Museum of Archaeology, cont.

Activities: **Gallery Talks**; **Guided Tours** (groups, reserve in advance, 647-0442); **Lectures**; **Permanent Exhibits**; **Temporary Exhibitions**.

Publications: "Kelsey Museum Studies"; bulletin, "Bulletin of the Museums of Art and Archaeology"; exhibition catalogues; gallery guide.

The Museum displays artifacts from its holdings of Near Eastern and classical Greek and Roman objects in its permanent galleries, supplemented by temporary thematic exhibitions.

The University of Michigan Museum of Art (C44)

Pablo Picasso, *Two Girls Reading*, 1934, Collection of and photograph courtesy of University of Michigan Museum of Art, Ann Arbor, Michigan.

525 S. State St.
Ann Arbor, MI 48109-1354
Tel: (734) 764-0395
Fax: (734) 764-3731
Internet Address: http://www.umich.edu/~umma
Interim Director: Ms. Carole McNamara
Admission: voluntary contribution.
Attendance: 80,000   *Established:* 1946
Membership: Y   *ADA Compliant:* Y
Parking: metered on street and nearby commercial lots.
Open: **June to August**,
      Tuesday to Wednesday, 11am-5pm;
      Thursday, 11am-9pm;
      Friday to Saturday, 11am-5pm;
      Sunday, noon-5pm.
    September to May,
      Tuesday to Wednesday, 10am-5pm;
      Thursday, 10am-9pm;
      Friday to Saturday, 10am-5pm;
      Sunday, noon-5pm.
Closed: New Year's Day, Independence Day, Thanksgiving Day, Christmas Day.

Facilities: **Architecture** (neo-classical Alumni Memorial Hall, 1910); **Galleries**; **Shop**.

Activities: **Education Programs** (adults and children); **Gallery Talks**; **Guided Tours** (call for group reservations); **Lectures**; **Temporary Exhibitions**; **Traveling Exhibitions**.

Publications: bulletin, "Bulletin, Museums of Art and Archaeology"; exhibition catalogues.

The University of Michigan Museum of Art houses the second-largest art collection in the state of Michigan. A community museum in an academic setting, the Museum offers a diverse permanent collection supplemented by a series of special exhibitions and a broad range of interpretive programs. The Museum maintains a collection of nearly 17,000 paintings, sculptures, prints, drawings, photographs, ceramics, and mixed-media works from around the world. From Italian Renaissance panel paintings and Han Dynasty tomb figures to 18th-century textiles and contemporary photography, the Museum is notable for both its range and its quality. Areas of particular strength include old master and contemporary works on paper (including 150 prints and drawings by James McNeill Whistler), 20th-century sculpture, Chinese ceramics and painting, and the art of central Africa.

University of Michigan School of Art and Design - Jean Paul Slusser Gallery (C44)

Art and Architecture Building, 2000 Bonisteel Blvd.
Ann Arbor, MI 48109-2069
Tel: (313) 936-2082
Fax: (313) 936-0469
Internet Address: http://www.umich.edu/~webteam/soad/
Director: Mr. Jon Rush
Admission: voluntary contribution.
Attendance: 15,000   *Membership:* Y   *ADA Compliant:* Y
Open: **Fall to Spring**, Daily, 11am-4pm.

Univ. of Michigan School of Art and Design - Jean Paul Slusser Gallery, cont.

Facilities: **Auditorium** (180 seats); **Classrooms**; **Gallery**; **Library**.

Activities: **Gallery Talks**; **Lectures**; **Temporary Exhibitions**.

Publications: exhibit brochure, "This Month in the School of Art and Design".

Located on the east side of the Art and Architecture Building on the North Campus, the Gallery provides an opportunity for students and faculty to exhibit their work to the public at large. The School also brings in the work of well-known visiting artists. The adjacent plaza often contains sculpture.

Bloomfield Hills

Cranbrook Academy of Art - Cranbrook Art Museum ⓒᴬᴬ

1221 N. Woodward Ave.

Bloomfield Hills, MI   48303-0801

Tel: (248) 645-3323   *Fax:* (248) 645-3324

Internet Address: http://www.cranbrook.edu/museum

Director: Mr. Gregory M. Wittkopp

Admission: museum fee: adult-$5.00, child-$3.00, student-$3.00, senior-$3.00.

Attendance: 30,000   *Established:* 1927   *Membership:* Y   *ADA Compliant:* Y

Parking: free on site.

Open: Tuesday to Wednesday, 11am-5pm; Thursday, 11am-9pm; Friday to Sunday, 11am-5pm.

Closed: Major Holidays.

Facilities: **Architecture** (home & studio of Eliel and Loja Saarinen, 1930); **Auditorium** (205 seats); **Exhibition Area** (16,000 square feet); **Sculpture Garden**; **Shop**.

Activities: **Films**; **Gallery Talks**; **Guided Tours**; **Lectures**; **Permanent Exhibits**; **Temporary Exhibitions** (of contemporary art); **Traveling Exhibitions**.

Publications: "Saarinen House & Garden: A Total Work of Art"; exhibition catalogues; newsletter, "What's Next" (5/yr).

Located at the heart of the Cranbrook Educational Community, the Museum examines Cranbrook's influence on 20th-century art through its permanent collection and tours of the campus, as well as mounting changing exhibitions of work by contemporary artists and Academy students. The permanent collection of the Museum highlights the history of Cranbrook, beginning with the Arts and Crafts Movement, and continuing with Art Deco and Modernism. The Museum features the work of Charles and Ray Eames; Duane Hanson; Eliel, Loja, and Eero Saarinen: Harry Bertoia: and Maija Grotell. In addition, there is outdoor sculpture by Carl Milles, Marshall Fredericks, Mark di Suvero, Juhani Pallasmaa, and Richard Nonas. The Cranbrook campus includes the Saarinen House (1930), designed by Eliel Saarinen and which served as his home and studio; Cranbrook House (1908), designed by Albert Kahn; and the Arts and Crafts-style home of George and Ellen Booth, the founders of Cranbrook and the Cranbrook Art Museum.

Detroit

Center for Creative Studies/College of Art and Design - Center Galleries

301 Frederick Douglass, Detroit, MI   48202

Tel: (313) 664-7800

Fax: (313) 664-7880

Internet Address: http://www.cc.scad.edu

Director: Ms. Michelle M. Spivak

Admission: free.

Attendance: 10,000   *Established:* 1989   *Membership:* Y   *ADA Compliant:* Y

Parking: parking lot.

Open: **September to July**, Tuesday to Saturday, 10am-5pm.

Closed: Independence Day, Thanksgiving Day, Christmas Day.

Facilities: **Exhibition Area** (4,000 square feet).

Activities: **Guided Tours**; **Lectures**; **Temporary Exhibitions**; **Traveling Exhibitions**.

Publications: exhibiting artist brochures.

Detroit, Michigan

Center for Creative Studies/College of Art and Design - Center Galleries, cont.

CCS' Center Galleries present contemporary visual, literary, and performance art from locally, nationally, and internationally recognized artists, faculty, alumni, and students. Included under the Center Galleries umbrella is the student-run U245 Gallery and Alumni/Faculty Hall, a space for regular exhibitions of alumni and faculty work.

Wayne State University Community Arts Gallery and Elaine L. Jacob Gallery ⓒ⁴⁴

150 Community Arts Building, Department of Art, Detroit, MI   48202

Tel: (313) 577-2423   *Fax:* (313) 577-3491

Internet Address: http://www.comm.wayne.edu/cfpca/spaces.html

Director: Ms. Sandra Ann Dupret

Admission: free.

Attendance: 15,000   *Established:* 1997   *ADA Compliant:* Y

Parking: pay on site.

Open: Tuesday to Friday, 10:30am-7pm; Saturday, 11am-5pm.

Facilities: **Auditorium**; **Exhibition Areas** (2 separate galleries).

Activities: **Concerts**; **Education Programs** (adults and students); **Lectures**; **Monthly Exhibitions**.

Publications: calendar (annual); exhibition catalogues.

The Galleries present temporary exhibitions of the work of students, faculty and professional artists, as well as traveling exhibitions.

East Lansing

Michigan State University - Kresge Art Museum ⓒ⁴⁴

Farm Lane and Dormitory Road

East Lansing, MI   48824-1119

Tel: (517) 353-9834

Fax: (517) 355-6577

Internet Address: http://www.msu.edu/unit/kamuseum

Director: Dr. Susan J. Bandes

Admission: voluntary contribution.

Attendance: 27,500   *Established:* 1959

Membership: Y   *ADA Compliant:* Y

Parking: pay on site.

Open: **mid-September to mid-May**,
          Monday to Wednesday, 9:30am-4:30pm;
          Thursday, noon-8pm;
          Friday, 9:30am-4:30pm;
          Saturday to Sunday, 1pm-4pm.

          Summer,
          Monday to Friday, 11am-4pm;
          Saturday to Sunday, 1pm-4pm.

Closed: Holiday Weekends, August, late Dec. to early Jan..

Facilities: **Galleries**; **Sculpture Garden**; **Shop**.

Activities: **Films**; **Gallery Talks**; **Guided Tours**; **Lectures**; **Permanent Exhibits**; **Temporary Exhibitions**.

Head of a Bull, Roman, second century A.D., marble. Kresge Art Museum. Photograph courtesy of Kresge Art Museum, Michigan State University, East Lansing Michigan.

Publications: bulletin, "Kresge Art Museum Bulletin"; exhibition catalogues; newsletter.

Kresge Art Museum houses Michigan State University's permanent collection of over 5,500 works of art. The collection includes representative examples of art produced over 5,000 years of human history, from ancient Cycladic figures to contemporary mixed-media installations. Greek, Roman, and Egyptian artifacts; medieval and Renaissance illuminations; and European paintings, prints, and sculptures document the intellectual and artistic development of Western civilization. Art and artifacts from African, Asian, Islamic, and pre-Columbian cultures offer insight into non-Western history, belief, and artistic traditions.

196

Grand Rapids

Calvin College - Center Art Gallery ⓒᴬᴬ

Calvin College, 3201 Burton St., S.E.
Grand Rapids, MI   49546-4388
Tel: (616) 957-6326
Fax: (616) 957-8551
Internet Address: http://www.calvin.edu
Director of Exhibitions: Ms. Virginia Bullock
Admission: free.
Attendance: 12,000   *Established:* 1974   *Membership:* N   *ADA Compliant:* Y
Parking: lot adjacent to site.
Open: Monday to Thursday, 9am-9pm; Friday, 9am-5pm; Saturday, noon-4pm.
Closed: School Vacations.
Facilities: **Auditorium** (350 seats); **Classrooms; Gallery; Library; Theatre.**
Activities: **Films; Guided Tours; Lectures; Permanent Exhibits; Temporary Exhibitions; Traveling Exhibitions.**
Publications: exhibition catalogues.

The Calvin College Center Art Gallery, located in the William Spoelhof College Center, installs an average of ten exhibitions per year. Juried selections, traveling shows, and invitationals of varied media are presented, along with works from the College's permanent collection.

Kendall College of Art and Design - Kendall Gallery ⓒᴬᴬ

111 N. Division Ave., Grand Rapids, MI   49503
Tel: (616) 451-2787   *Fax:* (616) 831-9689
Internet Address: http://www.kcad.edu/news_eve_pubs/gallery/gallery_2.html
Director of Exhibitions: Mr. Eric Jay Chad
Admission: free.
Open: Monday to Thursday, 9am-9pm; Friday, 9am-5pm; Saturday, 9am-4pm; Sunday, 1pm-5pm.
Facilities: **Exhibition Area.**
Activities: **Temporary Exhibitions.**

The Gallery offers a schedule of temporary exhibitions.

Holland

Hope College - De Pree Art Center and Gallery ⓒᴬᴬ

Hope College
275 Columbia Ave.
Holland, MI   49423
Tel: (616) 395-7000
Fax: (616) 395-7499
Internet Address: http://www.hope.edu
Gallery Director: Dr. John M. Wilson
Admission: free.
Attendance: 20,500   *Established:* 1982
Membership: Y   *ADA Compliant:* Y
Open: **September to April**,
         Monday to Saturday, 10am-5pm;
         Sunday, 1pm-5pm.
         May to August, reduced hours.
         College Breaks, reduced hours.

Exterior view, DePree Art Center Gallery. Photograph courtesy of DePree Art Center Gallery, Hope College, Holland, Michigan.

Closed: New Year's Day, Memorial Day, Thanksgiving Day, Christmas Day.
Facilities: **Auditorium** (100 seat); **Classrooms** (2); **Exhibition Area** (1,300 square feet); **Studios** (7).

Holland, Michigan

Hope College - De Pree Art Center and Gallery, cont.

Activities: **Education Programs** (college students); **Guided Tours**; **Lectures**; **Temporary Exhibitions**; **Traveling Exhibitions**.

The Gallery presents traveling and original exhibitions of fine art in a wide variety of styles, periods, and cultures, both historical and contemporary.

Kalamazoo

Western Michigan University Art Collection and Galleries ⓒᴬᴬ

Department of Art, College of Fine Arts, 1201 Oliver St.
Kalamazoo, MI   49008-5188
Tel: (616) 387-2455   *Fax:* (616) 387-2477
Internet Address: http://www.umich.edu/art/exhibitions/exhibitions/index.html
Chairman, Art Department: Mr. Charles Stroh
Admission: free.
Attendance: 60,000   *Established:* 1975   *Membership:* Y   *ADA Compliant:* Y
Parking: metered.
Open: **September to mid-April**,
              Gallery 2: Monday to Friday, 10am-5pm;
              Student Art Gallery: Monday to Friday, noon-5pm.
Closed: Academic Holidays.
Facilities: **Galleries** (2).
Activities: **Education Programs** (graduate and undergraduate college students); **Temporary/Traveling Exhibitions**.
Publications: exhibition catalogues.

The Department of Art offers opportunities to view exhibitions of work by visiting artists, faculty and students in a number of venues on campus: Gallery II in Sangren Hall; Student Art Gallery in East Hall; the Multi-Media Room in the Dalton Center, and the Sculpture Tour Program, which installs works at sites on campus.

Marquette

Northern Michigan University - University Art Museum ⓒᴬᴬ

1401 Presque Isle Ave., Marquette, MI   49855
Tel: (800) 682-9797
Internet Address: http://www.nmu.edu
Exec. Director: Mr. Wayne Francis
Admission: free.
Established: 1975
Open: Call for hours.
Facilities: **Galleries** (2).
Activities: **Guided Tours**; **Temporary Exhibitions** (15/year); **Visiting Artist Workshops**.

The Museum curates national and regional exhibitions, hosts traveling shows, and exhibits the work of faculty and students. In addition, its permanent collection is occasionally on exhibition.

Rochester

Oakland University - Meadow Brook Art Gallery ⓒᴬᴬ

Oakland University (between Adams and Squirrel Roads), Rochester, MI   48309-4401
Tel: (248) 370-3005   *Fax:* (248) 370-3108
Internet Address: http://www.oakland.edu
Manager: Debra Watson
Admission: voluntary contribution.
Attendance: 35,000   *Established:* 1959
Membership: Y   *ADA Compliant:* Y
Parking: free on site.

Oakland University - Meadow Brook Art Gallery, cont.

Open: Tuesday to Friday, 1pm-5pm;
Saturday to Sunday, 2pm-6:30pm.

Facilities: Concert Hall; Gallery; Outdoor Music Pavilion; Sculpture Garden; Theatre.

Activities: Arts Festival; Education Programs (undergraduate college students); **Gallery Talks; Temporary Exhibitions** (4 major/year).

Publications: exhibition catalogues.

The Gallery presents four exhibitions per year, including one-person and group shows, private collections, and collaborations with the Art and Art History Department. The permanent collection contains over 300 pieces of African art, and examples of Pre-Columbian, Oceanic, and Chinese art. The bulk of the collection consists of 20th-century paintings and prints by artists such as Fernando Botero, Alex Katz, Alexander Calder, and Lyonel Feininger.

Fernando Botero, *The Temptation of Sante Rita*, 1970, oil on canvas; 42 1/2 x 38 inches. Meadow Brook Art Gallery collection. Photograph courtesy of Meadow Brook Art Gallery, Oakland University, Rochester, Minnesota.

Traverse City

Northwestern Michigan College - Dennos Museum Center ⓒ

1701 E. Front St., Traverse City, MI   49686

Tel: (616) 922-1055

Fax: (616) 922-1597

Internet Address: http://dmc.nmc.edu/

Director: Mr. Eugene A. Jenneman

Admission: fee: adult-$2.00, child-$1.00, student-$1.00, senior-$2.00.

Attendance: 65,000   **Established:** 1991

Membership: Y   **ADA Compliant:** Y

Parking: free adjacent to site.

View of gallery, Dennos Museum Center (1991), designed by Robert Holdeman. Photograph by Curtis R. Frook, courtesy of the Dennos Museum Center of Northwestern Michigan College, Traverse City, Michigan.

Open: Monday to Saturday, 10am-5pm; Sunday, 1pm-5pm.

Closed: New Year's Day, Easter, Memorial Day, Independence Day, Labor Day, Thanksgiving Day to Thanksgiving Friday, Christmas Eve to Christmas Day, Good Friday.

Facilities: Discovery Gallery; Exhibition Area (8,000 square feet); **Library** (300 volumes, Inuit art and culture); **Sculpture Garden** (to be opened in 1999 or 2000); **Shop; Theatre** (367 seats).

Activities: Concerts; Dance Recitals; Education Programs (adults and children); **Films; Guided Tours; Lectures; Performances; Temporary Exhibitions; Traveling Exhibitions.**

Publications: newsletter, "Inside" (quarterly).

The Dennos Museum Center features three galleries devoted to changing exhibitions, a sculpture court, and an extensive collection of Inuit Art.

University Center

Delta College - Galleria ⓒ

Central Lobby, Fine Arts Bldg. (S-wing), Hotchkiss & Mackinaw Roads
University Center, MI   48710

Tel: (517) 686-9441

Internet Address: http://www.delta.edu/~humaniti/galleria.htm

Contact: Mr. Randal Crawford

Admission: free.

Delta College - Galleria, cont.

Open: Call for hours.
Facilities: **Exhibition Area**.
Activities: **Temporary Exhibitions**.

The Galleria exhibits works from the college's permanent collection as well as works by professional artists, faculty and students.

Saginaw Valley State University - Marshall M. Fredericks Sculpture Gallery ⓒᴬᴬ

Saginaw Valley State University
Arbury Arts Center, Bay Road
University Center, MI   48710
Tel: (517) 790-5667
Fax: (517) 791-7721
Internet Address: http://www.svsu.edu/mfsg
Director: Dr. Michael W. Panhorst
Admission: free.
Attendance: 10,000   *Established:* 1988
Membership: Y   *ADA Compliant:* Y
Parking: free on site.
Open: Tuesday to Sunday, 1pm-5pm.
Closed: Legal Holidays, Academic Holidays.
Facilities: **Exhibition Area** (8,000 square feet: 200 works of sculpture); **Shop**.
Activities: **Education Programs** (children); **Guided Tours**.

Exterior view of Marshall M. Fredericks Sculpture Gallery, with "Night and Day Fountain" by Fredericks in foreground. Photograph by Gary Bublitz, courtesy of Marshall M. Fredericks Sculpture Gallery, Saginaw Valley State University, University Center, Michigan.

Publications: newsletter, "Friends of the MFSG Newsletter".

The Gallery contains sculptures, models, drawings and paintings by Marshall M. Fredericks (American, b. 1908). There is also an adjacent sculpture garden with additional bronze works by Fredericks.

Ypsilanti

Eastern Michigan University - Ford Gallery ⓒᴬᴬ

Ford Hall, Summit St.
Ypsilanti, MI   48197
Tel: (734) 487-0465
Internet Address: http://www.art.acad.emich.edu/exhibitions/ford/
Gallery Director: Ms. Barbara Miner
Admission: free.
Open: Daily, 9am-5pm.
Facilities: **Exhibition Area**.
Activities: **Temporary Exhibitions**.

The Ford Gallery presents temporary exhibitions including student MFA Thesis Exhibitions. Also of possible interest on campus, the Intermedia Gallery Group mounts exhibitions of student work in McKenny Union.

Minnesota

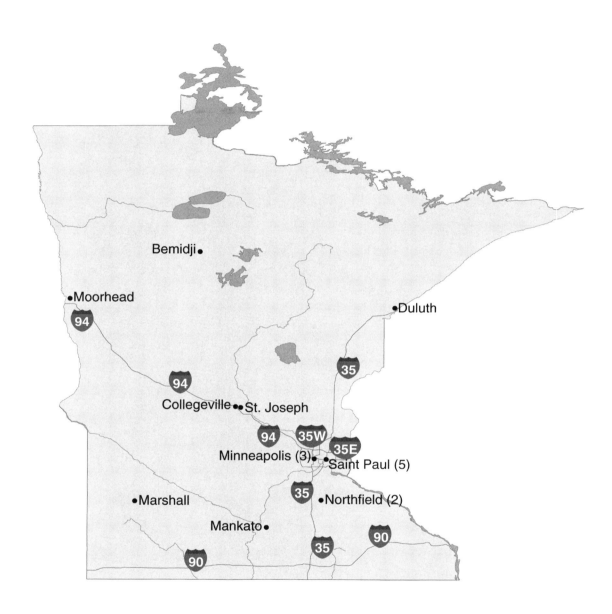

The number in parentheses following the city name indicates the number of museums/galleries in that municipality. If there is no number, one is understood. For example, in the text three listings would be found under Minneapolis and one listing under Bemidji.

Minnesota

Bemidji

Bemidji State University - Talley Gallery ⓒᴬᴬ

Education-Art Building (ground floor), 1500 Birchmont Drive N.E., Bemidji, MN   56601-2699
Tel: (218) 755-3708
Internet Address: http://www.cal.bemidji.msus.edu/VisArts/galleries
Director: Sandy Kaul
Admission: free.
ADA Compliant: Y
Open: **Academic Year**, Monday to Friday, 9:30am-9:30pm; Saturday, 9:30am-6:30pm.
Closed: Holidays, Academic Holidays, Between Exhibitions.
Facilities: **Exhibition Area**.
Activities: **Gallery Talks**; **Temporary Exhibitions**; **Visiting Artist Program**.

The Gallery presents temporary exhibitions of the work of professional artists, faculty and students. Holdings of the Department of Visual Arts include prints (Kleven Collection) and ceramics (Harlow Collection). Another exhibition space presenting temporary shows, Gallery X, is located on the second floor of the Education-Art Building (755-3740). Also of possible interest on campus, the Touché Gallery, located in the Hobson Memorial Union (755-3760), is open Monday to Friday, 8am-4:30pm.

Collegeville

St. John's Abbey and University - Museum at St. John's and Galleries ⓒᴬᴬ

Alice R. Rogers & Dayton Hudson Galleries, University Art Center
Collegeville, MN   56321-2015
Tel: (320) 363-2701   *Fax:* (320) 363-2504
Internet Address: http://www.users.csbsju.edu/~museum
Museum Director: Father Ian Dommer, OSB
Admission: voluntary contribution.
Attendance: 10,000   *Established:* 1996
Parking: free on site.
Open: **Museum**, Call for schedule.
          Galleries: Fall to Spring,
             Monday to Wednesday, 10am-4pm; Thursday, 10am-9pm; Friday to Sunday, 10am-4pm.
          Galleries: Summer,
             Monday to Friday, 9am-5pm; Saturday to Sunday, 10am-5pm.
Facilities: **Architecture** Art Center (designed by Hugh Newell Jacobson).
Activities: **Temporary Exhibitions**.

While St. John's does possess an art collection, it does not have a permanent exhibition facility. The Museum mounts occasional temporary exhibits in various facilities of the University. Two spaces presenting a schedule of temporary exhibitions throughout the school year are located in the University Art Center, the Alice R. Rogers Gallery and the Dayton Hudson Gallery. Saint John's University for men is the brother school of the College of Saint Benedict for women (Saint Joseph, Minnesota); exhibitions are coordinated and many of the student exhibitions include work by art students from both schools.

Duluth

University of Minnesota at Duluth - Tweed Museum of Art ⓒᴬᴬ

University of Minnesota at Duluth, 10 University Drive, Duluth, MN   55812
Tel: (218) 726-8222   *Fax:* (218) 726-8503
Internet Address: http://www.d.umn.edu/tma
Director and Curator: Mr. Martin DeWitt
Admission: suggested contribution: adult-$3.00, child-$1.00, family-$5.00.

University of Minnesota at Duluth - Tweed Museum of Art, cont.

Attendance: 50,000 *Established:* 1950 *Membership:* Y *ADA Compliant:* Y
Parking: free on site.
Open: Tuesday, 9am-8pm; Wednesday to Friday, 9am-4:30pm; Saturday to Sunday, 1pm-5pm.
Closed: Legal Holidays, Academic Holidays.
Facilities: **Galleries (8)**; **Lecture Room**; **Sculpture Conservatory and Courtyard**; **Shop**.
Activities: **Film Series**; **Guided Tours**; **Permanent Exhibits**; **Temporary Exhibitions**; **Traveling Exhibitions**.
Publications: exhibition catalogues; newsletter (quarterly).

The Tweed Museum's permanent collection consists of European paintings; American Impressionism (works by Hassam, Twachtman, Robinson, and Weir); Modernist works by Ajay, Biederman, Crawford, Reise, and Soto; and Contemporary works by Viveka Heino, Jun Kaneko, Lucy Lewis, and Steven Woodward.

Mankato

Mankato State University - Conkling Gallery Ⓒᴬᴬ

Maywood Ave., Mankato, MN 56002-8400
Tel: (507) 389-6412 *Fax:* (507) 389-2816
Internet Address: http://www.mankato.msus.edu/dept/artdept/Gallery/gallery.html
Gallery Coordinator: Mr. Brian Frink
Open: Call for hours.
Facilities: **Exhibition Area.**
Activities: **Temporary Exhibitions.**

The Gallery features temporary exhibitions by artists of both national and regional reputation. In addition to professional exhibitions, the Gallery presents exhibitions of work by graduating seniors and thesis exhibitions by graduate students.

Marshall

Southwest State University - William Whipple Gallery Ⓒᴬᴬ

Library, 1st Floor, Highways 19 and 23, Marshall, MN 56258
Tel: (507) 537-7191 *Fax:* (507) 537-6200
Internet Address: http://www.southwest.msus.edu/AcadSuppServ/whipple
Director: Mr. Edward Evans
Open: Monday to Thursday, 8am-11pm; Friday, 8am-4pm; Saturday, 1pm-5pm; Sunday, 1pm-11pm.
Facilities: **Exhibition Area.**
Activities: **Temporary Exhibitions.**

Located on the first floor of the library, the William Whipple Gallery exhibits the work of students, faculty, and regionally, nationally, and internationally recognized artists.

Minneapolis

Minneapolis College of Art and Design Gallery

2501 Stevens Ave., S., Minneapolis, MN 55404
Tel: (612) 874-3785 *Fax:* (612) 874-3704 *TDDY:* (612) 874-3800
Internet Address: http://www.mcad.edu/
Gallery Director: Mr. Brian Szott
Admission: free.
Established: 1886 *ADA Compliant:* Y
Open: Monday to Friday, 9am-9pm; Saturday, 9am-5pm; Sunday, noon-5pm.
Closed: Legal Holidays.
Facilities: **Exhibition Area.**
Activities: **Concerts**; **Dance Recitals**; **Education Programs** (undergraduate college students); **Films**; **Gallery Talks**; **Lectures**; **Temporary Exhibitions**; **Traveling Exhibitions**.
Publications: exhibition catalogues.

Minneapolis College of Art and Design Gallery, cont.

The Gallery mounts temporary exhibitions of contemporary works by local, regional, and national artists and designers.

University of Minnesota - Frederick R. Weisman Art Museum 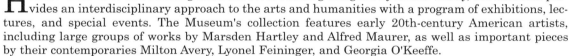 (WAM)

University of Minnesota, 333 E. River Road
Minneapolis, MN 55455
Tel: (612) 625-9494
Fax: (612) 625-9630
Internet Address: http://www.hudson.acad.umm.edu
Director: Lyndel King
Admission: voluntary contribution.
Attendance: 100,000 *Established:* 1934
Membership: Y *ADA Compliant:* Y
Parking: pay on site.
Open: Tuesday to Wednesday, 10am-5pm;
Thursday, 10am-8pm;
Friday, 10am-5pm;
Saturday to Sunday, 11am-5pm.
Closed: Academic Holidays.
Facilities: **Architecture** (1993 designed by Frank Gehry); **Galleries; Shop.**
Activities: **Art Rental; Education Programs** (graduate students); **Gallery Talks; Guided Tours; Lectures; Temporary Exhibitions; Traveling Exhibitions.**
Publications: exhibition catalogues.

Marsden Hartley, *One Portrait of One Woman,* 1916, oil on composition board, 30 x 25 inches. Bequest of Hudson Walker from the Ione and Hudson Walker Collection. Photograph courtesy of Frederick R. Weisman Art Museum, University of Minnesota, Minneapolis, Minnesota.

Housed since 1993 in a striking stainless steel building designed by Frank Gehry, the Museum provides an interdisciplinary approach to the arts and humanities with a program of exhibitions, lectures, and special events. The Museum's collection features early 20th-century American artists, including large groups of works by Marsden Hartley and Alfred Maurer, as well as important pieces by their contemporaries Milton Avery, Lyonel Feininger, and Georgia O'Keeffe.

University of Minnesota - Katherine E. Nash Gallery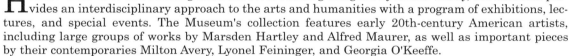

University of Minnesota, Willey Hall, 225 19th Ave., S., Lower Concourse
Minneapolis, MN 55404
Tel: (612) 624-6518
Fax: (612) 625-7881
Internet Address: Http://artdept.umn.edu/nash/genpage.htm
Managing Director: Ms. Tracey Zank
Admission: voluntary contribution.
Attendance: 20,000 *Established:* 1973 *ADA Compliant:* Y
Open: Tuesday, 10am-4pm; Wednesday, 10am-8pm; Thursday to Friday, 10am-4pm;
Saturday, 11am-5pm.
Closed: Academic Holidays, Semester Breaks.
Facilities: **Exhibition Area.**
Activities: **Temporary Exhibitions; Traveling Exhibitions.**

The Gallery presents temporary exhibitions.

Moorhead

Concordia College - Cyrus M. Running Gallery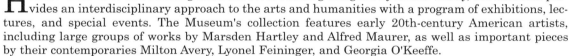

Olin Center, 901 8th St. South, Moorhead, MN 56562
Tel: (218) 294-4000
Internet Address: http://www.cord.edu/dept/art/gallery.html
Director: Ms. Barbara Thill Anderson

Concordia College - Cyrus M. Running Gallery, cont.

Admission: free.
Open: Call for hours.
Facilities: **Exhibition Area** (3,000 square feet, 240 running feet of wall space).
Activities: **Temporary Exhibitions**.

Beginning in the skyway connecting the Olin Center with the Francis Frazier Comstock Theatre building, the Gallery presents a schedule of temporary exhibitions, including annual faculty, senior student, and juried student shows, during the academic year.

Northfield

Carleton College Art Gallery ⓒ

Music and Drama Center, 1st St. and Winona (northeast of Skinner Memorial Chapel)
Northfield, MN   55057
Tel: (507) 646-4469
Internet Address: http://www.carleton.edu/curricular/Art-Gallery_Page.html
Dir., Exhibitions & Curator, Collections: Ms. Laura Bradley
Admission: free.
Open: Daily, noon-5pm; Tuesday to Friday, 7pm-10pm during exhibitions.
Facilities: **Exhibition Area**.
Activities: **Lectures**; **Temporary Exhibitions** (15/year); **Workshops**.

Located downstairs in the Music and Drama Center, the Gallery presents an exhibition program of borrowed works and objects from the Carleton College Art Collection. Totaling more than 800 works, the   College Art Collection features prints ranging from Old Masters and 19th-century European and American etchings and lithographs to contemporary work involving both traditional and more experimental techniques. Its photographic collection focusing on the work of 20th-century practitioners also includes a portrait collection of 20th-century authors. There are relatively few paintings and sculptures in the collection; of note are sculptures by Jacques Lipschitz and Constantin Meunier and canvases by Philip Evergood and Dean Warnholtz, a former faculty member. The most significant holdings in non-Western art are Chinese and Korean art and artifacts drawn from the Watson Collection.

St. Olaf College - Steensland Art Museum ⓒ

St. Olaf College, Northfield, MN   55057
Tel: (507) 646-3556   *Fax:* (507) 646-3776
Internet Address: http://www.stolaf.edu/other/steensland/index.html
Director: Ms. Karen Helland
Admission: voluntary contribution.
Attendance: 8,000   *Established:* 1976
Open: **September to June**, Monday to Wednesday, noon-5pm; Thursday, noon-8pm;
        Friday, noon-5pm; Saturday to Sunday, 2pm-5pm.
Closed: Easter, Thanksgiving Day, Christmas Day.
Facilities: **Exhibition Area** (2,400 square feet).
Activities: **Education Programs** (undergraduate college students); **Lectures**; **Temporary Exhibitions**; **Traveling Exhibitions**.
Publications: exhibition catalogues.

The Steensland Art Museum maintains a permanent collection of approximately 900 works and presents temporary exhibitions of the work of regional artists.

Saint Joseph

College of Saint Benedict - Galleries ⓒ

Benedicta Arts Center, College Ave., Saint Joseph, MN   56374
Tel: (320) 363-5777   *Fax:* (320) 363-6097
Internet Address: http://www.users.csbsju.edu/~bac/art/index.html
Director of Exhibitions: Ms. Lisa Cotton

College of Saint Benedict - Galleries, cont.

Admission: free.

Attendance: 8,125

Parking: parking lots #4 and #5 west and south (respectively) of Benedicta Arts Center.

Open: Monday to Thursday, 8am-4:30pm and 6:30pm-9:30pm; Friday to Saturday, 8am-4:30pm; Sunday, noon-4:30pm and 6:30pm-9:30pm.

Closed: Academic Holidays, Summer.

Facilities: **Exhibition Area** (gallery, 1,545 square feet; gallery lounge 88 running feet).

Activities: **Temporary Exhibitions** (every 6 weeks).

Publications: booklets, "CSB/SJU Fine Arts Programming Exhibtion Series" (annual); exhibition postcard; newsletter, "Fine Arts Programming Newsletter" (3/year).

Located on the southwest corner of the College of St. Benedict campus, the Benedicta Arts Center offers visual arts exhibitions in two spaces. Exhibitions include selections from the college's permanent collection, work by professional artists, and student work, including an annual senior exhibition and juried student exhibition. The College's permanent collection is housed in the Arts Center, but it is not a part of any ongoing exhibition series. A listing of holdings is not available. A joint department, the Director of Exhibitions schedules and oversees exhibitions at both the College of Saint Benedict and Saint John's University (see separate listing under Collegeville, Minnesota).

Saint Paul

Bethel College - Galleries ⓒᴬᴬ

Olson Gallery: Community Life Center. (2nd Floor)
Johnson Gallery: Fine Arts Building (2nd Floor)
Saint Paul, MN   55112

Tel: (651) 638-6263

Internet Address: http://www.bethel.edu/Campus_Activities/gallery.html

Admission: free.

Open: Monday to Saturday, 9am-8pm; Sunday, 11am-6pm.

Facilities: **Galleries** (2).

Activities: **Temporary Exhibitions**; **Visiting Artist Lecture Series**.

The Department of Art maintains two spaces, the Eugene Olson Gallery in the Community Life Center and the Eugene Johnson Gallery of Art in the Fine Arts Building. The Department offers exhibitions in a wide range of media by regionally, nationally, and internationally recognized artists. Student shows include Senior Thesis Exhibitions and the juried Raspberry Monday Exhibition in the spring.

College of St. Catherine - Catherine G. Murphy Gallery ⓒᴬᴬ

The Visual Arts Building, 2004 Randolph Ave., Saint Paul, MN   55105

Tel: (612) 690-6637

Internet Address: http://minerva.stkate.edu/PEC.nsf/$$Home

Director: Ms. Kathleen M. Daniels

Open: call for hours.

Facilities: **Exhibition Area.**

Activities: **Temporary Exhibitions**.

Located in the Visual Arts Building, the Murphy Gallery exhibits works by students, faculty, and local and national artists year-round.

Macalester College Gallery ⓒᴬᴬ

1600 Grand Ave., Saint Paul, MN   55105

Tel: (612) 696-6000   *Fax:* (612) 696-6689

Internet Address: http://www.macalaster.edu

Curator: Mr. Douglas Dagatano

Admission: free.

Established: 1964

Macalester College Gallery, cont.

Open: Call for hours
Closed: Academic Holidays.
Facilities: Exhibition Area (2,500 square feet).

The Gallery displays works from the College's permanent collection and mounts temporary exhibitions of a broad range of contemporary art in all media by artists of regional, national, and international reputation, as well as student and faculty shows.

University of Minnesota - The Goldstein: A Museum of Design ⊚

1985 Buford Ave., 244 McNeal Hall
Dept. of Design, Housing & Apparel
Saint Paul, MN 55108
Tel: (612) 624-7434
Fax: (612) 624-2750
Internet Address:
   http://www.goldstein.che.umn.edu
Director: Dr. Lindsay Shen
Admission: voluntary contribution.
Attendance: 15,000   *Established:* 1976
Membership: Y   *ADA Compliant:* Y
Parking: pay on site.
Open: Monday to Wednesday, 10am-4pm;
         Thursday, 10am-8pm;
         Friday, 10am-4pm;
         Saturday to Sunday, 1:30pm-4:30pm.

Items from collection of Goldstein Gallery. Photograph courtesy of Goldstein Gallery, Saint Paul, Minnesota.

Closed: Holidays.
Facilities: Gallery; Library (1,000 volumes, available to qualified researchers).
Activities: Gallery Talks; Guided Tours; Lectures; Temporary Exhibitions (3-4/year).
Publications: collection catalogue; exhibition catalogues; newsletter (2-3 per yr).

The Goldstein is a museum of design. It mounts three to four exhibitions per year that emphasize art in everyday life. The permanent collection of the Gallery consists of historic and designer costumes, textiles, decorative arts, and interior design archives.

University of St. Thomas - Art Space Gallery

Brady Educational Center, 2115 Summit Ave., Saint Paul, MN 55105
Tel: (612) 962-5877   *Fax:* (612) 962-5640
Internet Address: http://www.stthomas.edu/www/arthist_http/spec.html
Curator, Permanet Collections: Ms. Shelley Nordtorp-Madison
Open: Call for hours.
Facilities: Exhibition Area.
Activities: Temporary Exhibitions.

The Gallery mounts exhibitions of visual material whose content "explains and/or interprets a concept, a culture, a place, an historical or contemporary style, or the oeuvre/work from a limited period of a particular person or group." Also of possible interest on campus are exhibitions in the O'Shaughnessy-Frey Library Center and the Sculpture Garden at the Frey Science and Engineering Center. Additionally, the University mounts exhibitions on its Minneapolis campus (see separate listing under Minneapolis, Minnesota).

Mississippi

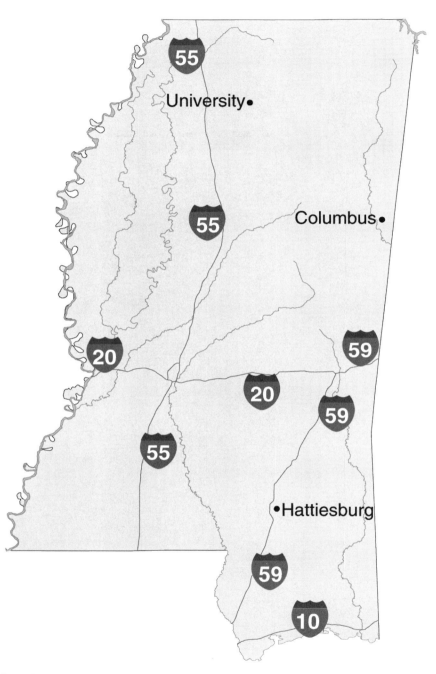

A number in parentheses following a city name indicates the number of museums/galleries in that municipality. If there is no number, one is understood. For example, in the text one listing would be found under each Mississippi city shown on map.

Mississippi

Columbus

Mississippi University for Women - Art Gallery ⓒᴬᴬ

Fine Arts Building, 1200 College St., Columbus, MS 39701
Tel: (662) 329-7341
Fax: (601) 241-7815
Internet Address: http://www.muw.edu/fine_arts/ArtEven.html
Director: Mr. Lawrence L. Feeney
Admission: free.
Attendance: 2,700   *Established:* 1960   *Membership:* N   *ADA Compliant:* Y
Parking: free on site - south side of building.
Open: Monday to Friday, 9am-noon and 1pm-4:30pm.
Closed: Academic Holidays.
Facilities: **Exhibition Area** (three galleries).
Activities: **Temporary Exhibitions**.

There are three exhibition areas in the Fine Arts Gallery, totaling almost 350 running feet of wall space. The Gallery mounts two major exhibitions each year, as well as additional shows of student art, work of visiting artists, and art having a connection to the curriculum. The permanent collection has a number of WPA prints, other twentieth-century prints, and work by Mississippi artists.

Interior view of Main South Gallery, Mississippi University for Women. Photograph courtesy of Mississippi University for Women, Columbus, Mississippi.

Hattiesburg

University of Southern Mississippi - USM Museum of Art ⓒᴬᴬ

2701 Hardy St., Hattiesburg, MS 39401
Tel: (601) 266-4972
Internet Address: http://www.arts.usm.edu/museum
Admission: free.
Open: Weekdays, 8am-5pm.
Facilities: **Exhibition Area**.
Activities: **Temporary Exhibitions**.

The Museum presents exhibits of national shows, in addition to solo and group exhibitions by professional and student artists. Selected works from the Art Department's permanent collection are always on display. Additional exhibits are on view in the Walter Lok Exhibition Lobby. Sculpture is also placed in numerous exterior sites around the campus. The Art Department's holdings consist primarily of prints, including works by Dürer, Rembrandt, and Whistler.

University

The University of Mississippi - University Museums ⓒᴬᴬ

The University of Mississippi, University Ave., University, MS 38677
Tel: (601) 232-7073
Fax: (601) 232-7010
Internet Address: http://www.olemiss.edu/depts/u-museum
Director: Ms. Bonnie J. Krause
Admission: voluntary contribution.
Attendance: 11,000   *Established:* 1977   *Membership:* Y   *ADA Compliant:* Y
Parking: free on site.

The University of Mississippi - University Museums, cont.

Open: Tuesday to Saturday, 10am-4:30pm; Sunday, 1pm-4pm.

Closed: Legal Holidays, Academic Holidays.

Facilities: Classrooms; Exhibition Areas (8); **Library** (1,500 volumes, on premises only).

Activities: Education Programs (children); **Guided Tours; Lectures; Permanent Exhibits; Temporary Exhibitions** (4 per year); **Traveling Exhibitions.**

Publications: brochures; exhibition catalogues; newsletter (quarterly).

The University Museums consist of the Mary Buie Museum and the adjoining Kate Skipwith Teaching Museum. The Museums display an important collection of Greek and Roman antiquities, and a large group of paintings by the Oxford folk artist Theora Hamblett, as well as works by other Southern folk artists, World War I posters, and small collections of African and Asian art. The Museums also mount eight to ten temporary exhibitions per year.

Volute Krater, Heroon with Youth and Old Man, Greek, c. 330-320 B.C. David M. Robinson Collection, University Museums. Photograph courtesy of University Museums, University, Mississippi.

Missouri

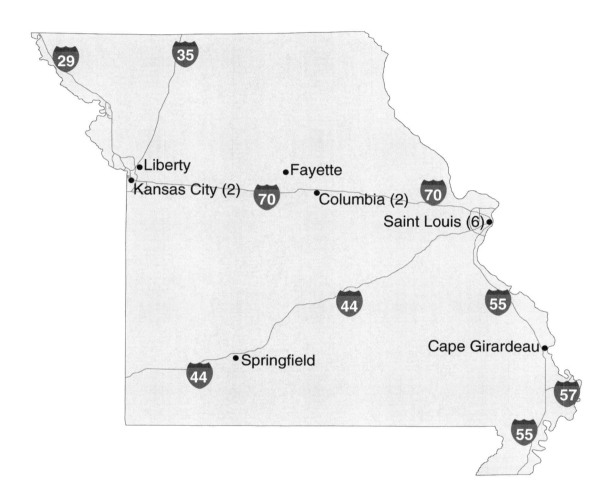

The number in parentheses following the city name indicates the number of museums/galleries in that municipality. If there is no number, one is understood. For example, in the text five listings would be found under Saint Louis and one listing under Springfield.

Missouri

Cape Girardeau

Southeast Missouri State University Museum

Southeast Missouri State University, 1 University Plaza, MS 4275
Cape Girardeau, MO   63701
Tel: (571) 651-2260   *Fax:* (571) 651-5103
Internet Address: http://www.semo.edu
Director: Ms. Jenny Strayer
Admission: free.
Attendance: 18,000   *Established:* 1976   *Membership:* Y   *ADA Compliant:* Y
Open: Monday to Friday, 9am-4pm.
Closed: Legal Holidays.
Facilities: **Exhibition Area**.
Activities: **Lectures**.
Publications: exhibition brochures.

The Museum holds collections of fine art, regional and American military history, and Mississippian archaeology. A gallery features monthly changing exhibits of art including the Annual Juried Student Assessment Exhibition.

Columbia

Stephens College - Davis Art Gallery ⒸⒶⒶ

Stephens College, 1220 East Broadway, Columbia, MO   65215
Tel: (573) 876-7173
Internet Address: http://www.stephens.edu
Director: Ms. Rosalind Kimball-Moulton
Admission: voluntary contribution.
Attendance: 500   *Established:* 1962   *ADA Compliant:* Y
Open: Monday to Friday, 10am-4pm.
Closed: Academic Holidays.
Facilities: **Gallery**.
Activities: **Temporary Exhibitions**.

The Gallery offers monthly exhibitions of work by professional artists, faculty and students.

University of Missouri-Columbia - Museum of Art and Archaeology ⒸⒶⒶ

Pickard Hall, Francis Quadrangle
(corner of University Ave. and 9th St.)
Columbia, MO   65211
Tel: (573) 882-3591   *Fax:* (573) 884-4039
Internet Address:
   http://www.research.missouri.edu/museum/index.htm
Director: Ms. Marlene Perchinske
Admission: voluntary contribution.
Attendance: 32,000   *Established:* 1957
Membership: Y   *ADA Compliant:* Y
Parking: visitors garage on University Ave. and 9th St.
Open: Tuesday to Wednesday, 9am-5pm;
           Thursday, 9am-5pm and 6pm-9pm;
           Friday, 9am-5pm;
           Saturday to Sunday, noon-5pm.

Unknown, *Durga on a Lion*, 17th century, cast bronze, Himachel Pradesh, India. Museum of Art and Archaeology. Gift of Dr. and Mrs. Samuel Eilenberg. Photograph courtesy of Museum of Art and Archaeology, University of Missouri-Columbia, Columbia, Missouri.

Columbia, Missouri

University of Missouri-Columbia - Museum of Art and Archaeology, cont.

Closed: Legal Holidays, Christmas Day to New Year's Day.

Facilities: **Galleries**; **Lecture Hall** (116 seats); **Library** (6,000 volumes); **Shop**.

Activities: **Education Programs** (undergraduate and graduate students); **Gallery Talks** (including "Midday Gallery Events", Wed, 12:15pm); **Guided Tours**; **Lectures**; **Permanent Exhibitions**; **Temporary Exhibitions**.

Publications: "Handbook of the Collections"; bulletin, "Muse, Annual of the Museum of Art and Archaeology" (annual); collection catalogue; exhibition catalogues; newsletter, "The News" (3/year).

Museum galleries house art and artifacts from six continents and five millennia. Special exhibitions, lectures, seminars, gallery talks, and educational programs associated with permanent and loan exhibitions provide a wide range of activities. Museum holdings include more than 13,000 objects from a wide variety of civilizations and cultures and spanning all periods from the Paleolithic to the present. Strengths include classical antiquities and Western art from the early Renaissance to contemporary. The cast gallery has casts of classical Greek and Roman sculpture. Also of possible interest is the George Caleb Bingham Gallery, located in the Fine Arts Building, which presents temporary exhibitions of work by professional artists, faculty, and students (573) 882-3555.

Fayette

Central Methodist College - Ashby-Hodge Gallery of American Art

Central Methodist College
411 Central Methodist Square
Fayette, MO 65248
Tel: (816) 248-3391   *Ext:* 563
Fax: (816) 248-2622
Internet Address: http://cmc2.cmc.edu/gal.html
Curator: Mr. Thomas Yancey
Admission: free.
Parking: free on site.
Open: Tuesday to Thursday, 1:30pm-4:30pm.
    For special exhibits, Sunday, 2:30pm-5pm.
Facilities: **Exhibition Area**.

The Ashby-Hodge Gallery of American Art is located on the campus of Central Methodist College, which has been designated a National Historic District. The Gallery presents temporary exhibitions, but its principle focus is its permanent collection of oil paintings, watercolors,, lithographs, bronzes, drawings, and acrylics by prominent American Regional artists, such as Thomas Hart Benton (and at least six of his followers), Emile Gruppe, and Birger Sandzen.

Charles Banks Wilson, *As Long As There Are Horses*, 1959, egg tempera on panel, 27 x 30 inches. Collection of and photograph courtesy of Ashby-Hodge Gallery of American Art, Fayette, Missouri.

Kansas City

Avila College - Thornhill Gallery

11901 Wornall Road, Kansas City, MO 64145
Tel: (816) 942-8400 *Ext:* 2259
Fax: (816) 942-3362
Internet Address: http://www.avila.edu
Director: Mr. George Christman
Admission: free.
Attendance: 2,000   *ADA Compliant:* Y
Open: Monday to Friday, 10am-noon and 1pm-5pm.
Closed: New Year's Day, Easter, Memorial Day, Thanksgiving Day, Christmas Day.
Facilities: **Exhibition Area** (850 square feet).
Activities: **Temporary/Traveling Exhibitions**.

Avila College - Thornhill Gallery, cont.

Publications: annual calendar.

The Gallery presents temporary exhibitions.

University of Missouri-Kansas City - Gallery of Art (CAA)

204 Fine Arts, 5100 Rockhill Road, Kansas City, MO   64110-2499

Tel: (816) 235-1502

Fax: (816) 235-5507

Internet Address: http://www.cctr.umkc.edu/gallery/index.html

Director: Mr. Craig A. Subler

Admission: free.

Attendance: 10,000   *Established:* 1975   *Membership:* Y   *ADA Compliant:* Y

Parking: metered parking adjacent to site.

Open: **September to April**, Tuesday to Friday, noon-5pm; Saturday to Sunday, 1pm-5pm.
   May to August, Tuesday to Friday, noon-5pm.

Closed: ML King Day, Memorial Day, Independence Day, Labor Day, Thanksgiving Day,
   Christmas Day to New Year's Day.

Facilities: **Exhibition Area**; **Theatre**.

Activities: **Education Programs** (undergraduate and graduate college students); **Guided Tours**
   (upon request); **Lectures** (upon request); **Traveling Exhibitions**.

Publications: exhibition catalogues (quarterly).

A non-collecting facility, the UMKC Gallery of Art presents temporary exhibitions of work by professional artists and students.

Liberty

William Jewell College - Stocksdale Gallery of Art

Brown Hall, 2nd Floor, 500 College Hill, Liberty, MO   64068

Tel: (816) 781-7700

Fax: (816) 415-5027

Internet Address: http://www.jewell.edu/academia/stocksdale/museums.html

Gallery Director: Nano Nore

Admission: free.

Open: Monday to Friday, 9am-6pm; Saturday, 9am-noon.

Facilities: **Gallery**.

Activities: **Temporary Exhibitions**.

The gallery presents temporary exhibitions, including a biennial faculty exhibition, student art competitions, and a graduating seniors art show.

Saint Louis

Maryville University - Morton J. May Foundation Gallery (CAA)

13550 Conway, Saint Louis, MO   63141

Tel: (314) 529-9300

Internet Address: http://www.maryville.edu

Director: Ms. Nancy N. Rice, MFA

Admission: voluntary contribution.

Attendance: 800   *ADA Compliant:* Y

Parking: free on site.

Open: Monday to Thursday, 8am-10pm; Friday to Saturday, 8am-6pm; Sunday, 2pm-10pm.

Facilities: **Exhibition Area** (400 square feet).

Activities: **Education Programs** (university students); **Guided Tours**; **Lectures**.

Publications: "Maryville Student Art Journal".

The Gallery presents temporary exhibitions of works by students, faculty, and professional artists.

Saint Louis University - Museum of Contemporary Religious Art ⊕ (MOCRA)

3700 John E. Connelly Mall, Saint Louis, MO   63108
Tel: (314) 977-7170   *Fax:* (314) 977-2999
Internet Address: http://www.slu.edu/the_arts/
Admission: voluntary contribution.
Attendance: 7,500   *Membership:* N   *ADA Compliant:* Y
Parking: metered on street.
Open: Tuesday to Sunday, 11am-4pm.
Closed: Academic Holidays.
Facilities: **Exhibition Area**.
Activities: **Guided Tours**; **Permanent Exhibits**; **Temporary Exhibitions**.
Publications: gallery guides.

The mission of MOCRA is to be an ongoing forum for the dialogue between contemporary artists and the various religious traditions, as well as a place for greater understanding among various religions. The Museum is located in a spacious chapel, which was renovated to make it suitable for the display of art without eliminating the sense that it was a sacred place. MOCRA is developing its own permanent collection and features group and solo exhibitions three times each year.

View of gallery, Museum of Contemporary Religious Art. Foreground: "Torso with Outstretched Arm", by Stephen DeStaebler (1990), bronze and nickel, 60.5 x 36 inches. Background: "Caelestis, Spatium, Res" (1989-1990), acrylic, canvas, aluminum, 36 x 22.25 inches. Photograph by Cheryl Pendleton courtesy of Museum of Contemporary Religious Art, Saint Louis University, Saint Louis, Missouri.

Saint Louis University - Samuel Cupples House

221 North Grand Blvd. (Frost Campus), Saint Louis, MO   63103
Tel: (314) 977-3025   *Fax:* (314) 977-3581
Internet Address: http://www.slu.edu/the_arts/cupples/index.html
Admission: fee: adult-$4.00, child-free, student-free, senior-$3.00.
Membership: Y
Parking: parking garage at Grand Blvd & Laclede Ave.
Open: Monday to Tuesday, by appointment only; Wednesday to Sunday, 11am-4pm.
Closed: Legal Holidays, January.
Facilities: **Architecture** (Romanesque Revival mansion, 1888).
Activities: **Guided Tours** (groups larger than 20 must reserve; $1.00 per person).

The Samuel Cupples House was acquired by the University in 1942, and restored beginning in 1970. It is a forty-two-room Richardsonian Romanesqe mansion built of purple Colorado sandstone. The House contains Tiffany windows, antique furniture, rare books, and decorative arts (Meissen, Staffordshire, English silver, and Oriental figurines), as well as the University's art collection, including Northern and Italian Renaissance paintings, nineteenth-century landscapes, and art glass.

University of Missouri at Saint Louis - Gallery 210

210 Lucas Hall, 8001 Natural Bridge Road, Saint Louis, MO   63121
Tel: (314) 553-5975
Internet Address: http://www.umsl.edu/~gallery
Director: Terry Suhre
Open: Tuesday, noon-8pm; Wednesday to Friday, 10am-5pm; Saturday, 10am-2pm.
Facilities: **Exhibition Area**.
Activities: **Temporary Exhibitions** (6/year).

Located in Lucas Hall, Gallery 210 hosts five exhibitions by outside artists and one student art competition each year.

Washington University Gallery of Art

Steinberg Hall, Forsyth and Skinker Blvds.
Saint Louis, MO 63130-4899
Tel: (314) 935-5490
Fax: (314) 935-7282
Internet Address:
  http://www.proserve.wustl.edu/wugallery
Director: Mr. Joseph D. Ketner
Admission: voluntary contribution.
Attendance: 30,000   *Established:* 1881
ADA Compliant: Y
Parking: free on site.
Open: **Labor Day to mid-May**,
     Monday to Friday, 10am-4:30pm;
     Saturday to Sunday, 1pm-4pm.
Closed: Legal Holidays.
Facilities: **Auditorium** (300 seats); **Exhibition
  Area**; **Library** (50,000 volumes); **Shop**.

Alexander Calder, *Five Rudders*, 1964, painted sheet metal and rods, height 154 inches. Behind sculpture is exterior view of Steinburg Hall (Washington University Gallery of Art) (1960), designed by Fumihiko Maki. Photograph courtesy of Washington University Gallery of Art, St. Louis, Missouri.

Activities: **Films**; **Gallery Talks**; **Guided Tours**; **Lectures**.
Publications: "An Illustrated Checklist of the Collection"; "Calendar of Events" (semi-annual); exhibition catalogues.

Each year the Gallery organizes special loan exhibitions, presents faculty and student shows, and arranges installations of works from the permanent collection. The Washington University Gallery of Art preserves 3,000 objects ranging from Egyptian mummies and Greek vases to contemporary mixed-media constructions. European paintings by Barbizon, Realist, and Academic masters, and American paintings of the Hudson River School reflect 19th-century St. Louis tastes. Works by Dupre, Daumier, Church, and Gifford are highlights of the collection. Twentieth-century art is represented by Picasso, Ernst, and Miró, as well as the post-war painters Pollock, de Kooning, and Gorky, among others.

Webster University - Cecille R. Hunt Gallery

8342 Big Bend Road, Saint Louis, MO 63119
Tel: (314) 968-7171
Internet Address: http://www.websteruniv.edu/depts/finearts/art/news/hunt.html
Admission: free.
Established: 1983
Open: Monday to Friday, 10am-4pm.
Facilities: **Gallery**.
Activities: **Temporary Exhibitions**.

The Gallery presents art by local, national, and international artists and hosts visiting artists, scholarly lectures, and seminars relating to each exhibition.

Springfield

Southwest Missouri State University - Art and Design Gallery

333 E. Jefferson Ave. at Walnut St., Springfield, MO 65804
Tel: (417) 866-4861
Internet Address: http://www.smsu.edu/contrib/art/resources/art_design_gallery.html
Admission: free.
Open: **Academic Year**, Tuesday to Saturday, noon-5pm.
Facilities: **Exhibition Area**.
Activities: **Temporary Exhibitions**.

The Gallery presents monthly exhibitions during the school year. Exhibitions have included the work of distinguished artists and designers from all regions of the country, as well as annual shows of faculty and senior students in design.

Montana

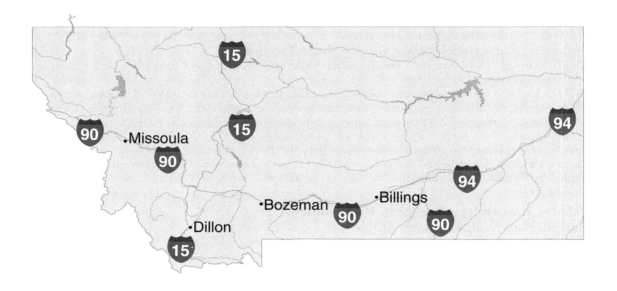

The number in parentheses following the city name indicates the number of museums/galleries in that municipality. If there is no number, one is understood. For example, in the text one listing would be found under each Montanan city.

Montana

Billings

Montana State University at Billings - Northcutt Steele Gallery

1500 N. 30th St., Billings, MT   59101
Tel: (406) 657-2324
Internet Address: http://www.msubillings.edu/art
Director: Tracy Linder
Open: Monday to Friday, 8am-5m.
Facilities: Exhibition Area.
Activities: Temporary Exhibitions.

The Northcutt Steele Gallery provides a program of six exhibitions each academic year supplemented by visiting artists lectures. A regional student art competition brings in student work from other locations, in addition to providing MSU Billings students the chance to showcase their own art work.

Bozeman

Montana State University - Museum of the Rockies

Montana State University, 600 W. Kagy Blvd.
Bozeman, MT   59717-2730
Tel: (406) 994-2251   *Fax:* (406) 994-2682
Internet Address: http://www.montana.edu/wwwmor/
Director: Mr. Arthur H. Wolf
Admission: fee: adult-$6.00, child-$4.00.
Attendance: 153,000   *Established:* 1956   *Membership:* Y   *ADA Compliant:* Y
Open: **Memorial Day to Labor Day**, Daily, 8am-8pm.
          Labor Day to Memorial Day, Monday to Saturday, 9am-5pm; Sunday, 12:30pm-5pm.
Closed: New Year's Day, Thanksgiving Day, Christmas Day.
Facilities: **Auditorium** (220 seats); **Building** (94,000 square feet); **Exhibition Area**; **Food Services** (picnic area); **Photoarchives**; **Shop**.
Activities: **Guided Tours**; **Lectures**.
Publications: newsletter, "MOR News" (quarterly).

Located on the campus of Montana State University-Bozeman, the Museum of the Rockies is a general museum focusing on the natural and cultural history of the Northern Rocky Mountain region. Exhibits encompass art, history and science and include a planetarium. The Exhibition Hall, Main Gallery, and Loft Gallery are reserved for changing exhibitions drawn from the Museum's permanent collection and traveling art, science, or history exhibits. The permanent collection consists of 280,000 objects, primarily in archaeology (45%); archival photographs (36%); history (10%); vertebrate paleontology (8%); and ethnology, geology, and fine arts (1%)

Dillon

Western Montana College Gallery-Museum

710 S. Atlantic, Dillon, MT   59725-3598
Tel: (406) 683-7126
Internet Address: http://www.wmc.edu/academics/finearts/gallery.html
Director: Ms. Eva Mastandrea
Admission: free.
Attendance: 5,000   *Established:* 1986
Open: In Session,
          Monday, 10am-3pm; Tuesday, 10am-3pm and 7pm-9pm; Wednesday to Friday, 10am-3pm.
Closed: Academic Holidays.
Facilities: **Exhibition Area** (2 galleries).
Activities: **Temporary Exhibitions.**

Dillon, Montana
Western Montana College Gallery-Museum, cont.
The Corr Gallery presents changing exhibitions of works by professional artists, faculty, and students. The Walton Gallery contains artwork from the private collection of the Walton family. Periodically, the Walton Gallery is also used for revolving exhibitions.

Missoula

University of Montana - Museum of Fine Arts ⊕
University of Montana, School of Fine Arts, Missoula, MT   59812
Tel: (406) 243-4970   *Fax:* (406) 243-5726
Internet Address: http://www.umt.edu/partv/famus/
Director: Ms. Margaret Mudd
Admission: voluntary contribution.
Attendance: 24,000   *Established:* 1956   *ADA Compliant:* Y
Parking: free parking with visitor's pass.
Open: **May to August**, Monday to Friday, 8am-noon and 1pm-5pm.
         September to April, Monday to Friday, 8am-noon and 1pm-5pm; Sunday, 11am-3pm.
Closed: Legal Holidays.
Facilities: **Gallery**; **Workshop**.
Activities: **Arts Festival**; **Concerts**; **Dance Recitals**; **Education Programs** (college students and children); **Films**; **Guided Tours**; **Lectures**; **Temporary Exhibitions**; **Traveling Exhibitions**.
The University of Montana Museum of Fine Arts collects, displays, and maintains contemporary and historical works of art for study by an academic community, public exhibition, and loans to other institutions. Objects from the permanent collection are rotated for display at the Paxson Gallery and satellite exhibition areas. The permanent collection contains more than 2,500 objects including antiquities, cast bronzes, paintings, drawings, sculpture, textiles, contemporary ceramics, period ceramics, photographs, prints, and student work.

Nebraska

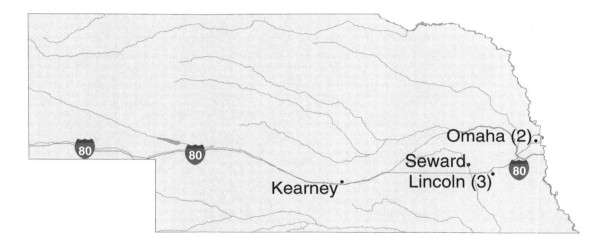

The number in parentheses following the city name indicates the number of museums/galleries in that municipality. If there is no number, one is understood. For example, in the text three listings would be found under Lincoln and one listing under Kearney.

Nebraska

Kearney

University of Nebraska at Kearney - Museum of Nebraska Art ⓒ⁴⁴ (MONA)

2401 Central Ave. at 24th St. (near entrance to the Kearney Centre)
Kearney, NE 68848
Tel: (308) 865-8559
Fax: (308) 865-8104
Internet Address: http://monet.unk.edu/mona
Interim Director: Mr. Gary Zaruba
Admission: voluntary contribution.
Established: 1986   *Membership:* Y   *ADA Compliant:* Y
Parking: free on site.
Open: Tuesday to Saturday, 11am-5pm; Sunday, 1pm-5pm.
Closed: Legal Holidays.
Facilities: **Architecture** (former Post Office building, 1911); **Exhibition Area**; **Library** (Nebraska art and artists); **Sculpture Garden**; **Shop** (artwork by Nebraska artists, books, cards, posters).
Activities: **Education Programs** (adults, U of NE graduate/undergraduate students, and children); **Guided Tours**; **Lectures**; **Temporary Exhibitions**; **Traveling Exhibitions**; **Workshops**.
Publications: catalogues (annual); exhibition catalogues; newsletter (quarterly).

MONA is a complementary partnership between the University of Nebraska at Kearney (UNK) and the Nebraska Art Collection Foundation (established 1976). Ranging from the historic artistic reporting of artist-explorers to contemporary regional work, the permanent collection focuses on art depicting Nebraska or by Nebraskans. Major strengths are in the works of Thomas Hart Benton, George Catlin, and Robert Henri. The Grant Reynard Collection comprises the largest single holding of the Museum and documents the career of this Nebraska native.

Lincoln

Nebraska Wesleyan University Galleries ⓒ⁴⁴

5000 St. Paul Ave., Lincoln, NE   68504-2230
Tel: (402) 466-2371
Fax: (402) 465-2179
Internet Address: http://www.nebrwesleyan.edu/
Director: Dr. Donald Paoletta
Admission: voluntary contribution.
Attendance: 4,000   *Established:* 1965   *ADA Compliant:* Y
Open: Tuesday to Friday, 10am-4pm; Saturday to Sunday, 1pm-4pm.
Closed: Academic Holidays.
Facilities: **Galleries** (2).
Activities: **Gallery Talks**; **Lectures**; **Temporary/Traveling Exhibitions**.

The Art Department at Nebraska Wesleyan maintains two art galleries. The Elder Gallery presents juried, invitational, and student exhibitions. The Kepler Gallery is reserved for student displays.

University of Nebraska-Lincoln - Great Plains Art Collection ⓒ⁴⁴ (GPAC)

University of Nebraska-Lincoln, 215-217 Love Library (13th & R Sts.)
Lincoln, NE   68588-0475
Tel: (402) 472-6220   *Fax:* (402) 472-5131
Curator: Ms. Martha H. Kennedy
Admission: voluntary contribution.
Attendance: 7,000   *Established:* 1980
Membership: Y   *ADA Compliant:* Y
Parking: metered parking.
Open: Monday to Friday, 9:30-5pm; Saturday, 10am-5pm; Sunday, 1:30pm-5pm.
Closed: Legal Holidays, Between Semesters, Between Exhibits.

University of Nebraska-Lincoln - Great Plains Art Collection, cont.

Facilities: **Exhibition Area**; **Library** (4,000 volumes).

Activities: **Gallery Talks**; **Guided Tours**; **Temporary Exhibitions**.

Publications: brochures; exhibition catalogues.

Apart of the Center for great Plains Studies at the University of Nebraska-Lincoln, GPAC presents five major exhibits each year accompanied by public programs pertaining to the exhibitions or other topics related to great Plains Studies. The permanent collection consists of more than 180 bronzes (including works by Frederic S. Remington and Charles M. Russell), 240 paintings and 390 works on paper (including works by Albert Bierstadt, William Cary, John Clymer, William Henry Jackson, Norman Rockwell, and Olaf Wieghorst).

Charles M. Russell, *Smoking Up*, 1904, bronze, height 11 7/8 inches, Christleib Collection, University of Nebraska-Lincoln. Photograph by Roger Bruhn, courtesy of Great Plains Art Collection, University of Nebraska-Lincoln, Lincoln, Nebraska.

Univ. of Nebraska-Lincoln - Sheldon Memorial Art Gallery & Sculpture Garden

University of Nebraska-Lincoln, 12th and R Sts.,Lincoln, NE   68588-0300

Tel: (402) 472-2461   *Fax:* (402) 472-4258

Internet Address: http://sheldon.unl.edu

Director: Mr. George Neubert

Admission: free.

Attendance: 150,000   *Established:* 1963   *Membership:* Y   *ADA Compliant:* Y

Parking: free on site.

Open: Tuesday to Wednesday, 10am-5pm; Thursday to Saturday, 10am-5pm and 7pm-9pm; Sunday, 2pm-9pm.

Closed: New Year's Eve to New Year's Day, Memorial Day, Independence Day, Labor Day, Thanksgiving Day, Christmas Day.

Facilities: **Architecture** (International Style, 1963 design by Philip Johnson); **Auditorium** (300 seats); **Film Theatre**; **Food Services** Café (Tues-Fri, 9:30am-3:30pm); **Galleries**; **Library** (15,000 volumes); **Picnic Areas**; **Sculpture Garden** (15 acres); **Shop** (Tues-Sat, 10am-5pm; Sun 2pm-5pm; art, cards, gift items).

Activities: **Concerts**; **Education Programs** (children); **Films**; **Gallery Talks**; **Guided Tours** (reservation, 2 weeks in advance); **Lectures**; **Temporary Exhibitions** (20/year); **Touring Exhibition** (annual, statewide); **Traveling Exhibitions**.

Publications: annual report; calendar, "Gallery Notes" (monthly); exhibition catalogues, "Sculpture Collection"; exhibition series, "The American Painting Collection of the Sheldon Memorial Art Gallery"; newsletter (quarterly).

Housed in an International Style building designed by architect Philip Johnson, the Sheldon Memorial Art Gallery and Sculpture Garden houses a comprehensive collection of 20th-century American art. Thirty-three monumental sculptures are exhibited in the sculpture garden. Approximately twenty exhibitions are presented each year featuring works in all media, including video and installation art. The exhibition program consists of displays drawn from the permanent collection organized by the curatorial staff and shows organized by peer institutions throughout the United States. The Sheldon houses both the Nebraska Art Association collection, founded in 1888, and the University of Nebraska collection, initiated in 1929. Together they consist of over 12,000 original art works in all media. There are significant holdings in 19th-century landscape and still life, American Impressionism, early Modernism, geometric abstraction, Abstract Expressionism, pop art, minimalism and contemporary art. Monumental sculpture includes works by including works by Mark di Suvero, Michael Heizer, Bryan Hunt, Gaston Lachaise, Jacques Lipchitz, Elie Nadelman,

University of Nebraska-Lincoln - Sheldon Memorial Art Gallery, cont.
Claes Oldenburg/Coosje van Bruggen, Richard Serra, Judith Shea, David Smith, and William Tucker. Also of possible interest, undergraduate and graduate student work is displayed in the Gallery of the Department of Art and Art History, 102 Richards Hall (472-2631), Monday-Thursday, 9am-5pm.

Omaha

Creighton University - Gallery ⓒ
Lied Education Center for the Arts, 2500 California Plaza, Omaha, NE   68178-0001
Tel: (402) 280-2700
Internet Address: http://leca.creighton.edu/events.html
Admission: free.
Open: Call for hours.
Facilities: **Exhibition Area**.
Activities: **Temporary Exhibitions**.

Located in the Lied Education Center for the Arts, the Gallery mounts temporary exhibitions of the work of professional and student artists, including an all-student show each spring.

University of Nebraska at Omaha - The UNO Art Gallery ⓒ
Weber Fine Arts Building, Dodge St., Omaha, NE   68182
Tel: (402) 554-2796
Internet Address: http://www.unomaha.edu/~fineart/art/gallery/html
Director: Ms. Nancy Kelly
Admission: free.
Open: Monday to Friday, 10am-4:30pm.
Facilities: **Architecture** Fine Arts Building (1992 design by Hardy, Holzman and Pfeiffer Associates (New York)); **Exhibition Area** (3 rooms, 2,175 square feet); **Sculpture Garden**.
Activities: **Temporary Exhibitions** (8-10/year).

Consisting of two large rooms and a hexagonal gallery, the UNO Gallery offers exhibitions of work by professional artists, as well as four student shows (two juried/two BFA thesis) and a biennial faculty show.

Seward

Concordia University - Marxhausen Art Gallery
Jesse Hall, 800 N. Columbia Ave., Seward, NE   68434
Tel: (402) 643-3651   *Fax:* (402) 643-4073
Internet Address: http://www.cune.edu
Curator of Incoming Exhibitions: Prof. Lynn R. Soloway
Admission: free.
Established: 1951
Open: **September to May**,
  Monday to Friday, 9am-noon and 1pm-4pm; Saturday to Sunday, 1pm-4pm.
  Summer School,
  by appointment.
Closed: Academic Holidays.
Facilities: **Exhibition Area**.
Activities: **Gallery Talks**; **Rental Gallery**; **Temporary Exhibitions**; **Traveling Exhibitions**.

The Gallery offers regional and national exhibitions approximately every month during the academic year. Exhibitions include both group and solo shows in a wide variety of media. The permanent collection is shown twice a year. There are also an annual student exhibition and a biennial faculty show. The permanent collection consists of contemporary original prints (lithographs, intaglios, screenprints, assemblages, aquatints, monotypes, etc.) by American and International artists. Among the artists represented are Baskin, Dine, Grooms, Hockney, Kunc, Lasansky, Lichtenstein, Murray, Nelson, Nevelson, Rauschenberg, Roualt, Salle, Scholder, Serra, and Stella.

Nevada

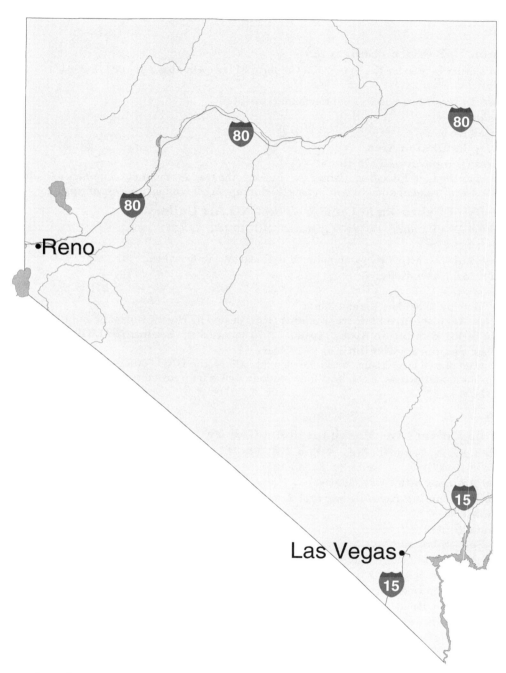

A number in parentheses following a city name indicates the number of museums/galleries in that municipality. If there is no number, one is understood. For example, in the text one listing would be found under each Nevadan city shown on map.

Nevada

Las Vegas

University of Nevada Las Vegas - Donna Beam Fine Arts Gallery ⒸⒶⒶ

UNLV, Alta Ham Fine Arts Building, 4505 Maryland Parkway
Las Vegas, NV   89154
Tel: (702) 895-3893
Fax: (702) 895-4194
Internet Address: http://www.nscee.edu/unlv/Art/gallery.html
Director: Mr. Jerry A. Schefcik
Admission: free.
Attendance: 7,500   *Established:* 1960   *ADA Compliant:* Y
Open: Monday to Friday, 9am-5pm.
Closed: Legal Holidays.
Facilities: **Exhibition Area**.
Activities: **Education Programs** (undergraduates); **Gallery Talks**; **Lectures**; **Temporary Exhibitions**; **Traveling Exhibitions**.
Publications: brochures; exhibition catalogues.

Located in the Alta Ham Fine Arts Building, the Donna Beam Fine Arts Gallery is dedicated to the exhibition, interpretation, documentation, and preservation of 20th-century visual art. The Gallery offers a variety of temporary exhibitions of four to six weeks duration featuring the work of nationally and internationally recognized artists, as well as works from the permanent collection.

Reno

University of Nevada, Reno - Galleries ⒸⒶⒶ

Art Department 224, Evans Ave., Reno, NV   89557-0007
Tel: (702) 784-6682
Fax: (702) 784-6655
Internet Address: http://www.unr.edu
Director: Ms. Suzanne Kanatsiz
Admission: voluntary contribution.
Attendance: 30,000   *Established:* 1960   *Membership:* Y   *ADA Compliant:* Y
Open: Monday to Friday, 9am-5pm.
Closed: Legal Holidays.
Facilities: **Galleries** (4; Sheppard 2,000 square feet).
Activities: **Concerts**; **Films**; **Gallery Talks**; **Guided Tours**; **Lectures**; **Temporary Exhibitions** (Exit Gallery, 8/year); **Travelling Exhibitions**.
Publications: exhibition catalogues.

The Sheppard Gallery, on the first floor of the Church Fine Arts Complex, presents temporary exhibitions of work in a variety of media by professional artists. Past exhibitions have featured artists in solo and group shows of local, regional, and international prominence and annual juried shows of student work. Also located in the Church Fine Arts Building, the Front Door Gallery often displays student work. In the Photography Department, The Exit Gallery, a nationally curated, photography-only gallery, presents one-month solo exhibitions September through May. Art exhibitions are also mounted in the McNamara Gallery, located in the Morrill Hall Alumni Center.

New Hampshire

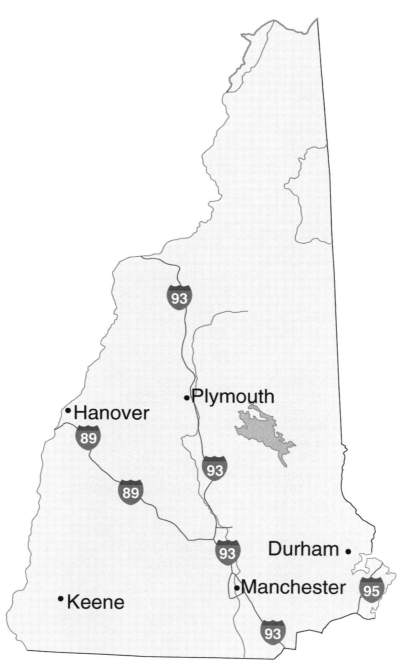

The number in parentheses following the city name indicates the number of museums/galleries in that municipality. If there is no number, one is understood. For example, in the text one listing would be found under each New Hampshire city shown on map.

New Hampshire

Durham

University of New Hampshire - The Art Gallery

Paul Creative Arts Center
30 College Road
Durham, NH   03824-3538
Tel: (603) 862-3712
Fax: (603) 862-2191
Internet Address: http://www.unh.edu
Director: Ms. Vicki C. Wright
Admission: voluntary contribution.
Attendance: 9,000   *Established:* 1960
Membership: Y
Parking: metered.
Open: **September to May,**
     Monday to Wednesday, 10am-4pm;
     Thursday, 10am-8pm;
     Saturday to Sunday, 1pm-5pm.
Closed: June to August, Academic Holidays.
Facilities: **Exhibition Area** (4,500 square feet).

John Laurent, *Artichokes and Lemons*, 1983, acrylic on paper, purchase, permanent collection, Art Gallery, University of New Hampshire. Photograph courtesy of Art Gallery, University of New Hampshire, Durham, New Hampshire.

Activities: **Concerts**; **Education Programs**; **Films**; **Gallery Talks**; **Lectures** ("Brown Bag Lecture Series"); **Readings** (poetry); **Temporary Exhibitions**.
Publications: booklets; exhibition catalogues.

The Art Gallery is an entity of the University of New Hampshire. Its exhibitions cover a range of periods, styles, and media, including paintings, sculpture, photography, ceramics, prints, and drawings.   Focusing on a variety of themes, shows have included the etchings of Dürer and Rembrandt, contemporary work by New Hampshire artists, New England landscape painting, and nineteenth-century Japanese prints, with works often borrowed from public and private collections throughout New England. The Art Gallery also mounts exhibitions of university's art faculty members and alumni, senior art students, and selections from the permanent collection. The permanent collection, totaling 1,500 works, emphasizes 19th- and 20th-century prints and drawings, including nearly 200 Japanese woodblock prints.

Hanover

Dartmouth College - Hood Museum of Art

Dartmouth College
Wheelock St.
Hanover, NH   03755
Tel: (603) 646-2808
Fax: (603) 646-1400
Internet Address: http://www.dartmouth.edu/~hood
Director: Mr. Timothy Rub
Admission: voluntary contribution.
Attendance: 42,000   *Established:* 1772
Membership: Y   *ADA Compliant:* Y
Parking: metered parking on site.
Open: Tuesday, 10am-5pm;
     Wednesday, 10am-9pm;
     Thursday to Friday, 10am-5pm;
     Saturday to Sunday, noon-5pm.

Abbott Handerson Thayer, *Below Mount Monadnock*, c. 1913, oil on panel, 9 x 7 5/16 inches, Hood Museum of Art, purchased through gifts from Class of 1955 and Lathrop Fellows. Photograph courtesy of Hood Museum of Art, Dartmouth College, Hanover, New Hampshire.

Dartmouth College - Hood Museum of Art. cont.

Facilities: **Architecture** (Post-Modern building, 1985 design by Charles W. Moore/Chad Floyd); **Auditorium** (200 seats); **Food Services** Restaurant; **Galleries** (10; 12,000 square feet); **Shop**.

Activities: **Gallery Talks**; **Guided Tours**; **Lectures**; **Traveling Exhibitions**.

Publications: exhibition catalogues; handbook, "Treasures of the Hood Museum".

The Hood Museum of Art is one of the oldest and largest college museums in the country. The Rev. David McClure gave the College its first artifacts, "a few curious Elephants bones" (actually mastodon fossils), in 1772, just three years after its founding. Since then, Dartmouth's collection of art and artifacts has grown to incorporate more than 60,000 objects. In addition to ongoing displays from its permanent collection, the Museum presents approximately eight changing exhibitions each year, with two new exhibitions on view each term. The Museum also presents two teaching exhibitions per term. The Dartmouth collection represents nearly every area of art history and ethnography and is particularly strong in African art, Oceanic art, Native North American art, early American silver, 19th- and 20th-century American painting, European Old Master, 19th- and 20th-century prints, and contemporary art. Highlights include 9th-century BC reliefs from the Palace of Ashurnaisirpal II; works by Thomas Eakins, Frederic Remington, Paul Sample, John Sloan, and Gilbert Stuart; works by modern masters including Marc Chagall, Wassily Kandinsky, Fernand Léger, Henri Matisse, Joan Miró, Georgia O'Keeffe, Pablo Picasso, and Mark Rothko; and the Harry A. Franklin Family Collection of Oceanic Art (1,300 artifacts). The largest mural by José Clemente Orozco in the United States, "The Epic of American Civilization", is housed in the Baker Library.

Keene

Keene State College - Thorne-Sagendorph Art Gallery ⊆⁴⁹

Keene State College, Wyman Way
Keene, NH   03435-3501
Tel: (603) 358-2720
Fax: (603) 358-2238
Internet Address:
   http://www.keene.edu/FACILITIES/TSAG
Director: Ms. Maureen Ahern
Admission: voluntary contribution.
Attendance: 5,000   *Established:* 1965
Membership: Y   *ADA Compliant:* Y
Parking: free on site.
Open: **Fall to Spring**,
         Monday to Wednesday, noon-4pm;
         Thursday to Friday, noon-7pm;
         Saturday to Sunday, noon-4pm.
      Summer,
         Sunday to Tuesday, noon-4pm.

Exterior view of Thorne-Sagendorph Art Gallery, Keene State College. Rendering courtesy of Thorne-Sagendorph Gallery, Keene State College, Keene, New Hampshire.

Closed: Academic Holidays, Semester Breaks.

Facilities: **Galleries** (4,000 square feet).

Activities: **Education Programs** (children); **Films**; **Gallery Talks**; **Guided Tours**; **Lectures**; **Temporary Exhibitions**; **Traveling Exhibitions**.

Publications: exhibition brochures; exhibition catalogues.

The Gallery is a comprehensive community and campus arts complex with space for programs, lectures, films and slides in concert with exhibits. Committed to local and regional, as well as national and international, art, the Gallery has hosted a retrospective of the work of Jules Olitski, five New Art-New Hampshire exhibits focusing on the best of New Hampshire's own artists, faculty shows, and regional juried exhibitions. The Thorne's permanent collection includes an extensive collection of nationally-recognized artists who worked in the Mount Monadnock area at the turn of the century, including Barry Faulkner, Alexander James, Richard Meryman, and Joseph Lindon Smith. The collection has grown through the years to include works by other contemporary artists, such as Vargian Bogosian, Robert Mapplethorpe, Jules Olitski, George Rickey, and Fritz Scholder.

Manchester

St. Anselm College - Chapel Art Center ⒸⒶⒾ

St. Anselm College
100 St. Anselm Drive
Manchester, NH 03102
Tel: (603) 641-7470
Fax: (603) 641-7116
Internet Address: http://www.anselm.edu
Director: Dr. Donald A. Rosenthal
Admission: free.
Attendance: 4,000   *Established:* 1967
ADA Compliant: Y
Open: **September to April**,
            Thursday, 10am-9pm;
            Friday to Saturday, 10am-4pm.
Closed: Academic Holidays, Legal Holidays.
Facilities: **Architecture** (former college chapel,
      1923; ceiling and wall painting c. 1930);
      Exhibition Area (2,800 square feet).

Interior view, Chapel Art Center, Saint Anselm College. Photograph courtesy of Chapel Art Center, Saint Anselm College, Manchester, New Hampshire.

Activities: **Gallery Talks**; **Lectures**; **Temporary Exhibitions**; **Traveling Exhibitions**.
Publications: exhibition catalogues.

The Chapel Art Center, adjoining Alumni Hall, organizes varied exhibitions of historical and contemporary art that are closely integrated with the curriculum in art history and studio fine arts courses. An important part of the schedule is devoted to displays of the most accomplished recent art works by students. The gallery is located in the former College Chapel, beautifully decorated with mural paintings. Other programs such as lectures, concerts and receptions, usually related to current exhibitions, are scheduled from time to time. The Chapel Art Center also houses a small permanent art collection, consisting mainly of contemporary American paintings and works on paper.

Plymouth

Plymouth State College - Karl Drerup Fine Arts Gallery ⒸⒶⒾ

Plymouth State College, Department of Fine Arts
Draper Maynard Building, High St.
Plymouth, NH 03264
Tel: (603) 535-2646   *Fax:* (603) 535-2938   *TDDY:* (603) 535-2679
Internet Address: http://eeyore.plymouth.edu/~rdecicco/art/gallery.html
Gallery Director: Mr. Joe Driscoll
Admission: free.
Attendance: 4,000   *Established:* 1969   *ADA Compliant:* Y
Open: **September to May**,
            Tuesday, 10am-5pm; Wednesday, 10am-8pm; Thursday to Friday, 10am-5pm;
            Saturday, noon-5pm.
Closed: Academic Holidays, Thanksgiving Day, Christmas Day.
Facilities: **Exhibition Area**.
Activities: **Education Programs** (undergraduate and graduate students); **Lectures**; **Traveling Exhibitions**.

Located in the Draper Maynard building on the campus of Plymouth State College, the Gallery offers art exhibits, adjunct programs, and lectures.

New Jersey

The number in parentheses following the city name indicates the number of museums/galleries in that municipality. If there is no number, one is understood. For example, in the text one listings would be found under each New Jersey city shown on the map.

New Jersey

Camden

Rutgers University, Camden - Stedman Gallery ⒸⒶ

Rutgers-Camden Center for the Arts, 3rd and Pearl Streets, Camden, NJ   08102-1403
Tel: (609) 225-6245
Fax: (609) 225-6330
TDDY: (609) 225-6648
Internet Address: http://camden-www.rutgers.edu
Director: Ms. Virginia Oberlin Steel
Admission: free.
Attendance: 18,500   *Established:* 1975   *Membership:* N   *ADA Compliant:* Y
Parking: free on site.
Open: Monday to Wednesday, 10am-4pm; Thursday, 10am-8pm; Friday to Saturday, 10am-4pm.
Closed: Memorial Day, Independence Day, Labor Day, Thanksgiving Day,
    Christmas Eve to January 2, Between Exhibitions.
Facilities: **Galleries**.
Activities: **Concerts**; **Education Programs** (children); **Films**; **Lectures**; **Temporary Exhibitions**.
Publications: exhibition catalogues.

The Gallery mounts a year-round series of temporary exhibitions.

Cranford

Union County College - The Tomasulo Gallery

1033 Springfield Ave.
Cranford, NJ   07016-1599
Tel: (908) 709-7155
Fax: (908) 709-0527
Internet Address: http://www.ucc.edu
Director: Valeri Larko
Admission: free.
Established: 1974
Membership: N   *ADA Compliant:* Y
Parking: parking available.
Open: Monday, 1pm-4pm;
    Tuesday to Thursday, 1pm-4pm and 6pm-9pm;
    Saturday, 1pm-4pm.
Facilities: **Exhibition Area** (625 square feet in Library).
Activities: **Temporary Exhibitions** (6 per year - 5 professional & 1 student).

Each year, the Gallery mounts five professional exhibits of contemporary painting, sculpture, and installation art. There is also an annual student exhibit of work in architecture. Usually, there are no exhibits in July and August.

Mary Beth McLenzie, *Self Portrait (yellow background)*, oil on canvas, 18 x 14 inches, from 1998 exhibition of the artist's work, Tomasulo Gallery. Photograph courtesy of Tomasulo Gallery, Union County College, Cranford, New Jersey.

Glassboro

Rowan University - Galleries ⒸⒶ

Route 322, Glassboro, NJ   08028
Tel: (609) 256-4521
Internet Address: http://www.rowan.edu
Director of the Galleries: Ms. Naomi Nelson
Admission: free.

Glassboro, New Jersey

Rowan University - Galleries, cont.

Open: **Wilson Art Gallery**, Monday to Friday, 9am-5pm.
Westby Art Gallery, Tues, 10am-4pm; Wed, 10am-6:30pm; Thurs to Fri, 10am-4pm.
Student Art Gallery, Monday to Friday, 9am-4pm.
Facilities: **Galleries** (3).
Activities: **Temporary Exhibitions.**

The Galleries at Rowan University exhibit traditional and contemporary work by nationally and internationally recognized artists, as well as innovative emerging artists. Rowan students present individual and group exhibitions in the Westby Student Gallery. Wilson Concert Hall's lobby is used for special exhibits, often in collaboration with musical and theatrical presentations.

Hackensack

Fairleigh Dickinson University - Edward Williams Gallery ⓒ

150 Kotte Place, Hackensack, NJ   07601
Tel: (201) 692-2449
Internet Address: http://www.fdu.edu
Director: Ms. Rachel Friedberg
Open: Monday to Friday, 9am-9pm; Saturday, 9am-2pm.
Facilities: **Exhibition Area.**
Activities: **Temporary Exhibitions.**

The gallery presents temporary exhibitions. Also of possible interest on the Teaneck-Hackensack campus are University College Art Gallery (Mon-Fri, 9am-5pm; Sat, noon-5pm, 692-2801), located in Becton Hall, presenting ten professional exhibitions annually, and University College Art Gallery II, The Maples, located next to Becton Hall, featuring student work.

Jersey City

New Jersey City University - Lemmerman and Courtney Galleries

2039 Kennedy Blvd., Jersey City, NJ   07305
Tel: (201) 200-3246
Fax: (201) 200-3224
Internet Address: http://www.njcu.edu
Director of Campus Galleries: Professor Hugo Xavier Bastidas
Admission: free.
Attendance: 7,000   *Established:* 1969   *ADA Compliant:* Y
Parking: Parking lot and on street.
Open: Monday to Friday, 11am-4pm.
Facilities: **Galleries** (2; 700 and 340 square feet).
Activities: **Temporary Exhibitions.**

The University maintains two galleries: the Harold B. Lemmerman Gallery and the Courtney Gallery both devoted to changing exhibitions of work by professional artists, faculty, and students. The permanent collection is not exhibited in the galleries; however, a potion of the holdings are on display on the third floor of Hepburn Hall.

Lawrenceville

Rider University - University Art Gallery ⓒ

Student Center, 2083 Lawrenceville Road, Lawrenceville, NJ   08648
Tel: (609) 895-5588
Internet Address: http://www.rider.edu
Director: Prof.. Harry Naar
Admission: free.
Attendance: 2,000   *ADA Compliant:* Y
Parking: free on site.
Open: **Academic Year**, Monday to Thursday, 2pm-8pm; Friday to Sunday, 2pm-5pm.

Rider University - University Art Gallery, cont.

Facilities: **Exhibition Area**.

Activities: **Gallery Talks**; **Temporary Exhibitions** (4/year).

Publications: exhibition catalogues.

The Gallery mounts four exhibitions per year (one each in September-October, November-December, January-February, and March-April). Exhibits include work by professional artists, primarily from New Jersey and its immediate region. The permanent collection at Rider focuses primarily on contemporary painting, but it also includes a small but strong collection of African sculpture. These works may be seen in the Presidential Lobby.

Madison

Drew University - Korn Gallery ⓒ

Brothers College
Route 124
Madison, NJ   07940

Tel: (973) 408-3011

Internet Address:
   http://www.depts.drew.edu/art/gallery.htm

Admission: free.

Parking: free on site.

Open: Tuesday to Friday, 12:30pm-4:00pm,
         or by appointment.

Facilities: **Exhibition Area**.

Activities: **Gallery   Talks**;   **Lectures**;
   Performances; **Temporary Exhibitions**.

The Gallery hosts temporary exhibitions of work by professional artists, as well as annual student and senior shows. Drew also presents rotating exhibits in the University Library, art receptions and displays in Brothers College, and photography exhibits in the University Center.

Steve Roden, *wandering, the world has become lovelier*, 1998-9, 8 inches x 10 inches, oil and acrylic on canvas. Temporary exhibition, 1999, Korn Gallery, Drew University. Photograph courtesy of Drew University, Madison, New Jersey.

New Brunswick

Rutgers University - Jane Voorhees Zimmerli Art Museum ⓒ

Rutgers: The State University of NJ,
George and Hamilton Sts.
New Brunswick, NJ   08903

Tel: (908) 932-7237

Fax: (908) 232-2444

Internet Address: http://www-rci.rutgers.edu/~zamuseum/

Director and Curator: Mr. Phillip Dennis Cate

Admission: fee: adult-$3.00, child-free.

Attendance: 30,000   *Established:* 1966   *Membership:* Y   *ADA Compliant:* Y

Parking: behind museum off George St..

Open: **September to June**,
         Tuesday to Friday, 10am-4:30pm; Saturday to Sunday, noon-5pm.
      July,
         Wednesday to Friday, 10am-4:30pm; Saturday to Sunday, noon-5pm.

Closed: August, Memorial Day, Independence Day, Labor Day,
      Thanksgiving Day to Thanksgiving Friday, Christmas Day to New Year's Day.

Facilities: **Galleries**; **Library** (3,500 volumes, French fin de siecle books & periodicals).

Activities: **Concerts**; **Education Programs** (children); **Guided Tours** (groups, minimum 10, reserve 4 weeks in advance); **Temporary Exhibitions**.

Publications: exhibition catalogues; newsletter, "Japonisme Newsletter" (semi-annual).

Rutgers University - Jane Voorhees Zimmerli Art Museum, cont.

The Museum presents exhibits drawn from the permanent collections and temporary exhibitions. The Museum houses the Rutgers University Art Collection composed of approximately 50,000 objects. A component, the International Center for Japonisme, mounts displays in the Kusakabe-Griffis Japonisme Gallery. Permanent collections include the Norton and Nancy Dodge Collection of Non-Conformist Art from the Soviet Union (over 10,000 works of art by over 900 artists); the French Graphic Arts Collection (50,000 works on paper from 1870-1918); the Gordon Henderson Collection of Stained Glass Design; the Japonisme Collection (turn-of-the-century French and American art inspired by Japanese aesthetics); the George Riabov Collection of Russian Art (1,100 works from the 18th through 20th centuries); the Rutgers Archives for Printmaking Studios; the Rutgers Collection of Children's Literature; and the Collection of Western Art (2,000 paintings, sculpture, and graphic art).

Newark

Rutgers University - Robeson Center Art Gallery ©44

350 Dr. Martin Luther King Jr. Blvd., Newark, NJ 07102
Tel: (973) 353-5119 *Ext:* 32   *Fax:* (973) 353-1392
Internet Address: http://newark.rutgers.edu/artgallery/
Admission: free.
Open: Monday to Tuesday, 11:30am-4:30pm; Wednesday, 1:30pm-6:30pm;
Thursday, 11:30am-4:30pm.
Facilities: **Exhibition Area**.
Activities: **Temporary Exhibitions**.

Located in the Paul Robeson Campus Center on the Newark Campus of Rutgers University, the Gallery presents temporary exhibitions, including annual fine arts and graphic design senior theses shows.

North Branch

Raritan Valley Community College Art Gallery

Route 28 and Lamington Road
North Branch, NJ 08876
Tel: (908) 218-8876
Fax: (908) 595-0213
Internet Address:
   http://rvcc2.raritanval.edu/~fapa/index.html
Director, Art Gallery: Prof. Ann Tsubota
Admission: free.
Attendance: 700   *Established:* 1985
Membership: N   *ADA Compliant:* Y
Parking: free on site.
Open: Monday, 3pm-8pm;
Tuesday, noon-3pm;
Wednesday, 1pm-8pm;
Thursday, noon-3pm.
Facilities: **Gallery** (1,575 square feet).
Activities: **Temporary Exhibitions** (8/year).

Interior view of Raritan Valley Community College Art Gallery during "No Apologies", a solo exhibition of work by John Atura in 1998. Photograph courtesy of Raritan Valley Community College, Pittstown, New Jersey.

The Main Gallery, located in the College Center building, presents eight exhibitions each year including annual student and faculty art exhibits, one to two solo shows and two to four group exhibitions of work by professional artists (curated by RVCC Art Department faculty). Additionally, an on-going series devoted to current student work is displayed in the Mini Gallery, located in the Art Building. There are also several alternative exhibition spaces on campus, including the theater lobby and the sculpture garden.

Paterson

Passaic County Community College Gallery

1 College Blvd., Paterson, NJ 07505-1179
Tel: (973) 684-6555   *Fax:* (973) 684-5843
Internet Address: http://www.pccc.cc.nj.us/
Art Curator: Ms. Lori Rattner
Admission: free.
Attendance: 2,000   *Established:* 1979   *ADA Compliant:* Y
Parking: metered parking.
Open: Monday to Friday, 9am-9pm; Saturday, 9am-5pm.
Facilities: **Exhibition Area** (2 galleries); **Sculpture Garden**.
Activities: **Temporary Exhibitions** (monthly or bi-monthly - local and regional artists).

The college exhibits work of interest and educational value in two galleries: the Broadway and the LRC. The galleries present monthly or bi-monthly exhibitions of work by artists from New Jersey and the tri-state areas.

Pomona

Richard Stockton College of New Jersey - Art Gallery ⒸⒶⒶ

Performing Arts Center, Room H113, College Drive, Pomona, NJ 08240
Tel: (609) 652-4214   *Fax:* (609) 652-4550
Internet Address: http://loki.stockton.edu/main/acad/artv/gallery.html
Admin. Asst: Ms. Denise McGarvey
Attendance: 4,000   *Established:* 1974   *Membership:* N   *ADA Compliant:* Y
Parking: two lots on site.
Open: Monday, 11:30am-4pm; Tuesday, 11:30am-8pm; Wednesday to Friday, 11:30am-4pm;
      Sunday, noon-4pm; 1 hour prior to PAC events.
Facilities: **Exhibition Area** (1,500 square feet).
Activities: **Temporary Exhibitions**.
Publications: brochures (occasional).

Stockton sponsors five or six professional fine art exhibitions of regionally and nationally known artists each academic year, as well as an equal number of student shows.

Princeton

Princeton University - The Art Museum ⒸⒶⒶ

Princeton University
McCormick Hall (off Nassau Street)
Princeton, NJ 08544-1018
Tel: (609) 258-3788
Fax: (609) 258-5949
Internet Address: http://www.princeton.edu
Director: Mr. Allen Rosenbaum
Admission: voluntary contribution.
Attendance: 72,000   *Established:* 1882
Membership: Y   *ADA Compliant:* Y
Parking: not available on campus, metered on street/commercial lots.
Open: Tuesday to Saturday, 10am-5pm;
      Sunday, 1pm-5pm.
Closed: Major Holidays.
Facilities: **Galleries**; **Shop**.
Activities: **Gallery Talks**; **Guided Tours**
      (groups 6+, by appointment, 258-3043);
      Lectures; **Temporary Exhibitions**.

Guido da Siena, *Annunciation*, Italian, 13th century. Tempera on panel, 35.1 x 48.8 cm. The Art Museum, Princeton University, Caroline G. Mather Fund (144). Photograph courtesy of The Art Museum, Princeton University, Princeton, New Jersey.

Princeton, New Jersey

Princeton University - The Art Museum, cont.

Publications: bulletin, "Record of the Art Museum, Princeton University" (semi-annual); exhibition catalogues; posters.

The founding principle and primary function of the Museum is to give students access to original works of art to complement and enrich the instructional and research activities of the University. The Art Museum also serves a much larger audience as an important cultural resource and as an active participant in the international community of museums. Many exhibitions, drawn from the permanent collection, are organized in conjunction with the curriculum of the Department of Art and Archaeology and programs in other departments of the University. The Museum also originates exhibitions, drawing on works of art from all over the world, with an emphasis on lesser known areas of the history of art deserving scholarly and aesthetic exploration. These exhibitions are often circulated to other museums. The collections range from ancient to contemporary art and concentrate, geographically, on the Mediterranean regions, Western Europe, China, the United States, and Latin America. There is an outstanding collection of Greek and Roman antiquities, including ceramics, marbles and bronzes, and Roman mosaics from Princeton University's excavations in Antioch. Medieval Europe is represented by sculpture, metalwork, and stained glass. The collection of Western European paintings includes important examples from the early Renaissance through the 19th century, and there is a growing collection of 20th-century and contemporary art. Among the greatest strengths in the Museum are the collections of Chinese art, with important holdings in bronzes, tomb figures, painting, and calligraphy; and pre-Columbian art, with remarkable examples of the art of the Maya. The Museum has important collections of old master prints and drawings and a comprehensive collection of original photographs. African art is represented as well as Northwest Coast Indian art, on loan to the Museum from the Department of Geology. Not housed in the Museum but part of the University collection, the John B. Putnam, Jr., Memorial Collection of 20th-century sculpture includes works by such modern masters as Henry Moore, Alexander Calder, Pablo Picasso, and Jacques Lipchitz, located throughout the campus.

Upper Montclair

Montclair State University Art Galleries ⒸⒶⒿ

Life Hall , Room 135, One Normal Avenue, Upper Montclair, NJ   07043
Tel: (973) 655-5113   *Fax:* (973) 655-7640
Internet Address: http://www.montclair.edu/Pages/FineArts/faevents.htm
Co-Director: Mr. Lorenzo Pace
Open: September to May, Monday/Wednesday/Friday, 10am-4pm; Tuesday/Thursday, 10am-6pm.
Facilities: Exhibition Area.
Activities: Artist Residencies; Lectures; Temporary Exhibitions (7/year).

Located in Life Hall, the University Gallery presents exhibitions of the work of professional artists, as well as the annuals: BFA Student Exhibition in May, Teen Art Festival in June, and Juried Small Works Show in July. Also managed by the University Art Gallery is Gallery One, which mounts exhibitions by professional artists, undergraduate students, and graduate students. Also of possible interest on campus, a student-run exhibition space, Gallery 3½, located in the Calcia Fine Arts Building (655-7295), presents shows of student work during the fall and spring semesters.

Wayne

William Paterson University of New Jersey - Ben Shahn Galleries ⒸⒶⒿ

300 Pompton Road, Wayne, NJ   07470-2103
Tel: (973) 720-2654   *Fax:* (973) 720-3273
Internet Address: http://www.wpunj.edu/arts_culture/index2.htm
Director: Dr. Nancy Einreinhofer
Admission: free.
Attendance: 10,000   *Established:* 1968
Membership: Y   *ADA Compliant:* Y
Open: Monday to Friday, 10am-5pm; Saturday to Sunday, by appointment.
Closed: Legal Holidays.

William Paterson University of New Jersey - Ben Shahn Galleries, cont.

Facilities: **Exhibition Area** (5,000 square feet, 3 galleries); **Sculpture Garden** (20 contemporary works).

Activities: **Guided Tours**; **Lectures**; **Traveling Exhibitions**.

Publications: collection catalogue, "Sculpture on Campus"; gallery guides.

The Ben Shahn Galleries at William Paterson University mount exhibitions of contemporary art and make these available to the students and faculty and to the residents of the surrounding communities. The Galleries also sponsor lectures on art and various related workshops on a regular basis. The goal of the Galleries' exhibition program is to create an environment that is challenging and that stimulates ideas, discussion, and discovery among the student body, faculty, staff, and the public. Holdings include artists books, decorative art, and the Tobias Collection of African and Oceanic art. Also of possible interest, the University's Sculpture on Campus program has developed a collection of contemporary sculpture displayed in public areas throughout the campus.

Exterior view of Ben Shahn Galleries; "Neon", sculpture by Stephen Antonakos. Photograph courtesy of Ben Shahn Galleries, William Paterson University, Wayne, New Jersey.

New Mexico

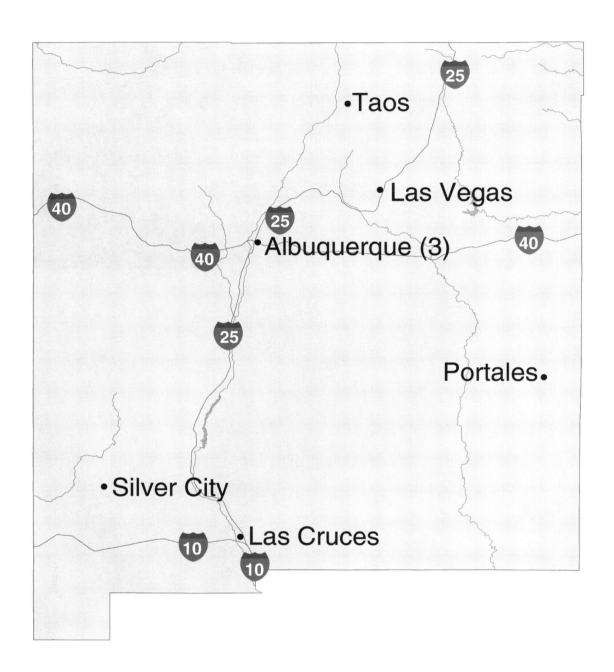

The number in parentheses following the city name indicates the number of museums/galleries in that municipality. If there is no number, one is understood. For example, in the text three listings would be found under Albuquerque and one listing under Portales.

New Mexico

Albuquerque

The University of New Mexico Art Museum (C44)

UNM Fine Arts Center (just north of Cornell and Central, NE)
Albuquerque, NM   87131-1416
Tel: (505) 277-4001
Fax: (505) 277-7315
Internet Address: http://www.unm.edu%7Efinearts/museum.htm
Director: Mr. Peter Walch
Admission: voluntary contribution.
Attendance: 43,000   *Established:* 1963
Membership: Y   *ADA Compliant:* Y
Parking: free behind Jonson Gallery, or pay lot in front of Museum.
Open: Tuesday, 9am-4pm and 5pm-8pm;
Wednesday to Friday, 9am-4pm;
Sunday, 1pm-4pm.
Closed: UNM Holidays.
Facilities: **Exhibition Area** (2 floors, 5 galleries); **Print and Photography Study Room** (by appointment); **Sculpture Garden**; **Shop** (gifts, jewelry, art books).
Activities: **Education Programs** (school groups and graduate students); **Gallery Talks**; **Guided Tours** (by appointment, reserve two weeks in advance); **Lectures** (during semester, Tues, 5:30pm; 1st Tues of month at Jonson Gallery); **Temporary Exhibitions**; **Traveling Exhibitions**.
Publications: calendar (semi-annual); exhibition catalogues; gallery guides.

Georgia O'Keeffe, *White Flowers*, 1926, oil on canvas. Estate of Georgia O'Keeffe. University Art Museum. Photo by Damian Andrus, courtesy of University Art Museum, University of New Mexico, Albuquerque, New Mexico.

The University Art Museum, located in the University of New Mexico's Center for the Arts, houses over 24,000 works of art. The permanent collection includes European art from the Renaissance to contemporary times, Hispanic traditions in the Old World and the New, and American 19th- and 20th-century art in the modernist tradition. A special strength is its photography and print collection, one of the finest of university art museums nationwide. The public can enjoy five galleries of changing exhibitions, and a print/photo seminar room, which may be visited by appointment. Also of possible interest is the 516 University Art Museum Downtown. A collaboration of the University Art Museum and the Maxwell Museum of Anthropology, the gallery presents changing exhibits (516 Central Ave., N.E.; open Tues-Sat, 10am-4pm; tel 242-8244).

University of New Mexico Art Museum - Jonson Gallery (C44)

1909 Las Lomas, N.E., Albuquerque, NM   87131
Tel: (505) 277-4967
Fax: (505) 277-3188
Internet Address: http://www.unm.edu%7Efinearts/museum.htm
Curator: Ms. Tiska Blankenship
Admission: free.
Attendance: 4,000   *Established:* 1950   *Membership:* Y   *ADA Compliant:* Y
Parking: free in lot behind Gallery.
Open: Tuesday, 9am-4pm and 5pm-8pm; Wednesday to Friday, 9am-4pm.
Closed: Legal Holidays.
Facilities: **Exhibition Areas** (permanent and temporary); **Galleries**; **Library** (400 volumes).
Activities: **Gallery Talks** (during semester, 1st Tues in month, 5:30pm); **Permanent Exhibits**; **Temporary Exhibitions**.
Publications: exhibition catalogues.

University of New Mexico Art Museum - Jonson Gallery, cont.

Abranch of the University of New Mexico Museum of Art, the Jonson Gallery, houses works by modernist painter Raymond Jonson, his contemporaries, and his students. For information on the University of New Mexico Art Museum see separate listing.

University of New Mexico - Tamarind Institute Gallery ⓒ⁴⁹

108-110 Cornell Drive S.E., Albuquerque, NM   87106
Tel: (505) 277-3901   *Fax:* (505) 277-3920
Internet Address: http://www.unm.edu/~tamarind/history.html
Director: Ms. Marjorie Devon
Admission: free.
Established: 1960
Open: Tuesday to Friday, 9am-5pm.
Facilities: **Archive** (3,000 lithographs); **Gallery**.
Activities: **Guided Tours** (1st Fri in month, 1:30pm, reserve in advance).
Publications: lithographs.

Established in Los Angeles in 1960 as the Tamarind Lithography Workshop, for the purpose of preserving the fine art of lithography, it became the Tamarind Institute in 1970, affiliating with the University of New Mexico and relocating to Albuquerque. The Institute engages in education, research, and creative programs funded partially by the University and supplemented by revenue from contract printing and the sale of its published limited edition lithographs. The Gallery, located adjacent to the workshop exhibits a selection of recent prints made at Tamarind by nationally and internationally recognized artists who have been invited to collaborate with Tamarind's master printers. The Institute's archives of approximately 3,000 lithographs is housed in the University of New Mexico Art Museum.

Las Cruces

New Mexico State University - University Art Gallery ⓒ⁴⁹

Williams Hall, University Ave. (east of Solano), Las Cruces, NM   88003-8001
Tel: (505) 646-2545
Fax: (505) 646-8036
Internet Address: http://www.nmsu.edu/campus_life/artgal.html
Director: Mr. Charles Muir Lovell
Admission: free.
Attendance: 18,000   *Established:* 1974
Membership: Y   *ADA Compliant:* Y
Parking: spaces reserved for gallery visitors.
Open: Tuesday to Wednesday, 10am-5pm;
          Thursday, 10am-7pm;
          Friday to Saturday, 10am-5pm;
          Sunday, 1pm-5pm.
Closed: Easter, Memorial Day, Labor Day,
          Independence Day, Thanksgiving Day,
          Christmas Day, University Holidays.
Facilities: **Facility** (12,000 square feet); **Galleries** (4,600
    square feet).
Activities: **Films/Videos**; **Gallery Talks**; **Guided Tours**
    (school and community groups, reservations required, 646-
    6110); **Lectures**; **Temporary Exhibitions** (10-12/year);
    Traveling Exhibitions; **Workshops**.

Anonymous, *El Alma de Maria (The Soul of Mary)*, 19th century, oil on tin, 14 x 10 inches, Mexico. University Art Gallery. Photograph by Mike Laurance, courtesy of University Art Gallery, New Mexico State University, Las Cruces, New Mexico.

New Mexico State University - University Art Gallery, cont.

Publications: newsletter, "Visiones" (semi-annual).

The University Art Gallery at New Mexico State University is the largest contemporary art gallery in South Central New Mexico. The Gallery presents 10-12 exhibitions annually of historical and contemporary art in various media, and works from the Gallery's permanent collection. Annual and biennial exhibitions feature the work of undergraduate students, graduate students, and faculty of the Department of Art at NMSU, and the juried "Close To The Border Exhibition" presents artists from the border region of the U.S. and Mexico. The Gallery also sponsors an extensive educational program. A permanent collection of approximately 2,750 objects includes 1,700 19th-century Mexican retablos, one of the largest collections of its kind in the country. Other objects in the collection include contemporary prints, historical and contemporary photographs, paintings, graphics, book arts, and works on paper.

Las Vegas

New Mexico Highlands University - Fine Arts Gallery Ⓒ⁴⁴

National Ave., Las Vegas, NM   87701

Tel: (505) 454-3338

Fax: (505) 454-0026

Internet Address: http://www.nmhu.edu

Director: Mr. Bob Read

Admission: free.

Attendance: 5,000   *Established:* 1982   *ADA Compliant:* P

Open: Monday to Friday, 8am-noon and 1pm-5pm.

Closed: Christmas Day to New Year's Day.

Facilities: **Exhibition Area** (800 square feet).

Activities: **Temporary Exhibitions**.

Publications: "Folklore Printouts".

The Gallery presents temporary exhibitions including an annual "retablo y bulto" show. NMHU's Donnelly Library collection of fine arts contains more than 100 artworks, including both student work as well as regionally and nationally known artists. Such painters as Fremont Ellis, a member of Los Cinco Pintores, and Joseph Fleck, a founding member of the Taos Society of Artists, are represented.

Portales

Eastern New Mexico University - Runnels Gallery Ⓒ⁴⁴

Golden Library, Portales, NM   88130

Tel: (505) 562-2778

Internet Address: http://www.enmu.edu/~bryant/runnels.html

Admission: free.

Open: **August 15 to June 6**,
   Monday to Thursday, 7:30am-11pm; Friday, 7:30am-8pm; Saturday, 10am-7pm;
   Sunday, noon-11pm.
  June 7 to August 14,
   Monday to Thursday, 7am-10pm; Friday, 7am-5pm; Saturday, 10am-5pm;
   Sunday, noon-10pm.

Facilities: **Exhibition Area**.

Activities: **Juried Exhibits**; **Temporary Exhibitions**.

Located in the University's Golden Library, the Runnels Gallery presents two national juried shows, "Scene/Unscene" and "New Mexico Photographer", along with a Student Art Show, Senior Art Shows, and other exhibits. Other artwork and displays, including sculptures from the Purcell African Art Collection, wood carvings from the Tex Hasse Collection, and numerous paintings, prints, and photographs, are on display at other locations throughout the Library.

Silver City

Western New Mexico University - Francis McCray Gallery ⓒᴬᴬ

Western New Mexico University, 1000 W. College Ave.
Silver City, NM   88062
Tel: (505) 538-6614
Fax: (505) 538-6155
Internet Address: http://www.wnmu.edu
Director: Ms. Gloria Maya
Admission: free.
Attendance: 2,400   *Established:* 1960   *ADA Compliant:* Y
Open: **September to May**, Monday to Friday, 9am-4pm.
Closed: University Holidays.
Facilities: **Exhibition Area** (1,600 square feet); **Theatre** (990 seats).
Activities: **Arts Festival**; **Concerts**; **Dance Recitals**; **Education Programs** (college students); **Films**; **Lectures**; **Rental Gallery**; **Temporary Exhibitions**; **Traveling Exhibitions**.
Publications: flyer (monthly).

The Gallery presents temporary exhibitions. The University's permanent collections feature 20th-century Japanese printmaking.

Taos

University of New Mexico - The Harwood Museum ⓒᴬᴬ

238 Ledoux St.
Taos, NM   87571-6004
Tel: (505) 758-9826
Fax: (505) 758-1475
Internet Address: http://www.laplaza.org/
   a.l/art/local.museums.harwood.html
Director: Mr. Robert M. Ellis
Admission: fee-$4.00.
Attendance: 24,000   *Established:* 1923
Membership: Y
Parking: across from museum, off Ranchitos
   Road.
Open: Tuesday to Saturday, 10am-5pm;
      Sunday, noon-5pm.
Closed: New Year's Day, ML King Day,
      Memorial Day, Independence Day,
      Labor Day, Thanksgiving Day,
      Christmas Day.

Interior view of Dorothy and Jack Brandenburg Gallery for Early 20th Century Art, Harwood Museum of University of New Mexico. Photograph courtesy of Harwood Museum of University of New Mexico, Taos, New Mexico.

Facilities: **Architecture** (Pueblo Revival structure with 1937 expansion by John Gaw Meem); **Exhibition Area** (7 galleries); **Shop** (books, catalogues, crafts).
Activities: **Concerts**; **Lectures**; **Permanent Exhibits**; **Temporary Exhibitions** (6-8/year).
Publications: exhibition catalogues; newsletter (quarterly).

Founded in 1923 and operated by the University of New Mexico since 1936, the Harwood is the second oldest museum in the state and is listed on the State and National Registers of Historic Places. In 1923, Elizabeth Case Harwood and a group of Taos artists created the Harwood Foundation as a private nonprofit organization to serve as a library, museum and educational center. Later the Foundation was given to the University of New Mexico. The Museum features paintings, drawings, prints, sculpture and photography by artists from Taos and the region displayed in seven galleries. A gallery for changing exhibitions mounts up to six installations per year dealing with traditional or historic issues as well as contemporary artistic trends. The Harwood's permanent collection consists of over 1,200 works of art and a photographic archive of 17,000 images spanning a period from the 19th

University of New Mexico - The Harwood Museum, cont.

century to the present. It includes 19th-century retablos (religious paintings on wood) and works by 20th-century artists. Works on view range from the early days of the art colony, including paintings by Victor Higgins, Oscar Berninghaus and other members of the Taos Society of Artists; through the Taos Moderns, a post-World War II group of modernist painters; to contemporary works by artists such as Larry Bell, Bea Mandelman, Louis Ribak, Agnes Martin, and Earl Stroh, as well as a special gallery housing seven paintings given to the Museum by internationally acclaimed artist and Taos resident, Agnes Martin. The Museum also has an important collection of Hispanic works that covers a broad range of the historic traditions of Northern New Mexico, including the largest public collection of wood sculptures by Patrociño Barela.

New York

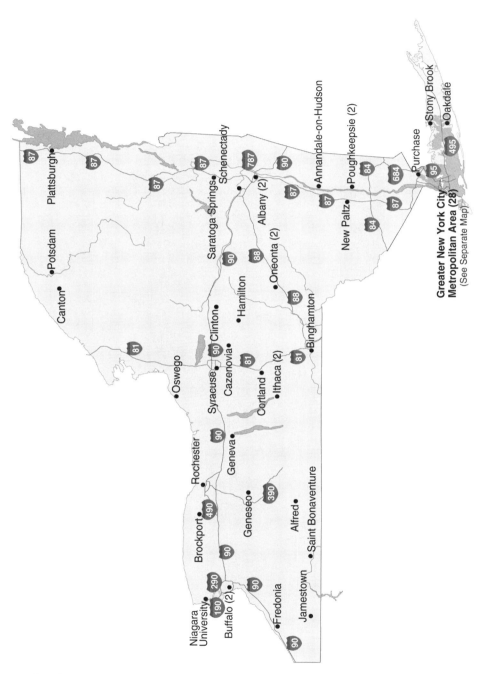

The number in parentheses following the city name indicates the number of museums/galleries in that municipality. If there is no number, one is understood. For example, in the text two listings would be found under Albany and one listing under Annandale-on-Hudson. Cities, boroughs, and communities within the greater New York metropolitan area will be found on the map on the facing page.

Greater New York City Metropolitan Area

(including, Bayside, Bronx, Brooklyn, Brookville, Flushing, Garden City, Hempstead, Jamaica, Long Island City, Manhattan,New Rochelle, Queens, and Staten Island.)

Please note that the boroughs of Bronx, Brooklyn, Manhattan, Queens, and Staten Island appear alphabetically under New York City. Any institution located in New York City not using a borough name in its address will be found under the borough in which the institution is located.

The number in parentheses following a city, borough, or community name indicates the number of museums/galleries in that place. If there is no number, one is understood. For example, in the text two listings would be found under Garden City and one listing under Hempstead. The number in parentheses following a borough name represents the total number of institutions in the borough including all institutions located in communities within that borough (i.e. Queens (5) includes institutions in Bayside, Flushing, Jamaica, and Long Island City).

New York

Albany

Sage Junior College of Albany - Rathbone Gallery

140 New Scotland Ave.
Albany, NY 12208
Tel: (518) 292-1778
Fax: (518) 292-1910
Internet Address: http://www.sage.edu/
   html/JCA/studlife/rathbone/gal.htm
Director: Mr. Jim Richard Wilson
Admission: free.
Attendance: 2,000
Membership: N   *ADA Compliant:* N
Open: **Fall to Spring**,
        Monday, 10am-4pm;
        Tues to Thurs, 10am-4pm & 6pm-8pm;
        Friday, 10am-4pm;
        Sunday, noon-4pm.
         Summer, call for hours.
Closed: between exhibitions.
Facilities: **Exhibition Area** (2 galleries,
   575 square feet).

Tony Reinemann, *East 32nd Street*, oil on maisonette, 8 x 12 inches. Alumni Juried Exhibition, 1998, Rathbone Gallery, Sage Junior College of Albany. Photograph courtesy of Rathbone Gallery, The Sage Colleges, Albany, New York.

Activities: **Temporary Exhibitions** (6/year).
Publications: collection catalogue (occasional).

Housed in Rathbone Hall on the Sage Albany Campus, the Rathbone Gallery is the formal exhibition space of The Sage Colleges. The Gallery mounts six exhibitions during the academic year focusing on the work of professional artists from outside the region. During the summer months, the Gallery hosts exhibitions organized by community-based arts organizations. The Gallery frequently features multi-disciplinary projects and also hosts poetry readings, recitals, and symposia, often in conjunction with its exhibitions

University at Albany, SUNY - University Art Museum ⓒ

University at Albany, SUNY, 1400 Washington Ave., Albany, NY 12222
Tel: (518) 442-4035   *Fax:* (518) 442-5075
Internet Address: http://www.albany.edu/museum/
Director: Ms. Marijo Dougherty
Admission: voluntary contribution.
Attendance: 38,000   *Established:* 1967   *ADA Compliant:* Y
Parking: Collins Circle at Washington Ave. campus entrance.
Open: Tuesday to Friday, 10am-5pm; Saturday to Sunday, noon-4pm.
Closed: Legal Holidays.
Facilities: **Galleries** (3).
Activities: **Films**; **Gallery Talks**; **Lectures**; **Temporary Exhibitions**.
Publications: exhibition catalogues.

The Museum's permanent collection consists of some 1,600 works of contemporary art, which it displays in temporary exhibitions.

Alfred

Alfred University - The International Museum of Ceramic Art ⓒ (IMCA)

Ceramics Corridor Innovation Center, 2nd Fl., Main St. (Route 244)
Alfred, NY 14802
Tel: (607) 871-2421   *Fax:* (607) 871-2615
Internet Address: http://nyscc.alfred.edu/mus/mus.html
Director and Chief Curator: Dr. Margaret Carney

Alfred University - The International Museum of Ceramic Art, cont.

Admission: free.

Established: 1900

Membership: Y   *ADA Compliant:* Y

Parking: free behind building.

Open: Tuesday to Sunday, 10am-5pm.

Closed: Academic Holidays.

Facilities: **Exhibition Area** (3 galleries); **Library** (5,000 volumes).

Activities: **Education Programs** (undergraduate and graduate college students); **Guided Tours** (groups, schedule 2 weeks in advance); **Lectures**; **Temporary Exhibitions**.

Publications: exhibition   catalogues;   newsletter, "Ceramophile" (semi-annual).

Charles   Fergus   Binns,   *ovate   vase*,   1929, stoneware,   glazed,   height   19.1   cm.   Binns Collection, International Museum of Ceramic Art. Photograph courtesy of the International Museum of Ceramic Art, Alfred University, Alfred, New York.

Apart of the New York State College of Ceramics at Alfred University, the International Museum of Ceramic Art presents exhibitions drawn from its permanent collection, temporary thematic displays on varying topics, and historical exhibits. IMCA houses nearly 8,000 ceramic and glass objects, ranging from small pottery shards recovered from ancient civilizations to contemporary sculpture and installation pieces to modern ceramics reflecting recent advances in ceramic technology. The collection, in addition to graduate thesis ceramics created by Alfred-educated ceramists, includes works by Rosanjin, Leach, Hamada, and Rie, Chinese funerary jars and tomb sculpture from the Neolithic period onward, Roman and Byzantine lamps, Nigerian market pottery, and European dinnerware. IMCA's current location is temporary, the New York City architectural firm of Hardy Holzman Pfeiffer has completed the design for a permanent facility. Also of possible interest at Alfred University, are the Fine Art Department's Fosdick-Nelson Gallery (871-2411) in Charles Harder Hall (open, Mon-Fri, 11am-4pm; Sat, 7pm-9pm; and Sun, 1pm-3pm) and the Student Gallery in Herrick Memorial Library.

Annandale on Hudson

Bard College - The Center for Curatorial Studies and Art in Contemporary Culture Museum Ⓒ⁴⁴

Bard College (off Route 9G)

Annandale on Hudson, NY   12504

Tel: (914) 758-7598   *Fax:* (914) 758-2442

Internet Address: http://www.bard.edu/

Director: Ms. Amanda Cruz

Admission: free.

Attendance: 4,200   *Established:* 1990   *ADA Compliant:* Y

Parking: free on site.

Open: **February to December**, Wednesday to Sunday, 1pm-5pm.

Closed: New Year's Day, Easter, Thanksgiving Day, Christmas Day.

Facilities: **Auditorium** (40 seats); **Exhibition Area** (9,500 square feet); **Library** (8,000 volumes).

Activities: **Education Programs** (adults, undergraduate & graduate college students); **Lectures**; **Temporary Exhibitions**.

The Museum presents an extensive schedule of exhibitions of works by internationally important contemporary artists. The Center, the only accredited program in the nation offering a graduate degree in curatorial studies, also sponsors a lecture series and public programs. The Center's permanent collection, The Rivendell Collection of Late Twentieth-Century Art, consists of nearly 1,000 works by over 200 artists including paintings, sculptures, photographs, works on paper, videos, and video

Bard College - Center for Curatorial Studies Museum, cont.

installations from the mid-1960s to the present. The collection is international in scope with works from Europe, Japan, Latin America, the Middle East, and the United States. Works in the Rivendell Collection are available to graduate students, faculty, and guest curators for study and for use in exhibitions at the Center, including students' master's degree exhibitions.

Binghamton

State University of New York at Binghamton - University Art Museum Ⓒᴬ

SUNY at Binghamton, Fine Arts Building (off Route 434 E., 1 mile west of Binghamton)
Binghamton, NY 13902-6000
Tel: (607) 777-2634
Fax: (607) 777-4000
Internet Address: http://www.binghamton.edu
Director: Lynn Gramwell
Admission: free.
Established: 1967
Open: Tuesday to Friday, 1pm-4pm.
Closed: Academic Holidays.
Facilities: **Exhibition Area**; **Library** (50,000 volumes).
Activities: **Lectures**; **Temporary Exhibitions**.
Publications: calendar; exhibition catalogues; newsletter.

The University Art Museum has an Asian Art Gallery and a permanent collection of art representing many periods and styles. On regular display are special traveling and loan exhibits as well as works of University artists.

Brockport

State University of New York, Brockport - Tower Fine Arts Gallery Ⓒᴬ

SUNY at Brockport, Tower Fine Arts Center, Holley St.
Brockport, NY 14420-2985
Tel: (716) 395-2209
Fax: (716) 395-2588
Internet Address: http://cc.brockport.edu/~art001/arthome.htm
Admission: free.
Attendance: 6,000   *Established:* 1964   *ADA Compliant:* Y
Parking: free on site.
Open: Tuesday to Wednesday, noon-5pm and 7pm-9pm; Thursday to Saturday, noon-5pm.
Facilities: **Exhibition Area** (1,500 square feet).
Activities: **Arts Festival**; **Exhibits** (7/year); **Lectures**.
Publications: exhibition catalogues.

The Gallery mounts temporary exhibitions of the work of both students and professional artists.

Brookville

C.W. Post Campus of Long Island University - Hillwood Art Museum Ⓒᴬ

Long Island University, C.W. Post Campus, 720 Northern Blvd.
Brookville, NY 11548-1300
Tel: (516) 299-4073
Fax: (516) 299-4180
Internet Address: http://www.liu.edu/cwis/cwp/but06/hillwood/museum.html
Director of Operations: Mr. Barry Stern
Admission: free.
Attendance: 12,500   *Established:* 1973   *Membership:* Y   *ADA Compliant:* Y
Parking: free on site.

C.W. Post Campus of Long Island University - Hillwood Art Museum, cont.

Open: **September to May**,
> Monday to Tuesday, 9:30am-4:30pm; Wednesday, 9:30am-7:30pm;
> Thursday, 9:30am-4:30pm; Friday, 9:30am-7:30pm; Saturday to Sunday, noon-4pm.
> **Summer**, Weekdays, call for hours.

Facilities: **Exhibition Area** (numerous galleries); **Food Services** Restaurant; **Sculpture Garden**; **Shop**.

Activities: **Guided Tours** (by appointment only, groups limited to 30); **Lectures**; **Performances**; **Temporary Exhibitions** (4-5 major shows/year).

Publications: exhibition catalogues.

The Museum presents a schedule of temporary exhibitions, lectures and demonstrations emphasizing the ethnic and cultural diversity of the region. Its permanent collection consists of over 350 works, including pre-Columbian artifacts, contemporary American and European prints, Asian art, Persian bronzes, Islamic glass, and contemporary photography, as well as a large portion of the archives of early abstract impressionist artist Esphyr Slobokina. The Museum mounts temporary exhibitions of works from its collection and from other institutions.

Buffalo

State University College at Buffalo - Burchfield-Penney Art Center Ⓒ⁴⁴

State University College at Buffalo
1300 Elmwood Ave., Rockwell Hall
Buffalo, NY 14222
Tel: (716) 878-6011
Fax: (716) 878-6003
TDDY: (716) 878-6012
Internet Address:
 http://www.burchfield-penney.org
Director: Mr. Ted Pietrzak
Admission: voluntary contribution.
Attendance: 50,000   *Established:* 1966
Membership: Y   *ADA Compliant:* Y
Parking: lot behind Rockwell Hall off Iriquois Drive.
Open: Tuesday to Saturday, 10am-5pm;
 Sunday, 1pm-5pm.
Closed: Legal Holidays.
Facilities: **Exhibition Area** (10 galleries; main gallery 3,060 square feet); **Library** (2,500 volumes); **Shop**.

Charles E. Burchfield, *Windblown Asters*, 1951, watercolor, 29 5/8 x 39 5/8 inches. Anonymous gift, 1967, Burchfield-Penney Art Center. Photograph courtesy of Burchfield-Penney Art Center, State University College at Buffalo, Buffalo, New York.

Activities: **Artist-in-Residence Program**; **Concerts** (approximately monthly); **Education Programs** (adults, college students and children); **Gallery Talks** (monthly); **Guided Tours** (by appointment); **Lectures** (monthly); **Readings** (poetry); **Temporary Exhibitions** (8 major/year).

Publications: exhibition catalogues; newsletter, "Burchfield-Penney Art Center" (bi-monthly).

Located on the third floor of Rockwell Hall on the campus of State University College at Buffalo (directly across from the Albright-Knox Art Gallery), the Art Center celebrates the excellence of contemporary and historic art from throughout the region. It organizes approximately eight major exhibitions a year for its main gallery, with rotating temporary installations and exhibitions of the permanent collection being held in the remaining galleries. Specific galleries are dedicated to watercolorist Charles E. Burchfield, beaux-arts sculptor Charles Cary Rumsey, craft art, and Roycroft objects. The Museum's holdings total more than 5,400 items, including the world's largest collection of the work of Charles E. Burchfield and augmented by works of his colleagues and contemporaries such as Thomas Hart Benton, John Carroll, George William Eggers, Marsden Hartley, Reginald Marsh, Eugene Speicher, and Grant Wood. In addition, the Center's collection includes paintings, prints, drawings, photographs, sculpture, and media art representing a broad spectrum of established and emerging Western New York artists.

Buffalo, New York

University at Buffalo Art Gallery (UBAG)

SUNY at Buffalo, North (Amherst) Campus
201A Center for the Arts (off Coventry St)
Buffalo, NY   14260-6000
Tel: (716) 645-6912   *Ext:* 1420
Fax: (716) 645-6753
Internet Address:
   http://www.artgallery.buffalo.edu
Director and Curator: Mr. Al Harris
Admission: free.
Attendance: 25,000   *Established:* 1994
Membership: N   *ADA Compliant:* Y
Parking: free after 3pm and weekends.
Open: **Fall to Spring**,
            Wednesday to Saturday, 10:30am-8pm
            Sunday, noon-5pm.
         Summer,
            Monday to Sunday, noon-5pm.

Harvey Breverman, *Cabal II* (center panel of triptych), 1987-1988, pastel on paper. Gift of Will and Nan Clarkson, University of Buffalo Art Gallery. Photograph courtesy of University of Buffalo Art Gallery, Buffalo, New York.

Closed: Independence Day, Labor Day, Thanksgiving Day, Christmas Break.
Facilities: **Exhibition Area** (10,000 square feet); **Library**.
Activities: **Education Programs** (adults and college students); **Temporary Exhibitions** (6-8/year);
      Traveling Exhibitions.
Publications: books; compilation (annual); exhibition brochures (8/year).

The Gallery emphasizes temporary exhibitions of contemporary art that reflect the diversity of issues and practices found in current art practice and theory. Its core program consists of six to eight exhibitions per year, occasionally featuring work from the University's permanent collection. The Gallery is housed in the Center for the Arts, designed by Gwathmey and Siegel.

Canton

St. Lawrence University - Richard F. Brush Art Gallery & Permanent Collection

Griffiths Art Center, Romoda Drive, Canton, NY   13617
Tel: (315) 229-5174   *Fax:* (315) 229-5502
Internet Address: http://www.stlawu.edu/gallery
Director: Ms. Catherine L. Tedford
Admission: free.
Attendance: 3,000   *Established:* 1967   *ADA Compliant:* Y
Open: Monday to Thursday, noon-8pm; Friday to Saturday, noon-5pm.
Closed: Academic Recesses.
Facilities: **Auditorium** (75 seat); **Galleries** (3).
Activities: **Arts Festival**; **Films**; **Gallery Talks**; **Lectures**; **Temporary Exhibitions**; **Traveling Exhibitions**.
Publications: exhibition brochures.

The Gallery's permanent collection includes nearly 7,000 art objects and artifacts, with particular strengths in 20th-century American and European works on paper, including photographs, prints, drawings, and artists' books. The gallery also mounts temporary exhibitions accompanied by related activities.

Cazenovia

Cazenovia College - Gertrude T. Chapman Art Center Gallery (CACG)

Nickerson St. (between Sullivan and Lincklaen Sts.), Cazenovia, NY   13035
Tel: (315) 655-7162   *Fax:* (315) 655-2190
Internet Address: http://www.cazcollege.edu
Director: Mr. John Aistairs

Cazenovia College - Gertrude T. Chapman Art Center Gallery, cont

Admission: free.

Attendance: 600   *Established:* 1978

Parking: on campus.

Open: **Academic Year**,
Monday to Thursday, 1pm-4pm and 7pm-9pm; Friday, 1pm-4pm;
Saturday to Sunday, 2pm-6pm.

Closed: Academic Holidays.

Facilities: **Exhibition Area** (1,064 square feet).

Activities: **Lectures** (occasional, by artists); **Temporary Exhibitions**.

The gallery houses a small permanent collection. In addition, it mounts one- and two-person exhibitions, as well as invitational and juried shows (e.g., student and faculty shows). Also of possible interest on campus is the Chapman Cultural Center Gallery (Tel 655-9446). A 1,000-square foot, bi-level gallery with a balcony overlooking a main exhibit hall, the Gallery presents seven to eight exhibitions of the work of local and regional artists each year. Holdings are minimal, with most artwork displayed on campus.

Clinton

Hamilton College - Emerson Gallery ⓒⁱⁱ

Hamilton College, 198 College Hill Road, Clinton, NY   13323

Tel: (315) 859-4396   *Fax:* (315) 859-4687

Internet Address: http://www.hamilton.edu

Director: Ms. Lise Holst

Admission: free.

Attendance: 5,500   *Established:* 1982   *Membership:* Y   *ADA Compliant:* Y

Parking: free on site.

Open: **Fall to Spring**,
Monday to Friday, noon-5pm; Saturday to Sunday, 1pm-5pm.
Summer,
Monday to Friday, 1pm-5pm.

Facilities: **Galleries** (3).

Activities: **Concerts**; **Films**; **Guided Tours**; **Lectures**; **Temporary Exhibitions** (6-7/year).

Publications: exhibition catalogues.

Located on the first floor of Christian A. Johnson Hall, the Emerson Art Gallery has an active schedule of temporary exhibitions. Its permanent collection is strong in American and British works on paper and also includes paintings and sculpture, collections of Greek vases, Roman glass and Native American objects.

Cortland

State University of New York at Cortland - Dowd Fine Arts Gallery ⓒⁱⁱ

SUNY at Cortland, Dowd Fine Arts Center (off State Route 222), Cortland, NY   13045

Tel: (607) 753-4216   *Fax:* (607) 753-5999

Internet Address: http://www.cortland.edu

Director: Ms. Janet B. Steck

Admission: voluntary contribution.

Attendance: 15,000   *Established:* 1967   *ADA Compliant:* Y

Parking: free adjacent to site.

Open: **Academic Year**, Tuesday to Saturday, 11am-4pm.

Closed: Academic Holidays, Thanksgiving Weekend.

Facilities: **Exhibition Area** (2,500 square feet); **Sculpture Garden**.

Activities: **Guided Tours**; **Lectures**; **Temporary Exhibitions**; **Visiting Artist Program**.

The Gallery presents a diverse program of exhibitions, visiting artists, and lecturers.

Fredonia

State University of New York at Fredonia - Michael C. Rockefeller Arts Center Galleries ⓒⁱⁱ

SUNY at Fredonia (off Central Ave.), Fredonia, NY   14063
Tel: (716) 673-3538
Internet Address: http://www.fredonia.edu
Director: Mr. Marvin Bjurlin
Admission: free.
Attendance: 2,000   *Established:* 1826   *ADA Compliant:* Y
Open: Wednesday to Sunday, 2pm-8pm.
Closed: Legal Holidays, Academic Holidays.
Facilities: **Architecture** Rockefeller Art Center (1969 design by I.M. Pei and Associates); **Galleries** (Main Gallery, 2,000 square feet; Christian Gallery, 600 square feet).
Activities: **Temporary Exhibitions**; **Traveling Exhibitions**.

The Rockefeller Arts Center (RAC) contains two galleries administered by the College's Department of Art .On the first floor, the Main Gallery presents temporary exhibitions of student work as well as faculty shows and group shows by off campus artists in a wide variety of media. The annual student exhibition program features three groups shows of work by graduating seniors (one at the end of the fall semester and two at the end of the spring semester) and a show each spring drawn from the best work created in fall semester art courses. The Emmitt Christian Gallery, located on the second floor, mounts small group and solo shows of student art work.

Garden City

Adelphi University Art Galleries ⓒⁱⁱ

Ruth S. Harley University Center Art Gallery (off South Ave.), Garden City, NY   11530
Tel: (516) 877-4460
Internet Address: http://www.adelphi.edu
Director: Professor Richard Vaux
Open: Monday to Friday, 1pm-7pm.
Facilities: **Exhibition Area.**
Activities: **Temporary Exhibitions.**

The Gallery presents a schedule of temporary exhibitions including faculty and alumni shows. Also of possible interest is the Adelphi University Manhattan Center Gallery located at 75 Varick St., 2nd Floor, New York, NY 10013 - (212) 431-5161.

Nassau Community College - Firehouse Art Gallery

1 Education Drive, Garden City, NY   11530
Tel: (516) 572-7165   *Fax:* (516) 572-7302
Internet Address: http://www.sunynassau.edu
Director: Ms. Janet R. Marzo
Admission: free.
Attendance: 12,000   *Established:* 1965   *Membership:* N   *ADA Compliant:* Y
Parking: student lot in front of building.
Open: **September to May,**
      Monday to Tuesday, 11:30am-4:30pm; Wednesday, 11:30am-7pm;
      Thursday, 11:30am-4:30pm; Saturday to Sunday, 1pm-5pm.
Closed: Academic Holidays, Summer.
Facilities: **Exhibition Area** (2 gallery rooms).
Activities: **Guided Tours** (available upon request); **Lectures** (monthly); **Temporary Exhibitions.**
Publications: calendar; exhibition catalogues (monthly).

The Gallery presents six temporary exhibits during the school year in conjunction with art courses being taught at Nassau.

Geneseo

State University of New York College at Geneseo - Bertha V.B. Lederer Fine Arts Gallery

SUNY at Geneseo, 1 College Circle, Brodie Fine Arts Building
Geneseo, NY 14454
Tel: (716) 245-5814   *Fax:* (716) 245-5815
Internet Address: http://www.geneseo.edu
C.E.O.: Ms. Janet Jackson
Admission: free.
Attendance: 2,000   *Established:* 1967   *ADA Compliant:* Y
Open: Monday to Wednesday, 2pm-5pm; Thursday, noon-8pm; Friday to Sunday, 2pm-5pm.
Facilities: **Architecture** (Brodie Fine Arts Building, 1967 design by Edgar Tafel); **Exhibition Area**; **Library** (100 volumes).
Activities: **Temporary Exhibitions.**
Publications: bulletins.

The Gallery presents temporary exhibitions of the work of students, faculty, and regional artists.

Geneva

Hobart and William Smith Colleges - Houghton House Gallery

Houghton House, 1 Kings Lane, Geneva, NY 14456
Tel: (315) 781-3487   *Fax:* (315) 781-3689
Internet Address: http://www.hws.edu/aca/depts/art/art_gallery.html
Director: Ms. Linda K. Karol
Admission: free.
Parking: off street parking available.
Open: Monday to Saturday, 9am-5pm.
Facilities: **Architecture** (Eclectic Victorian mansion, 1880); **Exhibition Area**.
Activities: **Temporary Exhibitions** (5-6/year).

Housed in a former summer residence, the Gallery presents exhibitions of the work of guest artists, faculty, and students.

Hamilton

Colgate University - The Picker Art Gallery

Charles A. Dana Center for the Creative Arts, 13 Oak Drive
Hamilton, NY 13346-1380
Tel: (315) 824-7746
Fax: (315) 228-7932
Internet Address: http://picker.colgate.edu
Director: Mr. Dewey F. Mosby
Admission: free.
Attendance: 12,000   *Established:* 1966
Membership: Y   *ADA Compliant:* Y
Parking: free on site.
Open: **In Session**,
   Daily, 10am-5pm.
   Academic Holidays
   Mon to Fri, 9am-noon & 1pm-4pm,
   walk in request.
Closed: National Holidays.

Sam Francis, *Untitled*, monotype. Gift of Dr. Luther W. Brady, DFA '88. Picker Art Gallery. Photograph courtesy of Picker Art Gallery, Colgate University, Hamilton, New York.

Colgate University - The Picker Art Gallery, cont.

Facilities: **Architecture** (Dana Arts Center, designed by Paul Rudolph); **Galleries** (3); **Graphic Arts Study Room**; **Sculpture Court** (outdoor).

Activities: **Films**; **Gallery Talks**; **Guided Tours**; **Lectures**; **Temporary Exhibitions**; **Traveling Exhibitions**.

Publications: bulletin; exhibition catalogues; journal (annual).

Located in the Dana Arts Center on the campus of Colgate University, the Gallery has collections in all media and from all periods of art history from Egyptian bronzes and Old Master paintings to African masks and Abstract Expressionist sculpture. Works from the permanent collection are displayed in the Inner and Outer galleries and on the Sculpture Court, while special exhibitions are usually on view in the Upper Gallery. Five to six exhibitions, many of them borrowed from national and international sources, are held each year with themes chosen to complement or highlight strengths of the permanent collection and the Colgate University curriculum. Holdings exceed 12,000 works. Highlights include the Dr. Luther W. Brady DFA '88 Collection of 20th-Century Works on Paper, the Gary M. Hoffer '74 Memorial Photography Collection, the Herman Collection of Chinese Woodcuts, the Luis de Hoyos '43 Guerrero Stones Collection, and the Evgeny Khaldei Collection of photographs.

Hempstead

Hofstra University Museum ⓒ

Emily Lowe Gallery, Lowe Hall
(off Hempstead Turnpike)
Hempstead, NY   11549
Tel: (516) 463-5671
Fax: (516) 463-4832
Internet Address: hyttp://www.hofstra.edu
Director: Mr. David C. Christman
Admission: voluntary contribution-$2.00.
Attendance: 15,000   *Established:* 1963
Membership: Y   *ADA Compliant:* Y
Parking: free on site.
Open: **September to May**,
   Tuesday, 10am-9pm;
   Wednesday to Friday, 10am-5pm;
   Saturday to Sunday, 1pm-5pm.
   June to August,
   Tuesday to Friday, 10am-4pm.
Closed: Legal Holidays.

Paul Gauguin, *Portrait of a Woman / The Model Julliette*, 1881-82. Hofstra Museum. Photograph courtesy of Hofstra Museum, Hofstra University, Hempstead, New York.

Facilities: **Arboretum** (238 acres); **Exhibition Areas** (5); **Library** (university library 1.4 million volumes); **Outdoor Sculpture Area** (encompassing most of the campus arboretum); **Shop**.

Activities: **Films**; **Gallery Talks**; **Guided Tours** (by arrangement); **Lectures**; **Temporary Exhibitions** (over 20/year).

Publications: exhibition catalogues.

With five exhibition areas and a sculpture park on the 238-acre Hofstra University campus, the Museum presents over twenty exhibitions each year. In addition to the Lowe Gallery and Museum Offices located at the above address, exhibits may be mounted in the Rochelle and Irwin A. Lowenfeld Conference and Exhibition Hall on the 10th Floor of the Axinn Library (open; Tues, 10am-9pm; Wed-Fri, 10am-5pm; Sat-Sun, 1pm-5pm); the David Filderman Gallery and Study Area, both located on the 9th Floor of the Axinn Library (open; Mon-Fri, 10am-9pm; Sat-Sun, 1pm-5pm); and Bits 'n Bytes in Memorial Hall. On permanent display are 75 objects from Oceanic Melanesia and fifty outdoor sculptures. The permanent collection holds slightly more than 4,000 painting, drawings, prints, sculptures, photographs, as well as ethnographic and decorative art objects. These works are grouped as follows: European paintings, drawings, and prints from the 16th to 20th centuries; American paintings, drawings, and sculpture of the 20th century; African and Oceanic artifacts; pre-Columbian

Hofstra University Museum, cont.

ceramic bowls and figurines; Asian stone and bronze work of the 10th to 19th centuries; Japanese Edo period woodblock prints, as well as scrolls and finger masks; 19th-and 20th-century Puerto Rican santos; paintings and prints by Latino, South American, and Israeli artists; Russian paintings of the 19th and 20th centuries; photographs, mostly 20th-century American; and American prints, the largest collection area, which includes the 19th-century Currier and Ives series, works by regionalists, social realists, and artists from the 1960's and 1970's.

Ithaca

Cornell University - Herbert F. Johnson Museum of Art ⊕

Cornell University
corner of Central and University Aves.
Ithaca, NY 14853-4001
Tel: (607) 255-6464
Fax: (607) 255-9940
Internet Address: http://www.museum.cornell.edu
Director: Mr. Franklin W. Robinson
Admission: voluntary contribution.
Attendance: 70,000   *Established:* 1973
Membership: Y   *ADA Compliant:* Y
Parking: metered adjacent to building site.
Open: Tuesday to Sunday, 10am-5pm.
Closed: Memorial Day, Independence Day, Labor Day,
  Thanksgiving Day, Christmas Day to New Year's Day.
Facilities: **Architecture** (1973 design by I.M. Pei);
  Auditorium (130 seat); **Galleries**; **Library** (4,000 volumes); **Reading Room**; **Sculpture Garden**.
Activities: **Education Programs** (adults, students, children and families); **Film Series**; **Gallery Talks**; **Guided Tours**; **Lectures**; **Performances**; **Temporary Exhibitions**; **Traveling Exhibitions**; **Workshops**.
Publications: exhibition catalogues.

Exterior view of Herbert F. Johnson Museum of Art, designed by I.M. Pei. Photograph courtesy of Herbert F. Johnson Museum of Art, Cornell University, Ithaca, New York.

Located on the northwest corner of the Cornell University campus, the Johnson Museum was designed by I.M. Pei and opened to the public in 1973. Spanning the history of art, the Museum's collections are especially strong in Asian art, 19th- and 20th-century American art, and the graphic arts. Special exhibitions complement the Museum's diverse collections and present a broad range of media and cultural and historical perspectives. The American collection includes works by Stuart Davis, Willem de Kooning, Red Grooms, Hans Hofmann, and Georgia O'Keeffe, as well as members of the Hudson River School and the American Impressionists. European holdings range from Old Master drawings and 17th-century Dutch landscapes and portraiture to 19th-century French impressionist and academic painting. The Museum also owns works by such modern masters as Henri Matisse and Alberto Giacometti. The print collection, selections from which are always on exhibition, consists of more than 13,000 works in all media from the 15th century to the present, with major examples by Dürer, Rembrandt, and Whistler, among others. Photography holdings include works by a number of acclaimed artists, including Berenice Abbott, Robert Frank, Alfred Stieglitz, and Garry Winogrand. The collection also has examples of African and pre-Columbian art.

Ithaca College - Handwerker Gallery ⊕

Ithaca College, 1170 Gannett Center, Ithaca, NY 14850-7276
Tel: (607) 274-3018   *Fax:* (607) 274-3474
Internet Address: http://www.ithaca.edu/arthistory/handwerker/handwerker.html
Director: Assoc Prof Thomas P. Somma
Admission: free.
ADA Compliant: Y

Ithaca College - Handwerker Gallery, cont.
Open: **September to May,**
Monday to Wednesday, 10am-6pm; Thursday, 10am-9pm; Friday, 10am-6pm;
Saturday, 10am-2pm.
Closed: Vacation Breaks.
Facilities: **Exhibition Area.**
Activities: **Temporary Exhibitions.**

Situated on the ground floor of the Caroline Wener Gannett Center on the Ithaca College campus, the Gallery presents five to six shows of historical or contemporary art each year.

Jamestown

Jamestown Community College - Weeks Gallery
Community Cultural Center, Jamestown Campus, Falconer St., Jamestown, NY   14701
Tel: (716) 665-9107   *Fax:* (716) 665-9110
Internet Address: http://www.sunyjcc.edu/jamestown/aca_arts/art
Director, Community Cultural Center: Mr. James D. Colby
Admission: free.
Attendance: 7,000   *Established:* 1969   *Membership:* Y   *ADA Compliant:* Y
Open: Tuesday to Wednesday, 11am-5pm; Thursday, 11am-7pm; Friday, 11am-5pm;
Saturday, 11am-1pm.
Closed: Academic Holidays.
Facilities: **Auditorium; Exhibition Area** (1,000 square feet).
Activities: **Education Programs** (adults and undergraduate/graduate college students); **Lectures;**
Temporary/Traveling Exhibitions.
Publications: exhibition catalogues.

The Forum Gallery presents temporary exhibitions of contemporary art, including an annual juried student art exhibition in the spring.

New Paltz

State University of New York at New Paltz - Samuel Dorsky Museum of Art ⒸⒶ
75 S. Manheim Blvd., New Paltz, NY   12561
Tel: (914) 257-3844
Fax: (914) 257-3854
Internet Address:
   http://www.newpaltz.edu/artgallery
Director: Mr. Neil C. Trager
Admission: voluntary contribution.
Attendance: 15,000   *Established:* 1963
ADA Compliant: Y
Parking: free on site.
Open: **September to May,**
Tuesday, 10am-4pm and 7pm-9pm;
Wednesday to Thursday, 10am-4pm;
Saturday to Sunday, 1pm-4pm.

Architectural rendering of Central Gallery, Samuel Dorsky Museum of Art. Rendering courtesy of State University of New York at New Paltz, New Paltz, New York.

Closed: Academic Holidays.
Facilities: **Galleries** (4 permanent collection, 2 temporary; total 9,000 square feet).
Activities: **Concerts; Dance Recitals; Lectures; Permanent Exhibits; Temporary**
Exhibitions; Traveling Exhibitions.
Publications: exhibition catalogues (semi-annual).

The Museum operates two galleries dedicated to changing temporary exhibitions and four galleries devoted to the exhibition of the permanent collection. Relevant publications and interpretive programming complement the exhibitions. The temporary exhibition program includes exhibitions of works of art by faculty, alumni, and students in the Art Department, and exhibitions, installations,

State University of New York at New Paltz - Samuel Dorsky Museum of Art, cont.
and projects by nationally and internationally recognized artists. Each summer the Museum sponsors thematic exhibitions featuring works by artists living in the mid-Hudson Valley and Catskill Mountain regions. The Museum is dedicated to collecting, housing, researching, interpreting, and exhibiting works of art from diverse cultures. The collection of approximately 4,000 works of art is encyclopedic, spanning a period of almost 4,000 years. Areas of specialization include 20th-century prints and paintings, Asian art, pre-Columbian art and artifacts, metals, and photographs. The Museum has a special commitment to collecting important works of art created by artists (past and present) who have lived and worked in the Hudson Valley and Catskill Mountain regions. In October 1998, ground was to have been broken to construct 5,000-square-feet of new exhibition space that will adjoin the existing galleries. The new facility will be primarily used for the exhibition of the College's permanent collection. The galleries will be closed until construction is completed in the Fall of 1999.

New Rochelle

The College of New Rochelle - Castle Gallery ©

29 Castle Place (Leland Castle, Main Campus), New Rochelle, NY   10805
Tel: (914) 542-5423
Internet Address: http://www.cnr.edu/cg.htm
Director: Wennie Huang
Admission: free.
Established: 1980
Open: Tuesday to Friday, 10am-5pm; Saturday to Saturday, noon-4pm.
Closed: Holidays.
Facilities: **Exhibition Area.**
Activities: **Guided Tours**; **Temporary Exhibitions** (four per year).

The Castle Gallery presents temporary exhibitions of contemporary art, applied design, fine craft, and material culture

New York City - Bronx

Hostos Community College of CUNY - Hostos Art Gallery

Hostos Center for the Arts and Culture, 450 Grand Concourse at 149th St., Bronx, NY   10451
Tel: (718) 518-4455
Internet Address: http://www.hostos.cuny.edu/culture/gallery.html
Open: **Call for hours.**
Facilities: **Gallery.**
Activities: **Temporary Exhibitions.**

Located on the campus of one of the colleges in the City University system, the Center consists of a museum-grade art gallery, a 367-seat theatre, and 906-seat concert hall. The Hostos Gallery presents temporary exhibitions of the work of artists of national and international reputation, as well as emerging and established local artists.

Lehman College Art Gallery ©

250 Bedford Park Blvd. W. & Goulden Ave., Bronx, NY   10468-1589
Tel: (718) 960-8731   *Fax:* (718) 960-8935
Internet Address: http://www.lehman.cuny.edu/lehmangallery.html
Director: Ms. Susan Hoeltzel
Admission: voluntary contribution.
Attendance: 15,000   *Established:* 1985   *Membership:* Y   *ADA Compliant:* Y
Open: **September to June**, Tuesday to Saturday, 10am-4pm.
            July to August, by appointment.
Facilities: **Exhibition Area.**
Activities: **Education Programs** (children); **Films**; **Guided Tours**; **Lectures**; **Temporary Exhibitions.**
Publications: exhibition catalogues; exhibition notes (bi-monthly).

Lehman College Art Gallery, cont.

Housed in a building designed by architect Marcel Breuer on the campus of Lehman College, a branch of City University of New York, the Gallery presents a range of temporary exhibitions and arts education programs, primarily in contemporary art.

New York City - Brooklyn

Brooklyn College/CUNY - Art Gallery ⓒⒶⒹ

LaGuardia Hall (under the bell tower), 2900 Bedford Ave., Brooklyn, NY   11210
Tel: (718) 951-5181
Internet Address: http://www.brooklyn.cuny.edu/bc/calendar/art/artcal.htm
Admission: free.
Open: Monday to Friday, 12:30pm-4:30pm.
Facilities: **Exhibition Area**.
Activities: **Lectures**; **Temporary Exhibitions**.

Located on the main floor of LaGuardia Hall, the Gallery presents several exhibitions featuring the work of nationally and internationally recognized artists each year. Also of possible interest on campus, the Art Department's Meier Bernstein Art Library and its Graduate Art Student Union sponsor lectures and slide presentations throughout the academic year by visiting artists, art historians, critics, museum curators, writers on art, gallery owners, and other art-world figures.

Long Island University Galleries ⓒⒶⒹ

1 University Plaza, Brooklyn, NY   11201
Tel: (718) 488-1198   *Fax:* (718) 488-1372
Internet Address: http://www.brooklyn.liunet.edu/cwis/bklyn/art/artEXHIBITS.htm
Open: Monday to Friday, 10am-6pm; Saturday to Sunday, 10am-5pm.
Facilities: **Exhibition Area** (2 galleries).
Activities: **Temporary Exhibitions**.

The University Art Department mounts temporary exhibitions in two galleries in the LLC Building, the Selena Gallery on the ground floor and the Resnick Showcase on the third floor.

Pratt Institute - The Rubelle and Norman Schafler Gallery ⓒⒶⒹ

Pratt Institute, 200 Willoughby Ave., Brooklyn, NY   11205
Tel: (718) 636-3517   *Fax:* (718) 636-3455
Internet Address: http://www.pratt.edu/exhibitions
Director: Ms, Eleanor Moretta
Admission: free.
Attendance: 10,000   *Established:* 1967
Parking: metered on street.
Open: Monday to Friday, 9am-5pm.
Closed: Legal Holidays.
Facilities: **Exhibition Area** (2,300 square feet); **Food Services** Restaurant; **Library** (185,000 volumes); **Multi-media Center**; **Studios and Classrooms**.
Activities: **Education Programs** (undergraduate and graduate students); **Lectures**; **Performances**.
Publications: calendar (semi-annual); exhibition announcements.

The Gallery presents temporary exhibitions of student work. The Pratt Institute has a branch gallery at 295 Lafayette St. at Houston St. in Manhattan.

New York City - Manhattan

Adelphi University Manhattan Center Gallery ⓒⒶⒹ

75 Varick St., 2nd Floor, New York, NY   10013
Tel: (516) 431-5161
Internet Address: http://www.adelphi.edu
Director: Professor Richard Vaux

Adelphi University Manhattan Center Gallery, cont.

Open: Monday to Friday, 9am-5pm.
Facilities: **Exhibition Area.**
Activities: **Temporary Exhibitions.**

The Gallery presents a schedule of temporary exhibitions.

The Bard Graduate Center for Studies in the Decorative Arts ⓒ (BGC)

18 West 86th St.
New York, NY   10024
Tel: (212) 501-3000
Fax: (212) 501-3099
TDDY: (212) 501-3012
Internet Address:
   http://www.bard.edu/graduate/BGC/exhibit/exhibit
Director: Ms. Susan Weber Soros
Admission: fee: adult-$2.00, student-$1.00, senior-$1.00.
Established: 1992
Membership: N   *ADA Compliant:* Y
Parking: nearby commercial garages.
Open: Tuesday to Wednesday, 11am-5pm;
     Thursday, 11am-8:30pm;
     Friday to Sunday, 11am-5pm.
Closed: New Year's Day, ML King Jr. Day, Memorial Day,
     Independence Day, Labor Day,
     Thanksgiving Day to Thanksgiving Friday,
     Christmas Day.

Exterior view of façade of Bard Graduate Center for Studies in the Decorative Arts. Photograph courtesy of Bard Graduate Center for Studies in the Decorative Arts, New York, New York.

Facilities: **Exhibition Area** (2 floors in town house);
   Library (25,000 volumes, by appointment, call 501-3035).
Activities: **Education Programs**; **Guided Tours** (for information call 501-3023); **Lectures.**
Publications: exhibition catalogues; journal, "Studies in the Decorative Arts" (semi-annual).

The BGC is primarily an educational institution offering both the Masters degree and Ph.D. in the decorative arts. It also presents 2-3 exhibitions each year on a diverse roster of subjects that could include architecture, jewelry, furniture, glass, and porcelain, among others. There are extensive public programs and continuing education programs as well.

Baruch College - Sidney Mishkin Gallery ⓒ

135 East 22nd St., New York, NY   10010
Tel: (212) 387-1006
Internet Address: http://www.cuny.edu/colleges/tpoframe-baruch.html
Director: Dr. Sandra Kraskin
Admission: free.
Established: 1981   *ADA Compliant:* Y
Parking: commercial adjacent to site.
Open: **September to May,**
     Monday to Wednesday, noon-5pm; Thursday, noon-7pm; Friday, noon-5pm.
Closed: January, June to August, Academic Holidays.
Facilities: **Architecture** (former Federal Courthouse, 1939); **Exhibition Area** (1,800 square feet).
Activities: **Education Programs** (undergraduate and graduate students); **Temporary Exhibitions**; **Traveling Exhibitions.**
Publications: brochures; exhibition catalogues.

Located on the ground floor of Baruch College's Administrative Center, the Gallery presents temporary exhibitions in a variety of media featuring scholarly, multicultural, one-person and group shows, and exhibitions out of the American mainstream. Three hundred artworks (primarily modern

New York City - Manhattan, New York

Baruch College - Sidney Mishkin Gallery, cont.

and contemporary paintings, sculpture, prints and photographs) comprise the Gallery's permanent collection. The core of the Gallery's holdings is the Mishkin Collection, which includes painting and sculpture by Surrealists Max Ernst, Andre Masson, and Man Ray, as well as works by Alexander Calder, Marsden Hartley, and Barbara Hepworth.

Columbia University - Miriam and Ira D. Wallach Art Gallery ⓒ

Schermerhorn Hall, 8th Floor, 116th St. and Broadway
New York, NY   10027
Tel: (212) 854-6800   *Fax:* (212) 854-7329
Internet Address: http://www/columbia.edu/cu/wallach/
Director and Curator, Art Properties: Ms. Sarah Elliston Weiner
Admission: free.
Attendance: 2,800   *Established:* 1986   *ADA Compliant:* Y
Parking: commercial adjacent to site.
Open: Wednesday to Saturday, 1pm-5pm.
Closed: Academic Holidays.
Facilities: **Exhibition Area** (2,300 square feet).
Activities: **Education Programs** (undergraduate and graduate college students); **Films**; **Lectures**.
Publications: exhibition catalogues.

The Wallach Art Gallery presents exhibitions that complement the educational mission of the University. Works are drawn from public and private collections as well as from University collections.

Cooper Union School of Art - Arthur A. Houghton, Jr. Gallery ⓒ

Cooper Union Foundation Building, 2nd Floor
7 East 7th St. (3rd Ave. and 7th St.)
New York, NY   10003
Tel: (212) 353-4203
Internet Address: http://www.cooper.edu/art
Director: Mr. Robert Rindler
Open: Monday to Friday, noon-7pm; Saturday, noon-5pm.
Facilities: **Exhibition Area**.
Activities: **Temporary Exhibitions**.

The Gallery presents temporary exhibitions. Also located on the second floor, The Herb Lubalin Study Center of Design and Typography (353-4214) mounts exhibitions related to the history and theory of graphic design.

Hunter College - Bertha and Karl Leubsdorf Art Gallery ⓒ

68th St. & Lexington Ave., West Building, New York, NY   10021
Tel: (212) 772-4991
Fax: (212) 772-4554
Internet Address: http://sapienta.hunter.cuny.edu/~art/galleries.html
Director: Mr. Sanford Warmfeld
Admission: voluntary contribution.
Attendance: 10,000   *Established:* 1984   *Membership:* Y   *ADA Compliant:* Y
Open: Monday to Saturday, 1pm-6pm.
Closed: New Year's Day, Memorial Day, Independence Day, Labor Day, Columbus Day, Thanksgiving Day, Christmas Day, Academic Holidays.
Facilities: **Architecture** (Eleanor Roosevelt house); **Galleries**.
Activities: **Temporary Exhibitions**.
Publications: exhibition catalogues.

The Leubsdorf Art Gallery houses professionally-organized exhibits that support the educational programs of the Hunter College Art Department.

Hunter College - The MFA Gallery

450 West 41st St. (between 9th & 10th Aves. at Dyer St.), New York, NY 10036
Tel: (212) 772-4991
Fax: (212) 772-4554
Internet Address: http://sapienta.hunter.cuny.edu/~art/galleries.html
Open: Tuesday to Saturday, 1pm-6pm.
Facilities: **Exhibition Area** (5,000 square feet).
Activities: **Temporary Exhibitions** (4/year).
Publications: exhibition catalogues (4/year).

Each semester, the Gallery mounts three major exhibitions organized by faculty, students, or alumni. There is also an end-of-semester MFA projects show.

Marymount Manhattan College - MMC Gallery Ⓒᴬᴬ (MMC Gallery)

Marymount Manhattan College, 221 East 71st St., New York, NY 10021
Tel: (212) 517-0634
Fax: (212) 517-0413
Internet Address: http://marymount.mmm.edu
Director: Ms. Karen Harris
Open: Monday to Sunday, 9am-9pm.
Facilities: **Exhibition Area**.
Activities: **Temporary Exhibitions**.

Located in the esplanade of the College, the MMC Gallery features exhibitions of new and innovative work by professional artists. Also of possible interest, student work is displayed in smaller galleries throughout the college.

New School University/Parsons School of Design - Exhibition Center & Galleries

2 West 13th St., New York, NY 10011 Ⓒᴬᴬ
Tel: (212) 229-8987
Fax: (212) 229-8975
Internet Address: http://newschool.edu
Director or Exhibitions: Mr. Clinton Kuopus
Open: **Exhibition Center**, Monday to Friday, 9am-9pm; Saturday, 10am-6pm.
     Aronson Gallery, Monday to Friday, 9am-9pm; Saturday, 10am-6pm.
     Student Gallery, Monday to Friday, 8am-11pm; Saturday, 9am-8pm; Sunday, 10am-10pm.
Facilities: **Galleries**.
Activities: **Temporary Exhibitions**.

An affiliate of the New School University, the Parsons School of Design features design and fine art in its Exhibition Center, as well as the work of student BFA and MFA candidates. Exhibitions may also be found at 66 5th Avenue in the Arnold and Sheila Aronson Gallery on the ground floor and in the PSD Student Gallery on the fourth floor.

New York University Art Collection - The Grey Art Gallery and Study Center Ⓒᴬᴬ

100 Washington Square East, New York, NY 10003-6619
Tel: (212) 998-6780
Fax: (212) 995-4024
Internet Address: http://www.nyu.edu/greyart
Director: Ms. Lynn Gumpert
Admission: suggested contribution-$2.50.
Attendance: 25,000   *Established:* 1975
Parking: commercial adjacent to site.
Open: Tuesday, 11am-6pm; Wednesday, 11am-8pm; Thursday to Friday, 11am-6pm;
     Saturday, 11am-5pm.
Closed: Legal Holidays.
Facilities: **Galleries**; **Library**; **Reading Room**.

New York University Art Collection - Grey Art Gallery and Study Center, cont.
Activities: **Education Programs** (adults, college students and children); **Films**; **Gallery Talks**; **Lectures**; **Temporary Exhibitions**; **Traveling Exhibitions**.
Publications: exhibition catalogues.

The Gallery mounts temporary exhibitions of works from the University's collection as well as hosting traveling exhibitions. The University has two main collections: the New York University Art Collection, consisting of 6,000 works, primarily late-19th- and 20th-century art, with particular strengths in American painting from 1940 to the present and 20th-century European prints; and the Grey Collection of Contemporary Asian and Middle Eastern Art, totaling some 1,000 works in various media. The University also maintains the following branch galleries: 80 Washington Square East Galleries (thesis exhibitions of masters candidates); Broadway Windows (at 10th Street; installations); Washington Square Windows (installations); and Rosenberg Gallery (student work).

Pratt Manhattan Gallery Ⓒ⁴⁴
295 Lafayette St., 2nd Floor, New York, NY   10012
Tel: (718) 636-3517   *Fax:* (718) 636-3455
Director: Ms. Eleanor Moretta
Admission: free.
Attendance: 30,000   *Established:* 1975
Parking: commercial adjacent to site.
Open: Monday to Saturday, 10am-5pm.
Closed: Legal Holidays.
Facilities: **Architecture** (Puck Building); **Exhibition Area** (1,200 square feet).
Activities: **Continuing Education Programs; Lectures**.
Publications: exhibition & events calendar (semi-annual); exhibition announcements.

The Gallery presents exhibitions of undergraduate and graduate student work in a range of media including painting, sculpture, computer graphics, and photography. The Pratt Institute also operates the Schafler Gallery at its campus in Brooklyn (see separate listing).

School of Visual Arts - Visual Arts Museum Ⓒ⁴⁴
School of Visual Arts
209 East 23rd St.
New York, NY   10010
Tel: (212) 592-2144
Fax: (212) 592-2095
Internet Address:
   http://www.schoolofvisualarts.edu
Director: Francis Di Tommaso
Admission: free.
Established: 1971
Membership: N   *ADA Compliant:* Y
Parking: metered on street.
Open: Monday to Wednesday, 9am-6:30pm;
         Thursday, 9am-8pm;
         Friday, 9am-6:30pm;
         Saturday, 10am-5pm.

View of gallery during Fifth Annual Digital Salon, 1997. Photograph courtesy of Visual Arts Museum, New York, New York.

Facilities: **Auditorium** (180 seats); **Exhibition Area** (2,000 square feet).
Activities: **Juried Exhibits; Lectures; Traveling Exhibitions**.

The Museum holds exhibitions each year to promote public awareness and appreciation of the visual arts. By invitation of the Board of Directors, affirmed professionals and renowned artists exhibit their work and hold lectures at the School of Visual Arts. Since its inception in 1971, the Visual Arts Museum has exhibited the work of David Hockney, Willem de Kooning, Roy Lichtenstein, Agnes Martin, Robert Motherwell, Robert Rauschenberg, Larry Rivers, Richard Serra, Frank Stella, Cy Twombly and many others. Graphic designers and illustrators who have exhibited include Henry Wolf, Tony Palladino, Robert Weaver, Marshall Arisman, and others. In 1988, the School initiated

School of Visual Arts - Visual Arts Museum, cont.

The Masters Series to honor the great visual communicators of our time. Past honorees include Saul Bass, Seymour Chwast, Ivan Chermayeff, Lou Dorfsman, Milton Glaser, George Lois, Mary Ellen Mark, Paul Rand, Deborah Sussman, George Tscherny, and Massimo Vignelli. The recipient of the 1998 Masters Series Award is Paul Davis. Since 1993 the Museum has held the New York Digital Salon, an annual international exhibition of computer art, which features installations, prints, photographs, CD-ROMS, animations, sculpture and works on the Internet. Also of possible interest are the Visual Arts Gallery, SOHO (137 Wooster Street, Tues-Fri, 11-6); the SVA Gallery (209 E. 23rd Street); the Eastside Gallery (214 E. 21st Street); and the Westside Gallery (141 W. 21st Street). The latter three galleries are open Mon-Thurs, 9-8, and Sat-Sun, 9-5. Information:212-592-2010.

Yeshiva University Museum ⊂A4⊃

2520 Amsterdam Ave. at 185th St.
New York, NY   10033
Tel: (212) 960-5390
Fax: (212) 960-5406
Internet Address: http://www.yu.edu/museum
C.E.O.: Ms. Sylvia A. Herskowitz
Admission: fee: adult-$3.00, student-$2.00, senior-$2.00.
Attendance: 35,000   *Established:* 1973
Membership: Y   *ADA Compliant:* Y
Parking: metered on street and pay lots.
Open: **September to July**,
        Tuesday to Thursday, 10:30am-5pm;
        Sunday, noon-6pm.
Closed: Jewish Holidays.
Facilities: **Exhibition Area** (8,000 square feet); **Library** (15,000 volumes); **Shop**.

View of gallery installation, "Sacred Realm: The Emergence of the Synagogue in the Ancient World", February - December, 1996, Yeshiva University Museum. Photograph courtesy of Yeshiva University Museum, New York, New York.

Activities: **Arts Festival**; **Concerts**; **Education Programs** (adults, undergraduates and children); **Guided Tours**; **Lectures**; **Temporary Exhibitions**; **Traveling Exhibitions**.
Publications: books; exhibition catalogues.

Yeshiva University Museum is a teaching museum that serves both Jewish and non-Jewish audiences with exhibitions, public programs, and publications focusing on Jewish themes. The Museum collects, preserves, and interprets Jewish life, history, art, and culture. Exhibitions explore a wide variety of topics from histories of diverse communities to the most current contemporary art.

New York City - Queens

La Guardia Community College Galleries

31-10 Thompson, Long Island City (Queens), NY   11101
Tel: (718) 482-5709
Fax: (718) 875-6957
Internet Address: http://lagcc.cuny.edu
Director: Mr. Gary Vollo
Open: Monday to Saturday, 8am-9pm.
Facilities: **Galleries**.
Activities: **Temporary Exhibitions**.

Exhibition areas include LSG East (Atrium), LSG West, Fourth Floor East (Dean's Gallery), Fifth Floor East (President's Gallery), and the East Stairwell Gallery.

Queensborough Community College-CUNY - QCC Art Gallery

Queensborough Community College/CUNY, 222-05 56th Ave., Bayside, NY   11364-1497
Tel: (718) 631-6396   *Fax:* (718) 631-6620
Internet Address: http://www.qcc.cuny.edu
Director: Mr. Faustino Quintanilla

Queensborough Community College-CUNY - QCC Art Gallery, cont.

Admission: free.

Attendance: 35,000   *Established:* 1966   *Membership:* Y   *ADA Compliant:* Y

Open: Monday to Friday, 9am-5pm.

Facilities: **Exhibition Area**; **Library**.

Activities: **Education Programs** (adults, graduates and undergraduates); **Guided Tours**; **Lectures**; **Temporary Exhibitions**.

Publications: exhibition catalogues.

The Gallery presents temporary exhibitions.

Queens College Art Center ⓒⓐ

Benjamin S. Rosenthal Art Library, 65-30 Kissena Blvd., Flushing, NY   11367-1597

Tel: (718) 997-3770   *Fax:* (718) 997-3753

Internet Address: http://www.qc.edu/Library/acpage.html

Director: Ms. Suzanna Simor

Admission: free.

Membership: N

Parking: parking lot, reserve in advance.

Open: Monday to Thursday, 9am-8pm; Friday, 9am-5pm.

Closed: Major Holidays.

Facilities: **Exhibition Area** (1,200 square feet).

Activities: **Gallery Talks**; **Lectures**; **Temporary Exhibitions** (6-7/year).

Located on the sixth floor of the Benjamin S. Rosenthal Library, the Queens College Art Center organizes in its gallery a continuous program of exhibitions of work by emerging and established artists supplemented by related gallery talks, lectures, and symposia. The Center, a part of the Art Library, focuses on artists who reflect the cultural diversity of New York City and the College. Spanish and Latin American art has been a concentration. The Art Center complements and cooperates with the College's Frances Godwin-Joseph Ternbach Museum (see separate listing). Also of possible interest within the Art Department, a separate student gallery is active.

Queens College - Frances Godwin and Joseph Ternbach Museum ⓒⓐ

Queens College, Paul Klapper Hall, 65-30 Kissena Blvd.

Flushing, NY   11367

Tel: (718) 997-5000 *Ext:* 4747

Fax: (718) 997-5738

Internet Address: http://www.qc.edu

Director: Mr. Jerald Green

Admission: free.

Established: 1957   *Membership:* Y

Parking: free, on campus.

Open: Monday to Thursday, 11am-7pm.

Facilities: **Gallery**; **Library** (20,000 volumes).

Activities: **Education Programs** (undergraduate and graduate students); **Lecture Series**; **Temporary Exhibitions** (4/year).

Publications: brochure, "Queens College Art Collection"; exhibition catalogues.

The collection of the Museum consists of 2,500 works in a variety of media from ancient to contemporary art. It mounts four temporary exhibitions each year. Also of possible interest on campus is the Queens College Art Center Gallery located in the Benjamin S. Rosenthall Library; see separate listing.

St. John's University - University Gallery ⓒⓐ

Bent Hall, Room 109, 8000 Utopia Parkway, Jamaica, NY   11439

Tel: (718) 990-7476

Internet Address: http://www.stjohns.edu/libraries/services/gallery/index.html

St. John's University - University Gallery, cont.
Director: Mr. Ross Barbera
Admission: free.
Established: 1994
Open: Monday to Thursday, 10am-3pm; Friday, 11am-2pm.
Facilities: **Exhibition Area**.
Activities: **Temporary Exhibitions** (7/year).

The gallery presents exhibitions of contemporary art in a variety of media by well-known and emerging artists of regional, national, and international repute. Categories of shows include an invitational, a juried national, theme, annual faculty and annual student exhibitions.

Niagara University

Niagara University - Castellani Art Museum
Senior Drive (center of campus), Niagara University, NY   14109
Tel: (716) 286-8200
Internet Address: http://www.niagara.edu/~cam
Director: Dr. Sandra H. Olsen
Admission: voluntary contribution.
Attendance: 100,000   *Established:* 1973   *Membership:* Y   *ADA Compliant:* Y
Parking: free on site.
Open: Wednesday to Saturday, 11am-5pm; Sunday, 1pm-5pm.
Closed: Good Friday, Easter, Thanksgiving Day, Christmas Day, Academic Holidays.
Facilities: **Auditorium** (196 seats); **Exhibition Area** (10 galleries).
Activities: **Arts Festival**; **Concerts**; **Education Programs**; **Films**; **Gallery Talks**; **Guided Tours**; **Lectures**; **Temporary Exhibitions**; **Traveling Exhibitions**.
Publications: exhibition catalogues; newsletter, "Arcadia Revisited".

This 23,000-square-foot facility houses a collection that ranges from the Hudson River School landscapes of Jasper Cropsey and Albert Bierstadt to 20th-century constructions by Louise Nevelson and Robert Rauschenburg. Contemporary works by Susan Rothenberg, Arnold Mesches, Judy Pfaff, Roger Brown, and others provide a survey of major movements in today's art world, while there is also a pre-Columbian collection. The Museum also houses contemporary sculpture, as well as drawing, photography, print, and folk art collections.

Oakdale

Dowling College - Anthony Giordano Gallery
Dowling College, Visual Arts Center (Idle Hour Blvd. at Biltmore Ave.), Oakdale, NY   11769
Tel: (516) 244-3016
Internet Address: http://www.dowling.edu
Gallery Director: Ms. Catherine Valenza
Admission: free.
Open: Tuesday to Saturday, 10:30am-4:30pm; Sunday, 2pm-4:30pm.
Facilities: **Gallery**.
Activities: **Temporary Exhibitions**.

A subsidiary gallery of the Islip Art Museum (see listing under East Islip, New York), the Gallery features installations, site-specific works, and theme shows.

Oneonta

Hartwick College - Yager Museum
Hartwick College, West St., Oneonta, NY   13820-4020
Tel: (607) 431-4480   *Fax:* (607) 431-4468
Internet Address: http://www.hartwick.edu
Director: Mr. George Abrams
Admission: free.

Hartwick College - Yager Museum, cont.

Attendance: 30,000   *Established:* 1928   *ADA Compliant:* Y

Parking: free on site.

Open: Tuesday, 11am-5pm; Wednesday, 11am-9pm; Thursday to Saturday, 11am-5pm;
Sunday, 1pm-5pm.

Closed: Academic Holidays.

Facilities: **Auditorium** (392 seats); **Galleries** (Yager Museum and The Gallery, Fine Arts Center);
Library (800 volumes on American Indian culture); **Shop**.

Activities: **Temporary Exhibitions**; **Traveling Exhibitions**.

In addition to mounting temporary exhibitions of the work of students and professional artists, the Museum houses a permanent collection of artifacts of Native Americans of the Northeastern woodlands and 19th-century landscapes.

State University of New York, Oneonta - Fine Arts Gallery ⓒⁱⁱ

Fine Arts Building, Room #155, Ravine Pkwy., Oneonta, NY   13820

Tel: (607) 436-2445

Internet Address: http://www.oneonta.edu

Assoc. Professor: Ms. Yolanda R. Sharpe

Admission: free.

Open: Monday to Friday, 11am-4pm.

Facilities: **Exhibition Area**.

Activities: **Temporary Exhibitions**.

The Gallery offers diverse exhibitions focusing on a range of contemporary critical issues and featuring the work of locally, regionally, and nationally recognized artists. Often the work of students, exploring the media presented by the professional artists in the main gallery, is presented concurrently in the Student Mini Gallery and the Quad Gallery.

Oswego

State Univ. of New York College of Arts & Sciences at Oswego - Tyler Art Gallery

SUNY at Oswego, Tyler Hall (off Rudolph Road), Oswego, NY   13126   ⓒⁱⁱ

Tel: (315) 341-2113

Fax: (315) 341-3394

Internet Address: http://www.oswego.edu/
other_campus/tylerart/index

Director: Dr. Barbara A. Perry

Admission: voluntary contribution.

Attendance: 20,000

Membership: N   *ADA Compliant:* Y

Parking: free on site.

Open: **September to May**,
Monday to Friday, 9:30am-4:30pm;
Saturday to Sunday, 12:30am-4:30pm.
June to July,
Monday to Friday, noon-4pm.

Closed: College Vacations.

View of gallery during exhibition, Tyler Art Gallery. Photograph courtesy of Tyler Art Gallery, Oswego, New York, New York.

Facilities: **Exhibition Area** (3,750 square feet).

Activities: **Gallery Talks**; **Lectures**; **Temporary Exhibitions**; **Traveling Exhibitions**.

Publications: brochures; posters.

Tyler Art Gallery, located in Tyler Hall, presents approximately twelve art exhibitions each year in two gallery spaces, including traveling exhibitions, locally-produced loan exhibitions, and the best work of students and faculty. Exhibitions are usually inter-disciplinary in nature so that the Gallery's programs will be of relevance to a wide range of campus interests as well as the public at large. The Gallery has a permanent collection of European, African, and American drawings, prints, paintings, ceramics, and sculpture from the 18th century to the present.

Plattsburgh

State University of New York at Plattsburgh - Plattsburgh Art Museum Ⓒᴬ

SUNY at Plattsburgh, 101 Broad St., Plattsburgh, NY   12901
Tel: (518) 564-2474
Fax: (518) 564-2473
Internet Address: http://www.plattsburgh.edu/museum/
Director: Mr. Edward R. Brohel
Admission: voluntary contribution.
Established: 1952   *ADA Compliant:* Y
Parking: free on site.
Open: Monday to Wednesday, noon-4pm; Thursday, noon-8pm; Friday to Sunday, noon-4pm.
Closed: University Holidays.
Facilities: **Galleries** (2, permanent and changing); **Sculpture Court**; **Shop**.
Activities: **Education Programs** (undergraduates); **Gallery Talks**; **Guided Tours**; **Temporary Exhibitions** (24/year).
Publications: calendar (semi-annual); exhibition announcements (monthly); exhibition catalogues; journal, "Kent Collector".

The Plattsburgh Art Museum is actually a number of venues for art located throughout the campus. The Rockwell Kent Gallery houses the Museum's permanent collection, including works of Rockwell Kent. The Burke Gallery presents a wide variety of changing exhibitions. The Winkel Sculpture Court displays the work of Nina Winkel in an indoor garden sanctuary. The Sculpture Park has both permanent installations and changing exhibitions. The Slatkin Study Room displays a decorative glass collection.

Potsdam

State University of New York College at Potsdam - Roland Gibson Gallery Ⓒᴬ

SUNY College at Potsdam, Brainerd Hall (off Pierrepont Ave., Route 56)
Potsdam, NY   13676
Tel: (315) 267-2250
Fax: (315) 267-4884
Internet Address: http://www.potsdam.edu
Director: Mr. Dan Mills
Admission: voluntary contribution.
Attendance: 15,000   *Established:* 1968   *Membership:* Y   *ADA Compliant:* Y
Parking: free on site.
Open: Monday/Wednesday/Friday, noon-5pm; Tuesday/Thursday, noon-5pm and 7pm-9pm; Saturday to Sunday, noon-4pm.
Closed: Academic Holidays.
Facilities: **Galleries**; **Sculpture Garden**.
Activities: **Arts Festival**; **Concerts**; **Education Programs**; **Films**; **Lectures**; **Temporary Exhibitions**; **Traveling Exhibitions**; **Workshops**.
Publications: brochures; bulletin (monthly); exhibition catalogues; newsletter; posters.

The Gallery hosts temporary exhibitions featuring both traditional and contemporary art, including student, faculty, and alumni work.

Poughkeepsie

Marist College Art Gallery

290 North Road, Poughkeepsie, NY   12601-1387
Tel: (914) 575-3000 *Ext:* 2903
Internet Address: http://www.academic.marist.edu/art/gallery/gallery.html
Contact: Donise English
Admission: free.
Open: Call for hours.

Marist College Art Gallery, cont.

Facilities: **Exhibition Area**.

Activities: **Temporary Exhibitions**.

The Gallery presents temporary exhibitions including annual faculty and student shows.

Vassar College - The Frances Lehman Loeb Art Center ⓒ⁴⁴

Vassar College, 124 Raymond Ave., Poughkeepsie, NY 12601-6198

Tel: (914) 437-5237 *Fax:* (914) 437-7304

Internet Address: http://www.vassun.vassar.edu/~fllac/

Director: Mr. James Mundy

Established: 1864 *Membership:* Y *ADA Compliant:* Y

Parking: free on site.

Open: Tuesday to Saturday, 10am-5pm; Sunday, 1pm-5pm.

Closed: Easter, Thanksgiving Day, Christmas Eve to New Year's Day.

Facilities: **Galleries**; **Library** (25,000 volumes); **Shop**.

Activities: **Gallery Talks**; **Temporary Exhibitions**.

Publications: exhibition catalogues; newsletter (quarterly).

Designed by Cesar Pelli, the Art Center houses a museum, home to one of the finest teaching collections in the country, consisting of 12,500 objects. Some 400 of the most important works from the collection are on view, arranged chronologically, with selections from the Asian collection in a separate section of the main Gallery. The exhibition includes Egyptian, Greek, and Roman antiquities, 15th- and 16th-century Italian painting (Giordano, Rosa), Northern Renaissance painting (Brueghel the Younger, van Cleve), 19th-century French painting (Cézanne, Delacroix, Doré), British and American art (Copley, Fuseli, Hamilton, Inness), and 20th-century works (Calder, Miró, Bacon, Hartley, O'Keeffe, Rothko, Miró, Pollock). There is also an extensive collection of works on paper, a sculpture court, and a sculpture garden.

Purchase

Purchase College, State University of New York - Neuberger Museum of Art ⓒ⁴⁴

Purchase College, State U. of New York
735 Anderson Hill Road
Purchase, NY 10577-1400

Tel: (914) 251-6100

Fax: (914) 251-6101

Internet Address: http://www.neuberger.org

Director: Dr. Lucinda H. Gedeon

Admission: suggested contribution: adult-$4.00, child-$2.00, senior-$2.00, family-$2.00.

Attendance: 54,000 *Established:* 1974

Membership: Y *ADA Compliant:* Y

Parking: free on site.

Open: Tuesday to Friday, 10am-4pm;
Saturday to Sunday, 11am-5pm.

Closed: Legal Holidays.

View of gallery. Photograph courtesy of Neuberger Museum of Art, Purchase, New York.

Facilities: **Exhibition Area** (30,000 square feet); **Food Services** Café; **Shop**.

Activities: **Art Workshops**; **Biennial Sculpture Exhibition**; **Concerts**; **Dance Recitals**; **Education Programs** (elementary and secondary students); **Films**; **Guided Tours**; **Lectures**; **Temporary Exhibitions**.

Publications: "CD ROM of Selected Works in Collection"; calendar (quarterly); exhibition catalogues.

The Neuberger Museum of Art is a major visual arts center and cultural resource; the Neuberger combines the scale and excitement of a city museum with the charm of a country setting. It is among the ten largest art museums in New York State and it is the eighth largest university art museum in the country. The Museum, a 65,000 square foot facility designed by Philip Johnson and

Purchase College, State University of New York - Neuberger Museum of Art, cont.

John Burgee, houses a permanent collection of over 6,000 objects in various media, including 20th-century American and European art, and works of art in the tradition of Constructivism. Artists represented include Avery, Bearden, de Kooning, Diebenkorn, Frankenthaler, Hartigan, Hopper, Lipton, Noguchi, and Pollock. It also houses a distinguished collection of African and ancient art. The Museum mounts between fifteen and twenty changing exhibitions each year, and hosts numerous exhibition-related lectures, concerts, workshops, and tours.

Rochester

University of Rochester - Memorial Art Gallery Ⓒ (MAG)

500 University Ave. at Goodman Ave.
Rochester, NY   14607
Tel: (716) 473-7720
Fax: (716) 473-6266
TDDY: (716) 473-6152
Internet Address: http://www.rochester.edu/MAG/
Director: Mr. Grant Holcomb, III
Admission: fee: adult-$5.00, child-$3.00, student-$4.00, senior-$4.00.
Attendance: 260,000   *Established:* 1913
Membership: Y   *ADA Compliant:* Y
Parking: free on site.
Open: Tuesday, noon-9pm; Wednesday to Friday, 10am-4pm;
      Saturday, 10am-5pm; Sunday, noon-5pm.
Closed: New Year's Day, Independence Day, Thanksgiving Day,
      Christmas Day.

Facilities: **Auditorium** (300 seats); **Food Services** Cutler's Restaurant (lunch, dinner, Sunday brunch); **Galleries**; **Library** (13,000 volumes; Tues, 1pm-8:30pm, Wed-Fri, 1pm-4pm; Sun, 12:30pm-4pm); **Reading Room**; **Sculpture Garden**; **Shop** (hand-crafted jewelry, ceramics, books, catalogues).

Hans Hofmann, *Ruby Gold*, 1959, Memorial Art Gallery. Photograph courtesy of Memorial Art Gallery, University of Rochester, Rochester, New York.

Activities: **Concerts**; **Crafts Festival** (Clothesline Festival, weekend after Labor Day); **Education Programs** (adults and children); **Films**; **Gallery Talks**; **Guided Tours** (Tues, 7:30pm; Fri & Sun, 2pm); **Lectures**; **Rental Gallery**; **Temporary Exhibitions**; **Traveling Exhibitions**.

Publications: calendar; exhibition catalogues; newsletter, "MAGazine" (bi-monthly); scholarly bulletin, "Porticus" (semi-annual).

Located on the original campus of the University of Rochester, MAG houses more than 5,000 years of world art, from ancient relics to the newest creations. The Museum presents approximately 15 temporary exhibitions a year, featuring the permanent collection, art from other collections, or the work of contemporary regional artists. MAG's permanent collection of over 10,000 objects includes European and American painting and sculpture, as well as art and artifacts from the ancient world, Asia, Africa, Native America, and Meso-America. Among the European and American artists represented in the collection are Thomas Hart Benton, Albert Bierstadt, Mary Cassatt, Paul Cézanne, Stuart Davis, Edgar Degas, El Greco, Hans Hofmann, Winslow Homer, Jacob Lawrence, Henri Matisse, Claude Monet, Henry Moore, Albert Paley, Rachel Ruysch, John Sloan, and Lilly Martin Spencer.

Saint Bonaventure

St. Bonaventure University Galleries

Regina A. Quick Center for the Arts, Route 417, Saint Bonaventure, NY   14778
Tel: (716) 375-2000   *Ext:* 2550   *Fax:* (255) 375-2690
Internet Address: http://www.dynamic.aol.com/cgi/redir?http://www.sbu.edu/
Curator: Brother David Haack
Admission: free.

St. Bonaventure University Galleries, cont

Attendance: 5,000 *Established:* 1856 *Membership:* N *ADA Compliant:* Y
Parking: in Hopkins parking lot.
Open: **Fall to Spring**,
Thursday to Sunday, 1pm-5pm.
Summer, call for hours.
Closed: Easter, Thanksgiving Day, Christmas Day.
Facilities: **Exhibition Area** (3 galleries); **Library** (200,000 volumes); **Reading Room**; **Theatre**.
Activities: **Guided Tours**; **Temporary Exhibitions** (8/year).

The Regina A Quick Center for the Arts contains two galleries. The Paul W. Beltz Gallery houses and exhibits the University's diverse permanent collection of art and artifacts. Four exhibits throughout the year each feature an aspect of art collecting. The Dresser Foundation Gallery hosts visiting artists' exhibitions and traveling shows.

Exterior view of entrance to Regina A. Quick Center for the Arts, St. Bonaventure University. Photograph courtesy of St. Bonaventure University, St. Bonaventure, New York.

Saratoga Springs

Skidmore College - The Schick Art Gallery (CAA)

Skidmore College, 815 N. Broadway
Saratoga Springs, NY 12866-1632
Tel: (518) 580-5049 *Fax:* (518) 581-8386
Internet Address:
http://www.skidmore.edu/art/
Director: Mr. David Miller
Admission: free.
Attendance: 18,000 *Established:* 1926
Membership: N *ADA Compliant:* Y
Parking: free on campus.

Interior view of Schick Art Gallery, Skidmore College. Photograph courtesy of Schick Art Gallery, Skidmore College, Saratoga Springs, New York.

Open: **September to May**, Monday to Friday, 9am-5pm; Saturday to Sunday, 1pm-3:30pm.
Summer, Monday to Friday, 9am-4pm; Saturday, 1pm-3:30pm.
Facilities: **Gallery** (1,200 square feet).
Activities: **Films**; **Gallery Talks**; **Lectures**; **Temporary Exhibitions** (10/year).
Publications: catalogue (occasional).

The Gallery presents temporary exhibitions of contemporary art by nationally recognized artists, student shows, and faculty exhibits. Group shows are theme-oriented and are often curated by Skidmore faculty. Skidmore is building a new facility, the Frances Young Tang Teaching Museum and Art Gallery. Designed by architect Antoine Predock and scheduled for completion in 2000, the Museum will house Skidmore's permanent collection of historical and contemporary art and host temporary exhibits.

Schenectady

Union College - Mandeville Gallery (CAA)

Union College, Union St., The Nott Memorial (between North & South Lane)
Schenectady, NY 12308
Tel: (518) 388-6004 *Fax:* (518) 388-6173
Internet Address: http://www.union.edu/PUBLIC/GALLERY/
Director/Curator: Ms. Rachel Seligman

Union College - Mandeville Gallery, cont.

Admission: free.
ADA Compliant: Y
Open: **September to June**,
      Monday to Thursday, 9am-10pm;
      Friday, 9am-5pm;
      Saturday, noon-5pm;
      Sunday, noon-10pm.
      July to August,
      Daily, 9am-5pm.
Facilities: **Architecture** Nott Memorial (Victorian Gothic 1850's, designed by Edward Tuckerman Potter); **Exhibition Area**.
Activities: **Temporary Exhibitions** (seven per year).
Publications: exhibition catalogues (7 per year).

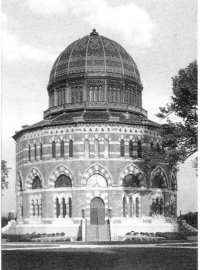

Exterior view of Nott Memorial (1850), designed by Edward Tuckerman Potter. Photograph courtesy of Union College, Schenectady, New York.

The Gallery is located on the second floor of the historic Nott Memorial, a National Historic Landmark, in the center of the Union campus. The Gallery hosts traveling exhibitions, mounts exhibits drawn from the Union College collection (including Audubon prints), and work by faculty and students. A frequent theme of Gallery exhibitions is the exploration of links between art and science. Exhibitions are also mounted in The Arts Atrium (Arts Building, ground level) and in the Photo Gallery (Arts Building, 2nd floor).

Stony Brook

State University of New York at Stony Brook - University Art Gallery ⓒⒶⒶ

Staller Center for the Arts, Center Drive, Stony Brook, NY 11794-5425
Tel: (516) 632-7240
Fax: (516) 632-7354
Internet Address: http://www.staller.sunysb.edu
Director: Ms. Rhonda Cooper
Admission: free.
Attendance: 12,000   *Established:* 1975   *ADA Compliant:* Y
Parking: pay parking garage on site.
Open: **early-September to July**, Tuesday to Friday, noon-4pm; Saturday, 6pm-8pm.
Closed: Legal Holidays.
Facilities: **Exhibition Area** (4,700 square feet).
Activities: **Education Programs**; **Temporary Exhibitions** (5-6/year).
Publications: exhibition catalogues (5/year).

The University Gallery at the Staller Center for the Arts offers a diverse schedule that includes an MFA Exhibition every February, a senior show of undergraduate work every May, a biannual faculty exhibition, and a variety of solo and group professional exhibitions. Most exhibitions are accompanied by an illustrated catalogue, which is offered free of charge to Gallery visitors. Additionally, the Department of Art sponsors the "Art History and Criticism Lecture Series".

Syracuse

Syracuse University - Joe and Emily Lowe Art Gallery ⓒⒶⒶ

Syracuse University, Shaffer Art Building, Sims Drive, Syracuse, NY 13244-1230
Tel: (315) 443-3127
Internet Address: http://students.syr.edu:80/events/artsadv/lave/html
Director: Dr. Edward A. Aiken
Admission: free.
Established: 1952   *ADA Compliant:* Y

Syracuse University - Joe and Emily Lowe Art Gallery, cont.

Open: **Academic Year**,
Tuesday, noon-5pm; Wednesday, noon-8pm; Thursday to Sunday, noon-5pm.
Summer,
Tuesday to Friday, 2pm-4pm.

Closed: National Holidays, During Installations.

Facilities: **Galleries**; **Library** (30,000 volumes).

Activities: **Gallery Talks**; **Lectures**; **Temporary Exhibitions**; **Traveling Exhibitions**.

Publications: exhibition catalogues.

Centrally located in the Shaffer Art Building in the southeast corner of the main quadrangle on the campus of Syracuse University, the Gallery cooperates closely with the Syracuse University Art Collection, which contains more than 45,000 objects. Exhibitions from the Collection can be found in the Lowe and in the University Art Collection space immediately adjacent to the Gallery. (For further information regarding the University Art Collection, please call (315) 443-4097.) Also of possible interest is The Gallery, located on the second floor of Joseph I. Lubin House, which presents exhibitions of faculty and student art and selections from the University Art Collection.

North Carolina

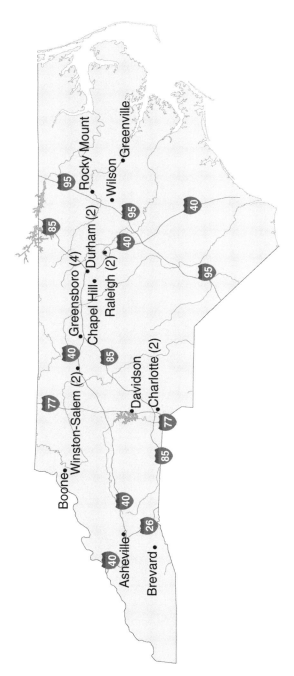

The number in parentheses following the city name indicates the number of museums/galleries in that municipality. If there is no number, one is understood. For example, in the text two listings would be found under Raleigh and one listing under Davidson.

North Carolina

Asheville

University of North Carolina at Asheville - Owen Galleries ⓒ

Owen Hall, 1 University Heights
Asheville, NC 28804-3299
Tel: (828) 251-6559
Internet Address: http://www.unca.edu/art/gallery/gallery.html
Director, University Gallery: Mr. Robert Tynes
Admission: free.
Open: Weekdays, 9am-6pm.
Facilities: **Exhibition Area**.
Activities: **Temporary Exhibitions**.

Located on the main floor of Owen Hall, the Art Department's main gallery features, in addition to work by professional artists, solo exhibitions by BFA candidates, an annual juried student show, and an annual faculty exhibition. Additionally, the Second Floor gallery mounts BA candidate exhibitions and faculty-curated exhibitions of student course work. Also of possible interest on campus, Ramsey Library often displays the work of senior students, faculty, and visiting artists in its exhibition space.

Boone

Appalachian State University - Catherine J. Smith Gallery ⓒ

Farthing Auditorium, 733 Rivers St.
Boone, NC 28608
Tel: (828) 262-3017   *Fax:* (828) 262-6370
Internet Address: http://www.oca.appstate.edu/csg/
Gallery Director: Mr. Hank Foreman
Admission: free.
ADA Compliant: N
Parking: in front of building.
Open: **Academic Year**, Monday to Friday, 10am-5pm.
Closed: Academic Holidays.
Facilities: **Exhibition Area** (2 floors).
Activities: **Gallery Talks** (reserve in advane); **Guided Tours of campus sculpture** (reserve in advance); **Temporary Exhibitions** (monthly).
Publications: exhibition brochures; exhibition catalogue, "Rosen Outdoor Sculpture Competition and Exhibtion" (annual).

Located in Farthing Auditorium, the Smith Gallery presents a schedule of exhibitions by locally, regionally, and nationally recognized artists. Annually, it hosts the Rosen Outdoor Sculpture Competition and Exhibition with works selected for the exhibition remaining on campus for one year. Tour maps for the outdoor sculpture on campus are available in the gallery. The Gallery also hosts the Halpert Biennial 2-D Competition and Exhibition. The permanent collection consists of 20th-century American works. Many of the two-dimensional works are on loan to various college offices and organizations; while the growing collection of permanent outdoor sculptures is sited around the campus. A new Visual Arts Center, which will include several galleries, is scheduled for opening in 2001.

Brevard

Brevard College - Spiers Gallery ⓒ

Brevard College, Sims Art Center, 400 N. Broad St.
Brevard, NC 28712
Tel: (704) 883-8292   *Fax:* (704) 884-3790
Internet Address: http://www.brevard.edu
Director: Mr. Bill Byers
Admission: free.

Brevard, North Carolina

Brevard College - Spiers Gallery, cont.

Attendance: 800   *ADA Compliant:* Y
Parking: free on site.
Open: **September to May**,
            Monday to Friday, 9am-3pm.
Closed: June to August,
            December 15 to January 15.
Facilities: **Exhibition Area** (2,000 square feet).
Activities: **Arts Festival**; **Lectures**; **Musical Performances**; **Readings**; **Temporary Exhibitions**.
Publications: exhibition notices.

Exterior view of Sims Art Center (site of Spiers Gallery). Photograph courtesy of Spiers Gallery, Brevard College, Brevard, North Carolina.

The Spiers Gallery at Brevard College houses a small permanent collection, including works by Thomas Sully and Walter Darby Bannard. The Gallery also presents temporary exhibitions of the work of Brevard students and regional artists.

Chapel Hill

University of North Carolina - The Ackland Art Museum Ⓒ

Columbia and Franklin Sts.
Chapel Hill, NC   27599-3400
Tel: (919) 966-5736
Fax: (919) 966-1400
TDDY: (919) 962-0837
Internet Address:
   http://www.unc.edu/depts/ackland
Director: Mr. Gerald D. Bolas
Admission: voluntary contribution.
Attendance: 32,000   *Established:* 1958
Membership: Y   *ADA Compliant:* Y
Parking: pay on site.
Open: Wednesday to Saturday, 10am-5pm;
            Sunday, 1pm-5pm.
Facilities: **Exhibition Area**; **Library** (39,000 volumes).

Emile Bernard, *Breton Woman and Haystacks*, Ackland Art Museum. Photograph courtesy of Ackland Art Museum, University of North Carolina, Chapel Hill, North Carolina.

Activities: **Gallery Talks**; **Guided Tours**; **Lectures**; **Temporary Exhibitions**.
Publications: newsletter (quarterly).

The Ackland Museum's permanent collection includes European painting, Indian miniature paintings and sculpture, Japanese paintings, Chinese ceramics, Thai sculpture, African art, and contemporary American art. The Museum also mounts temporary exhibitions. Also of possible interest on campus are the John and June Allcott Gallery (962-2015), located in the Hanes Art Center; the Alumni Sculpture Garden; the Carolina Union Gallery (996-3834); and the General Administration Building Gallery (962-1000).

Charlotte

Central Piedmont Community College - Pease Auditorium Art Gallery

Pease Bldg., 1201 Elizabeth Ave., Charlotte, NC   28204
Tel: (704) 330-5009
Internet Address: http://testwebext.cpcc.cc.nc.us
Admission: free.
Open: Monday to Thursday, 10am-4pm; Friday, 10am-noon.
Facilities: **Gallery**.
Activities: **Temporary Exhibitions**.

Central Piedmont Community College - Pease Auditorium Art Gallery, cont.

The CPCC Art Gallery presents temporary exhibits of work in a variety of media by students and professional artists. Every effort is made to combine workshops and special topics courses with gallery events. In doing so, the gallery seeks to promote an understanding of and an appreciation for the depth and diversity of the college and community at large.

University of North Carolina at Charlotte - UNC Charlotte Galleries Ⓒ

Rowe Gallery (137 Rowe Arts Center)
Cone University Center Gallery
Charlotte, NC   28223
Tel: (704) 547-2473
Internet Address: http://www.uncc.edu
Director: Mr. Donald R. Byrum
Open: **Rowe Gallery**.
        Call for hours.
        Cone Center Gallery,
        Monday to Friday, 9am-11pm; Saturday, noon-1am; Sunday, 1pm-11pm.
Facilities: **Exhibition Area**.
Activities: **Temporary Exhibitions**.

Galleries are located on the first floor of Rowe Arts Center and in the Bonnie E. Cone University Center. The Cone Center Gallery exhibitions include art by regionally, nationally, and internationally recognized artists, as well as work by student, faculty, staff, and alumni. The Cone Center permanent collection is displayed throughout the building and in the C.A. McKnight interior lobby. The North Carolina Print Drawing Society's permanent collection is shown in the northwest lounge..

Davidson

Davidson College - William H. Van Every Gallery & Edward M. Smith Gallery Ⓒ

Davidson College Visual Arts Center, Main St. and Concord Road, Davidson, NC   28036-1720
Tel: (704) 892-2344
Fax: (704) 892-2691
Internet Address: http://www.davidson.edu/academic/art/vac/ARTVAC.HTM
Director: Ms. Perry Nesbit
Admission: free.
Attendance: 12,000   *Established:* 1962   *ADA Compliant:* Y
Parking: free on site.
Open: **September to January**,
        Monday to Friday, 10am-4pm; Saturday to Sunday, 2pm-5pm.
Closed: Legal Holidays, Academic Holidays.
Facilities: **Galleries**.
Activities: **Gallery Talks**; **Lecture Series**; **Temporary Exhibitions**.

The work featured in the Van Every Gallery consists of contemporary art from throughout the United States, as well Davidson faculty work. In addition, selections from the College's permanent collection of 2,500 objects are shown occasionally in the space. The Edward M. Smith Gallery is used for one-person exhibitions required of every Davidson studio art major and for smaller temporary exhibitions.

Durham

Duke University Museum of Art Ⓒ

Buchanan Blvd. at Trinity, Durham, NC   27708
Tel: (919) 684-5135   *Fax:* (919) 681-8624
Internet Address: http://www.duke.edu/web/duma/
Director: Dr. Michael P. Mezzatesta
Admission: free.
Attendance: 30,000   *Established:* 1968   *Membership:* Y   *ADA Compliant:* Y

Duke University Museum of Art, cont.

Parking: free on site.

Open: Tuesday to Friday, 9am-5pm, Saturday, 11am-2pm, Sunday, 2pm-5pm.

Closed: Legal Holidays.

Facilities: **Galleries**; **Shop**.

Activities: **Concerts**; **Films**; **Gallery Talks**; **Guided Tours** (Tues-Fri, between 9:30am and 4pm, reserve 3 weeks in advance); **Lectures**; **Performances**; **Readings**; **Temporary Exhibitions**.

Publications: exhibition catalogues; posters.

Since its founding in 1969, Duke University Museum of Art has assembled an impressive collection - from ancient to modern, from Old Master and American to African, Asian, and contemporary Russian art. Highly regarded collection groups at the Museum include Medieval art and pre-Columbian art from Central and South America. Special exhibitions and programs complement the permanent collection.

Oleg Kudryashov, *Icon Composition*, 1994, drypoint, watercolor, 102 x 72 cm. Duke University Museum of Art. Photograph courtesy of Duke University Museum of Art, Durham, North Carolina.

North Carolina Central University - NCCU Art Gallery

Lawson St. (adjacent to Edwards Music Bldg.)

Durham, NC   27707

Tel: (919) 560-6211

Fax: (919) 560-5012

Internet Address: http://www.nccu.edu

Director: Mr. Kenneth Rodgers

Admission: free.

Established: 1977   *Membership:* Y   *ADA Compliant:* Y

Open: Tuesday to Friday, 9am-5pm; Sunday, 2pm-5pm.

Facilities: **Exhibition Area**.

Activities: **Education Programs** (undergraduate students); **Gallery Talks**; **Lectures**; **Temporary Exhibitions** (5/year); **Traveling Exhibitions**.

Publications: field guides.

The NCCU Art Museum presents temporary exhibitions and houses the University's growing art collection with selections on display in the Carol G. Belk Gallery. Primarily a teaching facility, the Gallery's collections and exhibitions are chosen to reflect diversity in style, technique, media, and subject. While focusing on American art, particularly works by African American artists, holdings also include works by European artists, traditional African objects, and some Oceanic examples.

Greensboro

Greensboro College - Irene Cullis Gallery

Cowan Building, 815 W. Market St., Greensboro, NC   27401-1875

Tel: (910) 272-7102

Internet Address: http://www.gborocollege.edu

Director: Mr. Robert Kowski

Admission: free.

Established: 1838   *ADA Compliant:* Y

Open: **September to April**, Monday to Friday, 10:30am-4pm; Sunday, 2pm-5pm.

Closed: Academic Holidays.

Facilities: **Gallery**.

Activities: **Gallery Talks**; **Temporary Exhibitions**.

Located in the Cowan Building on the Greensboro College Campus, the Gallery mounts six exhibitions per year.

Guilford College Art Gallery ⓒᴬᴬ

Hege Library, 800 W. Friendly Ave.
Greensboro, NC   27410
Tel: (336) 316-2438
Fax: (910) 316-2950
Internet Address:
   http://www.guilford.edu/library/art.html
Director and Curator: Ms. Theresa N. Hammond
Admission: free.
Attendance: 6,000   *Established:* 1990
ADA Compliant: Y
Parking: free on site.
Open: **Main Gallery**,
         Monday to Friday, 9am-5pm;
         Sunday, 2pm-5pm, during academic year.
Closed: Academic Holidays.
Facilities: **Exhibition Area** (main enclosed gallery, 8
   atrium galleries; 3,500 square feet).
Activities: **Guided Tours** (by appointment, 316-2438);
   Temporary Exhibitions.

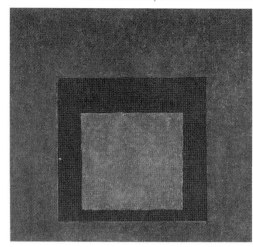

Josef Albers, *Homage to the Square, No. 167*, 1966, Oil on masonite. Gift of Otto Theodor Benfrey, Renate Wilkins, and Rudolf Benfrey. Guilford College Art Gallery. Photograph courtesy of Guilford College Art Gallery, Greensboro, North Carolina.

Located in the Hege Library, the Guilford College Art Gallery houses a permanent collection consisting of more than 600 works by more than 350 artists. Although 20th-century American art is emphasized, the collection also includes works by Rembrandt, Picasso, and Dali, works from the Renaissance and Baroque periods, contemporary Polish etchings, and works by Josef and Anni Albers.

North Carolina A&T State University - Mattye Reed African Heritage Center

North Carolina A&T State University, 1601 E. Market St.
Greensboro, NC   27411
Tel: (910) 334-7874
Internet Address: http://www.ncat.edu
Director and C.E.O.: Ms. Conchita F. Ndege
Admission: free.
Established: 1968   *Membership:* Y
Open: Monday to Friday, 9am-5pm.
Facilities: **Exhibition Area**; **Library** (1,200 volumes); **Reading Room**.
Activities: **Arts Festival**; **Education Programs** (college students and children); **Films**; **Guided Tours**; **Lectures**; **Temporary Exhibitions**; **Traveling Exhibitions**.
Publications: calendar; exhibition catalogues.

The Center has a long history of sponsoring events related to African culture. It presents exhibits drawn from its extensive collection of artifacts from Africa and its diaspora. It also presents traveling exhibits from other museums. The permanent collection includes of 3,500 artifacts from more than 30 African nations. The Center also operates a satellite gallery at the Greensboro Cultural Center at the corner of N. Davie and Friendly Streets. (See separate listing.) Also of possible interest on campus is the H.C. Taylor Gallery (334-7784).

University of North Carolina at Greensboro - Weatherspoon Art Gallery ⓒᴬᴬ

University of North Carolina at Greensboro, Spring Garden and Tate St.
Greensboro, NC   27412
Tel: (336) 334-5770
Fax: (336) 334-5907
Internet Address: http://www.uncg.edu/wag
Director: Mr. Nancy Doll
Admission: free.
Attendance: 23,000   *Established:* 1942   *Membership:* Y   *ADA Compliant:* Y

University of North Carolina at Greensboro - Weatherspoon Art Gallery, cont.

Parking: free on site, request parking permit at Welcome Desk.

Open: Tuesday, 10am-5pm;
Wednesday, 10am-8pm;
Thursday to Friday, 10am-5pm;
Saturday to Sunday, 1pm-5pm.

Closed: Academic Holidays.

Facilities: **Architecture** (designed by Romaldo Giurgola); **Galleries** (6); **Lecture Hall**; **Sculpture Courtyard**; **Shop** (limited edition prints, books, unique crafts).

Activities: **Education Programs** (undergraduate and graduate students); **Gallery Talks**; **Guided Tours** (1st Sun in month, 2pm; groups reserve 2 weeks in advance); **Lectures**; **Performances**; **Temporary Exhibitions**; **Traveling Exhibitions**.

Publications: bulletin (semi-annual); exhibition catalogues; newsletter.

Willem De Kooning, *Woman*, 1949-1950, oil on canvas. Lena Kernodle McDuffie Memorial Gift, 1954. Weatherspoon Art Gallery. Photograph courtesy of Weatherspoon Art Gallery, University of North Carolina, Greensboro, Greensboro, North Carolina.

Weatherspoon Art Gallery is the contemporary art museum of the University of North Carolina at Greensboro. Its permanent collection includes over 4,000 works by such 20th-century American artists as Calder, de Kooning, Nevelson, Rauschenberg, and Warhol; the Cone Collection of Henri Matisse prints and bronzes; the Dillard Collection of works on paper; and the Louise C. Wright Collection of traditional Japanese woodblock prints and scroll paintings. A series of temporary exhibitions by professional artists, faculty and students is mounted in six galleries in the facility.

Greenville

East Carolina University - Wellington B. Gray Gallery ⓒ

East Carolina University, Jenkins Fine Art Center, Elm and 10th Sts. Greenville, NC 27858-4353

Tel: (919) 328-6336

Fax: (919) 328-6441

Internet Address: http://www.ecu.edu/art/home.html

Director: Mr. Gilbert Leebrick

Admission: free.

Attendance: 23,000   *Established:* 1978   *ADA Compliant:* Y

Parking: free on site with pass.

Open: Monday to Wednesday, 10am-5pm; Thursday, 10am-8pm; Friday, 10am-5pm; Saturday, 10am-3pm.

Closed: Academic Holidays.

Facilities: **Exhibition Area** (6,000 square feet); **Sculpture Garden**.

Activities: **Films**; **Gallery Talks**; **Lectures**; **Temporary Exhibitions**; **Traveling Exhibitions**.

Publications: exhibition catalogues.

The Gallery has an extensive collection of African art. It also mounts temporary exhibitions of the work of students, faculty, and artists from outside the school community.

Raleigh

Meredith College - Art Galleries ⓒ

Gaddy-Hamrick Art Center, 3800 Hillsborough St., Raleigh, NC 27607-5298

Tel: (919) 829-8465   *Fax:* (919) 829-2347

Internet Address: http://www.meredith.edu

Director: Ms. Maureen Banker

Meredith College - Art Galleries, cont.

Admission: free.
Established: 1891
Parking: free on site.
Open: Monday to Friday, 9am-5pm;
  Saturday to Sunday, 2pm-5pm.
Facilities: **Exhibition Area** (2 galleries; Weems Gallery 1,320 square feet).
Activities: **Juried Exhibits**; **Temporary Exhibitions**.

The College presents a schedule of temporary exhibitions of work by professional artists, faculty, alumna, and students in two galleries: Frankie G. Weems Gallery, located in the Gaddy-Hamrick Art Center and Rotunda Gallery, located the administration building. Annual exhibitions include North Carolina Photographers Exhibition, Raleigh Fine Arts Society Juried Exhibition, and Juried Student Exhibition.

Exterior view of the Gaddy-Hamrick Art Center, which houses the Frankie G. Weems Gallery. Photograph courtesy of Meredith College, Raleigh, North Carolina.

North Carolina State University - The Gallery of Art and Design ⒸⒶⒹ

Visual Arts Center, Cates Ave., Raleigh, NC   27695
Tel: (919) 515-3503
Fax: (919) 515-6163
Internet Address: http://ACS.NCSU.edu/visual art/
Director: Dr. Charlotte V. Brown
Admission: free.
Attendance: 26,000   *Established:* 1979
Membership: Y   *ADA Compliant:* Y
Parking: free on site.
Open: Wednesday to Friday, noon-8pm;
  Saturday to Sunday, 2pm-8pm.
Closed: Academic Holidays.
Facilities: **Auditorium**; **Exhibition Area** (2 galleries); **Food Services** Cafeteria; **Theatre**.
Activities: **Education Programs** (graduate and under-graduate students); **Guided Tours** (on request); **Temporary Exhibitions**; **Traveling Exhibitions**.
Publications: exhibition catalogues.

The Gallery of Art and Design produces a series of exhibitions bringing regional, national and international design to the campus. The Gallery is also responsible for the development, conservation, and presentation of North Carolina State University's collections of architectural

Mark Hewitt, *Chub*, 1994, Two-handled planter, alkaline glaze. Gallery of Art and Design. Photograph by R. Jackson Smith, courtesy of Gallery of Art and Design, North Carolina State University, Raleigh, North Carolina.

drawings and works on paper, ceramics, paintings, photography, textiles and furniture. Notable holdings include extensive collections of textiles (American, Asian, European, historical, contemporary), ceramics (19th- and 20th-century American and international pottery), photography (Adams, Abbot, Arbus, Bourke-White, Mapplethorpe), and outsider art (Hooper, Burwell, Blizzard).

Rocky Mount

North Carolina Wesleyan College - Daisy Thorpe and Mims Galleries

3400 N. Wesleyan Blvd., Rocky Mount, NC   27804
Tel: (252) 985-5268
Internet Address: http://www.ncwc.edu

North Carolina Wesleyan College - Daisy Thorpe and Mims Galleries, cont.

Curator, Lynch Collection of Outsider Art: Mr. Everrett Adelman

Open: **Mimms Gallery,** Monday to Friday, 1pm-5pm & 1 hr before performances.
Daisy Thorpe Gallery, Call for hours.

Facilities: **Exhibition Area** (2 galleries).

Activities: **Permanent Exhibits**; **Temporary Exhibitions.**

The College maintains two galleries. Located in the Dunn Center for the Performing Arts, the Mims Gallery presents temporary exhibitions of contemporary art. The Daisy Thorpe Gallery, located in the Thomas J. Pearsall, Jr. building, is dedicated to displaying the Robert Lynch Collection of Outsider Art, over 400 works of contemporary folk art by eastern North Carolina artists.

Wilson

Barton College - Barton Museum

Barton College, Whitehead and Woodard Sts., Wilson, NC 27893

Tel: (919) 399-6477

Internet Address: http://www.barton.edu

Director: Mr. J. Chris Wilson

Admission: free.

Established: 1965   *ADA Compliant:* Y

Parking: free on site.

Open: **September to May**, Monday to Friday, 10am-4pm.

Closed: Spring Recess, Thanksgiving Day, Christmas Day.

Facilities: **Exhibition Area**; **Library** (4,000 volumes).

Activities: **Arts Festival**; **Education Programs** (undergraduates); **Gallery Talks**; **Lectures**; **Temporary Exhibitions**.

Publications: exhibition catalogues; gallery guides.

The Museum mounts about eight exhibitions per year, focusing on important regional artists. The Museum also has a permanent collection, which is periodically displayed.

Winston-Salem

Wake Forest University Fine Arts Gallery ⓒ⁴⁹

Art Department, 1834 Wake Forest Road
Winston-Salem, NC 27109

Tel: (336) 758-5795

Fax: (336) 758-5668

Internet Address: http://www.wfu.edu/
academic-departments/art/gall-index.html

Director: Mr. Victor Faccinto

Admission: free.

Attendance: 6,500   *Established:* 1976

Membership: N   *ADA Compliant:* Y

Parking: directly behind Fine Arts Center.

Open: **September to May**,
Monday to Friday, 10am-5pm;
Saturday to Sunday, 1pm-5pm.

Closed: Academic Holidays.

Exterior view of Scales Fine Arts Center (1976), designed by Caudill Rowlett Scott. Photograph courtesy of Wake Forest University, Winston-Salem, North Carolina.

Facilities: **Exhibition Area** (3,600 square feet).

Activities: **Lectures**; **Temporary Exhibitions** (approx. 8 per year); **Traveling Exhibitions**.

Publications: exhibition catalogues.

The Fine Arts Gallery at Wake Forest is located in the Scales Fine Arts Center. The Gallery mounts temporary exhibitions. In addition there are six permanent collections at the University, but they are spread among twenty-six buildings on campus.

Winston Salem State University - Diggs Gallery

601 Martin Luther King Jr. Drive
Winston-Salem, NC   27110
Tel: (336) 750-2458
Fax: (336) 750-2463
Internet Address:
   http://www.wssu.edu/diggs/home.htm
Director/Curator: Ms. Brooke D. Anderson
Admission: voluntary contribution.
Attendance: 15,000   *Established:* 1990
Membership: N   *ADA Compliant:* Y
Parking: free on site.
Open: Tuesday to Saturday, 11am-5pm.
Closed: ML King Jr. Day, Good Friday,
         Memorial Day, Independence Day,
         Labor Day, Veterans Day,
         Thanksgiving Day,
         Christmas Day to New Year's Day.

Tyrone Mitchell, *Po Tolo*, 1985, stone, steel, and granite, 8 feet x 40 feet. Funded by National Endowment for the Arts and Gordon Hanes. Digges Gallery. Photograph by Richard Hackel, courtesy of Diggs Gallery at Winston-Salem State University, Winston-Salem, North Carolina.

Facilities: **Exhibition Area** (6,000 square feet); **Library**.
Activities: **Concerts** (20-25 per year); **Education Programs** (adults, college students and children); **Films**; **Guided Tours** (schedule in advance); **Lectures**; **Temporary Exhibitions** (6/year); **Traveling Exhibitions** (6/year).
Publications: exhibition catalogues.

The Diggs Gallery offers ten to fifteen visual art exhibitions per year, half of which are curated by and originate from Winston-Salem State University. The exhibitions cover a broad range of artistic expression, with special concentration on African, African-American, and regional art. Visitors should also see the murals of John Biggers in the O'Kelly Library and the sculpture garden, boasting works by Mel Edwards, Beverly Buchanan, Roberto Bertoia, and Tyrone Mitchell.

North Dakota

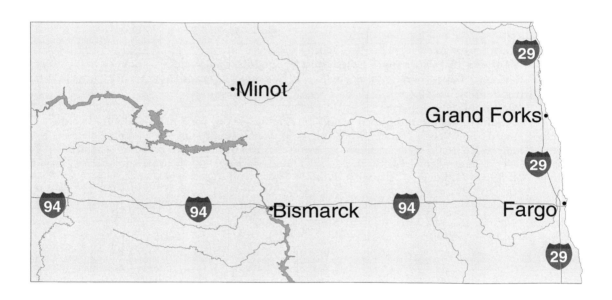

A number in parentheses following a city name indicates the number of museums/galleries in that municipality. If there is no number, one is understood. For example, in the text one listing would be found under each North Dakotan city shown on map.

North Dakota

Bismarck

Bismarck State College - Clell and Ruth Gannon Gallery

1500 Edwards Ave., Bismarck, ND   58501
Tel: (701) 224-5520
Fax: (701) 224-5550
Internet Address: http://www.bsc.nodak.edu/Library/Libgann.htm
Director: Ms. Michelle Lindblom
Admission: free.
Established: 1981
Open: Call for hours.
Facilities: **Exhibition Area**.
Activities: **Temporary Exhibitions**.

Located in the study, periodicals, and reference areas of the BSC Library, the Gallery presents temporary art exhibits ranging from traveling exhibits of works by nationally known artists to shows by local and regional artists and exhibits of student works.

Fargo

North Dakota State University Memorial Union Art Gallery ⒸⒶ

Memorial Union, 1301 N. University, North Dakota State University
Fargo, ND   58105
Tel: (701) 231-8239
Fax: (701) 231-8043
Internet Address: http://www.ndsu.rdu/lure/memorial union/gallery
Admission: free.
Attendance: 7,200   *Established:* 1975   *ADA Compliant:* Y
Parking: visitor lot at south entrance.
Open: **September to May**, Monday to Thursday, 9:30am-6pm; Friday, 9:30am-noon; Sunday, 5:30pm-9pm.
Closed: Legal Holidays.
Facilities: **Exhibition Area** (1,000 square feet).
Activities: **Concerts**; **Gallery Talks**; **Guided Tours**; **Lectures**; **Readings**; **Temporary Exhibitions**; **Traveling Exhibitions**.
Publications: calendar (biennial); exhibition notifications; posters.

The Gallery houses a permanent collection of 350 pieces, primarily American contemporary art. The Gallery also mounts temporary exhibitions.

Grand Forks

University of North Dakota - Witmer Art Gallery ⒸⒶ

2950 5th Ave. North (opposite the Newman Center)
Grand Forks, ND   58201
Tel: (701) 746-4211
Internet Address: http://www.operations.und.nodak.edu
Director: Ms. Sharon Webb
Admission: free.
Open: Monday to Friday, 9:30am-4:30pm; Saturday to Sunday, noon-3pm.
Facilities: **Exhibition Area**.
Activities: **Temporary Exhibitions**.

The Witmer Art Gallery represents the work of over 40 regional artists, many of which are UND faculty, staff, and students, as well as those who have received degrees from UND. Also of interest, the University Art Gallery is housed in North Dakota Museum of Art located on Centennial Drive.

Minot

Minot State University - Northwest Art Center Galleries (NAC Galleries)

11th Ave. Northwest, Minot, ND   58707

Tel: (701) 858-3264

Fax: (701) 858-3894

Internet Address: http://www.misu.nodak.edu

Director: Ms. Linda Olson

Admission: free.

Established: 1970   *Membership:* Y   *ADA Compliant:* Y

Parking: free on site.

Open: **Hartnett Gallery**, Monday to Friday, 8am-4:30pm.

  Library Gallery, regular library hours.

Closed: Academic Holidays.

Facilities: **Exhibition Area** (2 galleries).

Activities: **Guided Tours** (selected exhibitions); **Temporary Exhibitions**.

NAC presents exhibitions of contemporary and traditional art by local, regional, national, international artists in two galleries: the Library Gallery (located in the Gordon B. Olson Library) and the Hartnett Hall Gallery. Both galleries are located on the Minot State University campus along 11th Avenue Northwest. The exhibition schedule includes a biennial faculty exhibition and juried student exhibitions. The permanent collection consists of 300 pieces on or of paper and few canvases.

Ohio

The number in parentheses following the city name indicates the number of museums/galleries in that municipality. If there is no number, one is understood. For example, in the text three listings would be found under Columbus and one listing under Newark.

Ohio

Akron

University of Akron - Emily Davis Gallery ⊙

Folk Hall, 150 E. Exchange St., Akron, OH   44325-7801
Tel: (330) 972-5950
Internet Address: http://www.uakron.edu/faa/schools/art/galleries/edgallery/index.html
Director: Mr. Rod Bengston
Admission: free.
Open: Mon to Tues, 10am-5pm; Weds to Thurs, 10am-9pm; Fri to Sat, 10am-5pm.
Facilities: **Exhibition Area.**
Activities: **Temporary Exhibitions.**

The Emily Davis Gallery presents challenging exhibitions of contemporary art complemented by events that showcase the most current expressions and criticism evolving in today's visual arts; mounts regional and national traveling exhibitions; and hosts Meyers School of Art student, juried student, and scholarship exhibitions. In addition to the Projects and Atrium galleries also located in Folk Hall, works are exhibited in the Bierce Library, the Guzzetta Hall Atrium, and temporary spaces throughout the campus and community.

Athens

Ohio University - Kennedy Museum of Art ⊙

Ohio University, Lin Hall, The Ridges, Athens, OH   45701
Tel: (614) 593-1304
Fax: (614) 593-1305
Internet Address:
   http://www.cats.ohiou.edu/museum
Director: Mr. Kent Ahrens
Admission: free.
Established: 1993
Membership: Y   *ADA Compliant:* Y
Parking: free on site.
Open: Tuesday to Wednesday, noon-5pm;
       Thursday, noon-8pm;
       Friday, noon-5pm;
       Saturday to Sunday, 1pm-5pm.
Facilities: **Architecture** (renovated college
    hall); **Galleries.**

Exterior view of Lin Hall, location of Kennedy Museum of Art. Photograph courtesy of Kennedy Museum of Art, Ohio University, Athens, Ohio.

Activities: **Gallery Talks**; **Guided Tours** (by appointment); **Temporary Exhibitions**; **Traveling Exhibitions.**
Publications: brochures; exhibition catalogues; newsletter.

Located in a recently renovated Victorian building overlooking the campus, the Kennedy Museum of Art at Ohio University offers varied exhibitions and diverse learning opportunities for both adults and children. Selections from its permanent collection are exhibited periodically. Holdings include a major collection of southwest Native American weaving and jewelry and an important collection of contemporary works on paper by internationally recognized artists. The permanent collection also includes American painting and sculpture, and ceramics. The Foster Harmon Collection of Art is held on long-term loan. Selections from the Ohio University African Art Collection, owned and maintained by the Kennedy Museum, are displayed separately on the third floor of the Alden Library. Also of possible interest on campus are the galleries under the aegis of the School of Art ((593-0796). The Ohio University Art Gallery, located on the fifth floor of Siegfred Hall (open, Tues-Sat, 10am-4pm), focuses primarily on the work of regionally and nationally recognized artists with occasional displays of faculty and student work. The Trisolini Gallery, located at 48 E. Union St. (open, Tues-Sat, 10am-4pm), features student work, as well as exhibitions by nationally recognized artists. Student work is also on display in the Dungeon Gallery, located on the third floor of Siegfred Hall (open, daily 8am-5pm), and the student-run Undergraduate Art League (UAL) Gallery.

Berea

Baldwin-Wallace College - Thomas L. Fawick Art Gallery ⒸⒶⒶ
Kleist Center for Art and Drama, 95 E. Bagley Road at Beech St., Berea, OH   44017
Tel: (216) 826-2152
Internet Address: http://www.baldwinw.edu
Director: Mr. Jean Drahos
Admission: free.
Open: Monday to Friday, 2pm-5pm.
Facilities: **Exhibition Area**.
Activities: **Temporary Exhibitions**.

Located in the Kleist Center for Art and Drama, the Fawick Gallery presents temporary exhibitions and changing exhibitions of works from its permanent collection in four exhibition areas.

Bowling Green

Bowling Green State University Fine Arts Center Galleries ⒸⒶⒶ

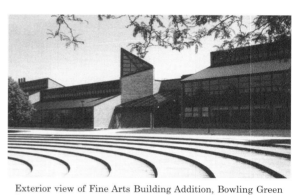

Fine Arts Center
(between Ridge and Wooster Sts.)
Bowling Green, OH   43403-0211
Tel: (419) 372-2786
Fax: (419) 372-2544
Internet Address:
   http://www.bgsu.edu/welcome/artshows.html
Ehhibition Program Administrator:
   Ms. Jacqueline S. Nathan
Admission: voluntary contribution.
Attendance: 9,000   *Established:* 1960
Membership: Y   *ADA Compliant:* Y
Parking: metered lot or visitor's parking pass.
Open: **September to April**,
   Tuesday to Saturday, 10am-4pm;
   Sunday, 2pm-5pm.

Exterior view of Fine Arts Building Addition, Bowling Green State University. Photograph courtesy of Fine Arts Center Galleries, Bowling Green State University, Bowling Green, Ohio.

Closed: Academic Holidays, Yom Kippur, December 1.
Facilities: **Galleries** (3).
Activities: **Guided Tours**; **Lectures**; **Temporary/Traveling Exhibitions** (change monthly).
Publications: exhibition catalogues.

The Fine Arts Center contains two galleries that present changing monthly exhibitions and a Japanese Ceremonial Arts Gallery. Exhibitions include the following annual shows: the New Music & Art Festival, Faculty/Staff, Undergraduate Art & Design, and MFA Thesis/BFA Senior Thesis. The Galleries are open only September through April when exhibitions are scheduled.

Cincinnati

Art Academy of Cincinnati - Chidlaw Gallery ⒸⒶⒶ

951 Eden Park Drive, Cincinnati, OH   45202
Tel: (513) 562-8777   *Fax:* (513) 562-8778
Internet Address: http://www.artacademy.edu
Admission: free.
Membership: N   *ADA Compliant:* Y
Open: Monday to Thursday, 9am-9pm; Friday, 9am-5pm;
   Saturday to Saturday, noon-5pm.
   Academic Holidays, Call for information.
   Legal Holidays, Call for information.

Work of Joe Newton, graduate student, on exhibition in Chidlaw Gallery. Photograph by Cal Kowal, courtesy of Art Academy of Cincinnati, Cincinnati, Ohio.

Art Academy of Cincinnati - Chidlaw Gallery, cont.

The Art Academy of Cincinnati is a college of art that offers both undergraduate and advanced degrees. Its exhibition facility, the Chidlaw Gallery, presents temporary exhibitions of national and international works of art, alumni exhibits, and student exhibits.

College of Mount Saint Joseph - Studio San Giuseppe Art Gallery ⒸⒶⒶ

College of Mount Saint Joseph, 5701 Delhi Road
Cincinnati, OH   45233-1670
Tel: (513) 244-4314
Fax: (513) 244-4222
Internet Address: http://www.msj.edu
Director: Mr. Gerald M. Bellas
Admission: voluntary contribution.
Attendance: 4,500   *Established:* 1962   *Membership:* Y   *ADA Compliant:* Y
Open: **Academic Year**, Monday to Friday, 10am-5pm; Saturday to Sunday, 1:30pm-4:30pm.
Closed: Legal Holidays.
Facilities: **Exhibition Area** (1,500 square feet).
Activities: **Films**; **Guided Tours**; **Lectures**; **Temporary Exhibitions**.
Publications: newsletter, "The Arts" (semi-annual).

Studio San Giuseppe presents temporary exhibitions.

Hebrew Union College - Skirball Museum, Cincinnati

3101 Clifton Ave., Cincinnati, OH   45220
Tel: (513) 221-1875
Fax: (513) 221-1842
Internet Address: http://www.huc.edu
Admission: free.
Open: Monday to Thursday, 11am-4pm; Sunday, 2pm-5pm.
Closed: Legal Holidays, Jewish Holidays.
Facilities: **Exhibition Area**.
Activities: **Temporary Exhibitions**.

The permanent collection at the Skirball Museum includes archeological artifacts, a special Torah and decorative ornaments, paintings, textiles, objects of Jewish celebration, and Israeli art. The museum also mounts three temporary exhibitions per year.

University of Cincinnati - DAAP Galleries ⒸⒶⒶ

Coll of Design, Architecture, Art & Planning
West Campus, DAAP Bldg., College Court
Cincinnati, OH   45221
Tel: (513) 556-4933
Fax: (513) 556-3288
Internet Address:
   http://www.daap.uc.edu/Gallery/gallery.html
Director: Ms. Anne Timpano
Admission: free.
Attendance: 10,000   *Established:* 1993
Membership: N   *ADA Compliant:* Y
Parking: visitor parking in Brodie Garage.
Open: **January to May**,
          Monday to Friday, 10am-5pm.
       September to November,
          Monday to Friday, 10am-5pm.
Closed: Academic Holidays.
Facilities: **Galleries** (3).

Guy Carlton Wiggins, *Brooklyn Bridge in Winter*, 1920, oil on canvas, 20½ x 24¼ inches. Gift of W.T.S. Johnson, University of Cincinnati Fine Arts Collection. Photograph courtesy of DAAP Galleries, University of Cincinnati, Cincinnati, Ohio.

Cincinnati, Ohio

University of Cincinnati - DAAP Galleries, cont.

Activities: **Lectures**; **Temporary Exhibitions**; **Traveling Exhibitions**.
Publications: brochures; calendar; exhibition catalogues.

Aunit of the College of Design, Architecture, Art, and Planning of the University of Cincinnati, DAAP Galleries administers three exhibition spaces: the Dorothy W. and C. Lawson Reed, Jr. Gallery at the Aronoff Center for Design, the Tangeman Fine Arts Gallery in the Tangeman University Center on the main campus, and the Machine Shop Gallery at Walnut Street and Central Parkway. All three galleries present temporary exhibitions. DAAP Galleries also administers the University of Cincinnati Fine Arts Collection of some 3,600 objects. International in scope, the permanent collection encompasses the art of the United States, Europe, pre-Columbian Ecuador, ancient Greece, and other cultures. A large portion of the collection consists of work by artists from the United States, many of whom were active in Cincinnati for at least a part of their careers. Perhaps the most well-known Cincinnati artist, Elizabeth Nourse, is represented by 32 works including oils, watercolors, and pastels. Other Cincinnati artists represented in some depth are Lewis Henry Meakin, Frank Harmon Myers, Herman Henry Wessel, Louis Charles Vogt, and John Ellsworth Weis.

Xavier University Art Gallery
3800 Victory Parkway, Cohen Center, Cincinnati, OH   45207-7311
Tel: (513) 745-3811   *Fax:* (513) 745-4301   *TDDY:* (513) 745-3811
Internet Address: http://www.xu.edu
Director: Mr. Robert C. Brasier
Admission: free.
Attendance: 1,800   *Established:* 1831   *Membership:* N   *ADA Compliant:* Y
Parking: free on site.
Open: **Academic Year**, Monday to Friday, 10am-4pm.
Closed: Legal Holidays, Academic Holidays.
Facilities: **Exhibition Area**.
Activities: **Films**.

The University Art Gallery presents temporary exhibitions, including shows of work by faculty and students.

Cleveland

Cleveland Institute of Art - Reinberger Gallery ☺
11141 E. Boulevard, Cleveland, OH   44106
Tel: (216) 421-7403
Internet Address: http://www.cia.edu/gallery_reinberger.html
Director: Mr. Bruce Checefsky
Admission: free.
Open: Monday, 9:30am-4pm; Tuesday to Saturday, 9:30am-9pm; Sunday, 1pm-4pm.
Facilities: **Gallery**.
Activities: **Temporary Exhibitions**.

In addition to gallery exhibitions featuring the work of professional artists, faculty and students, the Cleveland Institute of Art frequently offers slide lectures and symposia by visiting artists.

Cleveland State University Art Gallery ☺
2307 Chester Ave., Cleveland, OH   44114
Tel: (216) 687-2103
Fax: (216) 687-2275
Internet Address: http://www.csuohio.edu
Director and Curator: Mr. Robert Thurmer
Admission: voluntary contribution.
Attendance: 31,000   *Established:* 1973
Membership: Y   *ADA Compliant:* Y
Parking: metered on street and garage on East 21st St.

Cleveland State University Art Gallery, cont.

Open: Monday to Saturday, 10am-4pm.

Closed: Legal Holidays, Academic Holidays.

Facilities: **Exhibition Area** (4,500 square feet).

Activities: **Education Programs** (undergraduate and graduate college students); **Guided Tours**; **Lectures**; **Performances**; **Traveling Exhibitions**.

Publications: exhibition catalogues; exhibition schedule (annual).

Located on the ground floor of the Art Building, the Art Gallery features world-class thematic art exhibitions and related educational programs, including guided tours, lectures, and publications. Community based exhibitions, student shows, and programs dealing with important social and critical issues round out the gallery program.

Art Gallery, Cleveland State University during exhibition, "The Anxious Image: New Psychological Realism". Sculpture in foreground by Carole Jeanne Feuerman, polychrome polyester resin. Painting in background by Lawrence Krause, oil on canvas. Photograph courtesy of Art Gallery, Cleveland State University, Cleveland, Ohio.

Columbus

Capital University - The Schumacher Gallery

Capital University Library, 4th Floor, 2199 E. Main St., Columbus, OH   43209-2394

Tel: (614) 236-6319

Fax: (614) 236-6490

Internet Address: http://www.capital.edu

Director: Dr. Cassandra Tellier

Admission: voluntary contribution.

Attendance: 7,400   *Established:* 1964   *ADA Compliant:* Y

Parking: free on site.

Open: **September to mid-May**, Monday to Friday, 1pm-5pm; Saturday, 2pm-5pm.

Facilities: **Galleries**; **Library**.

Activities: **Concerts**; **Education Programs** (undergraduate and graduate college students); **Films**; **Gallery Talks**; **Guided Tours** (groups by appointment); **Lectures**; **Performances**; **Temporary Exhibitions**; **Traveling Exhibitions**.

Capital University's Schumacher Gallery offers the university and the community an extensive program of exhibitions, lectures, and arts-related events. It maintains a permanent collection of over 1,600 objects and features exhibits of Asian Art (traditional and contemporary art including Ming porcelain and Tang sculpture); Painting and Sculpture by notable artists (including Marin, Henry Moore, Nevelson, and Rodin); Ethnic Art featuring traditional art from many cultures (notably Inuit, Oceanic Islands, Haitian, African, and American Southwestern); Graphic Arts (including original works by Cassatt, Chagall, Dine, Gauguin, Picasso, Renoir, Toulouse-Lautrec, and Warhol); 16th-19th Century Period Works, a combination of paintings, prints, and tapestries (including works by Dürer, Jordaens, Willem Key, Rembrandt, and Goya); and Ohio Artists (focusing on prominent Ohio artists such as Elijah Pierce, Charles Burchfield, Edward Potthast, Alice Schille, and George Bellows). In addition to the permanent exhibits, the Gallery presents special focus exhibits, juried shows and displays of work by students.

Columbus College of Art & Design - Canzani Center Galleries ⓒ (CCAD)

Canzani Center, Cleveland Ave. and E. Gay Street, Columbus, OH   43215

Tel: (614) 222-4002   *Fax:* (614) 222-4040

Internet Address: http://www.ccad.edu

Director: Mr. Richard Aschenbrand

Columbus, Ohio

Columbus College of Art & Design - Canzani Center Galleries, cont.

Admission: free.
Established: 1879
Open: Monday to Wednesday, 11am-4pm; Thursday, 11am-9pm; Friday, 11am-4pm;
    Saturday, 10am-5pm.
Facilities: **Exhibition Area**.
Activities: **Student Art Sales** (held annually, December and in the Spring); **Temporary
    Exhibitions**.

The Canzani Center Gallery and Acock Gallery, located on the second floor of the Canzani Center, present temporary exhibitions, including work by professional artists, an annual student exhibition, and a biennial faculty show. Thesis shows by fine arts students are on display throughout the year in three on-campus locations: Beaton Hall (44 North 9th St.), V-Hall (470 E. Gay St.); and the Canzani Center Gallery (second floor).

Ohio State University - Wexner Center for the Arts C44

The Ohio State University
N. High St. at 15th Ave.
Columbus, OH 43210-1393
Tel: (614) 292-0330
Fax: (614) 292-3369
Internet Address:
  http://www.cgrg.ohio.state.edu/wexner
Director: Ms. Sherri Geldin
Admission: fee: adult-$3.00, child-free,
  student-$2.00, senior-$2.00.
Attendance: 205,000   *Established:* 1989
Membership: Y   *ADA Compliant:* Y
Parking: at Ohio Union Parking Ramp on
  High St..
Open: Tuesday to Wednesday, 10am-6pm;
  Thursday, 10am-9pm;
  Friday to Sunday, 10am-6pm.

View of Wexner Center for the Arts from the south. Photograph by Kevin Fitzsimons, courtesy of Wexner Center for the Arts, Ohio State University, Columbus, Ohio.

Facilities: **Architecture** (post-modern building, 1989, design by Peter Eisenman); **Cartoon Research Library**; **Film and Video Center** (278 seat theater); **Food Services** Café (Mon-Fri, 7am-4pm); **Galleries**; **Print Study Room**; **Shop** (books, periodicals, handcrafted jewelry, gifts); **Theatres** (3; Weigel Hall, the Performance Space, and Mershon Auditorium).
Activities: **Concerts** (jazz and world music); **Education Programs** (college students and general public); **Films** (weekly screenings); **Gallery Talks**; **Lectures**; **Performances** (dance and theater); **Temporary Exhibitions**.
Publications: calendar (bi-monthly); exhibition catalogues; gallery guides.

The Wexner Center for the Arts, Ohio State's multidisciplinary contemporary arts center, presents visual arts exhibitions, performing arts, films, videos, and educational programs for audiences of all ages. Visual arts exhibitions include contemporary painting, sculpture, architecture, photography, and multimedia installations featuring major modern artists and emerging talents. Also of possible interest on campus, the Hopkins Hall Gallery of the College of the Arts features faculty, student, and departmental exhibitions and quarterly shows of the work of visiting artists.

Dayton

University of Dayton - Rike Center Gallery C44

Rike Fine Arts Center (near St. Mary's Hall and the Post Office))
Dayton, OH 45469
Tel: (937) 229-3237
Internet Address: http:www.as.udayton.edu/visualarts/links.html
Gallery Manager: Mr. Jeff Jones
Admission: free.

University of Dayton - Rike Center Gallery, cont.

Open: Tuesday to Wednesday, 10am-4pm; Thursday, 10am-7pm; Friday, 10am-2pm.
Facilities: **Exhibition Area**.
Activities: **Temporary Exhibitions**.

The Gallery presents exhibitions of work by nationally and internationally recognized artists using a variety of media, as well as a juried exhibition of student works. Also of possible interest on campus, the Narrow Gallery, located in the Mechanical Engineering Building adjacent to the photography and video facilities, features exhibitions by artists using photographic methods and materials.

Wright State University Art Galleries ⓒᴬᴬ

Creative Arts Center
3640 Colonel Glenn Highway, A128-CAC
Dayton, OH   45435
Tel: (513) 775-2896
Internet Address: http://www.wright.edu
Gallery Coordinator: Mr. Craig Martin
Admission: free.
Attendance: 12,000   *Established:* 1974   *ADA Compliant:* Y
Open: **Academic Year**, Monday to Friday, 10am-4pm; Saturday to Sunday, noon-5pm.
Closed: Legal Holidays.
Facilities: **Galleries** (4).
Activities: **Education Programs** (undergraduate and graduate students); **Films**; **Gallery Talks**; **Lectures**.
Publications: exhibition catalogues; prints.

The galleries presents temporary exhibitions of work by professional artists, faculty, and students.

Findlay

The University of Findlay - Mazza Collection Galleria ⓒᴬᴬ

Virginia B. Gardner Fine Arts Pavilion
1000 N. Main St.
Findlay, OH   45840-3695
Tel: (419) 424-4560
Internet Address: http://www.findlay.edu/mazzaweb/mazzahm.htm
Open: Wednesday to Friday, noon-6pm; Sunday, 1pm-5pm; by appointment, 424-4777.
Closed: Legal Holidays.
Facilities: **Galleries** (5).
Activities: **Education Programs**; **Guided Tours**; **Permanent Exhibits**; **Temporary Exhibitions**.

With over 1,300 works, the Mazza Collection is the first and largest teaching gallery in the world specializing in children's book illustration.

Gambier

Kenyon College - Olin Art Gallery ⓒᴬᴬ

Kenyon College, Olin Library, East Gambier Street
Gambier, OH   43022
Tel: (740) 417-5000
Internet Address: http://www.kenyon.edu
Admission: free.
Open: Monday to Saturday, 8:30am-midnight; Sunday, 9:30am-midnight.
Facilities: **Gallery**.
Activities: **Lectures**; **Temporary Exhibitions**.

Located in the Olin Library on the Middle Way, the Olin Gallery at Kenyon features temporary exhibitions of the work of both students and professional artists.

Granville

Denison University Art Gallery ⓒ

Burke Hall of Music and Art (Cherry and Broadway), Granville, OH   43023
Tel: (614) 587-6255
Fax: (615) 587-5701
Internet Address: http://www.denison.edu
Director: Dr. Ankeney Weitz
Admission: free.
Established: 1946   *ADA Compliant:* Y
Open: **mid-September to May**, Daily, 1pm-4pm.
Closed: Academic Holidays.
Facilities: **Galleries** (4).
Activities: **Guided Tours**; **Lectures**; **Traveling Exhibitions**.
Publications: exhibition catalogues.

Consisting of a large gallery, three small galleries and a seminar room, the Fine Arts Gallery displays parts of Denison University's permanent collection as well as temporary exhibitions of contemporary art. The University's permanent collection is noted for one of the largest accumulations of Burmese art outside Myanmar; Chinese ceramics, textiles, and works on paper; and other small but significant collections of Eastern art. Western art is represented by a print collection, Baroque drawings of the Roman school, paintings on wood and canvas, and sculpture in all media.

Kent

Kent State University - School of Art Galleries ⓒ

School of Art Building (near Van Duesen Hall), Summit Street, Kent, OH   44242
Tel: (216) 672-7853   *Fax:* (216) 672-4729
Internet Address: http://www.kent.edu/art/soa_gall.html
Director: Prof. Fred T. Smith
Admission: voluntary contribution.
Attendance: 18,000   *Established:* 1950   *Membership:* Y   *ADA Compliant:* Y
Open: Monday to Friday, 10am-4pm; Sunday, 2pm-5pm.
Closed: Academic Holidays.
Activities: **Education Programs** (undergraduate and graduate students); **Guided Tours**; **Lectures**; **Performances**; **Temporary Exhibitions** (6 major/year).
Publications: booklets.

The School of Art galleries (The Art Gallery, Gallery 138, Student Galleries) hold a permanent collection of paintings, sculpture, prints, and graduate theses. Also of possible interest on campus, The Kent State University Museum, located in Rockwell Hall, features an international collection of costume and decorative arts in nine galleries. At a remove from the campus, the School of Art maintains a branch gallery, the William H. Eells Art Gallery, on the grounds of the Blossom Music Center, summer home of the Cleveland Orchestra, just north of Akron.

Newark

Ohio State University at Newark - Art Gallery ⓒ

1179 University Drive (off Crain Pkwy.), Newark, OH   43055
Tel: (740) 366-9369
Internet Address: http://www.newark.ohio-state.edu
Contact: Ms. Kathleen Keys
Open: Call for hours.
Facilities: **Exhibition Area**.
Activities: **Temporary Exhibitions**.

The Art Gallery is committed to exhibiting locally, nationally, and internationally recognized artists in all media. The Gallery has exhibited such prominent artists as Roy Lichtenstein.

Oberlin

Oberlin College - Allen Memorial Art Museum ⊕ (AMAM)

87 N. Main St. at E. Lorain St., Oberlin, OH 44074
Tel: (440) 775-8665   *Fax:* (440) 775-8799
Internet Address: http://www.oberlin.edu/~allenart
Acting Director: Ms. Marjorie Wieseman
Admission: voluntary contribution.
Attendance: 35,000   *Established:* 1917   *Membership:* Y   *ADA Compliant:* Y
Parking: free on site.
Open: Tuesday to Saturday, 10am-5pm;
        Sunday, 1pm-5pm.
Closed: Legal Holidays.

Facilities: **Architecture** Main building (designed by Cass Gilbert, 1917), subsequent addition (1977, designed by Venturi, Rauch & Scott Brown), Usonian House (by Frank Lloyd Wright, 1948-50); **Galleries** (5 permanent, 3 temporary exhibition); **Library** (43,000 volumes); **Print Study Room**; **Sculpture Garden**; **Shop** (39 S. Main St., 775-2086).
Activities: **Concerts** (2-4/year); **Education Programs** (adults and children); **Films**; **Gallery Talks** (2nd Tues in month, 2:30pm); **Guided Tours** (by request, 775-8048); **Lectures** (2-6/year); **Temporary Exhibitions** (10-12/year).

Piet Mondrian, *Brabant Farmyard*, 1904, oil/pulpboard/canvas, 39.8 x 48.3 cm. Allen Memorial Art Museum. Photograph courtesy of Allen Memorial Art Museum, Oberlin, Ohio.

Publications: brochures; collection catalogue; exhibition catalogues; journal, "Allen Memorial Art Museum Bulletin" (semi-annual); newsletter, "Allen Memorial Art Museum News" (3/year).

AMAM contains one of the nation's finest college or university art collections. Each year the Museum presents a variety of special exhibitions organized from its own collection, as well as loan exhibitions organized by the Museum staff or other institutions. In addition to the works on exhibit in the galleries, a number of sculptures from the Museum are located on the grounds around the building. The Museum collection of some 14,000 objects covers many cultures and time periods, and has particular strengths in Dutch and Flemish paintings of the 17th century, Islamic carpets, Old Master prints, Japanese prints, late 19th- and 20th-century European painting and sculpture, and modern and contemporary American art. Some of AMAM's finest works of art include "The Finding of Erichthonius" by Rubens, "Self Portrait" by Sweerts, "St. Sebastian Attended by St. Irene" by Terbrugghen, "View of Venice: Ducal Palace, Dogana, with Part of San Giorgio" by J.M.W. Turner, "Wisteria" and "The Garden of the Princess, Louvre" by Monet, "The Viaduct at L'Estaque" by Cézanne, "The Plough and the Song" by Gorky, and "Laocoön" by Eva Hesse. AMAM also operates a gallery and museum store, Uncommon Objects, at the New Union Center for the Arts, 39 S. Main St., Oberlin, Ohio - (440) 775-2086.

Oxford

Miami University Art Museum ⊕

Patterson Ave. (U.S. Route 27 between Western Drive and Chestnut St.)
Oxford, OH 45056
Tel: (513) 529-2232   *Fax:* (513) 529-6555   *TDDY:* (513) 529-1541
Internet Address: http://www.muohio.edu/artmuseum/
Director: Mr. Robert A. Kret
Admission: free.
Attendance: 51,000   *Established:* 1978   *Membership:* Y   *ADA Compliant:* Y
Parking: free on site.

Oxford, Ohio
Miami University Art Museum, cont.
Open: Tuesday to Sunday, 11am-5pm.

Closed: Legal Holidays, Academic Holidays.

Facilities: **Architecture** (1978 designed by Walter Netsch of Skidmore, Owings & Merrill); **Auditorium** (184 seats); **Galleries** (5); **Library**; **Sculpture Park**; **Shop**.

Activities: **Concerts**; **Education Programs**; **Films**; **Gallery Talks**; **Guided Tours** (by appointment, reserve two weeks in advance); **Lectures**; **Temporary Exhibitions**; **Traveling Exhibitions**.

Publications: annual report; brochure, "Calendar of Events"; exhibition catalogues; newsletter (quarterly).

George Bottini, *Addresse Sagot*, 1898, color lithograph on paper, 28.5 x 18.5 cm, Miami University Art Museum Purchase, Patrick A. Spensley Memorial Fund. Photograph courtesy of Art Museum, Miami University, Oxford, Ohio.

Located on the southern edge of the campus, the Art Museum houses five galleries of changing exhibitions, a growing permanent collection of approximately 16,000 art works, a lecture hall, and a library study room. Exhibitions feature historical and contemporary art, decorative arts, and art from diverse cultures of the world drawn from other museums, private and corporate collections, and national traveling exhibitions, as well as the University's permanent collection. Exhibitions are complemented by more than thirty public programs each year. The permanent collection is broad and eclectic with strengths in many fields from all parts of the world. Major holdings include European and American paintings, prints, drawings, watercolors and photographs; ancient art; European and American glass; ceramics (including Islamic, European, and Chinese porcelain); sculpture (including Gandharan, African, Oceanic, 19th century and contemporary works); a worldwide collection of textiles; folk art; and Leica cameras and accessories. Among the painters represented are Audrey Flack, Leon Golub, Hans Hofmann, Robert Indiana, Josef Israels, John Everett Millais, Ad Reinhardt, Miriam Schapiro, and Francesco Solimena. Sculptors include Fletcher Benton, Mark di Suvero, Nancy Holt, Richard Hunt, Marisol, and Claes Oldenburg. Prints include works by Josef Albers, Paul Cadmus, Marc Chagall, Francesco Clemente, Henri deToulouse-Lautrec, Jim Dine, Albrecht Dürer, Paul Gauguin, Käthe Kollwitz, Le Corbusier, Pablo Picasso, Odilon Redon, Georges Roualt, David Alfaro Sequeiros, Rufino Tamayo, June Wayne, Andy Warhol, and James McNeill Whistler.

Rio Grande

University of Rio Grande Sculpture Park ⒸⒶ
218 North College Avenue, Rio Grande, OH   45674-3131

Tel: (800) 288-2746

Internet Address: http://www.urggcc.edu

Curator: Mr. Kevin Lyles

Admission: free.

Open: Call for hours.

Facilities: **Sculpture Park**.

There are over a dozen outdoor sculptures located throughout the Rio Grande campus. All works are by professional sculptors from throughout the United States, including Fletcher Benton and Edward McCullough.

Toledo

University of Toledo - Center for the Visual Arts Galleries ⒸⒶ
620 Grove Place, Toledo, OH   43620

Tel: (419) 530-8300   *Fax:* (419) 530-8337

Internet Address: http://www.cva.utoledo.edu

Open: Daily, 9am-10pm.

University of Toledo - Center for the Visual Arts Galleries, cont.

Facilities: **Galleries** (3).

Activities: **Lectures**; **Temporary Exhibitions**.

The Center for the Visual Arts houses two galleries, the CVA Gallery and the Clement Gallery, which display the work of both students and professional artists. Also of possible interest on campus is the Eberly Center Gallery in Tucker Hall, which shows work created by woman artists.

Wooster

College of Wooster Art Museum Ⓒᴬᴬ

Ebert Art Center, 1220 Beall Ave. (south of Wayne Ave.), Wooster, OH   44691

Tel: (330) 263-2495

Fax: (330) 263-2633

Internet Address: http://www.wooster.edu/Art/artmuseum.html

Director: Ms. Thalia Gouma-Peterson

Admission: free.

Established: 1930

Open: Monday to Friday, 11am-5pm; Sunday, 2pm-5pm.

Facilities: **Galleries** (3; one large, two smaller).

Activities: **Films**; **Gallery Talks**; **Lectures**; **Temporary Exhibitions**.

Publications: exhibition catalogues.

The College of Wooster Art Museum exhibits the work of nationally known artists and has achieved a national reputation for exhibitions celebrating the works of contemporary woman artists. The College's permanent collection contains about 6,000 items, including the William Mithoefer Collection of African Art and the John Taylor Arms collection of prints and drawings, some of which date from the Renaissance.

Youngstown

Youngstown State University - The John J. McDonough Museum of Art Ⓒᴬᴬ

One University Plaza (across from The Butler Institute)

Youngstown, OH   44555

Tel: (330) 742-1400

Internet Address: http://www.ysu.edu/colleges/f&pa/art/mcd.htm

Director: Sandy Kreisman

Open: Tuesday, 11am-4pm; Wednesday, 11am-8pm; Thursday to Saturday, 11am-4pm.

Facilities: **Architecture** (design by Charles Gwathmey); **Exhibition Area**; **Sculpture Terraces**.

Activities: **Temporary Exhibitions** (15-20/year).

Funded in large part by the sale of a donated Childe Hassam painting, *Gloucester Harbor*, the John J. McDonough Museum of Art was designed by New York architect Charles Gwathmey. It serves as a professional exhibition venue for graduating BFA students in Studio Art, as well as for studio faculty. It presents visual arts programs of education and artistic significance, exhibits works of established and emerging artists as well as loaned works and/or collections from larger museums. The annual exhibition season is a balance of in-house curatorial efforts, touring temporary exhibits, and student and faculty shows. The Museum facility has three traditional galleries, a raw-space gallery and a two-story, sky-lit large installation gallery. Experimental galleries have plywood walls and concrete floors,-intentionally designed to accommodate installation works constructed on site. The outdoor sculpture terraces and grounds are used for site-specific works and special projects by artists.

Oklahoma

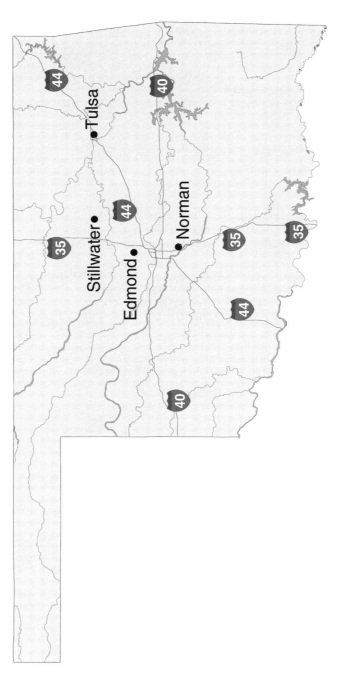

The number in parentheses following the city name indicates the number of museums/galleries in that municipality. If there is no number, one is understood. For example, in the text one listing would be found under each Oklahoman city.

Oklahoma

Edmond

University of Central Oklahoma - Museum of Art and Design ⒸⒶⒿ

Art and Design Building (south corner), 100 N. University Drive
Edmond, OK 73034
Tel: (405) 974-5931
Internet Address: http://www.libarts.ucok.edu/visual/html/museum.html
Admission: free.
Open: Monday to Wednesday, 9am-5pm; Thursday, 9am-8pm; Friday, 9am-5pm; Sunday, 1pm-5pm.
Facilities: **Exhibition Area.**
Activities: **Temporary Exhibitions.**

The Museum presents exhibitions of the work of professional artists, faculty and students.

Norman

University of Oklahoma - The Fred Jones Jr. Museum of Art ⒸⒶⒿ

University of Oklahoma
410 W. Boyd St.
Norman, OK 73019-3002
Tel: (405) 325-3272
Fax: (405) 325-7696
Internet Address: http://www.ou.edu/fjjma
Admission: free.
Established: 1936
Membership: Y   *ADA Compliant:* Y
Parking: free on site.
Open: **Academic Year**,
          Tuesday to Wednesday, 10am-4:30pm;
          Thursday, 10am-9pm;
          Friday, 10am-4:30pm;
          Saturday to Sunday, noon-4:30pm.
          Summer,
          Tuesday to Sunday, noon-4:30pm.
Closed: Legal Holidays, Academic Holidays.
Facilities: **Library** (3,000 volumes); **Shop.**
Activities: **Concerts**; **Films**; **Gallery Talks**; **Guided Tours**; **Lectures**; **Temporary Exhibitions**; **Traveling Exhibitions.**

Ernest L. Blumenschein, *Taos Valley and Mountain*, oil on panel, 22 x 25½ inches. Fred Jones Jr. Museum of Art, University of Oklahoma. Purchase, Richard H. and Adeline J. Fleischaker Collection, 1996. Photograph courtesy of Fred Jones Jr. Museum of Art, University of Oklahoma, Norman, Oklahoma.

Publications: brochures; calendar (3/year); exhibition catalogues; posters.

The Fred Jones Jr. Museum of Art is the art museum of The University of Oklahoma and reflects the University's commitment to research and scholarship in the visual arts. Its mission is to provide the best possible object-based learning experience through excellence in the collection, preservation, exhibition and interpretation of works of art. The museum strives to be a leader in fostering appreciation of the visual arts and serves as a resource center for the public, university, and scholarly communities. Strengths of the permanent collection include 20th-century American painting and sculpture, contemporary art, traditional and contemporary Native American art, photography, art of the Southwest, ceramics, Asian art, and European graphics from the 16th century to the present.

Stillwater

Oklahoma State University - Maude Gardiner Art Gallery ©

Oklahoma State University, 107 Bartlett Center for the Studio Arts
Stillwater, OK   74078
Tel: (405) 744-6016
Fax: (405) 744-5767
Internet Address: http://www.cas.okstate.edu/art/gallery.html
C.E.O. and Director: Dr. Nancy B. Wilkinson
Admission: free.
Attendance: 10,000   *Established:* 1965   *ADA Compliant:* Y
Open: Monday to Friday, 8am-5pm; Sunday, 1pm-4pm.
Closed: Legal Holidays.
Facilities: **Gallery**.
Activities: **Temporary Exhibitions**.
Publications: calendar; exhibition catalogues (occasional).

Exhibits at the Gallery vary from local shows, such as the annual student juried exhibitions and faculty exhibition, to national shows like the biennial Cimarron National Works on Paper Exhibition, to displays of traditional art of other cultures. The permanent collection began with graphic prints of the art department founder, Doel Reed, and has since grown to include over 240 pieces by such artists as Alexander Calder, Salvador Dali, Jasper Johns, Robert Motherwell, Robert Rauschenberg, and Larry Rivers.

Tulsa

University of Tulsa - Alexandre Hogue Gallery ©

School of Art, Phillips Hall
600 S. College Ave., Tulsa, OK   74104
Tel: (918) 631-2202
Fax: (918) 631-3423
Internet Address: http://www.utulsa.edu/arts/artfacilities.html
Director: Mr. Stephen Sumner
Open: **September to July**, Monday to Friday, 8:30am-4:30pm; Saturday, 1pm-4pm.
Facilities: **Exhibition Area**.
Activities: **Temporary Exhibitions**.

Used year-round for the exhibition of arts, crafts, performance art, and special events, the Alexandre Hogue Gallery provides flexible lighting and display areas for student, faculty, and touring art exhibitions. It is also the site of the annual Herbert Gussman Student Art Competition, the National Scholastic Art Awards Competition, and numerous shows by prominent artists, and can be comfortably used for poetry readings and chamber music performances. In addition, student work is displayed campus-wide in public areas and administrative offices.

Oregon

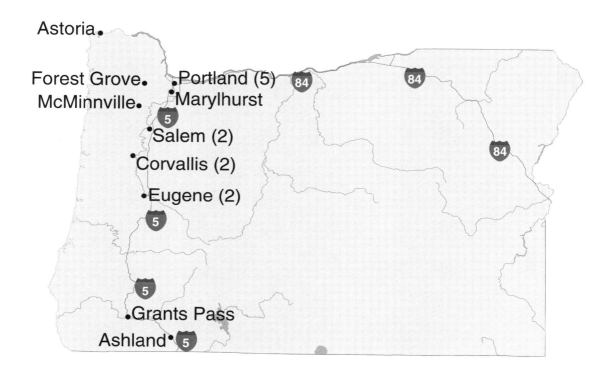

The number in parentheses following the city name indicates the number of museums/galleries in that municipality. If there is no number, one is understood. For example, in the text five listings would be found under Portland and one listing under Astoria.

Oregon

Ashland

Southern Oregon University - Schneider Museum of Art

Southern Oregon University, 1250 Siskiyou Blvd., Ashland, OR   97520-5095
Tel: (541) 552-6245   *Fax:* (541) 552-8241
Internet Address: http://www.sou.edu/schneider
Director: Mr. Greer Markle
Admission: suggested contribution-$2.00.
Attendance: 30,000   *Established:* 1986   *Membership:* Y   *ADA Compliant:* Y
Parking: 1 hour free, directly in front of museum.
Open: **Academic Year**, Tuesday to Saturday, 11am-5pm (1st Friday in month, 11am-7pm).
Closed: Legal Holidays, Thanksgiving Weekend, December 18 to January 4.
Facilities: **Architecture** (post-modernist building, 1985 design by Will Martin); **Galleries** (4).
Activities: **Guided Tours** (arrange in advance); **Lectures** (1st Friday in month and for specific exhibitions).
Publications: bulletin (quarterly).

A small, regional fine arts museum with four galleries at Southern Oregon University, the Museum hosts an eclectic program of contemporary art exhibitions, lectures, gallery talks and workshops. It is home to a permanent collection of more than 750 paintings, drawings, original prints and Native American objects. Also of possible interest on campus: The Gallery at Stevenson Union (552-6465) presents temporary exhibits of contemporary art by regionally and nationally recognized artists and an annual juried competition for SOSC students in the spring. The OtherArt Gallery in Siskiyou Commons mounts exhibitions of work by professional artists and by advance students. Student work is also displayed in the Central Art Gallery in Central Hall and in the lobby of the Dorothy Stolp Theatre.

Astoria

Clatsop Community College - Art Center Gallery

1653 Jerome, Astoria, OR   97103
Tel: (541) 325-0910   *Fax:* (541) 325-5738
Internet Address: http://www.clatsopcollege.com/Activities/actframe.html
Admission: free.
Open: Monday to Thursday, 9am-5pm and 7pm-10pm; Friday, 9am-5pm.
Facilities: **Gallery**.
Activities: **Temporary Exhibitions**.

Located at the southeast corner of the campus, the Art Center Gallery presents exhibition so work in a variety of media and styles by professional artists, as well as a juried exhibit of student work at the end of the spring term.

Corvallis

Oregon State University - Fairbanks and Giustina Galleries ⓒ

Fairbanks Hall: Jefferson Way and NW 26th St.
LaSells Stewart Center: College Drive and Western Blvd.
Corvallis, OR   97331-3702
Tel: (541) 737-4745
Internet Address: http://www.orst.edu
Director: Mr. Douglas E. Russell
Admission: free.
Open: Monday to Friday, 8am-5pm.
Facilities: **Galleries** (2).
Activities: **Temporary Exhibitions**.

Oregon State University - Fairbanks and Giustina Galleries, cont.

The Fairbanks Gallery, located in Fairbanks Hall on the OSU campus, exhibits monthly shows of contemporary art by local, regional and national artists. The Giustina Gallery, located in the LaSells Stewart Center, features art by regional and national artists. Exhibits rotate approximately every month with a show by senior art majors featured each spring. There is also a permanent exhibit of "Art about Agriculture" hanging in the conference wing. The University's Fine Arts Collection, consists of medieval illuminated manuscript pages, older European and Japanese prints, 20th-century paintings, prints, mosaics, sculpture, and crafts. Selections from the collection are exhibited occasionally in the Fairbanks and Giustina galleries.

Oregon State University Memorial Union Gallery Ⓒ

Oregon State University, Memorial Union Building, Jefferson St.
Corvallis, OR 97331-5004
Tel: (503) 737-6371
Fax: (503) 737-1565
Internet Address: http://www.orst.edu
Director: Mr. Kent Sumner
Admission: free.
Attendance: 50,000   *Established:* 1927   *ADA Compliant:* Y
Open: Daily, 9am-5pm.
Closed: Legal Holidays.
Facilities: **Exhibition Area.**
Activities: **Permanent Exhibits**; **Temporary Exhibitions.**

The Memorial Union Gallery includes collections of landscapes and marine paintings by William Henry Price and Leo Fairbanks. A permanent collection displays American Indian portraits by Carrie M. Gilbert and prints by Gordon Gilkey. Throughout the year temporary exhibits of cultural and social interest are displayed in the main concourse of the Union.

Eugene

Lane Community College Art Gallery

4000 East 30th Ave., Eugene, OR   97405
Tel: (541) 747-4501
Internet Address: http://www.lanecc.edu
Director: Mr. Harold Hoy
Admission: free.
Attendance: 6,000   *Established:* 1970   *ADA Compliant:* Y
Open: **September to June**, Monday to Thursday, 8am-10pm; Friday, 8am-5pm.
Closed: New Year's Day, Presidents' Day, Memorial Day, Labor Day, Thanksgiving Day,
        Christmas Day.
Facilities: **Exhibition Area** (875 square feet).
Activities: **Lectures.**

The Art Department Gallery presents temporary exhibitions including annual faculty, studio assistants, juried student and second-year graphic design student graduation shows.

University of Oregon Museum of Art Ⓒ

1430 Johnson Lane, Eugene, OR   97403
Tel: (541) 346-3027   *Fax:* (541) 346-0976
Internet Address: http://uoma.uoregon.edu
Director: Mr. David A. Robertson
Admission: suggested contribution-$3.00.
Attendance: 60,000   *Established:* 1930   *Membership:* Y   *ADA Compliant:* Y
Open: Wednesday, noon-8pm; Thursday to Sunday, noon-5pm.
Closed: Academic Holidays, Major Holidays.
Facilities: **Architecture**; **Exhibition Area**; **Garden and Sculpture Court**; **Shop.**

University of Oregon Museum of Art, cont.

Activities: **Gallery Talks**; **Guided Tours** (groups 10+ schedule in advance); **Temporary Exhibitions**.

Publications: brochures; exhibition catalogues; newsletter.

The Museum is widely recognized for its outstanding collection of Asian art. The collection also contains significant holdings of contemporary art from the Pacific Northwest, as well as 19th- and 20th-century European and American art and photography. Temporary exhibitions include an annual exhibition featuring the work of MFA graduate students.

Forest Grove

Pacific University - Kathrin Cawein Gallery of Art

2043 College Way, Forest Grove, OR 97116

Tel: (503) 357-6151

Internet Address: http://www.pacificu.edu

Admission: free.

Open: **September to May**, Weekdays, 8am-5pm.

Facilities: **Gallery**.

Activities: **Temporary Exhibitions**.

The Gallery features temporary exhibitions of work by regionally recognized artists.

Grants Pass

Rogue Community College Galleries

3345 Redwood Highway, Grants Pass, OR 97527

Tel: (541) 471-3500 *Ext:* 224

Fax: (541) 471-3588

Internet Address: http://www.rogue.cc.or.us

Director: Ms. Tommi Drake

Admission: voluntary contribution.

Attendance: 19,000   *Established:* 1988   *Membership:* N   *ADA Compliant:* Y

Parking: free on site.

Open: **Wiseman Gallery, Fall-Spring**,
Monday to Thursday, 8am-9pm; Friday, 8am-5pm; Saturday, 9am-4pm.
Wiseman Gallery, Summer, Reduced Summer Hours.
Fire House Gallery, Tuesday to Friday, 11:30am-4:30pm; Saturday, 11am-2pm.

Closed: Academic Holidays, Legal Holidays.

Facilities: **Galleries** (2); **Theatre** (250 seats).

Activities: **Education Programs** (adults and children); **Gallery Talks**; **Reception** (1st Friday in month, 6pm-8pm); **Temporary Exhibitions**; **Traveling Exhibitions**; **Workshops**.

Publications: "Northwest Women's Catalogue" (annual); exhibits schedule (annual).

The RCC galleries display contemporary art that deals with significant themes of the modern world. Representing a wide range of aesthetic styles, the exhibits originate from throughout the region, the nation, and the world. The Wiseman Gallery is located on the Redwood Campus of Rogue Community College. The Firehouse Gallery is located in the Historic Grants Pass City Hall at the corner of H and 4th streets.

Marylhurst

Marylhurst University - The Art Gym

Marylhurst University, 17600 Pacific Highway (Route 43), Marylhurst, OR 97036

Tel: (503) 636-8141   *Fax:* (503) 636-9526

Internet Address: http://www.marylhurst.edu

Director and Curator: Ms. Terri M. Hopkins

Admission: voluntary contribution.

Marylhurst, Oregon

Marylhurst College - The Art Gym, cont.
Attendance: 4,500   *Established:* 1980   *Membership:* Y   *ADA Compliant:* Y
Parking: free on site.
Open: **September to June**, Tuesday to Saturday, noon-4pm.
Closed: July to August, Thanksgiving Weekend, December 10 to January 5.
Facilities: **Exhibition Area** (2,500 square feet).
Activities: **Education Programs** (graduate and undergraduate students); **Guided Tours** (by arrangement); **Lectures**; **Temporary Exhibitions** (6-8/year).
Publications: exhibition announcements (bi-monthly); exhibition catalogues (semi-annual).

The goal of the Art Gym's program is to increase public understanding of contemporary art of the Pacific Northwest. Since 1980, the Art Gym has shown the work of more than 300 artists in many types of exhibitions, produced more than 25 exhibition catalogues, and sponsored numerous artist's talks and forums. Exhibitions include career retrospectives, mid-career surveys, thematic exhibitions, and large-scale sculpture exhibitions. Also of possible interest on campus, the Streff Gallery in Shoen Library exhibits artworks in a wide variety of media is shows running for one calendar month.

McMinnville

Linfield College - Renshaw Gallery ©
900 SE Baker Street, McMinnville, OR   97128
Tel: (503) 434-2275
Internet Address: http://www.linfield.edu
Open: Monday to Friday, 8am-5pm.
Facilities: **Galleries** (1600 square feet).

Each year, the Gallery presents exhibitions of regional, national, and international stature, as well as student work.

Portland

Oregon College of Art and Craft - Hoffman Gallery ©
8245 SW Barnes Road, Portland, OR   97225
Tel: (503) 297-5544
Internet Address: http://www.ocac.edu/exhibitions.html
Admission: free.
Open: Tuesday to Friday, 11am-5pm; Saturday to Sunday, 10am-5pm.
Facilities: **Exhibition Area**.
Activities: **Temporary Exhibitions**.

The Hoffman Gallery brings the work of regional, national, and international artists to the campus of the Oregon College of Art and Craft. The Gallery has a varied program of exhibits that range from traditional craft and ethnic art to work that challenges accepted concepts of craft and art. Student exhibitions include an annual juried show and a show of thesis work.

Pacific Northwest College of Art - Feldman Gallery
(PCNA)
1241 N.W. Johnson St., Portland, OR   97209
Tel: (800) 818-7622
Fax: (503) 226-3587
Internet Address: http://www.pnca.edu/
Dean, Academic Affairs: Mr. Gary Snyder
Admission: free.
Attendance: 20,000   *Established:* 1990
ADA Compliant: Y

Elizabeth Olbert, *Rod*, 1997, pigment in urethane on canvas, 24 inches by 17 inches. Photograph courtesy of Pacific Northwest College of Art.

Pacific Northwest College of Art - Feldman Gallery, cont.

Parking: on street.
Open: Tuesday to Saturday, 10am-6pm.
Facilities: **Exhibition Area** (3 spaces).
Activities: **Temporary Exhibitions**.

The Gallery presents temporary exhibitions of the work of nationally recognized contemporary artists and students in three spaces: the main gallery, project room, and student gallery. Also of possible interest at PNCA the 3-D Exhibition Space (3-D Annex), located in the Sculpture/Ceramics Building next to the main campus, showcases 3-dimensional work organized by the faculty of that department.

Portland Community College - Northview Gallery

Sylvania Campus, Communications Technology Bldg.
12000 SW 49th St., Room 214
Portland, OR   97219
Tel: (503) 977-4269
Internet Address: http://www.pcc.html
Director: Mr. Hugh Webb
Admission: free.
Open: Monday to Thursday, 8am-5pm; Friday, 8am-4pm.
Facilities: **Exhibition Area**.
Activities: **Temporary Exhibitions**.

Located on the second floor in the Communications Technology Building on PCC's Sylvania Campus, the Northview Gallery presents temporary exhibitions of work by contemporary Northwest artists and occasional thematic shows of educational importance.

Portland State Unversity - Autzen Gallery and Gallery 299 Ⓒ

Neuberger Hall, 724 S.W. Harrison, Portland, OR   97207
Tel: (503) 725-3344
Internet Address: http://www.fpa.pdx.edu/art.html
Contact: Ms. Mary McVein
Admission: free.
Open: Monday to Thursday, 8am-6pm; Friday, 8am-5pm.
Facilities: **Galleries**.
Activities: **Temporary Exhibitions**.

The Autzen Gallery (205 Neuberger Hall) and Gallery 299 (299 Neuberger Hall) present the work of regional and student artists, including MFA Thesis Exhibitions in the Spring. New exhibitions open on the first Thursday of each month. Also of possible interest on campus are the Littman and White Galleries on the second floor of Smith Memorial Center located at1825 S.W. Broadway. The Littman Gallery (Mon-Wed, noon-4pm; Thurs, noon-7pm) features painting, sculpture, and mixed media. The White Gallery (Mon-Fri, 7am-9pm; Sat-Sun, (9:30am-5pm) specializes in photography.

Reed College - The Douglas F. Cooley Memorial Art Gallery Ⓒ

Reed College, 3203 S.E. Woodstock Blvd.
Portland, OR   97202-8199
Tel: (503) 777-7790
Fax: (503) 777-7798
Internet Address: http://web.reed.edu/resources/gallery/index.html
Director: Ms. Susan Fellin-Yeh
Admission: free.
Attendance: 5,500   *Established:* 1989   *Membership:* Y   *ADA Compliant:* Y
Open: Tuesday to Sunday, noon-5pm.
Closed: Legal Holidays.
Facilities: **Galleries**.
Activities: **Gallery Talks**; **Lectures**; **Temporary Exhibitions**; **Traveling Exhibitions**.

Reed College - The Douglas F. Cooley Memorial Art Gallery, cont.

Publications: exhibition catalogues.

The Gallery functions as a venue for scholarly exhibitions both curated in-house and by other museums. Four major exhibitions of contemporary and historical work are displayed each school year. As a teaching gallery, it often links exhibitions to course offerings and other activities throughout the College's calendar year. Elsewhere on campus, the Vollum Lounge Gallery often exhibits the work of senior art majors.

Salem

Chemeketa Community College Art Gallery Ⓒᴬᴬ

4000 Lancaster Drive, N.E., Salem, OR   97309

Tel: (503) 399-2533

Internet Address: http://www.chemeketa.cc.or.us/arts/gallery.html

Contact: Tom Creeland

Admission: free.

Open: Monday to Thursday, 9:30am-5:30pm; Friday, 9:30am-4:30pm.

Facilities: **Gallery**.

Activities: **Temporary Exhibitions**.

The gallery presents temporary exhibitions of contemporary art in all media, including an annual juried student exhibition.

Willamette University - Hallie Ford Museum of Art Ⓒᴬᴬ

700 State St., Salem, OR   97301

Tel: (503) 370-6855

Fax: (503) 375-5458

Internet Address:
   http://www.willamette.edu/museum_of_art

Director: Mr. John Olbrantz

Admission: fee: adult-$3.00, child-free,
   student-$2.00, senior-$2.00.

Attendance: 24,000   *Established:* 1998

Membership: Y   *ADA Compliant:* Y

Parking: metered on street.

Open: **AcademicYear**,
            Tuesday to Saturday, noon-5pm.

Closed: Legal Holidays.

Facilities: **Galleries** (6); **Print Study Room**;
   Study Gallery.

Jean-Baptiste Camille Corot, *A Balmy Afternoon*, c. 1865, oil on canvas, 16 3/8 x 23 3/8 inches. Permanent collection, Hallie Ford Museum of Art. Photograph courtesy of Hallie Ford Museum of Art, Willamette University, Salem, Oregon.

Activities: **Guided Tours**; **Permanent Exhibits**; **Temporary Exhibitions**.

Publications: brochures (occasional); exhibition catalogues (occasional); newsletter/calendar, "Brushstrokes" (biennial).

The Museum is housed in an International Style building and consists of six galleries reflecting the range of the university's developing permanent art collection and its mission. Exhibitions focus on historic as well as contemporary art and present works from the permanent collection, as well as pieces loaned to the museum, and the work of locally and regionally recognized artists, university faculty, and students.

Pennsylvania

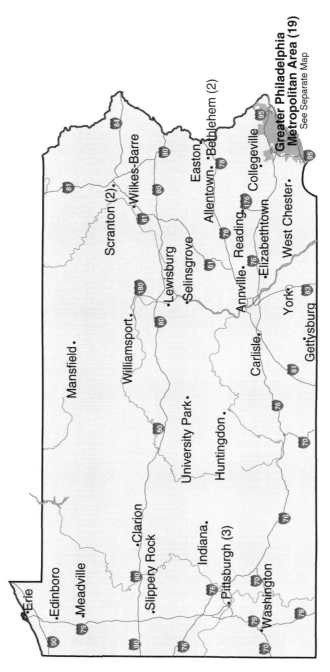

The number in parentheses following the city name indicates the number of museums/galleries in that municipality. If there is no number, one is understood. For example, in the text three listings would be found under Pittsburgh and one listing under Carlisle.

Greater Philadelphia Metropolitan Area

(including Bryn Athyn, Chester, Glenside, Haverford, Philadelphia,
Rosemont, Swarthmore, and Villanova.)

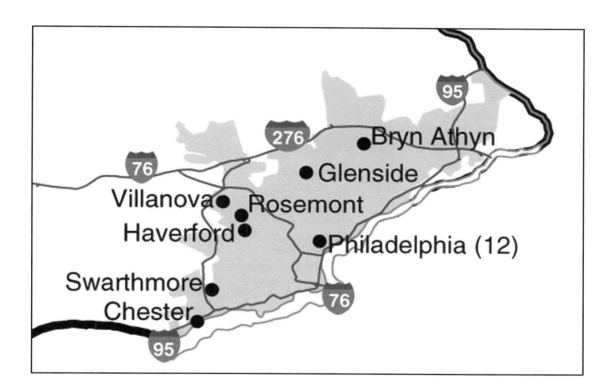

Pennsylvania

Allentown

Muhlenberg College - Martin Art Gallery ⓒ

Dorothy and Dexter Baker Center for the Arts, 2400 Chew St., Allentown, PA   18104-5586
Tel: (610) 821-3466
Internet Address: http://www.srt.net/mc/
Director: Ms. Lori Verderame, Ph.D.
Open: Tuesday to Saturday, noon-5pm.
Facilities: **Exhibition Area**.
Activities: **Permanent Exhibits**; **Temporary Exhibitions**.

Located in the Baker Center for the Arts, the Martin Art Gallery presents temporary exhibitions and changing selections from the permanent collection including a senior student art exhibition each spring.. Among the artists represented in the Florence Foerderer Tonner Print Collection are Heinrich Aldegrever, Richard Anuskiewicz, Harry Bertoia, William Blake, Mary Cassatt, Marc Chagall, Imogen Cunningham, Edward S. Curtis, Salvador Dali, Mark di Suvero, Albrecht Dürer, Philip Evergood, Leon Golub, Francisco Goya, Edward Hopper, Louis Kurz, Seymour Lipton, Ludwig Mies van der Rohe, Rembrandt van Rijn, Diego Rivera, Norman Rockwell, George Roualt, Andy Warhol, James Abbott McNeill Whistler, and William Zorach.

Annville

Lebanon Valley College - Suzanne H. Arnold Art Gallery ⓒ

Lebanon Valley College, 101 N. College Ave., Annville, PA   17003
Tel: (717) 867-6397   *Fax:* (717) 867-6124
Internet Address: http://www.lvc.edu/www/facilities/gallery_arnold.html
Asst. Professor, Art/Director: Dr. Leo Mazow
Admission: free.
Established: 1994
Open: **Academic Year**, Thursday to Sunday, 1pm-4:30pm.
Closed: Academic Holidays.
Facilities: **Exhibiton Area** (1001 square feet).
Activities: **Temporary Exhibitions** (6/year).
Publications: Exhibition catalogues (occasional); brochures (occasional).

A former Lutheran Church built in 1868, "The Gallery at Lebanon Valley College" includes the Suzanne H. Arnold Art Gallery, an intimate viewing area incorporating the highest standards of environmental and security controls, and the Zimmerman Recital Hall, a venue for small musical presentations. The Gallery presents temporary exhibitions and an annual juried student exhibition in the spring. Exhibitions have included the work of well-known artists, such as Joseph Cornell, Degas, Toulouse-Lautrec, O'Keeffe, Hopper, and Homer; as well as a more recent generation of artists including José Bedia, Patricia Bellan-Gillen, Susan Leopold, G. Daniel Massad, Kate Moran, and Rebecca Purdum.The Gallery also oversees the permanent collection of Lebanon Valley College. Among the highlights of this modest-sized collection are works on paper by such artists as Calder, Chagall, Miró, and Picasso. Audrey Flack's monumental sculpture, *Cuewe-Pehelle* (1997), graces the academic quadrangle.

Bethlehem

Lehigh University Art Galleries ⓒ (LUAG)

Zoellner Arts Center, 420 E. Packer Ave, Bethlehem, PA   18015-3007
Tel: (610) 758-3615   *Fax:* (610) 758-4580
Internet Address: http://www.lehigh.edu
Director and Curator: Prof. Ricardo Viera
Admission: free.
Attendance: 120,000   *Established:* 1864   *ADA Compliant:* Y
Parking: metered and parking garage ($1.00).

Lehigh University Art Galleries, cont.

Open: **Zoellner Gallery**,
Wednesday to Saturday, 11am-5pm;
Sunday, 1pm-5pm.
DuBois Gallery,
Monday to Friday, 9am-10pm;
Saturday, 9am-noon.
Siegel Gallery,
Monday to Thursday, 9am-10pm;
Friday, 9am-5pm.
Girdler Gallery,
Daily, 8am-midnight.

Closed: Academic Holidays.

Facilities: **Galleries** (2 additional galleries on campus); **Sculpture Garden**; **Shop**.

Activities: **Education Programs** (undergraduate college students); **Gallery Talks**; **Guided Tours**; **Lectures**; **Temporary Exhibitions**; **Traveling Exhibitions**.

Publications: calendar (semi-annual); exhibition catalogues; posters.

Maurice Prendergast, *La Rouge: Portrait of Miss Edith King*, c. 1910-1913, oil on canvas. Lehigh University Permanent Collection, gift of Ralph L. Wilson, '22. Photograph courtesy of Lehigh University Art Galleries, Bethlehem, Pennsylvania.

The Lehigh University Art Galleries maintain and develop the university's permanent art collection and present temporary exhibitions designed to make visual literacy a result of the university learning experience. More than twenty exhibitions a year in three campus galleries are planned to supplement formal classroom study in the visual arts, to create educational opportunities for the student body, and to enrich the cultural life of the campus and community at large. The annual schedule includes the exhibition of works from the permanent collection, the use of borrowed objects, and traveling exhibitions. The exhibition schedule is supplemented by gallery talks, lectures, films, workshops and research opportunities in the permanent collection. The art galleries occupy exhibition, storage, office, and workshop space in several campus locations. Permanent exhibitions are in the Zoellner Arts Center, Upper Gallery and Lower Gallery. Maginnes Hall houses the DuBois Gallery, and the Siegel Gallery is in Iacocca Hall on the mountaintop campus. The Muriel and Philip Berman Sculpture Gardens are located in the courtyard of Mudd, Mart, Whitaker and Sinclair buildings; on the mountaintop campus; and Saucon Field on the Murray H. Goodman campus. The Ralph L. Wilson Study Gallery and Open Storage Facility, accessible by appointment only, is located in Building J on the mountaintop campus. The permanent art collection is a work/study collection intended as a resource for students pursuing formal study in the visual arts and/or museum studies, for the faculty, and interested members of the community. The permanent art collection consists of a variety of works by old masters and contemporary artists. Important collection groups include the M. B. Grace Collection of European Paintings (Gainsborough, Reynolds, Goya, and others); the Dreyfus Collection of French Paintings (Bonnard, Sisley, Vuillard, Courbet); the Ralph L. Wilson Collection of American Art (paintings by Prendergast, Sloan, Henri, Lawson, Bellows, Davies, Burchfield; prints by Whistler, Hassam, Benton, Kent, Sloan, Davies, Frasconi); the Prasse Collection of Prints (Delacroix, Matisse, Renoir, Kunyoshi, Rivera, Orozco); the Muriel and Philip Berman Collection of Contemporary Sculpture (Kadishman, Unger, Tumarkin, Henry Moore, Bertoia, Shaw); the Fearnside Collection of European Old Master Prints and Drawings; the Baker Collection of Chinese Porcelains; the Berman Collection of Japanese Prints (Eishi, Hiroshige, Hokusai, Onshi, Sekino, Utamaro, Yoshika); the Folk and Outsider Art Collection (Finster, Adkins, Sperger, Kinney, Pickle, R.A.Miller, Tolliver); the Puerto Rican Poster Collection; Collection of Philatelics and Numismatics; Langermann Collection of Pre-Columbian Sculpture; Mr. and Mrs. Franklin H. Williams African Collection (gold weights of the Akam and West African objects); the Lehigh University Photography Collection (Fox-Talbot, Fenton, Cameron, Jackson, Atget, Rau, Kasebier, Sander, Bourke-White, Brassai, Brandt, Bravo, Callahan, Siskind, Fink, Porter, Hahn, Clark, Martinez-Canas, Serrano) and the Lehigh University Contemporary Prints Collection (Bearden, Rivers, Anuszkiewicz, Soto, Roth, Chryssa, Ruscha, Tobey, Calder, Kitaj, Marca-Relli, Genoves, Cruz Azaceta, Golub, Jimenez, Piper, Serrano, Simpson).

Bethlehem, Pennsylvania

Moravian College - Payne Gallery ⓒᴬᴬ

Main and Church Sts., Bethlehem, PA 18018
Tel: (610) 861-1680   *Fax:* (610) 861-1682
Internet Address: http://www.moravian.edu
Director: Dr. Diane Radycki
Admission: free.
Membership: N   *ADA Compliant:* Y
Parking: free on site.
Open: Tuesday to Sunday, 11am-4pm.
Closed: Legal Holidays.
Facilities: **Gallery**.
Activities: **Permanent Exhibits**; **Temporary Exhibitions**.
Publications: exhibition catalogues (1 per show).

The permanent collection at Moravian is particularly strong in late nineteenth- and early twentieth-century American art, including works by Albert Bierstadt, John Marin, Cecilia Beaux, Susan MacDowell Eakins, and the New Hope School of American Impressionism (works by Coppedge, Badura, Garber, Redfield, and Schofield).

Bryn Athyn

Bryn Athyn College of the New Church - Glencairn Museum ⓒᴬᴬ

1001 Cathedral Road, Bryn Athyn, PA 19009
Tel: (215) 938-2600   *Fax:* (215) 938-1056
Internet Address: http://www.newchurch.edu/college/glencairn.html
Director: Mr. Stephen H. Morley
Admission: fee: adult-$4.00, student-$2.00.
Attendance: 18,000   *Established:* 1878
Parking: free on site.
Open: Monday to Friday, 9am-5pm; alternate Sundays, 2pm-5pm.
Closed: Legal Holidays.
Facilities: **Library** (1,000 volumes).
Activities: **Concerts**; **Education Programs** (students); **Guided Tours**; **Temporary Exhibitions**.
Publications: journal; newsletter.

The Glencairn Museum was created to showcase the Raymond Pitcairn collection of religious art and to provide educational and cultural experiences for students at Bryn Athyn College. The holdings in Medieval sculpture and stained glass are notable. Galleries include Ancient Near East, Ancient Egyptian, Greek, Roman, Medieval, Far Eastern, Native American, and New Church Studies.

Carlisle

Dickinson College - The Trout Gallery ⓒᴬᴬ

Dickinson College, High St., Carlisle, PA 17013-2896
Tel: (717) 245-1344   *Fax:* (717) 245-1937
Internet Address: http://www.dickinson.edu/departments/trout
Director: Dr. Peter Lukehart
Admission: free.
Attendance: 12,000   *Established:* 1983 *Membership:* Y   *ADA Compliant:* Y
Parking: free on site.
Open: **late August to mid-June**,
          Tuesday to Saturday, 10am-4pm.
         late June to mid-August,
          Wednesday, 1pm-4pm; Saturday, 10am-4pm.
Closed: Legal Holidays.

Auguste Rodin, *St. John the Baptist Preaching*, bronze, 1878-1880. Gift of Dr. and Mrs. Meyer P. Potamkin.
Trout Gallery collection. Photograph courtesy of Trout Gallery, Dickinson College, Carlisle, Pennsylvania.

Dickinson College - The Trout Gallery, cont.

Facilities: **Auditorium** (250 seat); **Print Study Room.**
Activities: **Concerts**; **Education Programs** (undergraduate students); **Films**; **Guided Tours**; **Lectures**; **Temporary Exhibitions**; **Traveling Exhibitions**.
Publications: calendar (semi-annual); exhibition catalogues (biennial).

The Trout Gallery, along with housing Dickinson College's permanent collections of art (which range in time from Classical Greece to the 20th Century) maintains a varied and frequently changing exhibition schedule of historical, contemporary, and multicultural materials. The Trout Gallery is, at once, an educational branch of the College and a fine arts museum for the Carlisle/Greater Harrisburg area. The Gallery serves the college community as an interdisciplinary resource for studio art, art history, modern language, international studies, and classical archaeology courses.

Chester

Widener University Art Collection and Gallery ⓒ

14th and Chestnut, Chester, PA   19013
Tel: (610) 499-1189
Fax: (610) 499-4425
Internet Address: http://www.widener.edu
Collections Manager: Ms. Rebecca Warda
Admission: free.
Established: 1970   *ADA Compliant:* Y
Open: Tuesday, 10am-7pm;
        Wednesday to Saturday, 10am-4:30pm.
Closed: Legal Holidays, 2nd & 3rd weeks of July.
Facilities: **Shop**.
Activities: **Lectures**; **Temporary Exhibitions**.
Publications: brochures.

The Widener University Art Collection and Gallery features the Alfred O. Deshong Collection of 19th-century American and European paintings and 18th- and 19th-century Asian art. The paintings are mostly genre scenes by European-trained artists. The Oriental art includes Japanese carved ivory figures, Chinese carved hardstone vessels, lacquerware and bronzes. The Gallery also displays paintings by American Impressionists Edward Redfield, Robert Spencer, George L. Noyes, and others, as well as a collection of pre-Columbian pottery.

Clarion

Clarion University of Pennsylvania - Sandford Gallery

Clarion University of Pennsylvania
Marwick-Boyd Fine Arts Building
Clarion, PA   16214
Tel: (814) 226-2412
Fax: (814) 226-2723
Internet Address: http://vaxa.clarion.edu
Exec. Director: Ms. Carol B. Wickkiser
Admission: free.
Established: 1982   *Membership:* Y
Open: call for hours.
Closed: Academic Holidays.
Facilities: **Exhibition Area** (1,000 square feet).
Activities: **Education Programs** (students); **Lectures**; **Temporary Exhibitions**; **Traveling Exhibitions**.

The Gallery presents temporary exhibition throughout the year.

Collegeville

Ursinus College - Philip and Muriel Berman Museum of Art ⊚

Main St., Collegeville, PA   19426
Tel: (610) 409-3500
Fax: (610) 409-3664
Internet Address:
   http://www.ursinus.edu/berman/berman_exhibits.html#LOC
C.E.O.: Ms. Lisa Tremper Barnes
Admission: voluntary contribution.
Attendance: 55,000   *Established:* 1987
Membership: Y   *ADA Compliant:* Y
Parking: adjacent to the museum on campus.
Open: Tuesday to Friday, 10am-4pm;
        Saturday to Sunday, noon-4:30.
Closed: Academic Holidays.
Facilities: **Library** (1,200 volumes); **Shop**.
Activities: **Education Programs** (undergraduate and graduate
   students); **Films**; **Guided Tours**; **Lectures**; **Temporary
   Exhibitions**; **Traveling Exhibitions**.
Publications: "Friends of the Museum Newsletter" (quarterly);
   calendar (quarterly); exhibition catalogues.

Lynn Chadwick, *Diamond Seated Couple*, 1984, Bronze, each figure 78 x 40 x 96 inches. Collection of Philip and Muriel Berman Museum of Art, Ursinus College. Photograph courtesy of Ursinus College, Collegeville, Pennsylvania.

The Philip and Muriel Berman Museum of Art at Ursinus College, located in a classic Georgian facility readapted to house the museum, offers 12 exhibitions annually, both historical and contemporary in nature. Lectures, film series, symposia, and other programming are offered in conjunction with exhibitions. The permanent collection numbers approximately 3,500 pieces of paintings, prints, drawings, sculpture, and historical artifacts. Strengths of the collection include 18th-, 19th-, and 20th-century American art, 19th-century European landscapes, Japanese woodcuts, contemporary sculpture, and Pennsylvania German artifacts. The Museum holds the largest private collection of Lynn Chadwick sculpture in the United States.

Easton

Lafayette College Art Gallery ⊚

Williams Center for the Arts, Hamilton and High Sts., Easton, PA   18042
Tel: (610) 250-5361   *Fax:* (610) 559-4042
Internet Address: http://www.lafayette.edu
Director, Willliams Center for the Arts: Mr. H. Ellis Finger
Admission: free.
Attendance: 6,500   *Established:* 1983   *ADA Compliant:* Y
Open: **September to May**, Tuesday to Friday, 10am-5pm; Sunday, 2pm-5pm.
Closed: Academic Holidays.
Facilities: **Exhibition Area** (1,000 square feet).
Activities: **Lectures**; **Temporary Exhibitions**.
Publications: brochures; exhibition catalogues.

The Gallery presents exhibitions in a wide variety of media and genres each year.

Edinboro

Edinboro University of Pennsylvania - Bruce Gallery of Art ⊚

Doucette Hall, Ground Floor, near Diebold Center, Meadville Street, Edinboro, PA   16444-0001
Tel: (814) 732-2513   *Fax:* (814) 732-2629
Internet Address: http://www.edinboro.edu/cwis/Art/bruce.html

Edinboro University of Pennsylvania - Bruce Gallery of Art, cont.

Gallery Director: Mr. William Mathie
Admission: free.
Parking: Visitors must obtain parking pass from campus police.
Open: **September to April**,
    Monday to Tuesday, 2pm-5pm;
    Wednesday, 2pm to 5pm and 7pm-9pm;
    Thursday to Saturday, 2pm-5pm.
    Summer,
    Tuesday, 2pm-5pm;
    Wednesday, 2pm-5pm and 7pm-9pm;
    Thursday to Saturday, 2pm-5pm.

Facilities: **Exhibition Area** (1,400 square feet).
Activities: **Temporary Exhibitions** (7/year).

The Gallery mounts exhibitions of work by professional, faculty and student artists, including an annual faculty show, an annual juried student exhibition, and a biennial juried regional high school exhibition. Shows are generally of 3½ weeks duration. Shows during the academic year generally consist of the work of professional artists, while summer exhibitions are usually M.F.A. thesis shows.

Drew Thorne Dodson, *Segmented Oval Vase*. Vase exhibited in thesis exhibition, 1999. Photograph courtesy of Edinboro University of Pennsylvania, Edinboro, Pennsylvania.

Elizabethtown

Elizabethtown College - Galleries ©

Department of Fine and Performing Arts
1 Alpha Drive
Elizabethtown, PA   17022
Tel: (717) 361-1212   *Ext:* 1385
Internet Address:
   http://www.etown.edu/~fapa/art
Director: Prof. Milt D. Friedly
Admission: free.
Attendance: 6,000   *Established:* 1990
Membership: N   *ADA Compliant:* Y
Parking: free on site.
Open: **September 1 to December 15**,
    Daily, 9am-9pm.
    January 15 to May 15,
    Daily, 9am-9pm.
Closed: Academic Holidays.
Facilities: **Galleries** (3).
Activities: **Temporary Exhibitions**.

View of gallery, Elizabethtown College. Photograph courtesy of Elizabethtown College, Elizabethtown, Pennsylvania.

There are three gallery spaces at Elizabethtown where one-month exhibitions are presented, including works by local and regional artists, traveling exhibits, juried shows, and student work. The permanent collection is housed in the High Library and consists of early twentieth-century illustrations and paintings, African art, and contemporary art.

Erie

Gannon University - The Schuster Gallery ©

Nash Library, 3rd Floor, 619 Sassafras St. (at 7th St.), Erie, PA   16541
Tel: (814) 871-7332   *Fax:* (814) 871-5859
Internet Address: http://www.gannon.edu/resource/schuster/index.html

Gannon University - The Schuster Gallery, cont.

Director: Ms. Lisa Campbell
Admission: free.
Attendance: 1,000   *Established:* 1979   *Membership:* N   *ADA Compliant:* Y
Parking: commercial adjacent to site.
Open: **Fall to Spring**,
            Monday to Thursday, 8am-midnight; Friday, 8am-9pm; Saturday, 9am-4:30pm;
            Sunday, 12:30pm-midnight.
          Summer, restricted hours.
Closed: Independence Day Wkd.
Facilities: **Exhibition Area**.
Activities: **Temporary Exhibitions**.

The Gallery exhibits both student and faculty work. It has no permanent collection.

Gettysburg

Gettysburg College - Schmucker Hall Art Gallery ⓒᴬᴬ

Schmucker Hall, Lincoln Avenue, Gettysburg, PA   17325
Tel: (717) 337-6121
Internet Address: http://www.gettysburg.edu/academics.hold/visual_arts/art/Gallery.htm
Director: Mr. Mark Warwick
Admission: free.
Open: **September to May**, Monday to Friday, 9am-4pm; Saturday, 1pm-4pm, Sunday, 1pm-4pm.
          June-August, Monday to Friday, 9am-4pm; Saturday, 1pm-4pm.
Facilities: **Exhibition Area** (1,600 square feet).
Activities: **Temporary Exhibitions** (9-10/year).

The gallery presents works by invited professional artists and traveling exhibits of work from public and private collections, as well as an annual faculty show, an annual student show, and several senior art major show.

Glenside

Beaver College Art Gallery ⓒᴬᴬ

Spruance Fine Arts Center
Church and Easton Roads
Glenside, PA   19038
Tel: (215) 572-2131
Fax: (215) 881-8774
Internet Address: http://www.beaver.edu
Director: Mr. Richard Torchia
Admission: free.
Attendance: 3,750   *Established:* 1974
Membership: Y
Parking: free near gallery.
Open: **Academic Year**,
            Monday to Friday, 10am-3pm;
            Saturday to Sunday, noon-4pm.
Closed: Academic Holidays, Thanksgiving Day,
          Christmas Day.
Facilities: **Exhibition Area** (1,200 square feet);
          Theatre (150 seats).
Activities: **Guided Tours** (available upon request and by appointment); **Lectures** (directly related to exhibitions, usually weekdays at 6:30pm).
Publications: exhibition catalogues (2-3/year).

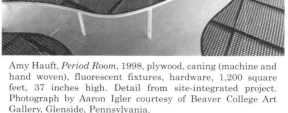

Amy Hauft, *Period Room*, 1998, plywood, caning (machine and hand woven), fluorescent fixtures, hardware, 1,200 square feet, 37 inches high. Detail from site-integrated project. Photograph by Aaron Igler courtesy of Beaver College Art Gallery, Glenside, Pennsylvania.

Beaver College Art Gallery, cont.

Housed in an historic 1893 power plant on the college campus, the Gallery provides a forum for contemporary art, offering a program of exhibitions and educational events of local to international scope. During its twenty-five year history, the Gallery has presented over one hundred exhibitions, bringing to the Philadelphia area the work of such artists as John Coplans, Mary Heilmann, Donald Lipski, Michael Lucero, Robert Morris, Elizabeth Murray, Alice Neel, Ken Price, Richard Prince, William Wegman, Fred Wilson, Yukinori Yanagi, and many others. Recent thematic group exhibitions have explored endurance-related performance, feminist practice, contemporary photorealist painting, and conceptual fiber works. Exhibitions also include a biennial juried exhibition for regional artists, a biennial show of student work selected by the faculty, and annual alumni and senior thesis exhibitions.

Haverford

Haverford College - Cantor Fitzgerald Gallery ⓒᴬᴬ

Whitehead Campus Center, 370 Lancaster Avenue
Haverford, PA   19041
Tel: (610) 896-1287
Internet Address: http://www.haverford.edu
Exhibitions Coordinator: Ms. Hilarie Johnston
Admission: free.
Attendance: 1,200   *Established:* 1994   *Membership:* Y   *ADA Compliant:* Y
Parking: free on site.
Open: **September to May**, Monday to Friday, 11am-4pm.; Saturday to Sunday, noon-4pm.
         June to August, Monday to Friday, 11am-4pm.
Closed: major holidays.
Facilities: **Exhibition Area** (1,600 square feet).
Activities: **Gallery Talks**; **Temporary Exhibitions** (monthly).

The Cantor-Fitzgerald Gallery presents well-reviewed exhibitions each month by serious working artists, who give a gallery talk at some point during the exhibition. There are also occasional historical exhibitions in a variety of media. Small exhibitions are also mounted in the Fine Art Building.

Huntingdon

Juniata College Museum of Art ⓒᴬᴬ

17th and Moore Sts.
Huntingdon, PA   16652
Tel: (814) 641-3505
Fax: (814) 641-3695
Internet Address: http://www.juniata.edu/museum
Director: Dr. Phillip J. Earenfight
Admission: free.
Established: 1998
Membership: Y   *ADA Compliant:* Y
Parking: lot behind museum, entrance off Mifflin Street.
Open: **Fall to Spring**,
         Monday to Friday, 10am-4pm;
         Saturday, noon-4pm.
         Summer,
         reduced hours, contact Museum.
Closed: Major Holidays.
Facilities: **Architecture** (Beaux-Arts former Carnegie Library Building, 1907 design by New York architect Edward Tilton); **Exhibition Area**.
Activities: **Permanent Exhibits** (scheduled for Spring, 2000); **Temporary Exhibitions**.

Charles Cromwell Ingham, *Portrait of Valentine Blanchard*, c. 1836, 1 5/6 inches x 1 3/8 inches portrait miniature. The Worth B. Stottlemyer Collection, Juniata College Museum of Art. Photograph courtesy of Juniata College Museum of Art.

Juniata College Museum of Art, cont.

The Museum houses a significant permanent collection, as well as hosting regional, national, and international exhibitions. The permanent collection includes paintings, prints, drawings, textiles, and photographs that date from the 17th century to the present. Of particular significance are landscapes by American painters Asher B. Durand, Arthur Fitzwilliam Tait, Jervis McEntee, and John Casilear. Holdings also include numerous 18th and 19th century American portrait miniatures; paintings by Sebastiano Conca and Egbert van Heemskerk; prints by Rembrandt, Whistler, and Hiroshige; and a collection of drawings and paintings by the German artist and humanist, Günther Spaltmann Collection. There is also a significant collection of 20th-century Navajo textiles, as well as photographic materials relating to the history of the college and the surrounding area. The Permanent Collection is in storage until spring 2000, when it will be reinstalled in a newly renovated permanent exhibition gallery. Only selections from the Permanent Collection will be on display during the 1999-2000 academic year.

Indiana

Indiana University of Pennsylvania - The University Museum ⓒ

John Sutton Hall, South Drive E. (between Pratt Dr. & 11th St.)
Indiana, PA 15705
Tel: (412) 357-7930
Fax: (412) 357-2332
Internet Address: http://shade.grove.iup.edu:80/FA/museum
Director: Mr. Ned Wirt
Admission: fee-$3.00.
Attendance: 8,000   *Established:* 1981   *Membership:* Y   *ADA Compliant:* Y
Parking: free on site.
Open: **Academic Year**,
            Tuesday to Wednesday, 11am-4pm; Thursday, 11am-4pm & 7pm-10pm; Friday, 11am-4pm;
            Saturday to Sunday, 1pm-4pm.
         Summer, call for hours.
Closed: Academic Holidays.
Facilities: **Galleries** (7).
Activities: **Guided Tours**; **Lectures**; **Temporary Exhibitions**.
Publications: newsletter, "Friends of the Museum Newsletter".

The University Museum presents six exhibitions per year, featuring art in all media by local, regional, and international artists. The permanent collection focuses on fine and folk arts and native arts of North and Central America, The Museum is located in John Sutton Hall, a National Register building built in 1875. Additionally, exhibitions are presented in the Department of Art's Kipp Gallery in Sprowls Hall (Monday-Friday 11:30am-2:30pm).

Lewisburg

Bucknell University - The Center Gallery ⓒ

Elaine Langone Center, 3rd Floor, 7th St. and Moore Ave.
Lewisburg, PA 17837
Tel: (717) 524-3792
Fax: (717) 524-3480
Internet Address: http://www.departments,bucknell.edu/center_gallery
Director: Ms. Johann J.K. Reusch
Admission: free.
Attendance: 3,200   *Established:* 1979   *ADA Compliant:* Y
Parking: free on site.
Open: **June to August**, Monday to Friday, 11am-5pm; Saturday to Sunday, 1pm-4pm.
Closed: Legal Holidays.
Facilities: **Auditorium** (125 seat); **Food Services** Restaurant; **Shop**.

Bucknell University - The Center Gallery, cont.

Activities: **Arts Festival**; **Concerts**; **Dance Recitals**; **Education Programs** (adults, college students and children); **Films**; **Guided Tours**; **Lectures**; **Temporary Exhibitions**; **Traveling Exhibitions**.

Publications: exhibition catalogues.

The Center Gallery presents temporary exhibitions centered on both its permanent collection and works on loan. The collection numbers approximately 7,500 objects. It features 24 items from the Samuel H. Kress Foundation, including works by Pontormo, Tintoretto, Veronese, and Sansovino. There are also collections of musical instruments and Japanese art. The museum's collection of American art includes works by Kensett, Prendergast, Burchfield, Shahn, and Benton. Its photographs include works by Mapplethorpe and Bravo, while works by Johns and Rauschenburg are found in its print collection.

Mansfield

Mansfield University - North Hall Gallery ⓒ

Mansfield University, Junction Routes 6 and 15, Mansfield, PA   16933

Tel: (570) 662-4000

Internet Address: http://www.mnsfld.edu

Open: Call for hours.

Facilities: Gallery.

Activities: Lectures.

Located in North Hall Library, the North Hall gallery presents several exhibits each year, featuring the work of both students and professional artists.

Meadville

Allegheny College Art Galleries ⓒ

Doane Hall of Art, N. Main St.

Meadville, PA   16335

Tel: (814) 332-4365

Fax: (814) 333-8180

Internet Address: http://www.alleg.edu

Director: Mr. Robert Raczka

Admission: free.

Attendance: 5,000   *Established:* 1970

Membership: N   *ADA Compliant:* Y

Parking: free on site.

Open: Tuesday to Friday, 12:30pm-5pm;
Saturday, 1:30pm-5pm;
Sunday, 2pm-4pm.

Installation view, Allegheny College Art Galleries. Photograph courtesy of Allegheny College, Meadville, Pennsylvania.

Facilities: **Exhibition Area** (3 galleries, 4,000 square feet).

Activities: **Guided Tours** (groups, on request); **Lectures** (usually five per year); **Temporary Exhibitions** (seven per year); **Traveling Exhibitions**.

The Galleries, Bowman, Megahan, and Penelec, are all located in Doane Hall of Art. Exhibitions consist mostly of contemporary art, but occasionally historical artworks are displayed. The permanent collection consists of 650 works, the majority being modern and contemporary.

Philadelphia

Drexel University-Nesbitt College of Design Arts - Design Arts Gallery ⓒ

Drexel University (northeast corner of 33rd and Market Sts.)

Philadelphia, PA   19104

Tel: (215) 895-2386

Fax: (215) 895-4917

Internet Address: http://www.post.drexel.edu/gallery

Director: Ms. Lydia Hunn

Drexel University-Nesbitt College of Design Arts - Design Arts Gallery, cont.

Attendance: 6,000 *Established:* 1986 *ADA Compliant:* Y
Parking: on and off street parking.
Open: Monday to Friday, 11am-5pm.
Facilities: **Gallery** (480 square feet).
Activities: **Temporary Exhibitions**.

Located on the ground floor of Nesbitt Hall, the Design Arts Gallery presents eight shows annually featuring contemporary fine and applied arts, including architecture, interior design, fashion design, photography, painting, sculpture, and drawing. Historical surveys are sometimes showcased, especially in connection with the Historic Costumes Collection, which is housed in the College. Faculty and student work is exhibited as well as that of regionally, nationally, and internationally recognized artists and designers.

View of the entrance to Design Arts Gallery, Nesbitt College of Design Arts. Photograph by Will Brown, courtesy of Design Arts Gallery, Nesbitt College of Design Arts, Drexel University, Philadelphia, Pennsylvania.

La Salle University Art Museum ©

20th and Olney Ave., Philadelphia, PA   19141
Tel: (215) 951-1221
Fax: (215) 951-1488
Internet Address: http://www.lasalle.edu/services/art-mus
Director: Brother Daniel Burke
Admission: free.
Attendance: 10,000 *Established:* 1975
Membership: Y *ADA Compliant:* Y
Parking: free on site.
Open: **September to July**,
          Tuesday to Friday, 11am-4pm; Sunday, 2pm-4pm.
Closed: Academic Holidays.
Facilities: **Galleries** (5); **Special Exhibition Gallery**.
Activities: **Concerts**; **Gallery Talks**; **Guided Tours**; **Lectures**; **Temporary Exhibitions**.
Publications: collection catalogue; exhibition catalogues.

The permanent collection of the Art Museum at La Salle University manifests a basic goal of the Museum to document the major styles and themes of Western art since the Middle Ages. The collection is highlighted by works by Provost, Van Cleve, Bourdon, Tintoretto, Ruisdael, Raeburn, Lawrence, West, Eakins, Corot, Degas, Pissarro, Boudin, Vuillard, and Rouault. The Museum also presents temporary exhibitions of works from its and other museums' collections.

Georges Rouault, *The Last Romantic*, 1937, oil on canvas, 26½ x 19½ inches. Collection of La Salle University Art Museum. Photograph courtesy of La Salle University, Philadelphia, Pennsylvania.

Moore College of Art and Design - Galleries ©

20th St. and The Parkway, Philadelphia, PA   19103
Tel: (215) 568-4515
Fax: (215) 568-5921
Internet Address: http://libertynet.org/~galmoore
Director: Ms. Elsa Longhauser

Moore College of Art and Design - Galleries, cont.

Admission: voluntary contribution.

Attendance: 50,000   *Established:* 1844   *Membership:* Y   *ADA Compliant:* Y

Open: **Academic Year**,
> Tuesday, 10am-5pm; Wednesday, 10am-7pm; Thursday to Friday, 10am-5pm; Saturday to Sunday, noon-4pm.

> **Summer**,
> Monday to Friday, 10am-5pm.

Closed: Academic Holidays, Legal Holidays.

Facilities: **Galleries** (2); **Library** (50,000 volumes).

Activities: **Concerts**; **Films**; **Gallery Talks**; **Guided Tours**; **Lectures**; **Temporary Exhibitions**; **Traveling Exhibitions**.

Publications: exhibition catalogues.

The Goldie Paley Gallery presents work by national and international artists who have made a distinctive contribution to their field, but have not always had mainstream exposure. The Gallery's exhibitions are linked by an underlying educational objective: to present traditional art in a contemporary context for reevaluation and contemporary art in an art-historical context for critical review. Moore College of Art and Design also maintains the Levy Gallery, which presents temporary exhibitions of the work of students, faculty, and alumnae.

Pennsylvania Academy of Fine Arts - Museum of American Art (PAFA)

118 N. Broad St. at Cherry St.
Philadelphia, PA   19102
Tel: (215) 972-7600
Fax: (215) 972-5564
Internet Address: http://www.pafa.org/~oafa
Director: Mr. Daniel Rosenfeld
Admission:
   fee: adult-$6.00, child-$4.00, student-$5.00, senior-$5.00.

Attendance: 75,000   *Established:* 1805

Membership: Y   *ADA Compliant:* Y

Parking:
   commercial adjacent to site and metered on street.

Open: Monday to Saturday, 10am-5pm;
   Sunday, 11am-5pm.

Closed: Legal Holidays.

Facilities: **Architecture** (Centennial Exhibition Bldg., 1876); **Auditorium** (130 seat); **Exhibition Area**; **Food Services** Café; **Library** (9,000 volumes); **Shop**.

Activities: **Concerts**;   **Guided   Tours**;   **Lectures**; **Temporary Exhibitions**; **Traveling Exhibitions**.

Publications: annual report; brochures; exhibition catalogues; newsletter.

View of gallery, Museum of Art of Pennsylvania Academy of Fine Arts (1876), designed by Frank Furness and George W. Hewitt. Photograph courtesy of Pennsylvania Academy of Fine Arts, Philadelphia, Pennsylvania.

The Museum of American Art is housed in a striking Victorian Gothic building designed by Philadelphia architect Frank Furness. It was designated a National Historic Landmark in 1975. The permanent collection of the Museum constitutes one of the finest and most comprehensive collections of American art in the United States and is especially strong in 19th-century genre and narrative paintings; 18th- and 19th-century portraiture; 18th- and 19th-century landscape painting; American Impressionist paintings; neoclassical sculpture; and works by "The Eight".

Philadelphia College of Textiles and Science - Paley Design Center ⊕

4200 Henry Ave., Philadelphia, PA   19144
Tel: (215) 951-2860
Internet Address: http://www.philacol.edu/paley
Director: Ms. Anne R. Fabbri

Philadelphia,Pennsylvania

Philadelphia College of Textiles and Science - Paley Design Center, cont.

Admission: free.
Established: 1978   *Membership:* Y   *ADA Compliant:* Y
Parking: free, opposite main entrance.
Open: Tuesday to Friday, 10am-4pm; Saturday to Sunday, noon-4pm.
Closed: National Holidays.
Facilities: **Architecture** (former residence, 1952 design by architect Earl Bolten); **Exhibition Area**; **Shop** (original hand-crafted work).
Activities: **Permanent Exhibits**; **Temporary Exhibitions**.

Located on the campus of the Philadelphia College of Textiles and Science, the Paley Center serves as the central repository for the College's collection of textiles and textile-related artifacts and presents them in temporary exhibitions. The Center's permanent collection of over 1.5 million items documents the history of textiles with particular focus on the American textile industry and the Philadelphia region in particular. Objects in the collection include fragments of 4th-century (A.D.) Egyptian Coptic textiles, 17th- to 20th-century lace, 18th- and 19th-century quilts, 19th- and 20-century American and European clothing and accessories including designer-wear and 19th-century undergarments, traditional ethnic costumes from throughout the world, and 19th-century Philadelphia textiles.

Saint Joseph's University - University Gallery ©

5600 City Line Ave., Boland Hall, Lapsley Lane, Philadelphia, PA   19131
Tel: (610) 660-1840
Internet Address: http://www.sju.edu/~corpus
Chairman, Fine & Performing Arts Dept.: Mr. Dennis Weeks
Admission: voluntary contribution.
Attendance: 600
Open: **September to May**, Monday to Friday, 10am-4pm.
Closed: Legal Holidays.
Activities: **Arts Festival**; **Concerts**; **Films**; **Lectures**.

The University Gallery hosts eight shows from September through May. The first five feature professional artists, usually from the Philadelphia area. The last three display student work.

Temple University - Temple Gallery ©

45 North 2nd St., Philadelphia, PA   19106
Tel: (215) 925-7379   *Fax:* (215) 782-2799
Internet Address: http://www.temple.edu
Director: Mr. Donald Desmett
Open: Tuesday to Saturday, 10am-5pm.
Facilities: **Exhibition Area**.
Activities: **Temporary Exhibitions**.

The Temple Gallery presents exhibitions of contemporary art.

Temple University - Tyler and Penrose Galleries ©

Tyler School of Art, Beech and Penrose Aves., Elkins Park, Philadelphia, PA   19027
Tel: (215) 782-2776
Fax: (215) 782-2799
Internet Address: http://www.temple.edu/tyler/home/exhibmain.html
Director: Mr. Donald Desmett
Open: Tuesday to Saturday, 10am-5pm.
Facilities: **Exhibition Area**.
Activities: **Temporary Exhibitions**.

The galleries at the Tyler School of Art present temporary exhibitions including an annual student exhibit in the spring.

University of Pennsylvania - Arthur Ross Gallery ⓒᴬᴬ

220 South 34th St., Philadelphia, PA 19104-6380
Tel: (215) 898-4401 *Fax:* (215) 573-2045
Internet Address: http://www.upenn.edu/ARG/index/html
Director: Dr. Dilys V. Winegrad
Admission: free.
Attendance: 10,000 *Established:* 1983 *Membership:* Y *ADA Compliant:* Y
Open: Tuesday to Friday, 10am-5pm; Saturday to Sunday, noon-5pm.
Closed: New Year's Day, Easter, Independence Day, Thanksgiving Day, Christmas Day.
Facilities: **Exhibition Area** (1,700 square feet).
Activities: **Education Programs** (children); **Lectures**; **Temporary Exhibitions**.
Publications: calendar (annual); exhibition catalogues.

Housed on the campus of the University of Pennsylvania in an historic building designed by Frank Furness, the Gallery presents temporary exhibitions, displaying objects from the University's collections and other major public and private collections. The Gallery also presents traveling exhibitions with an interdisciplinary appeal and an international focus.

University of Pennsylvania - Institute of Contemporary Art ⓒᴬᴬ

University of Pennsylvania
118 S. 36th St. at Sansom
Philadelphia, PA 19104-3289
Tel: (215) 898-7108
Fax: (215) 898-5050
Internet Address: http://www.upenn.edu/ica
Director: Mr. Patrick T. Murphy
Admission: fee: adult-$3.00, child-$2.00, student-$2.00,
    senior-$2.00.
Established: 1963
Membership: Y *ADA Compliant:* Y
Parking:
    commercial adjacent to site and metered on street.
Open: Wednesday, 10am-5pm;
        Thursday, 10am-7pm;
        Friday to Sunday, 10am-5pm.
Closed: New Year's Day, Easter, Thanksgiving Day,
        Christmas Day.
Facilities: **Auditorium**.
Activities: **Concerts**; **Education Programs** (children);
    Films; **Guided Tours**; **Lectures**; **Performances**;
    Readings; **Temporary Exhibitions**.

Exterior view of Institute of Contemporary Art, designed by Adele Naude Santos. Photograph courtesy of Institute of Contemporary Art, Philadelphia, Pennsylvania.

Publications: calendar; exhibition catalogues.

Established in 1963, the ICA is the only museum in Philadelphia committed to exhibiting only contemporary art. Through the presentation of individual, group, and thematic exhibitions that change throughout the year, the ICA has an international reputation for identifying artists of promise who later emerge in the national and international spotlight. Artists who had their first museum exhibition at the ICA include Andy Warhol, Robert Mapplethorpe, and Andres Serrano.

The University of Pennsylvania Museum of Archeology and Anthropology ⓒᴬᴬ

33rd and Spruce Sts., Philadelphia, PA 19104-6324
Tel: (215) 898-4000 *Fax:* (215) 898-0657
Internet Address: http://www.upenn.edu/museum
Director: Dr. Jeremy A. Sabloff
Admission: fee: adult-$5.00, student-$2.50, senior-$2.50.
Attendance: 140,000 *Established:* 1887 *Membership:* Y *ADA Compliant:* Y

The University of Pennsylvania Museum of Archeology and Anthropology, cont.

Parking: free on site.

Open: **Labor Day to Memorial Day**,
> Tuesday to Saturday, 10am-4:30pm;
> Sunday, 1pm-5pm.

> **Memorial Day to Labor Day**,
> Tuesday to Saturday, 10am-4:30pm.

Closed: Legal Holidays.

Facilities: **Food Services** Cafeteria (overlooking inner gardens); **Sculpture Garden**; **Shops** (one for adults and one for children).

Activities: **Concerts**; **Films**; **Gallery Talks**; **Guided Tours**; **Lectures**; **Temporary Exhibitions**; **Traveling Exhibitions**.

Publications: collection catalogue; exhibition catalogues; magazine, "Expedition" (quarterly); monograph series; newsletter (3/yr).

Sphinx Ramses II, 19th Dynasty, c.1293-1185 B.C., red granite, Memphis, Egypt; and pillars and gateways of Palace of Merenptah, c. 1236-1223 B.C., Memphis, Egypt. Collection of University of Pennsylvania Museum of Archeology and Anthropology. Photograph by Terry Wild, courtesy of University of Pennsylvania, Philadelphia, Pennsylvania.

The University of Pennsylvania Museum of Archeology and Anthropology houses more than 30 galleries of material from Egypt, Mesopotamia, Meso-America, Asia, and the Greco-Roman world, as well as artifacts from native peoples of North America, Africa, and Polynesia.

The University of the Arts - Rosenwald-Wolf Gallery ©

The University of the Arts, 333 S. Broad St. at Pine St.
Philadelphia, PA 19107
Tel: (215) 875-1116
Fax: (215) 875-2238
Internet Address: http://www.uarts.edu/events/rosenwolf.html
Director: Ms. Leah Douglas
Admission: free.
Established: 1876   *ADA Compliant:* Y
Parking: commercial adjacent to site and metered parking on street.
Open: Monday to Tuesday, 10am-5pm; Wednesday, 10am-9pm; Thursday to Friday, 10am-5pm; Saturday to Sunday, noon-5pm.
Closed: Academic Holidays, August.
Facilities: **Gallery** (2,000 square feet).
Activities: **Gallery Talks**; **Guided Tours**; **Lectures**; **Performances**; **Temporary Exhibitions**.
Publications: brochures; exhibition catalogues.

The Gallery is a non-collecting facility that features temporary exhibitions of contemporary art. Exhibitions are also mounted by the College of Art and Design (717-6300) in the Mednick Gallery (Open: Mon-Fri, 10am-4:30pm).

Pittsburgh

Carnegie Mellon University Galleries ©

Carnegie Mellon University, 5000 Forbes Ave., Pittsburgh, PA 15213
Tel: (412) 268-3618
Internet Address: http://www.-art.cfa.cmu.edu/exhibit
Admission: free.
Open: **Hewlett Gallery**,
> Monday to Friday, 11:30am-5pm; Saturday to Sunday, 11:30am-4pm.

> **Ellis Gallery**, Monday to Friday, 9am-5pm.

Facilities: **Exhibition Areas**.
Activities: **Temporary Exhibitions**.

Carnegie Mellon University Galleries, cont.

CMU has a number of exhibition spaces showing student work. Hewlett Gallery (268-3618), is located on the first floor of the College of Fine Arts. Ellis Gallery located on the third floor of the Center for Fine Arts, presents one-week exhibits. The University Center Gallery is located just off Kirr Commons in the University Center and features weekly shows. The University's student-run gallery, The Frame (268-2081 - formerly Forbes Gallery), is located at 5200 Forbes Ave., Oakland.

La Roche College - Cantellops Art Gallery

College Center, 9000 Babcock Blvd., Pittsburgh, PA   15237
Tel: (412) 536-1071
Internet Address: http://www.laroche.edu/TOC/student/art.html
Open: **Call for hours**.
Facilities: **Exhibition Area**.
Activities: **Temporary Exhibitions**.

Located in the College Center, the Gallery presents exhibitions of work by students in graphic design, interior design, and communication design as well as the work of professional artists.

University of Pittsburgh - University Art Gallery ☺ (UAG)

Frick Fine Arts Building, Schenley Drive (across from the Carnegie Library)
Pittsburgh, PA   15260
Tel: (412) 648-2400
Fax: (412) 648-2792
Internet Address: http://www.pitt.edu/~arthome/department/uag.html
Interim Director: Ms. Elizabeth Kennedy
Admission: free.
Established: 1966   *ADA Compliant:* Y
Open: **Academic Years**, Monday to Friday, 10am-4pm.
Closed: Academic Holidays, Easter, Christmas Day.
Facilities: **Auditorium** (200 seat); **Exhibition Area**.
Activities: **Lectures**; **Temporary Exhibitions**; **Traveling Exhibitions**.

The University Art Gallery (UAG) at the University of Pittsburgh has acquired works of art for nearly thirty years and the University's acceptance of valuable art and objects began even earlier. In addition to the permanent collection, specially curated shows occur annually. Traveling exhibitions and shows sponsored by the outside community make up the additional exhibition schedule. The permanent collection's strengths are works on paper dating from ca.1500 to the end of the 20th century with a distinguished assemblage of Callot and Callot-related prints. Paintings include works by Gilbert Stuart, Rembrandt Peale, George Hetzel, Aaron Gorson, and William Gropper, as well as selected works from past Carnegie Internationals. The permanent collection's Asian objects cover a variety of media and styles and include paintings by the modern Chinese artist, Ch'i Pai Shih. Special collections include the Nicholas Lochoff frescos of the 1930's located in the Frick Fine Arts Building Cloister; an extensive array of watercolors by Dr. Andrei Avinoff in the Cathedral of Learning's original 1938 Nationality Rooms, augmented by other drawings, prints and photographs of these unique, ethnically inspired classrooms; and the Gimbel Collection, scenes of western Pennsylvania from 1947 that celebrate its post- World War II technology prowess.

Reading

Albright College - Freedman Gallery

Albright College, 13th and Bern Sts., Reading, PA   19604
Tel: (610) 921-2381
Fax: (610) 921-7530
Internet Address: http://www.alb.edu
Director: Mr. Christopher Youngs
Admission: free.
Attendance: 11,000   *Established:* 1976   *Membership:* Y   *ADA Compliant:* Y
Parking: free on site.

Albright College - Freedman Gallery, cont.

Open: **Academic Year**,
Tuesday to Wednesday, noon-6pm; Thursday, noon-8pm; Friday, noon-6pm;
Saturday to Sunday, noon-4pm.
Summer, Tuesday to Sunday, noon-4pm.
Closed: Legal Holidays.
Facilities: **Auditorium** (250 seats); **Exhibition Area** (2,800 square feet).
Activities: **Films**; **Guided Tours**; **Lectures**; **Temporary Exhibitions**; **Traveling Exhibitions**.
Publications: brochures; exhibition catalogues.

The Freedman Gallery presents monthly exhibitions of nationally and regionally significant contemporary art.

Rosemont

Rosemont College - Lawrence Gallery Ⓒ⁴⁴

1400 Montgomery Ave., Rosemont, PA   19010
Tel: (610) 527-0200
Internet Address: http://www.rosemont.edu
Public Relations: Mr. Evan Welsh
Open: Monday to Friday, 9am-5pm.
Facilities: **Gallery**.
Activities: **Temporary Exhibitions**.

The Gallery presents temporary exhibitions of the work of students and professional artists.

Scranton

Marywood University Art Galleries Ⓒ⁴⁴

Visual Arts Bldg., 2300 Adams Ave., Scranton, PA   18509
Tel: (717) 348-6278
Fax: (717) 348-1817
Internet Address: http://www.marywood.edu/art/gallery.htm
Director: Ms. Sandra Ward
Admission: free.
Attendance: 8,000   *Established:* 1924   *ADA Compliant:* Y
Open: **Contemporary Gallery**,
Monday to Wednesday, 9am-8pm; Thursday to Friday, 9am-5pm;
Saturday to Sunday, 1pm-4pm.
Suraci Gallery,
Wednesday to Thursday, 10am-3pm; Friday, 10am-3pm and 5pm-8pm;
Saturday to Sunday, 1pm-4pm.
Facilities: **Exhibition Area** (5,500 square feet).
Activities: **Arts Festival**; **Guided Tours**; **Juried Exhibits**; **Lectures**; **Temporary Exhibitions**.

Marywood University maintains two exhibition spaces in the Visual Arts Center: the Contemporary Gallery and the Suraci Gallery. The Contemporary Gallery offers a varied program of group and solo shows by visiting artists, juried regional competitions, Marywood art faculty and student shows, and curated national exhibitions. Presenting the work of both emerging and established, well-known artists, exhibitions explore different media, stylistic approaches, issues, themes and techniques. Featured exhibitions are accompanied by artists' slide lectures, gallery talks, studio visits, workshops or demonstrations. The Suraci Gallery, located on the second floor, displays Marywood's permanent collection of fine and decorative arts from the 19th and 20th centuries. The Asian Collection consists of paintings, furniture, ivories, tapestries and ceramics. Bronze and marble sculptures, furniture and paintings comprise the American Collection. In addition, European ceramics, glass and other decorative arts are displayed and feature exhibitions are presented throughout the year.

University of Scranton - University Art Gallery ⓒᴬᴬ

Gallery Building, Floor 2F, Linden Street and Madison Ave., Scranton, PA   18510-4585
Tel: (717) 941-4214
Internet Address: http://www.uofs./edu/admin/exhibition.html
Director: Ms. Darlene Miller-Lanning, Ph.D.
Admission: free.
Open: Sunday to Tuesday, noon-4pm; Wednesday, noon-4pm and 7pm-9pm; Thursday to Friday, noon-4pm.
Facilities: **Exhibition Area.**
Activities: **Lectures**; **Temporary Exhibitions** (5-7/year).

Located in a building named in honor of former University President Eugene Gallery, S.J., the University Art Gallery presents exhibitions "designed to complement the university curriculum, encourage campus and community collaborations, support regional artists, provide art in education programming, and showcase student art work."

Selinsgrove

Susquehana University - Lore Degenstein Gallery ⓒᴬᴬ

Susquehana University, 514 University Ave., Selinsgrove, PA   17870-1001
Tel: (717) 372-4058   *Fax:* (717) 372-2745
Internet Address: http://www.susqu.edu/ac_depts/finearts/art_gall
Director and Curator: Dr. Valerie Livingston
Admission: free.
Attendance: 6,000   *Established:* 1993   *ADA Compliant:* Y
Open: **September to mid-May**, Monday to Sunday, 1pm-4pm.
Facilities: **Auditorium** (450 seat); **Exhibition Area** (2,500 square feet).
Activities: **Guided Tours**; **Lectures**; **Temporary Exhibitions**; **Traveling Exhibitions**.
Publications: exhibition catalogues.

The Gallery presents temporary exhibitions.

Slippery Rock

Slippery Rock University - Martha Gault Art Gallery ⓒᴬᴬ

Art Department, Maltby Avenue, Slippery Rock, PA   16057
Tel: (724) 738-2020
Internet Address: http://www.sru.edu/depts/artsci/art/margau.htm
Gallery Coordinator: Dr. Kurt Pitluga
Admission: free.
Open: **Fall to Spring**, Monday/Wednesday/Friday, 11am-3pm; Tuesday/Thursday, 3pm-7pm. **Other Times & Summer**, by appointment.
Facilities: **Exhibition Area.**
Activities: **Temporary Exhibitions** (8/academic year, plus single summer-long exhibition).

The gallery offers a schedule of exhibitions in a wide variety of media during the academic year and supplemented by a single summer-long exhibition. Shows include the work of professional artists, who range from those of special local interest to those of regional and national reputation, as well as an annual faculty exhibition in September and a juried student show in April.

Swarthmore

Swarthmore College - List Gallery ⓒᴬᴬ

Lang Performing Arts Center, 500 College Ave., Swarthmore, PA   19081-1397
Tel: (610) 328-8488
Fax: (610) 328-7793
Internet Address: http://www.swarthmore.edu/Humanities/art/Gallery/
Gallery Director: Ms. Andrea Packard

Swarthmore College - List Gallery, cont.

Admission: free.

Established: 1991   *ADA Compliant:* Y

Parking:

    DuPont visitors lot at College north entrance.

Open: Wednesday, noon-4pm;

          Friday, 1pm-5pm;

          Saturday to Sunday, 1pm-4pm; by appt.

Facilities: **Exhibition Area** (1,200 square feet).

Activities: **Permanent Exhibits**; **Temporary Exhibitions** (6/year).

Publications: exhibition brochures (1/year).

The Gallery presents exhibitions of the work of both emerging and nationally known artists and occasional historical exhibitions, as well as displaying works from the permanent collection. One-person exhibitions have featured such artists as Glenn Goldberg, Max and Joyce Kozloff, Alan Gussow, Mel Chin, Judy Moonelis, Alison Saar,

Edward Hicks, *Peaceable Kingdom,* Photograph courtesy of List Gallery, Swarthmore College, Swarthmore, Pennsylvania.

and Varjuan Boghosian. Curated exhibitions include "History, Memory and Representation: Responses to Genocide"; a traveling survey of works by Leslie Dill; and "The Mystical Arts of Tibet". The months of April and May feature a series of thesis exhibitions by senior art majors. A special exhibition is mounted for Alumni Weekend in June. The college's permanent collection includes works by Edward Hicks, John Steuart Curry, Robert Henri, and Benjamin West.

University Park

Pennsylvania State University - Palmer Museum of Art Ⓒᴬ

The Pennsylvania State University

Curtin Road

University Park, PA   16802-2507

Tel: (814) 865-7672

Fax: (814) 863-8608

Internet Address:

http://www.psu.edu/dept/palmermuseum

Director: Mrs. Jan Keene Muhlert

Admission: free.

Attendance: 54,000   *Established:* 1972

Membership: Y   *ADA Compliant:* Y

Parking: metered on street and commercial lot nearby.

Open: Tuesday to Saturday, 10am-4:30pm;

          Sunday, noon-4pm.

Closed: Legal Holidays,

          Christmas Day to New Year's Day.

Exterior view of Palmer Museum of Art (1983), designed by Charles W. Moore in association with Arbonies King Vlock. Photograph courtesy of Palmer Museum of Art, State College, Pennsylvania.

Facilities: **Auditorium** (150 seat); **Galleries** (10); **Sculpture Garden**; **Shop**.

Activities: **Guided Tours**; **Lectures**; **Temporary Exhibitions**; **Traveling Exhibitions**.

Publications: brochures; exhibition catalogues; newsletter (quarterly).

The Palmer Museum of Art presents selections from a permanent collection that comprises thirty-five centuries of painting, sculpture, ceramics, and works on paper from the United States, Europe, Asia, and South America. The Museum also maintains a comprehensive schedule of special exhibitions. The permanent collection at the Museum includes antiquities (ancient Greek earthenware pots, Phoenician glass, Roman bronzes), medieval art (Gothic architectural fragments, manuscripts), northern and southern European Renaissance painting, Baroque painting (works by Vanni, Ghezzi, van Mierevelt, Master Jacomo), nineteenth-century European painting (mostly in the academic manner), Asian art (third century B.C. to nineteenth-century ceramics and sculpture from China, Korea, Japan,

Pennsylvania State University - Palmer Museum of Art, cont.

and Cambodia), African art (sub-Saharan sculpture, masks, and textiles), American art (works by Rembrandt Peale, Stuart, Duveneck, Eakens, Kensett, Richards, Frieseke, Marsh, Sloan, Henri, Shinn, Prendergast, Glackens, and others), and contemporary art (examples by Diebenkorn, Bischoff, Goodnough, Delfino, Moore, Oldenburg, Segal, Nevelson, and LeWitt). There is also a separate gallery devoted to contemporary ceramics. Also of possible interest on campus is the EMS Museum and Art Gallery, which boasts the country's largest collection of paintings and sculpture depicting mining-related industries. It is open weekdays, 9am-5pm, and Saturday and Sunday, 1pm-5pm. Telephone: 814-865-6427.

Villanova

Villanova University Art Gallery ⓒᴬ⁹

Connelly Center, 800 Lancaster Ave., Villanova, PA   19085
Tel: (610) 519-4612   *Fax:* (610) 519-6046
Internet Address: http://www.artgallery.vill.edu
Admission: free.
Attendance: 2,000   *Established:* 1979
ADA Compliant: Y
Parking: free on site.
Open: Monday to Friday, 9am-5pm.
Facilities: **Gallery**.
Activities: **Temporary Exhibitions** (6 per year).

The Gallery presents approximately six changing exhibitions per year, in a variety of media, which have included international exhibitions as well student art shows. The University has a small collection of 20th-century art.

Jay J. Dugan, *Cosmos*, marble, 5 x 4 feet, located in Atrium of Connelly Center, Villanova University. Photograph courtesy of Villanova University, Villanova, Pennsylvania.

Washington

Washington and Jefferson College - Olin Fine Arts Gallery

E. Wheeling St., Washington, PA   15301
Tel: (412) 222-4400   *Fax:* (412) 223-5271
Internet Address: http://www.washjeff.edu
Acting Director: Prof. Hugh Taylor
Admission: free.
Attendance: 5,300   *Established:* 1982   *ADA Compliant:* Y
Parking: public parking adjacent to site.
Open: **Academic Year**, Daily, noon-7pm.
Facilities: **Exhibition Area** (1,925 square feet); **Theatre** (488 seat).
Activities: **Lectures**; **Student Art Shows**; **Temporary Exhibitions**.
Publications: exhibition catalogues.

The Gallery has specialized lighting and supports for the display of three-dimensional and hanging works. In recent years the gallery has presented works by such nationally and internationally acclaimed artists as Malcolm and Evans Parcell and Nat Youngblood. The gallery is also the home of the W&J National Painting Show. The show contributes directly to the enlargement of college's permanent art collection through purchase awards. A senior art majors show is held each spring.

West Chester

West Chester University - Art Galleries ⓒᴬ⁹

North Campus, Mitchell Hall, S. Church St. (between Sharpless & Union), West Chester, PA   19383
Tel: (610) 436-2755
Internet Address: http://www.wcupa.edu

West Chester, Pennsylvania

West Chester University - Art Galleries, cont.
Department Chairperson: John Baker
Admission: free.
Open: Call for hours.
Facilities: **Exhibition Area.**
Activities: **Temporary Exhibitions.**
The galleries present temporary exhibitions of work from all areas of the visual arts, including a senior student art show.

Wilkes-Barre

Wilkes University - Sordoni Art Gallery ©
150 S. River St., Wilkes-Barre, PA   18766-0001
Tel: (717) 831-4325   *Fax:* (717) 829-2434
Internet Address: http://www.wilkes.edu
Director: Mr. Stanley I. Grand
Admission: free.
Attendance: 13,000   *Established:* 1973   *Membership:* Y   *ADA Compliant:* Y
Parking: free on site.
Open: Monday to Wednesday, noon-5pm; Thursday, noon-9pm; Friday to Sunday, noon-5pm.
Closed: Legal Holidays.
Facilities: **Exhibition Area** (1,600 square feet).
Activities: **Gallery Talks; Guided Tours; Lectures; Temporary Exhibitions; Traveling Exhibitions.**
Publications: exhibition catalogues, "American Art".
The Sordoni Art Gallery houses a permanent collection featuring 19th- and 20th-century American art and a print collection including work of Old Masters and contemporary artists.. It also mounts temporary exhibitions.

Williamsport

Lycoming College - Art Gallery ©
John D. Snowden Library, 700 College Place, Williamsport, PA   17701
Tel: (570) 321-4000   *Fax:* (570) 321-4090
Internet Address: http://www.lycoming.edu/dept/art/gallery/gallery.htm
Chair, Art Dept.: Ms. B. Lynn Estomin
Admission: free.
Attendance: 700   *Established:* 1968   *Membership:* N   *ADA Compliant:* Y
Parking: free on site.
Open: Monday to Thursday, 11am-8pm; Friday, 8am-4:30pm; Saturday, 9am-5pm;
          Sunday, 1pm-11pm.
Closed: Academic Holidays.
Facilities: **Exhibition Area** (30 feet by 40 feet).
Activities: **Gallery Talks; Temporary Exhibitions.**
The Gallery features five to six temporary exhibitions each year of works by artists of regional or national reputation, as well as a show of the work of senior art majors.

York

York College of Pennsylvania - Art Galleries ©
Music, Art & Communication Center, 1st Floor (off Country Club Road)
York, PA   17405-7199
Tel: (717) 815-1354
Internet Address: http://www.ycp.edu/artgallery
Gallery Coordinator: Ms. Pamela Hemzik
Admission: free.

York College of Pennsylvania - Art Galleries, cont.

ADA Compliant: Y

Parking: free adjacent to site.

Open: **Academic Year**,
   Monday to Tuesday, 10am-4pm; Wednesday, 10am-9pm; Thursday to Friday, 10am-4pm; Saturday to Sunday, noon-4pm.

Closed: Academic Holidays.

Facilities: **Galleries** (2).

Activities: **Gallery Talks**; **Guided Tours** (groups by appointment, 815-1402); **Temporary Exhibitions**; **Workshops**.

Comprising two contiguous venues, the Cora Miller Gallery and the Brossman Gallery, the York College Galleries feature a varied program of juried and invitational exhibits, student and faculty shows, and touring exhibitions.

Puerto Rico

A number in parentheses following a city name indicates the number of museums/galleries in that municipality. If there is no number, one is understood. For example, in the text two listings would be found under San Juan.

Puerto Rico

San Juan

University of Puerto Rico - Museum of Anthropology, History and Art ⓒ⁴⁴
(Museo U.P.R.)

University of Puerto Rico, San Juan, PR   00931
Tel: (787) 763-3939   *Fax:* (787) 763-4799
Internet Address: http://www.upr.clu.edu
Curator, Art Collections: Ms. Flavia Marichal
Admission: free.
Attendance: 20,000   *Established:* 1940   *ADA Compliant:* Y
Open: Monday to Friday, 9am-4:30pm; Saturday to Sunday, 9am-3pm.
Closed: Legal Holidays.
Facilities: **Exhibition Area** (4,582 square feet); **Library** (non-circulating).
Activities: **Concerts**; **Guided Tours**; **Permanent Exhibits**; **Temporary Exhibitions**; **Traveling Exhibitions**.
Publications: exhibition catalogues.

The Museum houses a collection of 17th- to 20th-century Puerto Rican paintings, sculpture, prints, and drawings.

University of the Sacred Heart - Museum of Contemporary Art ⓒ⁴⁴
Universidad del Sagrado Corazón
Edif. Baralt, San Antonio, Santurce, San Juan, PR   00914
Tel: (787) 268-0049
Internet Address: http://www.museocontemporaneopr.org
Exec. Director: Dr. Maria Emilia Somoza
Established: 1984   *Membership:* Y
Open: Monday to Friday, 9am-4pm.
Facilities: **Exhibition Area**.
Activities: **Temporary Exhibitions**.

The Museum features the work of contemporary Puerto Rican artists. Its permanent collection includes contemporary work by artists from Puerto Rica, the Caribbean, Central and South American. Also of possible interest on campus are the Galeria de Arte (728-1515 x2561) and the Galeria José "Pepin" Mendez (728-1515 x2566), which features student work.

Rhode Island

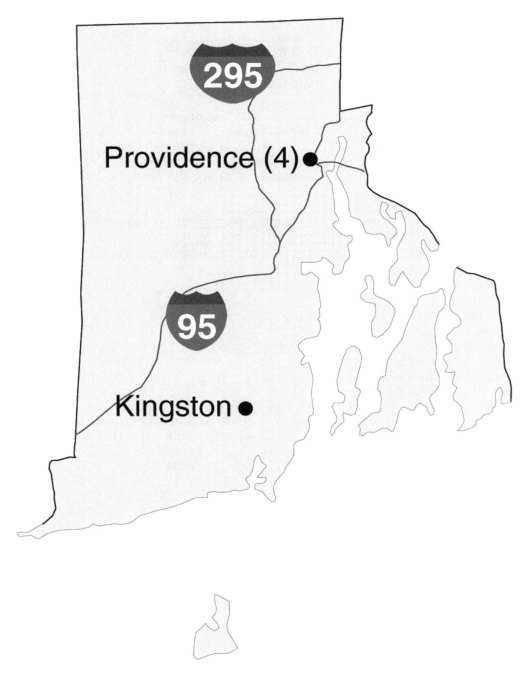

The number in parentheses following the city name indicates the number of museums/galleries in that municipality. If there is no number, one is understood. For example, in the text four listings would be found under Providence and one listing under Kingston.

Rhode Island

Kingston

University of Rhode Island Fine Arts Center Galleries ⓒ⁴⁴

105 Upper College Road, Kingston, RI   02881-0820
Tel: (401) 874-2775
Fax: (401) 874-2729
Internet Address: http://nick.uri.edu/artsci/art/URI_Art_FAC_Galleries.html
Director: Ms. Judith E. Tolnick
Admission: voluntary contribution.
Attendance: 25,000   *Established:* 1968   *ADA Compliant:* Y
Parking: free on site.
Open: **Main Gallery**,
    Tuesday to Friday, noon-4pm & 7:30pm-9:30pm; Saturday to Sunday, 1pm-4pm.
    Photography Gallery, Tuesday to Friday, noon-4pm.
    Corridor Gallery, Daily, 9am-9pm.
Facilities: **Exhibition Areas** (3; 1,424 square feet); **Library** (21,000 volumes); **Recital Hall** (525 seats); **Theatre** (550 seats).
Activities: **Temporary Exhibitions** (20-25/year).
Publications: annual report; brochures; field guides.

The Fine Arts Center Galleries offers temporary exhibitions at three venues: Main Gallery, Photography Gallery, and Corridor Gallery. The Corridor Gallery is reserved for exhibitions of work by faculty of the Department of Art, University of Rhode Island, and regional, invited guests.

Providence

Brown University - David Winton Bell Gallery ⓒ⁴⁴

Brown University, List Art Center, 64 College St., Providence, RI   02912
Tel: (401) 863-2932
Fax: (401) 863-1680
Internet Address: http://www.brown.edu/Facilities/David_Winton_Bell_Gallery/Bell.html
Director: Ms. Jo-Ann Conklin
Admission: voluntary contribution.
Attendance: 17,000   *Established:* 1971   *ADA Compliant:* Y
Parking: metered on street.
Open: **September to June**, Monday to Friday, 11am-4pm; Saturday to Sunday, 1pm-4pm.
Closed: New Year's Day, Thanksgiving Day, Christmas Day.
Facilities: **Architecture** (List Art Center, designed by Philip Johnson); **Auditorium** (250 seat); **Gallery**.
Activities: **Films**; **Gallery Talks**; **Lectures**; **Temporary Exhibitions**; **Traveling Exhibitions**.
Publications: calendar; exhibition catalogues.

Located in the List Art Center, the David Winton Bell Gallery presents temporary exhibitions including an annual juried student exhibition in the Spring and an occasional art faculty show.

Providence College - Hunt/Cavanagh Art Gallery ⓒ⁴⁴

East Campus, Hunt/Cavanagh Building, 549 River Ave.
Providence, RI   02918
Tel: (401) 865-1000
Internet Address: http://www.providence.edu/art/gallery1.html
Admission: free.
Open: **Call for hours.**
Facilities: **Exhibition Area**.
Activities: **Temporary Exhibitions**.

The Gallery presents exhibitions of the work of professional artists, as well as the work of senior students. There is also sculptural work by Thomas McGlynn, O.P., on campus.

Rhode Island College - Bannister Gallery

600 Mt. Pleasant Ave., Providence, RI   02908
Tel: (401) 456-9765
Fax: (401) 456-8379
Internet Address: http://www.ric.edu/bannister
Director: Mr. Dennis O'Malley
Admission: free.
Established: 1978
Open: **September to May**, Tuesday, 11am-4pm and 6pm-9pm; Wednesday, 11am-4pm;
         Thursday, 11am-4pm and 6pm-9pm; Friday to Saturday, 11am-4pm.
Closed: Holidays.
Facilities: **Exhibition Area** (1,450 square feet).
Activities: **Temporary Exhibitions** (8-10/year).

Initially developed as a teaching forum for the department of art, the scope of exhibitions has expanded in recent years to include major shows addressing college and world-wide issues. The Gallery mounts eight to ten exhibitions annually and provides a forum for diverse selection of contemporary art. Exhibits range from student and faculty shows to presentations by internationally renowned artists and scholars.

Rhode Island School of Design - Museum of Art Ⓒ⁴⁴ (RISD Museum)

224 Benefit St., Providence, RI   02903-2723
Tel: (401) 454-6500
Fax: (401) 454-6556
TDDY: (401) 454-5555
Internet Address: http://www.risd.edu/museum
Asst. Director: Mr. Richard Benefield
Admission: fee: adult-$2.00, child-$0.50, student-$0.50,
   senior-$1.00.
Attendance: 95,000   *Established:* 1877
Membership: Y   *ADA Compliant:* Y
Parking: commercial lot at N. Main and Steeple Sts..
Open: Wednesday to Thursday, 10am-5pm;
          Friday, 10am-8pm;
          Saturday to Sunday, 10am-5pm.
Closed: New Year's Day, Easter, Independence Day,
          Thanksgiving Day, Christmas Day.
Facilities: **Exhibition Area**; **Sculpture Garden**; **Shop**.
Activities: **Concerts**; **Education Programs** (adults, college students and children); **Guided Tours**; **Lectures**; **Readings**; **Temporary Exhibitions**; **Traveling Exhibitions**.
Publications: "Museum Notes"; calendar (bi-monthly); exhibition catalogues.

Edouard Manet, *Le Repos*, c. 1870. Rhode Island School of Design Museum. Photograph courtesy of Rhode Island School of Design Museum, Providence, Rhode Island.

With more than 65,000 works of art ("some of the finest examples of their kind from every part of the world"), RISD Museum is Rhode Island's leading museum of fine and decorative arts. The collection is displayed in 45 galleries on three floors. The history of Western art from antiquity to the 20th century fills the main floor. Galleries housing Greek and Roman antiquities lead to the Medieval gallery. A sequence of European galleries with painting, sculpture, and decorative arts ranging from the Renaissance to the 20th century follows. Highlights include works by Cézanne, Corot, Degas, Delacroix, Manet, Matisse, Monet, Poussin, Renoir, Rodin, and Tiepolo. Braque, Matisse, and Picasso are but a few of the 20th-century European painters in the collection. Pendleton House showcases American furniture, silver and decorative arts in period rooms, as well as paintings by American masters, such as Chase, Cassatt, Copley, Stuart, Cole, Homer and Sargent. Significant works by Franz Kline, Hans Hoffman, Neel, Nevelson, O'Keeffe, Pollock, Rothko, and Twombly represent the achievements of 20th century American art. The Museum's Egyptian gallery is located on the upper

Rhode Island School of Design - Museum of Art, cont.

floor, along with galleries devoted to the art of Africa, pre-Columbian cultures of Central and South America, India, Iran, China, and Japan. A nine-foot wooden Buddha from a medieval temple west of Kyoto occupies one gallery; extensive, rotating collections of Asian textiles and Japanese prints are also on view. Special exhibitions are presented on the Museum's lower floor, where selections from the more than 18,000 prints, drawings, and photographs, and the large collection of costumes and textiles are often featured. Exhibitions focusing on particular themes or periods, including contemporary crafts, complete the annual schedule. Handicapped access is available through the ramp entrance of the Farago Wing.

South Carolina

The number in parentheses following the city name indicates the number of museums/galleries in that municipality. If there is no number, one is understood. For example, in the text one listing would be found under each South Carolina city.

South Carolina

Beaufort

University of South Carolina - Beaufort Gallery at the Performing Arts Center

(USCB Art Gallery)

801 Carteret St., Beaufort, SC 29902

Tel: (803) 521-4144

Internet Address: http://vm.sc.edu/~beaulib/gallery.html

Admission: voluntary contribution.

Established: 1992

Parking: free on site.

Open: Monday to Friday, 9am-5pm.

Facilities: **Gallery** (2 rooms).

Activities: **Gallery Talks**; **Guided Tours**; **Temporary Exhibitions**.

Publications: magazine, "Arts Council Art News" (bi-monthly).

The Art Gallery mounts temporary exhibitions of the work of USCB students and professional artists. It also serves as the venue for exhibitions organized by the Arts Council of Beaufort County, the Beaufort Art Association, and Taste of the Arts.

Exterior view of University of South Carolina-Beaufort Performing Arts Center, site of the Art Gallery. Photograph courtesy of University of South Carolina-Beaufort Art Gallery, Beaufort, South Carolina.

Charleston

College of Charleston - Halsey Gallery

College of Charleston, School of the Arts

Simons Center for the Arts, St. Philip St.

Charleston, SC 29424

Tel: (803) 953-5680   *Fax:* (803) 953-8212

Internet Address: http://www.cofc.edu

Director: Mr. Mark Sloan

Admission: free.

Attendance: 5,000   *Established:* 1978   *Membership:* Y   *ADA Compliant:* Y

Open: **September to June**, Monday to Saturday, 11am-4pm.

Facilities: **Auditorium** (125 seat).

Activities: **Education Programs** (undergraduate students); **Gallery Talks**; **Guided Tours**.

Publications: exhibition catalogues.

Located on the first and second floors of the Simons Center for the Arts, the Gallery offers a schedule of temporary exhibitions.

Clemson

Clemson University - Rudolph E. Lee Gallery ⓒ

Arts and Humanities, Lee Hall, Fernow St.

Clemson University, Clemson, SC 29634

Tel: (864) 656-3881   *Fax:* (864) 656-0204

Internet Address: http://hubcap.clemson.edu/aah/arch/leegall.html

Director: Mr. David Houston

Admission: free.

Established: 1956

Open: Monday to Friday, 9am-4:30pm.

Closed: Legal Holidays.

Facilities: **Exhibition Area** (2,400 square feet).

Activities: **Temporary Exhibitions**.

Clemson University - Rudolph E. Lee Gallery, cont.

Publications: "Clemson National Print and Drawing Catalogue"; posters.

The full-time director and staff of the Lee Gallery organize regional, national, and international exhibitions, including the Clemson National Print and Drawing Exhibition. In addition the Art Department has a small gallery space operated by the students for flexible short-term exhibitions and experimental works.

Columbia

The University of South Carolina - McKissick Museum ⓒ

Pendleton and Bull Sts., Columbia, SC   29208
Tel: (803) 777-7251
Fax: (803) 777-2829
Internet Address: http://www.cla.sc.edu/MCKS/index.html
Exec. Director: Lynn Robertson
Admission: free.
Attendance: 150,000   *Established:* 1976
Membership: Y   *ADA Compliant:* Y
Parking: parking garage and on street.
Open: Monday to Friday, 9am-4pm;
          Saturday to Sunday, 1pm-5pm.
Closed: Independence Day, Labor Day, Thanksgiving Day,
          Christmas Day to New Year's Day.
Facilities: **Exhibition Area**; **Library**.
Activities: **Concerts**; **Demonstrations**; **Guided Tours**; **Lectures**; **Temporary Exhibitions**; **Traveling Exhibitions**.
Publications: brochures; exhibition catalogues; gallery guides; magazine.

Located in the historic part of the University of South Carolina campus in the center of downtown Columbia, the McKissick boasts two floors of galleries featuring national and local exhibi-tions devoted to art ranging from centuries-old cultural traditions

Exterior view of McKissick Museum. Photograph courtesy of McKissick Museum, University of South Carolina, Columbia, South Carolina.

to modern art forms. Permanent exhibitions include decorative arts and extensive natural science col-lections. The McKissick has received national recognition for its work in documenting and presenting the multicultural heritage of the Southeast. Exhibitions and public programs feature items from its permanent collection including Native and African American artifacts, traditional pottery, baskets, and quilts, as well as draw on the resources of artists and communities throughout the region. The Museum is devoted to the University's educational mission and promotes it through a variety of work-shops, classes, lectures, films, and travel programs throughout the year. In addition, the Museum fre-quently publishes catalogs, posters, and other materials.

Florence

Francis Marion University - Art Galleries ⓒ

Hyman Fine Arts Ctr. & Smith University Ctr., Route 301 North
Florence, SC   29501-0012
Tel: (843) 661-1385
Internet Address: http://alpha1.fmarion.edu/famc/gallery.htm
Admission: free.
Established: 1971
Parking: free on site.
Open: **September to April**, Monday to Friday, 8:30am-6pm.
Closed: Academic Holidays.
Facilities: **Architecture** Hyman Fine Arts Center (Post-Modern building, 1980 designed by Boston firm of Perry, Dean, Stahl & Roger); **Galleries** (3).

Francis Marion University - Art Galleries, cont.

Activities: **Temporary Exhibitions** (monthly).

Art galleries may be found in both the Hyman Fine Arts Center and the Smith University Center. The Fine Arts Center Gallery and the lobby adjacent to the theater and recital hall display both two and three-dimensional works; while the University Center Gallery, located in the main commons area, is best suited for the display of large two-dimensional work. Senior shows are required of all art majors. Additionally, at the end of each semester, the galleries display student work produced in studio art classes. Exhibitions of work by regional artists are selected to fill out the schedule in order to have two- and three-dimensional shows changing monthly throughout the academic year. Whenever possible, gallery openings are timed to coincide with First Tuesday Arts Event concerts, a series of chamber music recitals.

Interior view, Hyman Fine Arts Center Gallery. Photograph courtesy of Francis Marion University, Florence, South Carolina.

Greenville

Bob Jones University Museum & Gallery, Inc.

1700 Wade Hampton Blvd.
Greenville, SC   29614
Tel: (864) 242-5100   *Ext:* 1050
Fax: (864) 233-9829
Internet Address: http://www.bju.edu/art_gallery/index.html
Director: Ms. Joan Davis
Admission: voluntary contribution.
Attendance: 20,000   *Established:* 1951
Parking: commercial adjacent to site.
Open: Tuesday to Sunday, 2pm-5pm.
Closed: New Year's Day, Commencement Day, Independence Day,
        December 20 to Christmas.
Facilities: **Galleries** (30); **Shop.**
Activities: **Education Programs** (undergraduate and graduate stu-
        dents); **Guided Tours** (Nov-Apr, Tues-Fri, 1pm; groups 10-15, by
        reservation only).
Publications: collection catalogue, "Bob Jones University Collection of
        Religious Art: Italian Paintings, Furniture in Bob Jones Univ".

The Museum displays European sacred art from the 13th through the 19th centuries including important works of many major artists such as Botticelli, Cranach, Gerard David, Della Robbia, Doré, Honthorst, Murillo, Sebastiano del Piombo, Rembrandt, Ribera, Rubens, Tintoretto, Titian, van Dyck, and Veronese. Also worthy of note are the Museum's collections of Russian icons and European furniture.

Cranach (1472-1553), *Salome with Head of John the Baptist*, Bob Jones University Art Collection. Photograph courtesy of Bob Jones University Museum and Gallery, Inc., Bob Jones University, Greenville, South Carolina.

Hartsville

Coker College - Cecilia Coker Bell Gallery

Gladys Coker Fort Art Building (corner of Home Ave. & Campus Drive),
Hartsville, SC   29550
Tel: (803) 383-8152   *Fax:* (803) 383-8048
Internet Address: http://www.coker.edu/gallery/index.html

Coker College - Cecilia Coker Bell Gallery, cont.

Exhibition Director: Mr. Larry Merriman

Admission: free.

Attendance: 4,000   *Established:* 1983   *ADA Compliant:* Y

Open: **September to mid-May**, Monday to Friday, 10am-4pm.

Closed: New Year's Day, Easter, Labor Day, Thanksgiving Day, Christmas Day.

Facilities: **Exhibition Area** (750 square feet).

Activities: **Guided Tours.**

Coker College uses the Cecelia Coker Bell Gallery to broaden its students' exposure to artists with regional, national, and international reputations. Presenting four to five one-person shows each year, the exhibition review committee selects thought- provoking works of art by artists who desire exposure in an academic setting,. The focus is on the educational value provided to students, faculty, and the Coker college community. There are also annual shows of student and faculty work.

Rock Hill

Winthrop University - Winthrop Galleries ⓒᴬ

College of the Visual and Performing Arts

133 McLaurin, Rock Hill, SC   29733

Tel: (803) 323-2323

Internet Address: http://www.winthrop.edu/wingall.html

Established: 1998

Open: **Call for hours..**

Facilities: **Galleries** (3).

Activities: **Temporary Exhibitions** (9/year).

The Winthrop Galleries offer nine challenging professional exhibitions of work by established artists and designers throughout the year. Student work is featured in the Edmund D. Lewandowski Gallery, one of three exhibition spaces, located on the first floor of McLaurin.

Spartanburg

Converse College - Milliken Gallery ⓒᴬ

580 E. Main St., Spartanburg, SC   29302

Tel: (864) 596-9177

Internet Address: http://www.converse.edu

Director: Mayo Mac Boggs

Admission: free.

Attendance: 1,700   *Established:* 1971   *ADA Compliant:* Y

Open: **September to May**, Monday to Friday, 11am-4pm.

Closed: New Year's Day, Thanksgiving Day, Christmas Day.

Facilities: **Gallery**.

Activities: **Temporary Exhibitions**.

The Gallery presents temporary exhibitions, including an annual faculty art exhibition.

South Dakota

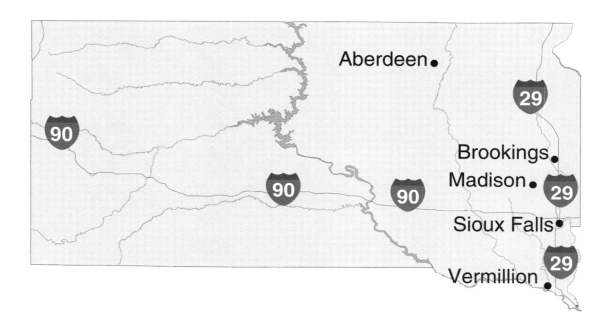

The number in parentheses following the city name indicates the number of museums/galleries in that municipality. If there is no number, one is understood. For example, in the text one listing would be found under each South Dakotan city.

South Dakota

Aberdeen

Northern State University - NSU Galleries ⓒᴬᴬ

1200 South Jay Street, Aberdeen, SD   57401
Tel: (605) 626-2263
Internet Address: http://www.northern.edu
Gallery Director: Mr. Bill Hoar
Open: call for hours.
Facilities: **Galleries** (3).
Activities: **Temporary Exhibitions**.

The work of professional artists is exhibited in the Isaac Lincoln Gallery, which is also a setting for guest artist workshops, conferences, and other cultural events. Professional artists and students also exhibit in the President's Gallery and the Memorial Union Gallery. Student work is also displayed in the Dakotah Hall Gallery and the Johnson Fine Arts Center. Additionally, the Gladys and Edgar Light Collection of the work of Paul "Warcloud" Grant and Tino Walking Bull is on permanent exhibition in Spafford Hall.

Brookings

South Dakota Art Museum at South Dakota State University ⓒᴬᴬ (SDAM)

1000 Medary Ave. at Harvey Dunn St.
Brookings, SD   57007-0899
Tel: (605) 688-5423
Fax: (605) 688-4445
Internet Address:
   http://www.sdstate.edu/~wsam/http/art1.html
Director: Ms. Lynda K. Clark
Admission: voluntary contribution.
Attendance: 69,000   *Established:* 1970
Membership: Y   *ADA Compliant:* Y
Parking: free on site.
Open: Monday to Friday, 8am-5pm;
       Saturday, 10am-5pm; Sunday, 1pm-5pm.
       Legal Holidays, 1pm-5pm.
Closed: New Year's Day, Thanksgiving Day,
       Christmas Day.
Facilities: **Auditorium** (150 seat); **Library** (2,000 volumes); **Reading Room**; **Sculpture Garden**; **Shop**.
Activities: **Films**; **Gallery Talks**; **Guided Tours**; **Temporary/Traveling Exhibitions** (approximately 30/year).

Man's Beaded Vest (Ojibwa and Blackfeet), c 1915. Frank and Adam Dudeck Memorial Collection of Native American Art, South Dakota Art Museum. Photograph courtesy of South Dakota Art Museum, Brookings, South Dakota.

Publications: exhibition catalogues; newsletter (quarterly).

South Dakota State University was instrumental in the founding of the Museum (originally the Memorial Art Center) and continues to provide assistance particularly in the areas of funding, management, and advocacy. In 1986, the name was changed to the South Dakota Art Museum to reflect its extensive collections and broad programming. Works from the Harvey Dunn, Oscar Howe, Native American Tribal, and Marghab Linen collections are on permanent display in their respective galleries. Other galleries feature temporary exhibitions representing a wide spectrum of themes, styles and media. SDAM serves South Dakota and the region with approximately thirty exhibitions per year, public programs and educational outreach. When it opened, the museum's collection consisted of 50 paintings by Harvey Dunn. It now houses 4,579 works of art in the Harvey Dunn Collection (94 works, photographs, personal possessions, memorabilia); the Oscar Howe Collection; the Native American Tribal Collection (640 artifacts, primarily the work 18th- and 19th-century Sioux artisans); the South Dakota Collection (including works by Arthur Amiotte, Karl Bodmer, Don Boyd,

South Dakota Art Museum at South Dakota State University, cont.

Charles Greener, Carol Hepper, Myra Miller, Dorothy Morgan, Robert Penn, Signe Stuart, and Michael Warrick); the American Collection (including works by artists of national and international stature such as Thomas Hart Benton, Sidney Chafetz, Eric Fischl, Marsden Hartley, Robert Mangold, and James McNeill Whistler and outstanding regional artists); the Marghab Linen Collection (1,800 pieces); and the Paul Goble Collection. Also of possible interest on campus, the Ritz Gallery (698-4103) exhibits art and design works by students, faculty, and visiting artists throughout the year.

Madison

Dakota State University - Mundt Library Gallery

Karl E. Mundt Library, 1st Floor, Madison, SD   57042-1799

Tel: (605) 256-5270

Fax: (605) 256-5208

Internet Address: http://www.departments.dsu.edu/library/gallery.html

Asst. Professor of Art: Mr. Allan Fisher

Admission: free.

Open: **Fall to Spring**,
        Monday to Thursday, 8am-10pm; Friday, 8am-5pm; Saturday, 1pm-5pm;
        Sunday, 2pm-10pm.
    Summer,
        Monday to Thursday, 7:30am-5:30pm; Friday, 7:30am-4:30pm.
    Holidays & Breaks,
        call for hours.

Facilities: **Exhibition Area**.

Activities: **Temporary Exhibitions**.

The Gallery presents a series of temporary exhibitions of work by students and professional artists. Since 1991 DSU has purchased the best student art work created in studio art classes in order to create the DSU Sudent Permanent Collection.

Sioux Falls

Augustana College - Eide/Dalrymple Art Gallery ⓒᴬᴬ

29th and S. Summit Ave., Sioux Falls, SD   57197

Tel: (605) 336-4609

Fax: (605) 336-4368

Internet Address: http://www.augie.edu

Director: Dr. Adrien Hannus

Admission: free.

Open: Tuesday to Sunday, noon-5pm.

Facilities: **Gallery**.

Activities: **Temporary Exhibitions**.

The Gallery presents temporary exhibits by professional artists. Its permanent collection consists of fine art prints and ethnographic works. Also of possible interest on campus is the Center for Western Studies, whose permanent collection includes wildlife art by Roger Pruess, photographs by Fred Farrar, watercolors by Herb Fisher, sculpture by Palmer Eide, and paintings by Belva Curtis, Robert Wood, and Oscar Howe. (Hours: Mon-Fri, 8am-5pm; tel: 605-336-4007.)

Vermillion

University of South Dakota - University Art Galleries ⓒᴬᴬ

Warren M. Lee Center for Fine Arts, 414 E. Clark St., Vermillion, SD   57069

Tel: (605) 677-5481

Fax: (605) 677-5988

Internet Address: http://www.usd.edu/cfa/Art/gallery.html

Director: Mr. John A. Day

University of South Dakota - University Art Galleries, cont.

Admission: free.

Attendance: 20,000   *Established:* 1976   *ADA Compliant:* Y

Parking: free on site.

Open: **Main Gallery**,
   Monday to Friday, 10am-4pm; Saturday to Sunday, 1pm-5pm.
   Gallery 110,
   Monday to Friday, 8am-5pm.
   Oscar Howe Gallery,
   Monday to Sunday, 1pm-4:30pm.

Closed: Legal Holidays.

Facilities: **Galleries**; **Library**.

Activities: **Films**; **Gallery Talks**; **Lectures**; **Temporary Exhibitions**; **Traveling Exhibitions**.

Publications: exhibition catalogues.

The University Art Galleries' primary purpose is to support the formal educational process of the University, but its impact extends beyond the academic community to serve artists and audiences in South Dakota and the region. UAG's Main Gallery, located in the Warren M. Lee Center for the Fine Arts, is a large modern exhibition facility, which presents twelve to fifteen art shows annually. Also located in the Lee Center, Gallery 110 is a small exhibition space for solo and group shows. In the recently renovated historic Old Main building at the heart of the University campus, the Oscar Howe Gallery is home to the largest collection of works by this celebrated American Indian artist, who taught at USD for over twenty-five years. The University Art Galleries program is also responsible for developing and maintaining the Permanent Art Collection of the University of South Dakota which currently numbers over 1,000 pieces, emphasizing South Dakota artists, contemporary art, and Asian and African study collections.

Tennessee

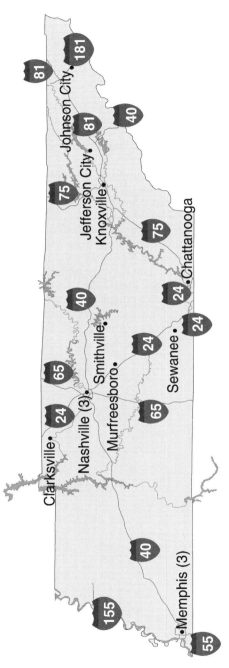

The number in parentheses following the city name indicates the number of museums/galleries in that municipality. If there is no number, one is understood. For example, in the text three listings would be found under Nashville and one listing under Sewanee.

Tennessee

Chattanooga

University of Tennessee at Chattanooga - George Ayers Cress Gallery of Art ⓒᴬᴬ
University of Tennessee at Chattanooga, Fine Arts Center, Vine and Palmetto Sts.
Chattanooga, TN   37403
Tel: (423) 755-4178
Fax: (423) 785-2101
Internet Address: http://www.utc.edu/cressgallery/campus.html
Gallery Director: Mr. George Ayers Cress
Admission: free.
Established: 1952
Open: Monday to Friday, 9am-4pm.
Closed: Academic Holidays.
Facilities: **Exhibition Area.**
Activities: **Gallery Talks**; **Temporary Exhibitions**; **Traveling Exhibitions**.

The Cress Gallery offers a schedule of temporary exhibitions. Shows include the Chattanooga Area Art Instructors and UTC Senior exhibitions, both held annually, and the biennial faculty exhibition.

Clarksville

Austin Peay State University - Trahern Gallery ⓒᴬᴬ
Margaret Fort Trahern Art and Drama Building, College and 8th Sts.
Clarksville, TN   37044
Tel: (931) 648-7333
Fax: (615) 572-1024
Internet Address: http://www.apsu.edu
Director: Ms. Bettye Holte
Admission: free.
Attendance: 7,000   *Established:* 1974   *ADA Compliant:* Y
Open: Monday to Friday, 9am-4pm; Saturday, 10am-2pm; Sunday, 1pm-4pm.
Closed: Academic Holidays.
Facilities: **Gallery.**
Activities: **Education Programs** (adults); **Temporary Exhibitions**; **Traveling Exhibitions**.
Publications: exhibition catalogues.

Each year the Gallery hosts the Annual Student Art Exhibition, the Studio exhibits (for senior art majors graduating in December and May), and an annual schedule featuring regionally, nationally, and internationally recognized artists. The Larson Drawing Collection is housed separately in Harned Hall.

Jefferson City

Carson-Newman College - Omega Gallery ⓒᴬᴬ
Warren Building, CNC Box 71995
Jefferson City, TN   37760
Tel: (423) 471-3572
Internet Address: http://www.cn.edu/academics/departments/art/exhibitions.html
Director: Mr. David Underwood
Open: Call for hours.
Facilities: **Exhibition Area.**
Activities: **Temporary Exhibitions.**

The Art Department presents temporary exhibitions in two galleries: the Omega Gallery and the Student Gallery.

Johnson City

East Tennessee State University - B. Carroll Reece Memorial Museum ⓒ

Gilbreath Drive
Johnson City, TN   37614-0660
Tel: (423) 439-4392
Fax: (423) 461-7075
Internet Address: http://cass.etsu.edu/museum
Co-Director: Ms. Margaret Carr
Admission: voluntary contribution.
Attendance: 16,000   *Established:* 1965
Membership: Y   *ADA Compliant:* Y
Parking: free on site.
Open: Monday to Saturday, 9am-4pm;
Sunday, 1pm-4pm.
Closed: ML King Day, Easter Weekend,
Independence Day, Labor Day,
Christmas Day to New Year's Day.

Exterior view of B. Carroll Reece Memorial Museum.
Photograph courtesy of B. Carroll Reece Memorial Museum,
East Tennessee State University, Johnson City, Tennessee.

Facilities: **Galleries**.
Activities: **Education Programs** (adults and children); **Gallery Talks**; **Guided Tours**; **Lectures**; **Temporary Exhibitions**; **Traveling Exhibitions**.
Publications: brochures; calendar (quarterly); exhibition catalogues; newsletter (quarterly).

Centrally located behind Sherrod Library on the campus of East Tennessee State University, the Museum houses approximately 10,000 objects ranging from prints by Picasso and other masters to frontier artifacts, musical instruments, costumes, and furniture. The galleries feature permanent and changing exhibits of historical significance, fine art and craft items. Also of possible interest on campus are the Slocumb Galleries, located in Ball Hall (open Mon-Fri, 9am-4pm; tel 439-7078). The Galleries offer a series of temporary and travelling exhibitions including a visiting artist series and MFA/BFA candidates exhibitions.

Knoxville

University of Tennessee, Knoxville - C. Kermit Ewing Gallery of Art and Architecture ⓒ

Art and Architecture Building, 1st Floor, 1715 Volunteer Blvd.
Knoxville, TN   37996
Tel: (423) 974-3200   *Fax:* (423) 974-3198
Internet Address: http://funnelweb.utcc.utk.edu/~spangler/owlfo.html
Director: Mr. Sam Yates
Admission: free.
Established: 1981
Open: **Fall to Spring**,
Monday to Thursday, 8:30am-8pm; Friday, 8:30am-4:30pm; Sunday, 1pm-4pm.
Facilities: **Exhibition Area** (3,000 square feet).
Activities: **Films**; **Lectures**; **Temporary Exhibitions**; **Workshops**.

Administered jointly by the Department of Art and the School of Architecture, the Gallery presents programming that emphasizes historic and current trends in art and architecture and stresses exhibits on subjects not frequently dealt with in the immediate area. The Gallery schedule reflects various media and disciplines taught in the academic programs and provides opportunities for students, faculty, and regional artists to exhibit their work. The permanent collection consists of approximately 3,000 objects, focusing on contemporary works in all media, Asian art, graphic design/illustration, and architectural drawings/photographs.

Memphis

Memphis College of Art - Tobey Gallery ⓒ

Overton Park ,1930 Poplar St., Memphis, TN   38104

Tel: (901) 726-4085

Fax: (901) 272-6830

Internet Address: http://www.mca.edu.

President: Mr. Jeffrey D. Nesin

Admission: free.

Attendance: 20,000   *Established:* 1936

ADA Compliant: Y

Parking: in front of school.

Open: Monday to Friday, 8:30am-4:30pm;
Saturday, 10am-3pm.

Closed: Academic Holidays.

Exterior view of Memphis College of Art. Photograph courtesy of Memphis College of Art, Memphis, Tennessee.

Facilities: **Auditorium** (342 seats); **Galleries** (2); **Library** (16,000 volumes); **Shop**.

Activities: **Arts Festival**; **Education Programs** (adults, undergraduates and children); **Films**; **Guided Tours**; **Lectures**; **Temporary Exhibitions** (10-12/year).

Publications: exhibition catalogues.

Located in historic Overton Park in a nationally-acknowledged, design-award building, MCA presents temporary exhibitions in two galleries. Regularly scheduled exhibitions include shows of the work of student MFA and BFA candidates and faculty.

Rhodes College - Clough-Hanson Gallery ⓒ

2000 North Parkway, Memphis, TN   38112

Tel: (901) 843-3442

Fax: (901) 843-3727

Internet Address: http://artslides2.art.rhodes.edu/gallery.html

Director: Ms. Marina Pacini

Admission: free.

Attendance: 2,800   *Established:* 1970   *Membership:* N   *ADA Compliant:* Y

Open: Tuesday to Saturday, 11am-5pm.

Closed: Academic Holidays, Summer.

Facilities: **Exhibition Area**.

Activities: **Lectures**; **Temporary Exhibitions**.

Publications: in-house exhibit publication (annual).

The Gallery presents temporary exhibitions of the work of professional artists as well as annual juried student and senior thesis exhibits.

University of Memphis – Art Museum ⓒ

3750 Norriswood (opposite McWherter Library)
Communication and Fine Arts Building
Memphis, TN   38152-6540

Tel: (901) 678-2224

Fax: (901) 678-5118

Internet Address:
http://www.people.memphis.edu/~artmuseum/Amhome.html

Director: Leslie Luebbers

Admission: suggested contribution-$2.00.

Attendance: 17,000

Membership: Y

Parking: parking garage at Norriswood and Deloach.

Gail Rothschild, *"Muted Belles" - A Monument to the Women of Memphis*, 1994, sculpture, located in front of CFA Building, Art Museum. Photograph courtesy of Art Museum of University of Memphis, Memphis, Tennessee.

University of Memphis - Art Museum, cont.
Open: Monday to Saturday, 9am-5pm.

Facilities: **Exhibition Area** (5,000 square feet); **Library** Institute of Egyptian Art & Archaeology (6,000 volumes).

Activities: **Guided Tours; Lectures; Temporary Exhibitions; Traveling Exhibitions**.

Publications: collection catalogue; exhibition catalogues; newsletter, "AM Edition"; newsletter, "Annual Institute of Art and Archeology".

Located on the campus of The University of Memphis, the Museum holds the permanent collection of the Institute of Egyptian Art and Archaeology, over 150 objects ranging in date from 3500 BC to 700 AD. There are permanent exhibits of Egyptian antiquities, West African Art, and miniature furniture. Each year the Museum also produces several exhibitions of primarily contemporary art in the main gallery, including the annual MAX (Memphis Art Exhibition), juried student, and MFA thesis exhibitions. Selections from the print collection are regularly displayed in conjunction with art classes.

Murfreesboro

Middle Tennessee State University - Baldwin Photographic Gallery ☉
Middle Tennessee State University, McWherter Learning Resources Center
Murfreesboro, TN   37132
Tel: (615) 898-2085
Fax: (615) 898-5682
Internet Address: http://www.mtsu.edu
Curator: Mr. Tom Jimison
Admission: free.
Attendance: 30,000   *Established:* 1961   *ADA Compliant:* Y
Parking: Free, adjacent to site.
Open: **Academic Year**, Monday to Friday, 8am-4:30pm; Saturday, 8am-noon; Sunday, 6pm-10pm.
          July to August, by appointment.
Closed: Academic Holidays.
Facilities: **Photographic Archive**.
Activities: **Lectures; Temporary Exhibitions**.
Publications: posters; show announcements (monthly).

The Gallery, focusing on contemporary photography, presents temporary exhibitions. Its permanent collection totals approximately 1,000 photographs. Also of possible interest on campus is the Art Barn Gallery, which presents temporary exhibitions, including juried student and senior BFA candidate shows (open Mon-Fri, 8am-4:30pm; tel 898-5653).

Nashville

Fisk University - Carl Van Vechten Gallery ☉
1000 17th Ave., N., Nashville, TN   37208-3051
Tel: (615) 329-8720   *Fax:* (615) 329-8715
Internet Address: http://www.fisk.edu
Director: Mr. Kevin Grogan
Admission: suggested contribution-$3.50.
Attendance: 40,000   *Established:* 1949
ADA Compliant: Y
Parking: free on site.
Open: **Academic Year**, Tuesday to Friday, 10am-5pm; Saturday to Sunday, 1pm-5pm.
          Summer, Tuesday to Friday, 10am-4pm.
Facilities: **Architecture** (first Fisk University gymnasium, 1888); **Library** (4,500 volumes); **Shop**.
Activities: **Arts Festival; Films; Gallery Talks; Guided Tours; Lectures; Traveling Exhibitions**.
Publications: calendar; exhibition catalogues.

Fisk University - Carl Van Vechten Gallery, cont.

Fisk University, founded in 1866 as the Fisk Free School, has been a collecting institution almost since its beginning. Its first faculty members had been, before joining Fisk, missionary educators among the Mende people of West Africa, and they brought with them to Nashville examples of the indigenous arts and crafts of the Mende. Since then, Fisk has built extensive collections of African American art, as well as collections of work by the photographer Carl Van Vechten, the painter/designer/teacher Winold Reiss, and artist/ethnographer Cyrus L. Baldridge. In 1949, American painter Georgia O'Keeffe donated a collection of 101 paintings, sculptures and works on paper from the collection of her late husband, photographer Alfred Stieglitz. The collection, in addition to 18 photographs by Stieglitz, includes work by O'Keeffe; American artists Charles Demuth, Arthur Dove, Marsden Hartley, John Marin, and Alfred Maurer; and such prominent artists as Cézanne, George Grosz, Picasso, Renoir, Rivera, Gino Severini, and Toulouse-Lautrec. The Carl Van Vechten Gallery of Art, Fisk's first gymnasium (1888), houses a considerable part of the Alfred Stieglitz Collection of modern art. Also on campus, the Aaron Douglas Gallery (329-8685) features rotating exhibits.

Exterior view of Carl Van Vechten Gallery of Art at Fisk University, former gymnasium (1888), converted to present use in 1949 to house Alfred Stieglitz Collection of Modern Art. Photograph courtesy of Fisk University, Nashville, Tennessee.

Vanderbilt University Fine Arts Gallery ⊖

Fine Arts Building (Old Gym), 23rd and West End Aves., Nashville, TN 37203
Tel: (615) 322-0605   *Fax:* (615) 343-1382
Internet Address: http://www.vanderbilt.edu/AnS/finearts/gallery.html
Art Curator: Mr. Joseph S. Mella
Admission: free.
Attendance: 5,000   *Established:* 1961   *Membership:* N
Parking: adjacent to gallery.
Open: **Academic Year**, Monday to Friday, noon-4pm; Saturday to Sunday, 1pm-5pm.
    Summer, Tuesday to Friday, noon-4pm; Saturday, 1pm-5pm.
Closed: Academic Holidays.
Activities: **Gallery Talks & Special Tours** (arrange with curatorial staff in advance, 343-1704);
    Lectures; **Temporary Exhibitions**; **Traveling Exhibitions**.
Publications: exhibition catalogues.

The Vanderbilt University Fine Arts Gallery features five exhibitions each year that represent the diversity of artistic production throughout the history of Eastern and Western art. In addition to thematic exhibitions drawn from the permanent collection, traveling exhibitions are presented. Beginning with Anna C. Hoyt's generous donation of 105 Old Master and modem prints more than a century ago, the collection has continued to flourish and increase the depth, diversity, and number of its holdings. Now totaling more than 5,000 works from more than forty countries, it serves to illustrate the history of world art in its most creative and comprehensive aspects. The collection has grown to include works of East Asian art with the Harold P. Stern Collection and the Herman D. Doochin Collection; European Old Master paintings with the Kress Study Collection; paintings from the Barbizon school; and African, Oceanic, and pre-Columbian art and artifacts from the Marjorie and Leon Marlowe Collection. Also of possible interest on campus is the Sarratt Student Center Gallery (open Mon-Sat, 9am-9pm, Sun, 11am-9pm; reduced hours in summer; tel 322-2471). The Gallery, located in the main lobby of the Sarratt Student Center, is known for its unique exhibits featuring paintings, sculpture, drawings, photography, prints and multi-media works of the mid-South's contemporary artists. Student and faculty/staff shows, lectures and discussions by the artists, plus poster sales and special craft sales highlight the year's schedule.

Nashville, Tennessee

Watkins Institute College of Art and Design ⒸⒶⒶ

601 Church St., Nashville, TN   37219
Tel: (615) 242-1851
Fax: (615) 242-4278
Internet Address: http://www.watkinsinstitute.org
Director of Exhibitions: Professor Madeline Reed
Admission: free.
Established: 1885
ADA Compliant: Y
Open: Monday to Thursday, 9am-8pm; Friday, 9am-3pm.
Closed: New Year's Day, Independence Day, Labor Day,
          Thanksgiving Day, Christmas Day.
Facilities: **Galleries**.
Activities: **Arts Festival**; **Education Programs** (adults and chil-
      dren); **Lectures**; **Traveling Exhibitions**.
Publications: exhibition catalogues.

Bruce Matthews, oil painting, Tennessee All-State Art Collection. Photograph courtesy of Watkins Institute, Nashville, Tennessee.

The Institute displays the Tennessee All-State Art Collection, art-work by Tennessee artists from 1954 to the present, in its library, reception area and student lounge. Changing exhibitions are mounted in the John A. Hood auditorium. Seven works in pastel and oil by Elihu Vedder are in the President's office.

Sewanee

The University of the South - The University Gallery ⒸⒶⒶ

735 University Ave. at Georgia Ave., Sewanee, TN   37383-1000
Tel: (931) 598-1708   *Fax:* (931) 598-1145
Internet Address: http://www.sewanee.edu/Gallery/websitegfb/galinfo
Gallery Director: Mr. Geof Bowie
Admission: voluntary contribution.
Attendance: 3,500   *Established:* 1965   *ADA Compliant:* Y
Open: Tuesday to Friday, 10am-5pm; Saturday to Sunday, noon-5pm.
Closed: Academic Holidays.
Activities: **Education Programs** (undergraduate and graduate students); **Films**; **Gallery Talks**;
      Guided Tours; **Lectures**; **Temporary Exhibitions**; **Traveling Exhibitions**.
Publications: bulletin.

The gallery features temporary exhibitions of contemporary artwork.

Smithville

Tennessee Technological University - Joe L. Evins Appalachian Center for Crafts

1560 Craft Center Drive, Smithville, TN   37166   ⒸⒶⒶ
Tel: (615) 597-6801
Fax: (615) 597-6803
Internet Address:
   http://www.tntech.edu/www/life/orgs/vas
Director: Mr. Ward Doubet
Admission: voluntary contribution.
Attendance: 150,000   *Established:* 1979
ADA Compliant: Y
Open: Daily, 9am-5pm.

Exterior view of Appalachian Center for Crafts. Photograph courtesy of Appalachian Center for Crafts, Tennessee Technological University, Smithville, Tennessee.

Tennessee Technological Univ. - J.L. Evins Appalachian Center for Crafts, cont.

Closed: Easter, June 29-30, Thanksgiving Day, Christmas Day to New Year's Day.

Facilities: **Exhibition Area** (1,500 square feet); **Food Services** Restaurant (70 seat); **Library**; **Sales Gallery**.

Activities: **Education Programs** (adults and graduate students); **Guided Tours**; **Lectures**.

A component of Tennessee Technological University, The Joe L. Evins Appalachian Center for Crafts is dedicated to expanding the context of contemporary art while sustaining the vitality of traditional crafts. In two exhibition areas adjacent to the sales gallery, works of national, regional, and historic interest are on view. The Sales Gallery showcases the work of Tennessee craftspersons and Craft Center faculty and students, along with that of artisans from 13 Appalachian states. Traditional Appalachian crafts of quilting, basketry, woodworking, and pottery are offered, as well as a selection of contemporary works including jewelry and handblown glass. Also of possible interest, the Joan Derryberry Art Gallery is located in the University Center on the campus of TTU in Cookeville, Tennessee.

Texas

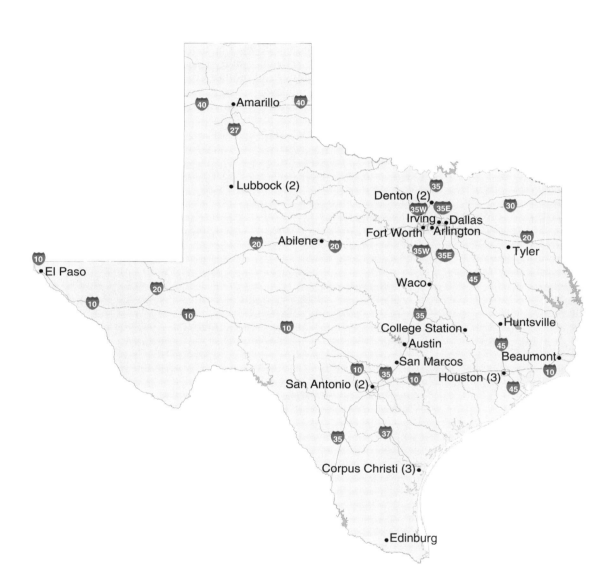

The number in parentheses following the city name indicates the number of museums/galleries in that municipality. If there is no number, one is understood. For example, in the text three listings would be found under Houston and one listing under Irving.

Texas

Abilene

Abilene Christian University - Virginia Clover Shore Art Gallery ⓒⁿ

142 Don H. Morris Center, North Wing (near Moody Coliseum)
Abilene, TX   79699-7987
Tel: (915) 674-2085
Internet Address: http://www.acu.edu/academics/art/htmlpages/gallery
Director: Dr. Brent Green
Admission: free.
Open: **Academic Year**, Monday to Friday, 9am-5pm.
Facilities: **Exhibition Area** (1,500 square feet).
Activities: **Gallery Talks**; **Temporary Exhibitions** (7/year); **Visiting Artist Program**.

The Shore Gallery presents temporary exhibitions of work by regionally and nationally recognized artists, faculty, alumni, and students. An annual juried student competitions is held during the spring semester, The Department's growing holdings are stored in the gallery's permanent collection storage room.

Amarillo

Amarillo College - Amarillo Museum of Art ⓒⁿ

2200 S. Van Buren at 22nd St., Amarillo, TX   79109
Tel: (806) 371-5050   *Fax:* (806) 373-9235
Internet Address: http://www.amarilloart.org
Director: Mr. Patrick McCracken
Admission: free.
Attendance: 56,000   *Established:* 1972   *Membership:* Y   *ADA Compliant:* Y
Parking: free on site.
Open: Tuesday to Friday, 10am-5pm; Saturday to Sunday, 1pm-5pm.
Closed: New Year's Day, Memorial Day, Independence Day, Labor Day, Thanksgiving Day,
          Christmas Eve to Christmas Day.
Facilities: **Architecture** (late International-style building, designed by Edward D. Stone, 24,000
          square feet); **Bookstore**; **Galleries** (6); **Library**; **Sculpture Courtyard**.
Activities: **Arts Festival**; **Education Programs** (adults and children); **Films**; **Gallery Talks**;
          Guided Tours; **Lectures**; **Performances**; **Temporary Exhibitions** (16/year); **Traveling
          Exhibitions**.
Publications: exhibition catalogues; gallery guides; newsletter (quarterly); posters.

Located on the campus of Amarillo College, a two-year community college, the Museum features loan exhibitions and art for the Museum's permanent collection. Museum holdings including works of mid-20th-century modernists (including Frankenthaler, Kline, Marin, Nevelson, and O'Keeffe), photography (particularly the work Russell Lee, but also including representative examples of the work of Delano, Lange, Rothstein, Steichen, Stieglitz, Strand, Wolcott, and Weston), 17th- to 19th-century European paintings (including two paintings by Francesco Guardi), 18th- through 20th-century Middle Eastern textiles, Japanese Edo period woodblock prints, and South and Southeast Asian sculpture (Buddhist and Hindu works ranging from 2nd-century B.C. Gandharan to 9th-century A.D. Java and 14th-century A.D. Khmer pieces).

Arlington

University of Texas at Arlington - The Gallery at UTA ⓒⁿ

Fine Arts Bldg., U. of TX at Arlington, 700 West 2nd St., Arlington, TX   76019
Tel: (817) 272-3143
Internet Address: http://www.uta.edu/art/
Director: Mr. Benito Huerta
Admission: free.
Attendance: 5,000   *Established:* 1976   *ADA Compliant:* Y

University of Texas Arlington - The Gallery at UTA, cont.

Open: Monday to Friday, 10am-5pm; Saturday, noon-5pm.
Closed: Academic Holidays.
Facilities: **Gallery** (4,000 square feet).
Activities: **Films**; **Lectures**; **Temporary Exhibitions** (6/year).

Located on the first floor of the Fine Arts building, The Gallery at UTA presents works by recognized contemporary artists in a critical and creative context. Also of possible interest on campus are Gallery 171, operated by the Student Art Association, and The Gallery in the University Center.

Austin

University of Texas at Austin - Jack S. Blanton Museum of Art ⓒ⁴⁴

Harry Ransom Humanities Research Center
21st & Guadalupe Sts.
Austin, TX   78712-1205
Tel: (512) 471-7324
Fax: (512) 471-7023
Internet Address: http://www.utexas.edu/cofa/hag
Director: Mr. Jessie Otto Hite
Admission: voluntary contribution.
Attendance: 100,000   *Established:* 1963
Membership: Y   *ADA Compliant:* Y
Parking: free on site.
Open: Monday/Wednesday/Friday, 9am-5pm;
          Thursday, 9am-9pm;
          Saturday to Sunday, 1pm-5pm.
Closed: Legal Holidays.
Facilities: **Exhibition Spaces** (2).
Activities: **Education Programs** (children); **Films**; **Guided Tours**; **Lectures**; **Temporary Exhibitions**; **Traveling Exhibitions**.
Publications: exhibition catalogues; newsletter.

Thomas Hart Benton, *Romance*, 1932, tempera and oil varnish glazes on gesso panel. Jack S. Blanton Museum of Art, University of Texas at Austin, gift of Mari and James A. Michener, 1991. Photograph by George Holmes, courtesy of University of Texas, Austin, Texas.

The Jack S. Blanton Museum of Art, formerly known as the Archer M. Huntington Art Gallery, is the fine arts museum of the University of Texas at Austin. With a collection of almost 13,000 objects, a full-time staff of 24, and an operating budget of approximately $1.8 million, the Blanton describes itself as one of the top five university museums in this country. Housed at two separate locations, the Museum's permanent collection, on view in the Harry Ransom Center, includes Ancient Art, European Art, 19th- and 20th-Century American Art, and Contemporary Latin American Art. The Collection of Prints and Drawings is exhibited in the Museum in the Art Building at 23rd and San Jacinto Streets. Each year over 15,000 people participate in programs at the Blanton, which include two public school outreach programs. The Museum hosts the best public collection of post-60's Latin American art in the U.S. Its Prints and Drawings Collection, with over 11,000 works on paper, is the best collection in the Southwest. Works range from Old Masters like Rembrandt and Dürer, to 18th century European, to contemporary American. The James and Mari Michener Collection is the core of the Museum's 20th-century American art exhibit. It consists of 375 paintings dating from 1907 to the present.

Beaumont

Lamar University - Dishman Art Gallery ⓒ⁴⁴

Lamar University, 1030 Lavaca, Beaumont, TX   77705
Tel: (409) 880-8959   *Fax:* (409) 880-1799
Internet Address: http://www.lamar.edu
Director: Dr. Lynn Lokensgard

Lamar University - Dishman Art Gallery, cont.

Admission: voluntary contribution.
Attendance: 4,000   *Established:* 1983   *Membership:* N   *ADA Compliant:* Y
Parking: free parking next to building.
Open: Monday to Friday, 8am-5pm.
Closed: New Year's Day, Good Friday, Memorial Day,
          Independence Day, Labor Day, Thanksgiving Day
          to Thanksgiving Friday, Christmas Day, between
          semesters.
Facilities: **Exhibition Area** (3,000 square feet); **Library**.
Activities: **Arts Festival**; **Lectures**.
Publications: exhibition catalogues.

The Dishman Art Gallery presents monthly exhibitions of the work of contemporary artists, in addition to its permanent collection. The permanent collection of the Dishman Art gallery consists of the Eisenstadt Collection: 147 paintings from the 17th- through the 20th century, including works by Lawrence, Ladell, Moran, and Gisson, as well as over 250 porcelains, and eight sculptures. The Eisenstadt Collection may be viewed on Tuesday, 1pm-3pm, and Wednesday, 2pm-4pm.

Sir Thomas Lawrence, *Portrait of a Young Lady (Lady Emily Cowper)*, 1814, oil on canvas. Dishman Art Gallery, Heinz and Ruth Eisenstadt Collection. Photograph courtesy of Dishman Art Gallery, Beaumont, Texas.

College Station

Texas A&M University - MSC Forsyth Center Galleries ⓒ

Texas A&M University, Memorial Student Center, Joe Routt Blvd., College Station, TX   77844-9081
Tel: (409) 845-9251
Fax: (409) 845-5117
Internet Address: http://charlotte.tamu.edu/services/Forsyth
Curator: Mr. Timothy Novak
Admission: free.
Attendance: 30,000   *Established:* 1989   *ADA Compliant:* Y
Parking: free on site.
Open: Monday to Friday, 9am-5pm; Saturday to Sunday, noon-5pm.
Closed: Independence Day, Thanksgiving Day, Christmas Day to New Year's Day.
Facilities: **Exhibition Area** (9,000 square feet).
Activities: **Films**; **Guided Tours**; **Lectures**; **Traveling Exhibitions**.
Publications: exhibition catalogues.

The Galleries are located in the Memorial Student Center of Texas A&M University and schedule tours, receptions, and other events. The permanent collection of the Galleries includes art glass (English cameo glass, and works by Louis Comfort Tiffany, Frederick Carder, and many others), and works by American artists such as Frederic Remington, Charles Russell, Mary Cassatt, Winslow Homer, and Grandma Moses. Also of possible interest on campus are the J. Wayne Stark University Center Galleries (open Tues-Fri, 9am-8pm, and Sat-Sun, noon-6pm; Tel 845-8501).The Galleries focus on works by 20th-century Texas artists.

Corpus Christi

Del Mar College - Joseph A. Cain Memorial Art Gallery ⓒ

East Campus, Fine Arts Center (off Ayers St.), Corpus Christi, TX   78404-3987
Tel: (512) 886-1216
Internet Address: http://www.edlmar.edu/art/artdept.html
Director: Mr. William E. Lambert

Del Mar College - Joseph A. Cain Memorial Art Gallery, cont.

Open: **Fall to Spring**, Monday to Thursday, 11am-4pm; Friday, 9am-noon.
Summer, Monday to Thursday, 10am-4pm; Friday, 10am-noon.

Facilities: **Exhibition Areas** (Cain Gallery, 1,750 square feet and hallway gallery space, 450 linear feet).

Activities: **Temporary Exhibitions**.

The Joseph A. Cain Memorial Art Gallery presents temporary exhibitions focusing on issues in the academic study of contemporary art. Exhibitions include the annual National Drawing and Small Sculpture Show (the only such competition and show to be held at a community college), an annual student exhibition, and an annual stone carving sculpture exhibition.. The permanent collection, begun in 1967 by former Art Department Chairman Joseph A. Cain, constitutes a solid body of work by emerging artists.

Texas A&M University-Corpus Christi - Art Museum of South Texas

1902 N. Shoreline
Corpus Christi, TX   78401
Tel: (512) 884-3844
Fax: (512) 980-3500
Director: Dr. William G. Otton
Admission: fee: adult-$3.00, child-$1.00, student-$2.00, senior-$2.00.
Established: 1960
Membership: Y   *ADA Compliant:* Y
Parking: free on site.
Open: Tuesday to Wednesday, 10am-5pm;
Thursday, 10am-9pm
Friday to Saturday, 10am-5pm;
Sunday, 1pm-5pm.
Closed: New Year's Day, Independence Day, Thanksgiving Day, Christmas Day.

Exterior view of Art Museum of South Texas, designed by Philip Johnson (1972). Photograph courtesy of Art Museum of South Texas, Corpus Christi, Texas.

Facilities: **Architecture** (designed by Philip Johnson); **Auditorium** (231 seats); **Food Services** Restaurant; **Gift Shop**; **Library** (2,500 volumes).

Activities: **Concerts**; **Education Programs** (adults and children); **Films**; **Gallery Talks**; **Guided Tours**; **Lectures**; **Temporary Exhibitions**; **Traveling Exhibitions**.

Publications: exhibition catalogues.

Affiliated with Texas A&M University-Corpus Christi, the Art Museum of South Texas has as its mission the collection and exhibition of visual art, with particular emphasis on the art of the Americas and of the region, and to provide educational programs in support of visual art. The collection of the Museum emphasizes the region, including Texas, surrounding states, and Northern Mexico. Its holdings include works by Edward Laning, Lahib Jaddo, Alexander Hogue, Antonio E. Garcia, Ricardo Ruiz, Bruno Andrade, Lucas Johnson, David Bates, Ken Holder, and Dennis Blagg.

Texas A&M University-Corpus Christi - Weil Gallery ⓒ⁴⁴

6300 Ocean Drive, Corpus Christi, TX   78412
Tel: (512) 994-2314   *Fax:* (512) 994-6097
Internet Address: http://www.tamucc.edu
Director: Mr. Jim Edwards
Admission: free.
Open: Monday, 10am-4pm; Tuesday, 10am-7pm; Wednesday to Thursday, 10am-4pm;
Friday, 10am-3pm.
Facilities: **Exhibition Area**.
Activities: **Temporary Exhibitions**.

The Gallery presents temporary exhibitions of contemporary art including an annual student exhibition. Exhibitions are often coordinated with related shows at the South Texas Institute for the Arts.

Dallas

Southern Methodist University - The Meadows Museum ⓒ

SMU School of the Arts
Bishop Blvd. at Binkley Ave.
Dallas, TX   75275-0356
Tel: (214) 768-2516
Fax: (214) 768-1688
Internet Address:
   http://www.smu.edu/meadows/museum
Admission: suggested contribution-$3.00.
Attendance: 30,000   *Established:* 1965
Membership: Y   *ADA Compliant:* Y
Parking: free on site.
Open: Monday to Tuesday, 10am-5pm;
          Thursday, 10am-8pm;
          Friday to Saturday, 10am-5pm;
          Sunday, 1pm-5pm.

Murillo, *Jacob Laying Peeled Rods before the Flocks of Laban*, c. 1665. Meadows Museum. Photograph courtesy of Meadows Museum, Dallas, Texas.

Closed: New Year's Day, Easter, Independence Day, Thanksgiving Day, Christmas Day.
Facilities: **Sculpture Garden**; **Shop**.
Activities: **Guided Tours**.
Publications: brochures.

The Meadows Museum was founded in 1965 , after Texas philanthropist and oil financier Algur H. Meadows donated his collection of paintings and prints to Southern Methodist University. Meadows had begun to acquire the collection, which is particularly strong in Spanish art, after a series of visits to the Prado in 1950. The Meadows presents major works from the Middle Ages to the present, including masterpieces by Velasquez, Ribera, Zurburan, Murillo, Goya, Miró, and Picasso. The sculpture garden displays works by Rodin, Maillol, Moore, Noguchi, and Lipchitz.

Denton

Texas Woman's University Fine Arts Gallery ⓒ

Texas Woman's University, 1 Circle Drive, Denton, TX   76204
Tel: (817) 898-2530   *Fax:* (817) 898-3198
Internet Address: http://www4.twu.edu/as/art/gallery
Director: Ms. Correy Stuckenbruck
Admission: free.
Established: 1901   *ADA Compliant:* Y
Open: Monday to Friday, 9am-4pm.
Closed: Legal Holidays.
Activities: **Education Programs** (adults, students and children); **Films**; **Gallery Talks**; **Guided Tours**; **Lectures**; **Temporary Exhibitions**.

The Fine Arts Gallery presents temporary exhibitions of student and faculty work, as well as that of artists from outside the University community.

University of North Texas Art Gallery ⓒ

School of Visual Arts, Mulberry at Welch, Denton, TX   76203
Tel: (940) 565-4005   *Fax:* (940) 565-4717
Internet Address: http://www.art.unt.edu/sova/galleries/index.html
Director: Ms. Diana Block
Admission: voluntary contribution.
Attendance: 5,000   *Established:* 1972   *ADA Compliant:* Y
Open: **September to May**, Monday to Tuesday, noon-8pm; Wednesday to Saturday, noon-5pm.
          June to August, call for hours.
Closed: Between Semesters, Spring Break.

University of North Texas Art Gallery, cont.

Facilities: **Exhibition Area** (2,250 square feet).

Activities: **Temporary Exhibitions**.

Publications: exhibition catalogues.

The University of North Texas Art Gallery presents temporary exhibitions, with emphasis on curatorial projects in contemporary art. Also of possible interest on campus is the Cora Stafford Gallery.

Edinburg

University of Texas-Pan American - Galleries 🆑

1201 West University Drive

Edinburg, TX   78539-2999

Tel: (956) 381-2655

Fax: (956) 384-5072

Internet Address: http://www.panam.edu/dept/art/gallery.htm

Director: Ms. Valerie Innella

Admission: free.

Attendance: 15,000   *Established:* 1973

Membership: N   *ADA Compliant:* Y

Parking: parking lots nearby.

Open: Monday to Friday, 9am-4pm.

Closed: Academic Holidays.

Facilities: **Galleries** (3 - total of 4,400 square feet).

Activities: **Guided Tours** (by appointment); **Lectures** (by exhibiting artists).

The University of Texas-Pan American has three galleries on its main campus: the Clark, University, and Lamar Galleries. The galleries offer temporary exhibitions by award-winning contemporary artists from the United States and Mexico, as well as BFA student shows. The Permanent Collection is housed in the Lamar Gallery and includes works by Dali, Garcia, Ray, Picabia, and Goya.

Maria Alba Gonzalez, *Dancers*, 1999, exhibited as part of a bachelor of fine art exhibition, 1999, University of Texas-Pan American Art Gallery. Photograph courtesy of University of Texas-Pan American, Roma, Texas.

El Paso

University of Texas at El Paso - University Art Galleries

Fox Fine Arts Center (off Sun Bowl Drive), El Paso, TX   79968

Tel: (915) 747-7837   *Fax:* (915) 747-6749

Internet Address: http://www.utep.edu/arts/calendar.htm

Director: Mr. Gene Flores

Open: Monday to Friday, 10am-5pm.

Facilities: **Galleries**.

Activities: **Temporary Exhibitions**; **Visiting Artists Series**.

The Gallery maintains two galleries in the Fox Fine Arts Center. The Main Gallery mounts temporary group exhibitions of work by visiting artists, faculty and students; the Glass Gallery presents the work of professional artists as well as MA and BA exhibitions. Past exhibitions have included work by Eric Avery, Robert Colescott, Dan Flavin, Gronk, Donald Judd, and Hermann Nitsch.

Fort Worth

Texas Christian University - Moudy Exhibition Hall 🆑

University Drive and Cantey, Fort Worth, TX   76129

Tel: (817) 257-7643   *Fax:* (817) 257-7399

Internet Address: http://www.tcu.edu

Director and Chairman: Mr. Ronald Watson

Texas Christian University - Moudy Exhibition Hall, cont.

Admission: free.

Established: 1874   *ADA Compliant:* Y

Open: **Academic Year**,

Monday, 11am-6pm; Tuesday to Friday, 11am-4pm; Saturday to Sunday, 1pm-4pm.

Closed: Easter, Christmas Day, Summer.

Activities: **Education Programs** (adults and students); **Lectures**.

The Moudy Exhibition Hall presents juried shows and exhibitions of student and faculty work.

Houston

Rice University Art Gallery ⓒᴬᴬ

6100 S. Main St., Sewall Hall

Houston, TX   77005

Tel: (713) 527-6069

Internet Address: http://www.rice.edu/ruag

Director: Ms. Kimberly Davenport

Admission: free.

Established: 1968

ADA Compliant: Y

Parking: free on site.

Open: Monday to Wednesday, 11am-5pm;
Thursday, 11am-8pm;
Friday to Saturday, 11am-5pm;
Sunday, noon-5pm.

Closed: Academic Holidays, Summer.

Facilities: **Auditorium**; **Library** (36,000 volumes).

Exterior view of Rice University Art Gallery. Photograph courtesy Rice University Art Gallery, Houston, Texas.

Activities: **Gallery Talks**; **Lectures**; **Temporary Exhibitions**.

Publications: brochures; exhibition catalogues.

The aim of the Rice University Art Gallery is to focus on content and critical public dialogue. Gallery personnel describe it as Houston's primary public space for the creation of new installation works by artists of national and international reputation. It also presents occasional group exhibitions organized around provocative themes.

University of Houston - Blaffer Gallery ⓒᴬᴬ

Fine Arts Building, UH Entrance #16, off Cullen Blvd.

Houston, TX   77204-4891

Tel: (713) 743-9530

Fax: (713) 743-9525

Internet Address:
   http://www.hfax.uh.edu/blaffer/

Director and Chief Curator: Dr. Don Bacigalupi

Admission: voluntary contribution.

Attendance: 35,000   *Established:* 1973

Membership: Y   *ADA Compliant:* Y

Parking: pay on site, 1st lot on left after Entrance #16.

Open: Tuesday to Friday, 10am-5pm;
Saturday to Sunday, 1pm-5pm.

Closed: Academic Holidays, New Year's Day, Independence Day, Thanksgiving Day, Christmas Day.

Interior view, Blaffer Gallery. Photograph courtesy of Blaffer Gallery, Houston, Texas.

University of Houston - Blaffer Gallery, cont.

Facilities: **Exhibition Area** (6,500 square feet).

Activities: **Education Programs** (adults and children); **Guided Tours**; **Lectures**; **Traveling Exhibitions**.

Publications: newsletter, "Blaffer" (biennial).

Through exhibitions, programs, and publications, the Blaffer Gallery presents art that is visually stimulating and relevant to the university and the Community. It presents temporary exhibitions of student work, as well as that of professional artists. Shows include the biennial Houston Area Exhibition. The Blaffer Gallery is a non-collecting institution.

University of Houston-Downtown - O'Kane Gallery ⓒ④④

University of Houston-Downtown, One Main St., Suite 323 South, Houston, TX   77002

Tel: (713) 221-8042   *Fax:* (713) 226-5207

Internet Address: http://www.dt.uh.edu/studaff/803oka.htm

Director: Ms. Ann Trask

Parking: on Girard.

Open: Monday to Friday, 10am-5pm.

Facilities: **Gallery.**

Activities: **Temporary Exhibitions.**

Located on the third floor of the One Main Street building, the Gallery offer exhibits mixed media works by Houston and Texas professional artists and faculty, as well as an annual student show.

Huntsville

Sam Houston State University - Gaddis Geeslin Gallery ⓒ④④

Art Building F, 1028 21st St. (SW Corner of Campus), Huntsville, TX   77341

Tel: (409) 294-1315

Internet Address: http://www.shsu.edu/~pin_www/T@S/gallery.html

Admission: free.

Open: Monday to Friday, noon-5pm.

Facilities: **Exhibition Area.**

Activities: **Temporary Exhibitions.**

The Gaddis Geeslin Gallery presents temporary exhibitions of work by professional artists, as well as faculty and student shows. Also of possible interest on campus is the Student Organization of Fine Art (SOFA) Gallery, located in Art Building A (open: Mon-Fri, 8am-5pm) and the Lowman Student Center (LSC) Gallery, adjacent to the Student Center's main lobby.

Irving

North Lake College - Gallery

5001 N. MacArthur Blvd., Irving, TX   75038

Tel: (972) 273-3574

Internet Address: http://www.dccd.edu/nlc/vparts/art/gal-sch.htm

Gallery Director: Mr. Bob Nunn

Admission: free.

Open: Call for hours.

Facilities: **Exhibition Area.**

Activities: **Temporary Exhibitions.**

North Lake is one of seven campuses that make up the Dallas County Community College District. The Gallery presents temporary exhibitions.

Lubbock

Texas Tech University - Landmark Arts ⓒ④④

Art Building, 18th and Flint Sts. Lubbock, TX   79409-2081

Tel: (806) 742-1947

Texas Tech University - Landmark Arts, cont.

Internet Address: http://www.art.ttu.edu/artdept/artdepinfo/lndmrk.html
Director: Mr. Ken Bloom
Admission: free.
Attendance: 5,000   *Established:* 1983
ADA Compliant: Y
Parking: free on site.
Open: Monday to Friday, 10am-4:30pm;
         Saturday, 1pm-4pm.
Facilities: **Exhibition Area** (5 galleries).
Activities: **Temporary Exhibitions**.
Publications: collection catalogue (2-3/yr).

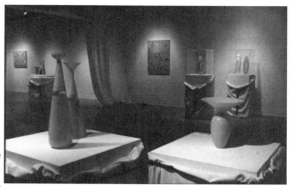

View of temporary exhibition at Landmark Arts, " Four in Glass" (1997). Photograph courtesy of Landmark Arts, Lubbock, Texas.

The Landmark Arts Program promotes fine arts growth and development through a comprehensive program of exhibitions; symposia and workshops; publications; and hands-on experience with working artists. Temporary exhibitions are presented in four galleries: the Landmark Gallery, displaying work by recognized professional artists; the Studio Gallery, presenting a weekly changing series of final examination by MFA/BFA students in all media; the Sculpture Alternative, an ongoing series of experimental sculpture and ceramics by graduate and undergraduate sculpture/installation-art students; and SRA-Photo, a continuing series of photographic displays by a national selection of artists. The permanent collection includes prints and photographs.

Texas Tech University - Museum of Texas Tech University Ⓒᴬᴬ (MoTTU)

4th St. and Indiana Ave., Lubbock, TX   79409
Tel: (806) 742-2490
Fax: (806) 742-1136
Internet Address: http://www.ttu.edu/~museum/
Exec. Director: Mr. Gary Edson
Admission: free.
Attendance: 244,000   *Established:* 1929   *Membership:* Y   *ADA Compliant:* Y
Open: Tuesday to Wednesday, 10am-5pm; Thursday, 10am-8:30pm; Friday to Saturday, 10am-5pm;
         Sunday, 1pm-5pm.
Closed: New Year's Day, ML King Day, Independence Day, Thanksgiving Day, Christmas Day.
Facilities: **Exhibition Area**; **Library** (10,000 volumes); **Shop**.
Activities: **Films**; **Gallery Talks**; **Guided Tours** (information: (806) 742-2456); **Temporary Exhibitions**; **Traveling Exhibitions**.
Publications: journal, "The Museum Journal"; newsletter, "MuseNews".

MoTTU is a general museum with collections in the arts, humanities, and the sciences, primarily focusing on natural and cultural material from Texas, the Southwest, and other regions related by natural history, heritage and climate. Temporary and permanent exhibitions in the social and natural sciences, and visual arts are presented in the main museum building on both the first and second floors. A new wing was constructed in 1995 to house the Diamond M Fine Art Collection (painting and sculpture of the American West; American illustration; jade, ivory, and porcelain objects; and Eskimo carvings). The Museum's collections number approximately two million objects.

San Antonio

San Antonio College - Visual Arts Instructional Gallery Ⓒᴬᴬ

Visual Arts and Technology Building, 950 Lewis Street
San Antonio, TX   78212-4299
Tel: (210)733-2894
Internet Address: http://www.accd.edu
Fine Arts Coordinator: Prof. Mark Pritchett

San Antonio College - Visual Arts Instructional Gallery, cont.

Admission: free.
Open: Monday to Thursday, 7am-9:45pm; Friday, 7am-4pm; Saturday, 9am-noon.
Closed: Legal Holidays.
Facilities: **Exhibition Area**.
Activities: **Temporary Exhibitions**.

The Gallery presents an annual schedule of approximately six temporary exhibitions by professional artists as well as the work of students.

University of Texas at San Antonio - UTSA Art Gallery ⓒ

6900 N. Loop 1604 West, San Antonio, TX 78249-0641
Tel: (214) 581-4391
Fax: (512) 691-4347
Internet Address: http://www.utsa.edu
Director: Mr. Ron Boling
Admission: free.
Established: 1982   *ADA Compliant:* Y
Open: Monday to Friday, 10am-4pm; Sunday, 2pm-4pm.
Closed: Academic Holidays.
Facilities: **Gallery**.
Activities: **Temporary Exhibitions**.
Publications: exhibition catalogues.

Changing exhibitions at the Gallery feature aspects of contemporary and historical art. Additionally, undergraduate works are displayed in the UTSA Satellite Space (open Friday-Sunday, noon-6pm). Occasional gallery talks, lectures, and poetry readings are presented for the UTSA and San Antonio communities.

San Marcos

Southwest Texas State University - University Art Gallery ⓒ

SW Texas State University, Art Building, University Drive
San Marcos, TX 78666
Tel: (512) 245-2611
Internet Address: http://www.swt.edu
Admission: free.
Open: Monday to Friday, 7:30am-4pm.
Facilities: **Exhibition Area**.
Activities: **Juried Exhibits**; **Temporary Exhibitions**.

The Gallery presents exhibitions of work in a variety of media and styles by prominent artists, faculty, alumni, and students. The Art Department also sponsors Works on Paper, an annual international juried competition and The Creative Summit Conference and Exhibition. Also of possible interest on campus, is the Special Collections Gallery located on the seventh floor of the Alkek Library.

Tyler

University of Texas-Tyler - Art Galleries ⓒ

3900 University Blvd., Tyler, TX 75799
Tel: (903) 566-7250
Internet Address: http://www.uttyler.edu/~art/
Director: Ms. Karen Gilliam
Admission: free.
Open: Monday to Friday, 9am-5pm.
Facilities: **Galleries** (2).
Activities: **Temporary Exhibitions**.

University of Texas-Tyler - Art Galleries, cont.

University of Texas-Tyler maintains two galleries: the Meadows Gallery located in the R. Don Cowan Fine and Performing Arts Center and the University Gallery. Exhibitions include work by professional artists, the annual National Works on Paper, selections from the Department of Art's permanent collection of prints and drawings, and an annual student competition and exhibition. The Department of Art's permanent collection includes prints and drawings by nationally recognized artists.

Waco

Baylor University - Martin Museum of Art and University Art Gallery ☺

Hooper-Schaefer Fine Arts Center, 1221 S. University Ave., Waco, TX   76706
Tel: (254) 710-1867
Fax: (254) 710-1566
Internet Address: http://www.baylor.edu/
Director, Martin Museum of Art: Dr. Heidi J. Hornik, Ph.D.
Admission: free.
Open: Tuesday to Friday, 10am-5pm; Saturday, noon-5pm; Baylor Theatre evening performances.
Facilities: **Exhibition Area**.
Activities: **Temporary Exhibitions**.

Located in the Hooper-Schaefer Fine Arts Center, both the Martin Museum of Art and the University Art Gallery, a teaching gallery, present changing exhibits of work by nationally and internationally recognized artists, as well as student and faculty shows.

Utah

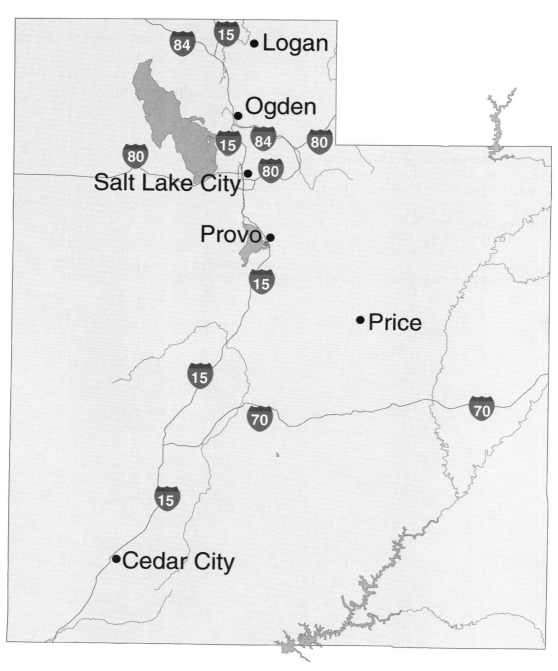

The number in parentheses following the city name indicates the number of museums/galleries in that municipality. If there is no number, one is understood. For example, in the text one listing would be found under each Utahan city.

Utah

Cedar City

Southern Utah University - Braithwaite Fine Arts Gallery

Southern Utah University, 351 W. Center St.
Cedar City, UT   84720
Tel: (435) 586-5432
Fax: (435) 865-8012
Internet Address: http://www.suu.edu/webpages/museumgaller
Acting Director: Ms. Lydia Johnson
Admission: free.
Attendance: 20,000   *Established:* 1976   *Membership:* Y   *ADA Compliant:* Y
Parking: Call for directions.
Open: **October to May**, Monday to Friday, noon-7pm.
          July to August, Monday to Saturday, noon-8:30pm.
Closed: Academic Holidays, Legal Holidays.
Facilities: **Exhibition Area** (2 galleries, total 2,000 square feet); **Reading Room**.
Activities: **Films**; **Guided Tours**; **Lectures**.

The Gallery is dedicated to providing varied visual arts experiences for a broad rural area of southern Utah. The Gallery mounts educational exhibits throughout the year, offers related programs, preserves and collects fine art, and serves as a resource center for the visual arts. The Braithwaite Gallery permanent collection consists of paintings, prints, photographs, sculpture, and weavings by artists of the Colorado Plateau and the Great Basin, including works by Bary Bastow, Allen Bishop, Maynard Dixon, Edith Hamlin, Julius Moessel, Paul Salisbury, and A.B. Wright. There is also a variety of public sculpture on the campus of SUU, including works by Frank Adams, Jerry Anderson, Jim DeVore, and Nolan Johnson.

Logan

Utah State University - Nora Eccles Harrison Museum of Art Ⓒᴬᴬ

Utah State University, 650 North 1100 East
Logan, UT   84322-4020
Tel: (801) 797-0163
Fax: (801) 797-3423
Internet Address: http://www.usu.edu
C.E.O. and Director: Mr. Steven W. Rosen
Admission: voluntary contribution.
Attendance: 24,000   *Established:* 1982
Membership: Y   *ADA Compliant:* Y
Parking: commercial adjacent to site.
Open: Tuesday, 10:30am-4:30pm;
          Wednesday, 10:30am-9pm;
          Thursday to Friday, 10:30am-4:30pm;
          Saturday to Sunday, 2pm-5pm.
Closed: Legal Holidays.
Facilities: **Architecture** (1982 design by Edward Larrabee Barnes, 23,000 square feet); **Food Services** Restaurant; **Gallery**; **Sculpture Plaza**; **Temporary Exhibition Space**.

John Ferren, *Untitled*, Nora Eccles Harrison Museum of Art collection. Photograph courtesy of Nora Eccles Harrison Museum of Art, Utah State University, Logan Utah.

Activities: **Guided Tours**; **Lectures**; **Temporary Exhibitions**.
Publications: "ARTSPECS"; brochures; exhibition catalogues; newsletter.

Specially designated exhibition spaces, including the Marie Eccles Caine Gallery, the Nora Eccles Harrison Ceramics Gallery, and the Boyden Collection of Native American Materials in the Chase Fine Arts Center; present continuing exhibitions of artworks from the permanent collection. The

Logan, Utah

Utah State University - Nora Eccles Harrison Museum of Art, cont.

Museum also mounts fourteen temporary exhibitions each year, including important traveling exhibitions. The permanent collection numbers 3,400 pieces and consists chiefly of 20th-century art by artists living or working in the western half of America. The 500-piece collection of the Museum's benefactor, Nora Eccles Treadwell Harrison, serves as the basis of an extensive ceramics collection, currently numbering over 1,200 works.

Ogden

Weber State University Art Gallery ⒸⒶⒶ

Art Department, 2001 University Circle
Ogden, UT   84408-2001
Tel: (801) 626-7689   *Fax:* (801) 626-6976
Internet Address: http://www.weber.edu/dova
Director: H. Barendse
Admission: free.
Established: 1960   *ADA Compliant:* Y
Open: **Academic Year**, Monday to Thursday, 9am-9pm; Friday, 9am-4pm.
Closed: Summer.
Facilities: **Gallery** (2,000 square feet).
Activities: **Education Programs** (undergraduate & graduate students); **Films**; **Lecture Series** (visiting artists).

The Gallery presents temporary exhibitions and a visiting artist lecture series, "Issues in Contemporary Art".

Price

College of Eastern Utah - Gallery East

451 East 400 North, Price, UT   84501
Tel: (801) 637-2120 *Ext:* 5297
Fax: (801) 637-4102
Internet Address: http://www.ceu.edu/Academics/DivisionB/FineArts/galleryeast
Department Chairman: Mr. James L. Young
Admission: free.
Attendance: 2,250   *Established:* 1937   *ADA Compliant:* Y
Parking: nearby lot with space for 200 cars.
Open: **September 15 to May**, Monday to Friday, 8:30am-5pm.
Closed: Legal Holidays.
Facilities: **Gallery** (3,000 square feet); **Library** (college).
Activities: **Education Programs**; **Gallery Talks** (on request); **Guided Tours** (on request); **Lectures** (7/year); **Temporary/Traveling Exhibitions**.

The Gallery presents temporary exhibitions.

Provo

Brigham Young University – Museum of Art ⒸⒶⒶ

N. Campus Drive, Provo, UT   84602-1400
Tel: (801) 378-2787   *Fax:* (801) 378-8222
Internet Address: http://www.byu.edu/moa
Director: Mr. James A. Mason
Admission: free.
Attendance: 100,000   *Established:* 1965   *ADA Compliant:* Y
Parking: in front of museum.
Open: Monday, 10am-9pm; Tuesday to Wednesday, 10am-6pm; Thursday, 10am-9pm; Friday, 10am-6pm; Saturday, noon-5pm.

Brigham Young University Museum of Art, cont.

Facilities: **Food Services** Café ((Mon-Fri, 11am-2:30pm)); **Library** (Mon-Fri, 10am-4pm; 378-8213); **Print Study Room** (Mon-Fri, 10am-4pm; 378-8272); **Tours** Mini-Tours, (Thurs, 11:30am-noon).

Activities: **Education Programs** (undergraduate, graduate and adult); **Gallery Talks**; **Lectures**; **Temporary Exhibitions**; **Traveling Exhibitions**.

Publications: exhibition catalogues.

The Museum presents changing exhibitions drawn from the permanent collection and elsewhere. Also of possible interest on campus are the Brimhill Gallery, located in the George H. Brimhill Building; Gallery 303, located in F303, Harris Fine arts Center (378-3882); and the B.F. Larsen Gallery, also located in the Harris fine arts Center.

Salt Lake City

University of Utah - Utah Museum of Fine Arts

University of Utah
370 South 1530 East South Campus Drive
Salt Lake City, UT 84112

Tel: (801) 581-7332

Fax: (801) 585-5198

Internet Address: http://www.utah.edu/umfa

Director and Curator: E.F. Sanguinetti

Admission: free.

Attendance: 120,000   *Established:* 1951

Membership: Y   *ADA Compliant:* Y

Parking: free on site.

Open: Monday to Friday, 10am-5pm;
        Saturday to Sunday, noon-5pm.

Closed: Legal Holidays.

Facilities: **Auditorium** (450 seat); **Library**; **Shop** (gifts, stained glass, lacquerware, jewelry, folk art).

Activities: **Concerts**; **Education Programs** (children and undergraduate); **Films**; **Gallery Talks**; **Guided Tours**; **Lectures**; **Temporary Exhibitions**; **Traveling Exhibitions**.

Publications: collection catalogue, "Selected Works of the Museum of Fine Arts"; exhibition catalogues.

Ambrosius Benson, *Elegant Couples Dancing in a Landscape*, 1495-1550. Gift of Howard J. and Jenny Creer Stoddard in honor of John Preston and Mary Elizabeth Brockbank Creer, Utah Museum of Fine Arts. Photograph courtesy of Utah Museum of Fine Arts, University of Utah, Salt Lake City, Utah.

The Utah Museum of Fine Arts, University of Utah, is Utah's primary cultural resource in the visual arts. It is the state's only public institution with the goal of collecting and exhibiting a general collection of art objects selected for quality and representation of the principal art styles and periods of civilization. The Museum's collections have long since outgrown available gallery space. Preliminary plans for a new wing with additional galleries and other required facilities have been completed. Meanwhile, the permanent collection is subject to regular rotation. The Museum presents approximately fifteen changing exhibitions each year drawn from other museums here and abroad. Temporary exhibitions are selected to complement or expand the permanent collections. Temporary exhibits present material not otherwise available to the public, or they respond to current events (Bicentennial of the French Revolution, Quinquecentennial of the discovery of America, Soviet Art, Contemporary Chinese Painting, etc.) The permanent collection consists of over 10,000 objects. A partial overview of the Museum's collections is available through the following list of galleries: the Jennie Creer Stoddard Entrance Gallery, 17th- and 18th-century French works of art; the Helen Druke Shaw Gallery, Dutch and Flemish art; the Natacha Rambova Collection (Gallery 6), Egyptian artifacts; the Bert G. Clift Gallery, Chinese porcelains; the LaReta Creer Madsen Kump Gallery, English art; the William H. and Wilma T. Gibson Gallery, Italian art; the Herbert I. and Elsa Bamberger Michael Gallery, late 18th- and early 19th- century American art; the E. Parry and Peggy Chatterton Thomas Gallery, art of Utah and the West; Gallery 2, traditional arts of Africa, Oceania, Indonesia, and the Americas; the Beatrice M. Hansen Gallery, decorative arts; and the Sculpture Court.

Vermont

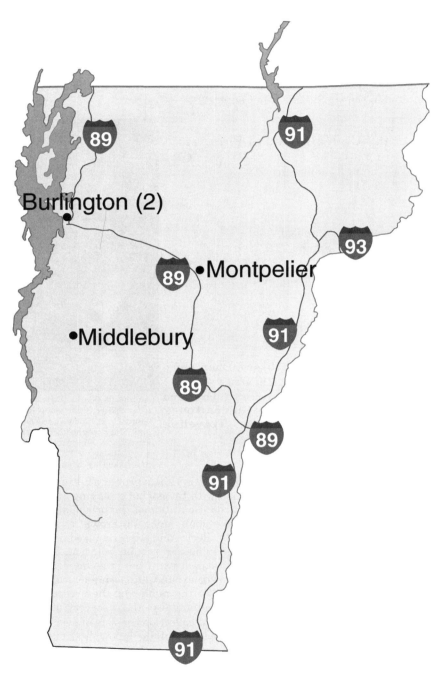

The number in parentheses following the city name indicates the number of museums/galleries in that municipality. If there is no number, one is understood. For example, in the text two listings would be found under Burlington and one listing under Montpelier.

Vermont

Burlington

University of Vermont - Francis Colburn Gallery ⓒ

University of Vermont, Williams Hall, University Place Road
Burlington, VT   05405
Tel: (802) 656-2014
Fax: (802) 656-2064
Internet Address: http://www.uvm.edu/~colburn/index.html
Admission: free.
Established: 1975
Parking: visitor's pay parking lot on College Street.
Open: **September to May**, Monday to Friday, 9am-5pm.
Closed: June to August.
Facilities: **Galleries.**
Activities: **Education Programs**; **Films**; **Gallery Talks**; **Lectures**; **Temporary Exhibitions**.
Publications: exhibition announcements.

The Francis Colburn Gallery, located on the second floor of Williams Hall, is a teaching gallery with exhibitions by visiting artists, faculty and honor students. Occasionally there are talks connected with the current exhibition. All shows are during the academic year and are primarily directed toward the student community.

University of Vermont - Robert Hull Fleming Museum ⓒ

University of Vermont, 61 Colchester Ave.
Burlington, VT   05405
Tel: (802) 656-2090
Fax: (802) 656-8059
Internet Address: http://www.uvm.edu/%7euvmiac/fleming.html
Director: Ms. Ann Porter
Admission: suggested contribution: adult-$3.00, student-$2.00, senior-$2.00.
Established: 1931   *Membership:* Y   *ADA Compliant:* Y
Parking: metered lot on site.
Open: **Labor Day to April 30**, Tuesday to Friday, 9am-4pm; Saturday to Sunday, 1pm-5pm.
          May to Labor Day, Tuesday to Friday, noon-4pm; Saturday to Sunday, 1pm-5pm.
Closed: Legal Holidays.
Facilities: **Architecture** (designed by McKim, Mead & White, 1931); **Auditorium**; **Library** (2,000 volumes); **Museum Shop** (books, educational items for children, jewelry); **Reading Room**.
Activities: **Arts Festival**; **Concerts**; **Films**; **Gallery Talks**; **Guided Tours** (groups, reserve in advance); **Lectures**; **Temporary Exhibitions**; **Traveling Exhibitions**.
Publications: brochures; calendar; exhibition catalogues; posters.

Located on the University of Vermont campus, the Museum houses Vermont's most comprehensive collection of art and anthropological artifacts. Ongoing exhibits from the permanent collection include displays of African, American, ancient Egyptian, Asian, European, and Middle Eastern art, and paintings by 20th-century Vermont artists.

Middlebury

Middlebury College Museum of Art ⓒ (MCMA)

Middlebury College, Center for the Arts
Route 30 (½ mile from junction with Route 7)
Middlebury, VT   05753-6177
Tel: (802) 443-5000   *Ext:* 5007
Fax: (802) 443-2069
Internet Address: http://www.middlebury.edu/~museum
Director: Mr. Richard H. Saunders

Middlebury College Museum of Art, cont.

Admission: free.

Attendance: 12,000   *Established:* 1968   *Membership:* Y

ADA Compliant: Y

Parking: free lot behind building.

Open: Tuesday to Friday, 10am-5pm;
Saturday to Sunday, noon-5pm.

Closed: Academic Holidays, last 2 weeks in Aug.

Facilities: **Architecture** (postmodern, 1992 design by Hardy Holzman Pfeiffer Associates); **Food Services** Café (adjacent to entrance, light fare); **Galleries** (5, total 4,800 square feet); **Shop** (catalogues, posters, cards).

Activities: **Films**; **Gallery Talks**; **Guided Tours** (groups 10+, reserve in advance (802) 388-3711 x 5007, fee); **Lectures**; **Traveling Exhibitions**.

Publications: annual report; brochures (semi-annual); exhibition catalogues; newsletter (semi-annual).

Circle of the Antimenes painter. Greek, attic black figure amphora, height 15½ inches, c. 539-520 BC. Purchase of the Friends of Art Acquisition Fund, The Christian A. Johnson Memorial Fund, the Walter Cerf Acquisition Fund and the Memorial Fund, Middlebury College Museum of Art. Photograph courtesy of Middlebury College Museum of Art, Middlebury, Vermont.

Located in the Middlebury College Center for the Arts, the Museum houses the permanent collection of the college as well as the Christian A. Johnson Memorial Gallery, a space designated for traveling exhibitions. Since its inception, the Museum has endeavored to be a forum for the visual arts in the college community and a catalyst for widely varied forms of artistic expression and criticism. In addition, it has strived to create a rich and diverse collection that is an integral component in the teaching of art and art history. The Museum displays works from the permanent collection and special exhibitions throughout the year. A senior studio art majors show is scheduled each spring. The collection of several thousand objects ranges from antiquities through contemporary art and includes distinguished collections of Cypriot pottery, 19th-century European and American sculpture, and contemporary prints.

Montpelier

Vermont College - T.W. Wood Gallery and Arts Center

Vermont College, College Hall
Montpelier, VT 05602

Tel: (802) 828-8743

Fax: (802) 828-8855

Internet Address:
   http://www.norwich.edu/vermontcollege

Director: Mr. Phillip A. Robertson

Admission: fee-$2.00.

Attendance: 7,000   *Established:* 1897

Membership: Y   *ADA Compliant:* Y

Parking: on street.

Open: Tuesday to Sunday, noon-4pm.

Closed: Legal Holidays.

Facilities: **Architecture** (19th century college campus); **Museum Shop.**

Activities: **Classes**; **Films**; **Guided Tours**; **Lectures**; **Traveling Exhibitions**.

Thomas Waterman Wood, *A Southern Cornfield*, 1861, oil on canvas, 28 x 40 inches. T.W. Wood Art Gallery. Photograph courtesy of T.W. Wood Gallery and Art Center, Montpelier, Vermont.

In 1895, the portrait and genre painter, Thomas Waterman Wood (1823-1903) contributed his personal art collection to the citizens of his home town, Montpelier, and in 1897 the T.W. Wood Gallery was opened.   In addition to his own work, his collection included the work of his contemporaries Asher B. Durand, J.G. Brown, W.H. Beard, and Alexander Wyant.   Paintings from the Works Progress Administration, completed during the depression era, are an especially interesting element

Vermont College - T.W. Wood Gallery and Arts Center, cont.

of the Gallery's holdings and include the work of artists such as Yasuo Kunioshi, Reginald Marsh, and Joseph Stella. The Gallery also presents contemporary shows by local and regional artists and sculptors and national exhibits.

Virginia

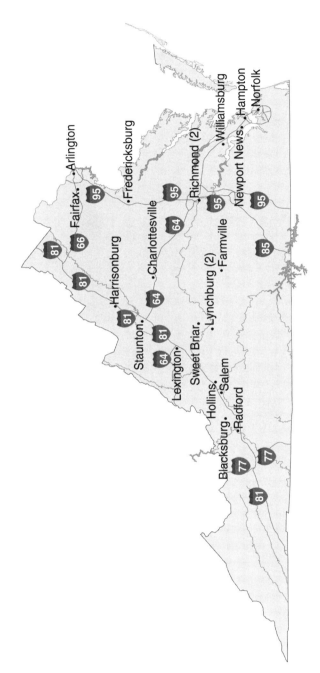

The number in parentheses following the city name indicates the number of museums/galleries in that municipality. If there is no number, one is understood. For example, in the text two listings would be found under Richmond and one listing under Farmville.

Virginia

Arlington

Marymount University - Barry Art Gallery ⓒᴬᴬ

Reinsch Library, 2807 N. Glebe Road, Arlington, VA 22207-4299
Tel: (703) 284-1561
Internet Address: http://www.mu.marymount.edu
Curator: Ms. Judy Bass
Open: Monday to Thursday, 10am-8pm; Friday to Saturday, 10am-6pm.
Facilities: **Exhibition Area.**
Activities: **Temporary Exhibitions.**

The Gallery offers a schedule of temporary exhibitions, including an annual juried Student Art and Design Exhibition.

Blacksburg

Virginia Polytechnic Institute - Armory Art Gallery ⓒᴬᴬ

201 Draper Road, Blacksburg, VA 24061-7623
Tel: (540) 231-5200
Internet Address: http://www.art.vt.edu
Admission: free.
Open: Tuesday to Friday, noon-5pm; Saturday, noon-4pm.

Formerly a gymnasium, the Armory Art Gallery presents work by students, faculty, and artists of regional and national reputation. Also of possible interest on campus is the XYZ Gallery, which shows work by students and local artists.

Charlottesville

University of Virginia - Bayly Art Museum ⓒᴬᴬ

Thomas H. Bayly Memorial Building, Rugby Road
Charlottesville, VA 22903-2427
Tel: (804) 924-3592   *Fax:* (804) 924-6321
Internet Address: http://www.virginia.edu/~bayly/bayly.html
Director: Ms. Jill Hartz
Admission: free.
Attendance: 30,000   *Established:* 1935   *Membership:* Y   *ADA Compliant:* Y
Parking: behind museum (limited) and university visitor lots.
Open: Tuesday to Sunday, 1pm-5pm.
Closed: Thanksgiving Day, Christmas Day to New Year's Day.
Facilities: **Exhibition Area**; **Shop.**
Activities: **Concerts**; **Gallery Talks**; **Guided Tours** (group tours by appointment, (804) 924-7458); **Permanent Exhibits**; **Temporary Exhibitions** (8-10/year); **Traveling Exhibitions.**
Publications: exhibition catalogues (occasional); newsletter (semi-annual).

The Bayly Art Museum at the University of Virginia exhibits art from around the world dating from ancient times to the present. Each year the Museum presents eight to ten temporary exhibitions drawn both from the Museum's collections and from a multitude of other sources nationwide. Installations of the permanent collection rotate throughout the year. Extensive programming, including lectures and symposia conducted by visiting scholars and artists, and publications, from brochures to major catalogues, enhance the critical interpretation offered by the exhibitions. The Museum's permanent collection is wide ranging. The Western tradition is represented by painting and sculpture of the 15th- to 19th-centuries with emphasis on American art and art from the Age of Thomas Jefferson (1775-1825). An important collection of old master and later prints spanning five centuries continues to be augmented. Highlights of the collection of 20th-century painting, sculpture and works on paper include American figurative art and photography. Art from ancient Mediterranean, pre-Columbian, American Indian, Asian, and African cultures affords Museum visitors access to a rich variety of human cultural achievements.

Fairfax

George Mason University - University Fine Arts Galleries ⓒ

Center Gallery: Atrium of G.W. Johnson Center
Gallery FAB: Fine Arts Bldg., Room B104
Fairfax, VA 22030
Tel: (703) 993-1010
Internet Address: http://www.gmu.edu/gallery
Director: Mr. Kirby Malone
Admission: free.
Parking: Visitor Parking garage off Mason Drive.
Open: Weekdays, 9am-5pm.
Facilities: **Galleries** (2).
Activities: **Temporary Exhibitions** (6/year).

Managed by GMA's Institute for the Arts, the University maintains two gallery spaces: the Center Gallery, located in the main atrium of the George W. Johnson Center and Gallery FAB, located in the adjacent Fine Arts building, Room B104. The galleries present the work of outside artists, an annual student exhibition at the end of the spring semester, and a biennial faculty exhibition. The campus also has several outdoor sculpture sites.

Farmville

Longwood College - Longwood Center for the Visual Arts ⓒ (LCVA)

Longwood College, 129 N. Main St., Farmville, VA 23901
Tel: (804) 395-2206   *Fax:* (804) 392-6441
TDDY: (800) 828-1120
Internet Address:
   http://web.lwc.edu/administrative/visualart/index.htm
Director: Dr. Georgia Coopersmith
Admission: free.
Attendance: 8,000   *Established:* 1978
Membership: Y   *ADA Compliant:* Y
Open: Monday to Saturday, 11am-4:30pm.
Closed: Memorial Day, Thanksgiving Day, Christmas Day.
Facilities: **Galleries** (3).
Activities: **Education Programs**; **Gallery Talks**; **Lectures**; **Traveling Exhibitions**.
Publications: exhibition catalogues.

Nell Blaine, *Sunlit Room with Figure*, 1963, oil on canvas, 36 x 25 inches. Longwood College purchase for the Contemporary Virginia Artists Collection. Photograph courtesy of the Longwood Center for the Visual Arts, Farmville, Virginia.

The Longwood Center for the Visual Arts is the art museum of Longwood College. Each year the Center presents six to eight exhibitions drawn both from its collections and from other sources accompanied by related publications and education programs. Collections focus on Virginia art and crafts and 19th-century American art. Initiated in 1951, the Virginia Collection of Contemporary Artists is the cornerstone of the Center, and the focus of new acquisitions and exhibitions. Also of note is the collection of paintings by the 19th-century American portrait painter Thomas Sully and his contemporaries. Additional artwork and art objects from around the world are collected and maintained in the Study Collection.

Fredericksburg

Mary Washington College Galleries ⓒ

College Ave., Fredericksburg, VA 22401-5358
Tel: (540) 654-2120   *Fax:* (540) 654-1070   *TDDY:* (540) 654-1104
Internet Address: http://www.mwc.edu/gallery/

Mary Washington College Galleries, cont.

Director: Dr. Forrest McGill

Admission: free.

Attendance: 5,000   *Established:* 1956   *ADA Compliant:* Y

Parking: free in area designated for gallery in lot on College Ave..

Open: **During Exhibitions,**
Monday/Wednesday/Friday, 10am-4pm; Saturday to Sunday, 1pm-4pm.

Closed: New Year's Day, Thanksgiving Day, Christmas Day.

Facilities: **Galleries** (2).

Activities: **Education Programs; Guided Tours; Lectures; Temporary Exhibitions.**

The Ridderhof Martin Gallery (College Avenue at Seacobeck Street) hosts exhibitions brought in from museums around the country, or drawn from the permanent collection. The duPont Gallery (College Avenue at Thornton Street) features painting, drawing, sculpture, photography, ceramics, and textiles by art faculty and students as well as other contemporary artists. The permanent collection of over 5,000 works is strongest in mid-20th-century and Asian art. Milton Avery, Nicholas P. Brigante, Hans Burkhardt, Sue Coe, Werner Drewes, Arshile Gorky, Karl Knaths, William Lathrop, Helen Lundeberg, Roger Mühl, Robert Andrew Parker, Ben Shahn. William Thon, Theo Tobiasse, John Twachtman, and Andy Warhol are among the artists represented in the permanent collection. The College also holds extensive collections of the artwork and personal papers of artists Phyllis Ridderhof Martin and Margaret Sutton.

Hampton

Hampton University Museum ©

Hampton University, Huntington Building
Hampton, VA   23668

Tel: (757) 727-5308

Fax: (757) 727-5170

Internet Address:
http://www.hamptonu.edu/other/museum/index.htm

Director: Ms. Jeanne Zeidler

Admission: free.

Attendance: 50,000   *Established:* 1868

Membership: Y   *ADA Compliant:* Y

Parking: free on site.

Open: Monday to Friday, 8am-5pm;
Saturday to Sunday, noon-4pm.

Closed: Legal Holidays, Academic Holidays.

Facilities: **Exhibition Area** (12,000 square feet); **Library** (1,000 volumes); **Shop** (handcrafted ethnic works of art, books, prints).

Activities: **Education Programs; Gallery Talks; Guided Tours** (by appointment); **Lectures; Permanent Exhibits; Temporary Exhibitions; Traveling Exhibitions.**

Henry Ossawa Tanner, *The Banjo Lesson*, 1893, oil on canvas. Hampton University Museum. Photograph courtesy of Hampton University Museum, Hampton, Virginia.

Publications: journal, "International Review of African American Art" (quarterly); monographs.

The Hampton University Museum is the oldest African American museum in the United States and one of the oldest museums in Virginia. The Museum has over 12,000 square feet of exhibition space, including permanent galleries for the fine arts collection. Its holdings feature over 9,000 objects such as traditional African, Native American, Asian and Pacific Island art; fine arts; and objects relating to the history of the University. The fine arts collection consists of some 1,500 paintings, works on paper, and sculpture. The Museum's holdings in the art of the Harlem Renaissance period are among the finest in the nation. The Museum also has a significant collection of works by 19th-century artist Henry Ossawa Tanner, including the "The Banjo Lesson" (1893). Artists represented in the holdings also include Ron Adams, Edward Mitchell Bannister, Romare Bearden, Dr. John T. Biggers, Elizabeth Catlett, Aaron Douglas, Robert Scott Duncanson, Joseph Gilliard, Persis Jennings, Joshua Johnson,

Hampton, Virginia

Hampton University Museum, cont.

Malvin Gray Johnson, Sargent Claude Johnson, William Henry Johnson, Lois Mailou Jones, Gwendolyn Knight, Jacob Lawrence, Dr. Samella Sanders Lewis, Archibald Motley, Jr., Charles Ethan Porter, Augusta Savage, Albert Alexander Smith, James Lesesne Wells, and Charles White. The African collection consists of approximately 3,500 objects representing nearly 100 ethnic groups and cultures, including one of the finest collections of Kuba art in the world. The Native American collection features over 1,600 objects from approximately 93 Native American tribes.

Harrisonburg

James Madison University - Art Galleries ⓒⒶⒶ

Sawhill Gallery: Duke Hall
New Image Gallery: Zirkle House, 800 S. Main St.
Harrisonburg, VA 22807
Tel: (540) 568-6407   *Fax:* (540) 568-6598
Internet Address: http://www.jmu.edu
Coordinator: Mr. Stuart Downs
Admission: free.
Attendance: 10,000   *Established:* 1967   *ADA Compliant:* Y
Open: September to April,
          Monday to Friday, 10:30am-4:30pm; Saturday to Sunday, 1:30pm-4:30pm.
Facilities: **Galleries.**
Activities: **Temporary Exhibitions.**

Sawhill Gallery, located in Duke Hall, features art of international, national and regional interest. New Image Gallery in Zirkle House focuses on contemporary photography. The Zirkle House Student Galleries present the work of JMU graduate and undergraduate students.

Hollins

Hollins University - Art Gallery ⓒⒶⒶ

7916 Williamson Road, Hollins, VA 24020
Tel: (540) 362-6468
Internet Address: http://www.hollins.edu/html/art/artexhibit/artexhibit.htm
Admission: free.
Open: Monday to Friday, 9am-9pm; Saturday to Sunday, 1pm-4pm.
Facilities: **Exhibition Area.**
Activities: **Temporary Exhibitions** (9/year).

Located in the Art Annex, the gallery presents exhibitions of work by regionally and nationally recognized artists, as well as by faculty and students. Exhibitions are also mounted in the Ballator Gallery, located in the Moody Center.

Lexington

Washington and Lee University - The Reeves Center ⓒⒶⒶ

Washington and Lee University, Back Campus, Lexington, VA 24450
Tel: (540) 463-8744   *Fax:* (540) 463-8741
Internet Address: http://liberty.uc.wlu.edu
Director: Mr. Thomas V. Litzenburg, Jr.
Admission: free.
Attendance: 5,000   *Established:* 1982   *ADA Compliant:* Y
Open: Monday to Friday, 9am-4:30pm; Saturday to Sunday, by appointment.
Closed: New Year's Eve to New Year's Day, Thanksgiving Day, Christmas Eve to Christmas Day.
Facilities: **Architecture** (1840 Greek Revival house and Palladian-style pavilion); **Exhibit Spaces**
          (2 - 3,500 square feet); **Library** (900 volumes).
Activities: **Education Programs; Guided Tours; Temporary Exhibitions; Traveling Exhibitions.**

388

Washington and Lee University - The Reeves Center, cont.

Publications: catalogues.

The Reeves Center presents loan exhibitions and temporary exhibitions of objects from its own collection, which includes Chinese ceramics, European ceramics, and 17th- to 19th-century paintings. Also of possible interest on campus is the duPont Gallery (open Mon-Fri, 9am-5pm during academic year; tel 463-8861). The Gallery presents temporary exhibitions of work by contemporary artists of regional and national reputation. Student work is also presented.

Lynchburg

Lynchburg College - Daura Gallery ⓒ⁴⁴

Dillard Fine Arts Center (off College St.)
Lynchburg, VA 24504
Tel: (804) 544-8343
Internet Address: http://www.lynchburg.edu/daura/
Director: Ms. Barbara Rothermel
Admission: free.
Established: 1974
Open: Monday to Friday, 9am-2pm; Sunday, 1pm-5pm.
Closed: Academic Holidays.
Facilities: **Exhibition Area.**
Activities: **Gallery Talks; Guided Tours** (by appointment, reserve two weeks in advance); **Lectures; Temporary Exhibitions.**

Located in the Dillard Fine Arts Center on the campus of Lynchburg College, the Gallery presents changing exhibitions of works drawn from its permanent collection and from public and private sources and features a permanent exhibit of the work of Catalan-American artist Pierre Daura. Established in 1974, the Gallery was dedicated in 1990 to the memory of Daura, former chairman of the Art Department, and his wife Louise Blair Daura. The permanent collection consists of more than 1,000 paintings, sculpture, and works on paper focusing on Virginia artists, including 150 works by the Dauras.

Randolph Macon Woman's College - Maier Museum of Art ⓒ⁴⁴

Randolph-Macon Woman's College
2500 Rivermont Ave.
Lynchburg, VA 24503
Tel: (804) 947-8136
Fax: (804) 947-8726
Internet Address: http://www.rmwc.edu/Maier
Director: Ms. Sarah Cash
Admission: free.
Attendance: 6,000   *Established:* 1920
Membership: Y   *ADA Compliant:* Y
Parking: free on site (limited).
Open: **late August to late May,**
        Tuesday to Sunday, 1pm-5pm.
        late May to late August,
        Wednesday to Sunday, 1pm-4pm.
Closed: Academic Holidays,
        late December to mid-January.

George Bellows, *Men of the Docks*, 1912, oil on canvas, 45 x 63½ inches. Maier Museum of Art, Randolph-Macon Woman's College. Photograph courtesy of Maier Museum of Art, Randolph-Macon Woman's College, Lynchburg, Virginia.

Facilities: **Galleries** (6); **Shop** (catalogues, cards).
Activities: **Concerts; Education Programs; Gallery Talks; Guided Tours** (group tours reserve in advance); **Lectures; Temporary Exhibitions.**
Publications: collection catalogue, "American Art: American Vision"; exhibition catalogues (2-3/year); newsletter (semi-annual).

Lynchburg, Virginia

Randolph Macon Woman's College - Maier Museum of Art, cont.

The Maier Museum of Art at Randolph-Macon Woman's College houses a growing collection of over 2,000 objects, with a focus on 19th- and 20th-century American paintings and works on paper. The Museum serves the academic community as well as the general public and offers changing exhibitions, permanent displays and special programs, including lectures and concerts. Virtually unique among college and university collections for its exclusive focus on American art, the Maier Museum's strengths lie in American impressionism, as seen in paintings such as Childe Hassam's "Early Evening after Snowfall", and early-20th-century realism, exemplified by Bellows's "Men of the Docks". Works by woman artists such as Marion Boyd Allen's "Portrait of Anna Vaughn Hyatt" play important roles in the collection. Early American portraiture is represented by Gilbert Stuart's "Portrait of Mrs. Polly Hooper", and among Hudson River School landscapes is John Frederick Kensett's "On the Connecticut Shore". Also included are examples by largely untrained painters, such as Edward Hicks's "Peaceable Kingdom", and paintings by artists more formally trained, such as Georgia O'Keeffe, Thomas Cole, Thomas Eakins, Robert Henri, Winslow Homer, Edward Hopper, George Inness, and James McNeill Whistler. A large collection of paintings and works on paper by Arthur B. Davies make the Museum an important center for the study of his works. Other works on paper include selections by Mary Cassatt, Childe Hassam, John Marin, and Maurice Prendergast. Prints by Sally Mann and William Eggleston number among a small, but growing, collection of American photographs.

Newport News

Christopher Newport University - Falk Art Gallery ©

University Place (off Route 60), Newport News, VA 23606
Tel: (757) 594-7089
Internet Address: http://www.cnu.edu
Art Department Chairman: Dr. Rita C. Hubbard
Admission: free.
Open: Monday to Friday, 1pm-4pm.
Facilities: **Exhibition Area**.
Activities: **Temporary Exhibitions**.

The Gallery presents seven temporary exhibitions each year.

Norfolk

Old Dominion University - University Gallery ©

765 Granby St., Norfolk, VA 23507
Tel: (757) 683-2843   *Fax:* (757) 683-5923
Internet Address: http://iris.arts.odu.edu:443/artleague/artgallery.html
C.E.O. and Director: Mr. David Johnson
Admission: free.
Attendance: 2,100   *Established:* 1971   *Membership:* Y
Open: Saturday to Sunday, noon-4pm.
Closed: Academic Holidays.
Activities: **Lectures**.
Publications: newsletter; posters.

The Gallery presents a schedule of temporary exhibitions.

Radford

Radford University Galleries ©

200 Powell Hall, Adams St., Radford, VA 24142
Tel: (703) 831-5754   *Fax:* (540) 831-6799
Internet Address: http://www.runet.edu/~museum
Director: Ms. Anna Fariello

Radford University Galleries, cont.

Admission: free.

Attendance: 6,000   *Established:* 1985   *Membership:* Y   *ADA Compliant:* Y

Parking: free on street and metered parking in lot off Norwood St..

Open: **September to June**,
 Tuesday to Wednesday, 10am-4pm; Thursday, 10am-4pm & 6pm-9pm; Friday, 10am-4pm; Sunday, noon-4pm.
 Summer, Tuesday to Friday, noon-6pm; Sunday, noon-6pm.

Closed: Legal Holidays.

Facilities: **Exhibit Space** (2,000 square feet); **Sculpture Garden** (16,000 square feet).

Activities: **Lectures**; **Temporary Exhibitions**.

Publications: brochures; exhibition catalogues.

The Radford University Galleries present an extensive schedule of exhibitions and events. A traveling exhibition of the works of Dorothy Gillespie from the permanent collection is scheduled on national tour through 2001. The Flossie Martin and Spotlight Galleries and the Burdé Sculpture Courtyard are located at Powell Hall, one block off Norwood Street on Adams Street. Exhibits are also regularly scheduled at the Bondurant Center for the Arts, 1115 Norwood Street (open Mon-Fri, 9am-8pm; Sat 10am-6pm). On-going exhibits of student work may be viewed in Tyler and Muse Halls.

Richmond

University of Richmond - Marsh Art Gallery ⓒ₄₄

University of Richmond
George M. Modlin Center for the Arts, Keller Road
Richmond, VA   23173

Tel: (804) 289-8276

Fax: (804) 287-6006

Internet Address: http://chemweb.urich.edu/~marshart

Director: Mr. Richard Waller

Admission: free.

Attendance: 12,000   *Established:* 1968

ADA Compliant: Y

Parking: ample free parking in Center parking lot.

Open: **September to April**, Tuesday to Saturday, 1pm-5pm.
 May to August, Thursday to Saturday, 1pm-5pm.

Closed: Spring Break, Fall Break, Thanksgiving Week, Christmas Day to New Year's Day.

Facilities: **Exhibit Space**; **Shop**.

Activities: **Concerts**; **Education Programs** (undergraduate and graduate students); **Films**; **Gallery Talks**; **Guided Tours** (reserve in advance); **Lectures**; **Temporary Exhibitions**; **Traveling Exhibitions**.

Reginald Marsh, *Star Burlesk*, 1933, etching, 11¾ x 8¾ inches. I. Webb Surratt, Jr. Print Collection, Marsh Art Gallery. Photograph by Katherine Wetzel, courtesy of Marsh Art Gallery, University of Richmond, Richmond, Virginia.

Publications: brochures; exhibition catalogues; posters.

The Gallery offers a schedule of temporary exhibitions, including an annual juried student exhibition. The Gallery also organizes the National Works on Paper Biennial juried exhibition.

Virginia Commonwealth University - Anderson Gallery, School of the Arts ⓒ₄₄

Virginia Commonwealth University, 907½ W. Franklin St
Richmond, VA   23284-2514

Tel: (804) 828-1522   *Fax:* (804) 828-8585   *TDDY:* (804) 367-0100

Internet Address: http://www.vcu.edu/artweb/gallery

Acting Director: Mr. Charles F. Bleick

Admission: free.

Attendance: 14,000   *Established:* 1969   *Membership:* Y

Virginia Commonwealth University - Anderson Gallery, School of the Arts, cont.

Parking: metered on street.

Open: Tuesday to Friday, 10am-5pm; Saturday to Sunday, 1pm-5pm.

Closed: Academic Holidays, Legal Holidays.

Facilities: **Exhibition Space** (6 spaces, total 10,000 square feet); **Shop**.

Activities: **Films**; **Gallery Talks**; **Guided Tours**; **Lectures**; **Temporary Exhibitions**; **Traveling Exhibitions**.

Publications: exhibition catalogues; posters.

Exhibitions at the Gallery focus on contemporary art of national and international importance. Similar to other contemporary art museums, the AG concentrates on emerging art and new ideas, showing artists who have not been presented in major venues and creating a forum for ideas that have not yet been fully appreciated. The Museum concentrates on showing work that challenges and expands concepts in art. Exhibitions embrace an extremely diverse range of media from glass to video. Some exhibitions show works that are not traditionally shown in museums, such as fashion, interior design, and graphic design, or focus on works that push the boundaries of the museum environment, such as installations and electronic media. Annual faculty focus exhibitions present works by School of the Arts professors in fine art and design. Students exhibit in two large annual shows and in MFA thesis exhibitions. With more than 2,000 objects, the Anderson Gallery's collection is available for teaching and research for the School of the Arts and VCU as well as for loan to other museums and art institutions. The areas of greatest concentration are prints, photography, drawings, paintings and sculptures. The print collection encompasses examples from the 15th century through the present, including works by Albrecht Dürer, Henri Matisse, Rembrandt van Rijn, and Vincent van Gogh, as well as contemporary works, including pieces by Andy Warhol and David Salle. Photography is strongly represented, including works by Larry Clark, Thomas Florschuetz, and Garry Winogrand. The AG owns works by contemporary artists Ross Blechner and Francesc Torres and many works by lesser-known artists, including former members of the School of the Arts faculty and local artists. Works of folk art include examples by Miles Carpenter and Sister Gertrude Morgan. The AG also has a collection of Asian art that is an excellent resource for the Department of Art History and supplements the extensive Asian art holdings of the Virginia Museum.

Salem

Roanoke College - Olin Hall Galleries ⓒ⁴⁴

F.W. Olin Hall, Thompson Memorial Blvd., Salem, VA   24153

Tel: (540) 375-2354

Internet Address: http://www2.roanoke.edu/finearts/Galleries/main.htm

Director: Ms. Linda Atkinson

Admission: free.

Open: Daily, 1pm-4pm.

Closed: Legal Holidays, Academic Holidays.

Facilities: **Galleries**.

Activities: **Temporary Exhibitions**.

The Olin Gallery, supplemented by The Smoyer Gallery and Corridor Gallery, present traveling and invitational exhibits along with the rotational display of the College's permanent collection. Each spring, graduating studio and art history majors mount an exhibition in the Olin Gallery. Also of possible interest are several works by the illustrator, Walter Biggs, displayed on the main floor in the Fintel library.

Staunton

Mary Baldwin College - Hunt Gallery ⓒ⁴⁴

Market and Vine Sts., Staunton, VA   24401

Tel: (540) 887-7196

Internet Address: http://www.mbc.edu

Director: Mr. Paul Ryan

Admission: free.

Mary Baldwin College - Hunt Gallery, cont.

Attendance: 1,100 *Established:* 1842 *ADA Compliant:* Y
Parking: parking lot behind Hunt Hall.
Open: **September to May**, Monday to Friday, 9am-5pm.
Facilities: **Gallery**.
Activities: **Education Programs** (adults); **Lectures**; **Temporary Exhibitions** .

The Gallery presents temporary exhibitions of work by regionally and nationally recognized artists.

Sweet Briar

Sweet Briar College Art Galleries ©

Sweet Briar College, Sweet Briar, VA 24595
Tel: (804) 381-6248
Fax: (804) 381-6173
Internet Address: http://www.artgallery.sbc.edu/
Director: Ms. Rebecca Massie Lane
Admission: free.
Attendance: 4,000 *Established:* 1901 *Membership:* Y *ADA Compliant:* Y
Parking: free on site.
Open: **Pannell**, Monday to Thursday, noon-9:30; Friday to Sunday, noon-5pm.
        Babcock, Daily, 9am-9pm.
Closed: Academic Holidays.
Facilities: **Food Services** Restaurant; **Library**; **Sculpture Garden**; **Shop**.
Activities: **Guided Tours**; **Traveling Exhibitions**).
Publications: exhibition catalogues; newsletter.

The Sweet Briar College Art Gallery is dedicated to the enrichment of cultural life on campus, in the community, and throughout central Virginia. The Gallery program supports the educational mission of Sweet Briar College through its active education program and through the collecting, preservation, and formal exhibition of works of art at the three campus galleries: Pannell, Babcock, and Benedict. Centrally located, the Pannell Center houses the Sweet Briar Gallery and the College's permanent art collection. As a dynamic learning tool, the gallery supports diverse hands-on learning projects throughout the year. Students help organize and publicize exhibits, learn curatorial practice, work as docents in the gallery, or undertake research. The Babock Gallery, located in the lobby of the Babcock Fine Arts Center, is host to several exhibitions throughout the year. The Benedict Gallery, located in the main lobby of Benedict Hall, is host to several exhibitions during the academic year, most of which place an emphasis on the humanities. Sweet Briar's survey collection numbers more than 1,000 pieces, ranging from medieval illuminated manuscripts to post-modem prints. Of particular note are six Hudson River School paintings by Albert Bierstadt, John William Casilear, Sanford Robinson Gifford, Daniel Huntington, David Johnson, and Arthur Fitzwilliam Tait. Other artists with representative works in the collection include Louise Bourgeois, Charles Burchfield, Vija Celmins, Jon Corbino, Mary Cassatt, Albrecht Dürer, Andy Goldsworthy, Roy Lichtenstein, Sally Mann, Pablo Picasso, Miriam Schapiro, Pat Steir, and Rembrandt van Rijn.

Williamsburg

College of William and Mary - Muscarelle Museum of Art ©

College of William and Mary, Jamestown Road
Williamsburg, VA 23187-8795
Tel: (757) 221-2700
Fax: (757) 221-2711
Internet Address: http://www.wm.edu/muscarelle
Director: Dr. Bonnie G. Kelm
Admission: free.
Attendance: 40,000 *Established:* 1983 *Membership:* Y *ADA Compliant:* Y
Parking: free on site.

Williamsburg, Virginia

College of William and Mary - Muscarelle Museum of Art, cont.

Open: Monday to Friday, 10am-4:45pm;
Saturday to Sunday, noon-4pm.

Closed: Legal Holidays, Academic Holidays.

Facilities: **Exhibition Galleries** (permanent and temporary); **Print Study Room; Shop.**

Activities: **Gallery Talks; Guided Tours; Lectures; Temporary Exhibitions.**

Publications: calendar; exhibition catalogues; newsletter (3/year).

South façade of Muscarelle Museum of Art at dusk, showing "Sun Sonata", a solar painting by Gene Davis. Photograph by Fred Miller, courtesy of Muscarelle Museum of Art, College of William and Mary, Williamsburg, Virginia.

The Joseph and Margaret Muscarelle Museum of Art, an integral part of the College of William and Mary, is dedicated to enriching cultural life on campus while also serving the general public of Williamsburg and the Tidewater area. A selection of the permanent collection is always on display in the second-floor galleries. Opportunities for close study of selected works on paper are offered in the Herman Graphic Arts Study Room of the Museum on the first floor. The permanent collections are supplemented by special temporary exhibitions in the first floor galleries. These exhibitions include national traveling shows from other institutions and works lent from distinguished private and corporate collections. Every year, many varied educational offerings are scheduled. Exhibitions are frequently the subject of coordinated symposia, lectures, demonstrations, films, and gallery talks. Studio art classes, workshops, a variety of travel tours, and special events are offered throughout the year. When the Museum was established in 1983, it assumed responsibility for the College art collection, which began in 1732 with a gift from the third Earl of Burlington. In the intervening 250 years, a substantial number of works of art had been acquired by the College and were housed in various buildings on the campus. Objects were relocated to the Museum's protective environment where works of art could be given appropriate care. The Museum also embarked upon an ambitious program to increase the permanent collection, and the number of objects has since grown to over 3,000 paintings, sculptures, works on paper, and decorative objects. A particular strength of the permanent collection is the large number of 17th-, 18th- and 19th-century portraits of important historical individuals by distinguished English and American painters. The Museum also has a notable collection of Old Master prints and Inuit drawings. The contemporary section of the permanent collection has also grown significantly and includes painting, sculpture, and works on paper by major 20th-century American artists.

Washington

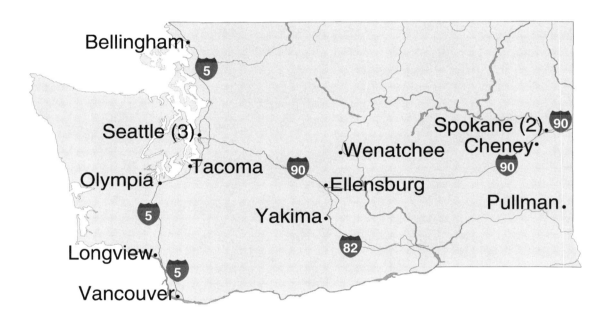

The number in parentheses following the city name indicates the number of museums/galleries in that municipality. If there is no number, one is understood. For example, in the text three listings would be found under Seattle and one listing under Tacoma.

Washington

Bellingham

Western Washington University - Western Gallery and Sculpture Collection ⓒⁱⁱ

Western Washington University, Fine Arts Complex, FI124
Bellingham, WA 98225-9068
Tel: (360) 650-3963
Fax: (360) 650-6878
Internet Address: http://www.wwu.edu
Director and C.E.O.: Sarah Clark-Langager, Ph.D.
Admission: voluntary contribution.
Attendance: 55,000 *Established:* 1950 *Membership:* Y *ADA Compliant:* Y
Parking: parking passes available at visitor's center.
Open: **Academic Year**, Monday to Friday, 10am-4pm; Saturday, noon-4pm.
Closed: Academic Holidays, Between Sessions.
Facilities: **Gallery Space** (4,500 square feet); **Sculpture Collection** (throughout campus, brochure available).
Activities: **Education Program** (undergraduate and graduate students); **Guided Tours** (by appointment); **Lectures**; **Temporary/Traveling Exhibitions**.
Publications: exhibition catalogues.

The Western Gallery and its plaza stand as a central focus between the northern and southern parts of campus. Through historical, contemporary, and experimental art exhibitions, through publications and interpretive interdisciplinary programs, and through its outdoor collection of contemporary sculpture, the Gallery acts as a focus for the display, discussion and exchange of ideas on critical issues in contemporary art from the region, and the national and international art scenes. Extending from the Western Gallery's plaza and integrated with other campus buildings, quadrangles, lawns, and playing fields is Western's Outdoor Sculpture Collection featuring works by major international, national and regional artists. Also on campus, the Viking Union Gallery, a student-run gallery located on the sixth floor of the Viking Addition, mounts three to four shows a quarter featuring the work of faculty, students and professional artists. The sculpture collection includes works by Magdalena Abakanowicz, Alice Aycock, Fred Bassetti, Richard Beyer, Anthony Caro, Mark di Suvero, James Fitzgerald, Lloyd Hamrol, Nancy Holt, Donald Judd, John Keppelman, Robert Maki, Michael McCafferty, Robert Morris, Bruce Nauman, Isamu Noguchi, Beverly Pepper, Mia Westerlund Roosen, Richard Serra, Steve Tibbetts, George Trakas, and Norman Warsinske.

Cheney

Eastern Washington University - University Galleries ⓒⁱⁱ

Gallery of Art: Art Bldg. (Main Floor)
Gallery of Photography: Art Bldg. (Room 129)
Cheney, WA 99004-2453
Tel: (509) 359-9707
Fax: (509) 359-4841
Internet Address:
http://www.visual.arts.ewu.edu/galleries/galleries.html
Director, University Galleries: Mr. Richard L. Twedt
Admission: free.
Attendance: 5,000
ADA Compliant: Y
Open: Monday to Friday, 8am-5pm.
Facilities: **Exhibition Area**.

Joseph Grigely, *Conversations with the Hearing*, 1993, Installation. Photograph courtesy of Eastern Washington University Gallery of Art, Cheney, Washington.

Eastern Washington University - University Galleries, cont.
Activities: **Temporary Exhibitions**.

The Gallery of Art presents exhibitions of work in all media by locally, regionally, and nationally recognized artists, faculty shows, and an annual juried student exhibition. It also sponsors the biennial National Computer Art Invitational traveling exhibition and occasionally sponsors other national juried shows. The Gallery of Photography mounts monthly exhibitions spanning the spectrum of photography from traditional black and white prints, to collage and digital images that push the boundaries of the photographic medium. University holdings include The Anne Harder MacKenzie Wyatt print collection of "Modern American Masters", the Percent-for-Art collection, the Ceramics collection, the National Computer Art collection, the Andy Warhol "Endangered Species" collection, many pre-Columbian artifacts, and a variety of works by regional artists including Ruben Trejo, Karen Guzak, Tom Askman, Mel McCuddin, and Richard Twedt. Also of possible interest on campus is the Student Gallery, located in the Art Department, which exhibits the work of student artists, including BFA and MFA Thesis Exhibitions. Off campus, the University's "Modern American Masters" Collection is located on the second floor of Eastern's Spokane Center in downtown Spokane (see separate listing). EWU's Exhibit Touring Services program, also part of the University Galleries, provides a wide variety of exhibitions internationally to museums; college, university, and community galleries; arts and cultural centers; and libraries.

Ellensburg

Central Washington University - Sarah Surgeon Gallery Ⓒᴬᴬ
Randall Hall, Ellensburg, WA 98926
Tel: (509) 963-2665
Fax: (509) 963-1918
Internet Address: http://www.cwu.edu
Open: Call for hours.
Facilities: **Exhibition Area**.
Activities: **Lectures**; **Temporary Exhibitions**.

With the assistance of the Associated Students of Central, the gallery features exhibitions of contemporary art throughout the year.

Longview

Lower Columbia College - Art Gallery
1600 Maple St., Longview, WA 98632
Tel: (360) 577-2314
Fax: (360) 577-3400
Internet Address: http://lcc.ctc.edu/events/cultural
Advisor: Ms. Trudy Woods
Admission: free.
Attendance: 5,437   *Established:* 1978   *ADA Compliant:* Y
Parking: free on site.
Open: **September to June**,
        Monday to Tuesday, 10am-4pm; Wednesday to Thursday, 10am-8pm; Friday, 10am-4pm.
Closed: July to August.
Activities: **Lectures/Workshops Series**; **Temporary/Traveling Exhibitions**.

The Gallery presents a series of scheduled temporary exhibitions.

Olympia

The Evergreen State College - Evergreen Galleries Ⓒᴬᴬ
The Evergreen State College, 2700 Evergreen Pkwy.
Olympia, WA 98505-0002
Tel: (360) 866-6000 *Ext:* 6488   *Fax:* (360) 866-6794
Internet Address: http://www.evergreen.edu/user/galleries/

The Evergreen State College - Evergreen Galleries, cont.

Director: Mr. Peter Ramsey

Admission: free.

Established: 1970   *ADA Compliant:* Y

Open: **Gallery II**,

    Monday to Friday, 8:45am-10:45pm; Saturday, 10:45am-6pm; Sunday, noon-6pm.

    Gallery IV,

     Monday to Friday, noon-5pm; Saturday, 1pm-4pm.

Closed: Academic Holidays.

Facilities: **Exhibition Space**; **Galleries** (2).

Activities: **Gallery Talks**; **Temporary/Traveling Exhibitions**.

Located in the Evans Library Building on the campus of The Evergreen State College, Gallery II is in the second floor foyer of the library proper, and Gallery IV is on the fourth floor. The mission of the two galleries is to supplement the current programs offered by the academic faculty. Exhibitions are developed from a variety of sources, including purchase from museums and galleries, works of visual arts faculty and staff, senior thesis or program shows, and student work. Evergreen maintains a permanent collection, although only a small portion of it is on view at any one time. It consists of some 200 works of both two-dimensional and three-dimensional art. The majority of the collection was acquired during the 1970s and reflects the work of both nationally recognized artists and local artists. Photographs in the collection include work by Dianne Arbus, Marsha Burns, Judy Dater, Ralph Meatyard, Karen Truzak, Jerry Uelsman, and Edward Weston. In addition to photography the collection includes hand-woven wall hangings, ceramics, off-hand glass works, ceramic sculpture, paintings, drawings, and prints.

Pullman

Washington State University - Museum of Art ⒸⒶⒶ

Wilson Road (across from Martin Stadium)

Pullman, WA 99164-7460

Tel: (509) 335-1910

Fax: (509) 335-1908

Internet Address: http://www.wsu.edu

Admission: free.

Attendance: 28,639   *Established:* 1973

Membership: Y   *ADA Compliant:* Y

Parking: beneath the Fine Arts Center after 5pm and on weekends.

Open: Monday, 10am-4pm;

    Tuesday, 10am-10pm;

    Wednesday to Friday, 10am-4pm;

    Saturday to Sunday, 1pm-5pm.

View of gallery during annual Fine Arts Graduate Thesis Exhibition at Museum of Art. Photograph courtesy of Museum of Art, Washington State University, Pullman, Washington.

Closed: Academic Holidays, During Installation.

Facilities: **Auditorium** (145 seat); **Gallery** (6,000 square feet).

Activities: **Concerts**; **Education Program** (high school, undergraduate and graduate students); **Films**; **Gallery Talks**; **Guided Tours**; **Lectures** (including a noon-time program - "Art à la carte"); **Performances**; **Temporary Exhibitions** (6-7/year); **Workshops** (children, on Saturdays).

Publications: exhibition catalogues; posters.

The Museum strives to provide a diverse and balanced range of offerings, including photography, design, ceramics, and textiles, as well as painting and sculpture. Shows of wide appeal alternate with more challenging exhibitions. The schedule includes exhibitions examining issues in contemporary art, an annual exhibit series focusing on art of the Northwest, exhibitions that examine the history of art, shows elaborating on works in the permanent collection, displays of art and artifacts from diverse cultures, and exhibits by faculty and graduate students. Each summer an exhibition is drawn

Washington State University - Museum of Art, cont.

from the museum's permanent collection. The Museum houses a small, but significant collection of American paintings, including works by such artists as William Merritt Chase, Frank Duveneck, William Glackens, Robert Henri, George Inness, Ernest Lawson, and Maurice Prendergast, and a selection of paintings by Northwest artists. The print collection includes historical works by European masters Goya, Hogarth, and Daumier, as well as contemporary prints by British and American artists, among them Leon Golub, Stanley William Hayter, David Hockney, R.B. Kitaj, Robert Motherwell, Robert Rauschenburg, Frank Stella, and Andy Warhol.

Seattle

Cornish College of the Arts - Art Galleries ⓒᴬ

Behnke Gallery: Cornish North, 1501 10th Ave. East
Fisher Gallery and Annex: Kerry Hall, 710 E. Roy St.
Alumni Exhibition Gallery: Harvard House 1, 723 Harvard Ave. East
Seattle, WA 98102
Tel: (206) 726-5066
Internet Address: http://www.cornish.edu/art/artexhbt.htm
Admission: free.
Open: Call for hours.
Facilities: **Galleries** (2).
Activities: **Temporary Exhibitions**.

The college maintains three exhibition spaces. The Behnke Gallery, located on the third floor of Cornish North, exhibits student work throughout the year, including the fall juried student exhibition and BFA candidates thesis exhibits in May. Exhibitions in the Fisher Gallery and Annex focus on work by Northwest artists, as well as Cornish faculty, students, and staff. The Alumni Exhibition Gallery presents artwork by alumni. Also of possible interest, the SOS Gallery, located in Cornish North (1501 10th Ave. East), features the work of current students.

Photographic Center Northwest Gallery

Photographic Center Northwest
900 12th Ave.
Seattle, WA 98122-4412
Tel: (206) 720-7222
Fax: (206) 720-0306
Internet Address: http://www.speakeasy.org/photocen/gallery.html
Gallery Coordinator: Ms. Ann Pallesen
Open: Monday, noon-9:30pm; Tuesday to Sunday, 9am-9:30pm.
Facilities: **Exhibition Area**.
Activities: **Temporary Exhibitions**.

The gallery features the work of nationally recognized and emerging Northwest photographic artists.

University of Washington - Henry Art Gallery ⓒᴬ

Faye G. Allen Center for the Visual Arts
15th Ave. NE & NE 41st St.
Seattle, WA 98195-3070
Tel: (206) 543-2280
Fax: (206) 685-3123
Internet Address: http://www.henryart.org
Director: Mr. Richard Andrews
Admission: fee: adult-$5.00, child-free, student-free, senior-$3.50.
Attendance: 65,000   *Established:* 1927   *Membership:* Y   *ADA Compliant:* Y
Parking: underground UW Central Parking garage at NE 41st Street.
Open: Tuesday, 11am-5pm; Wednesday to Thursday, 11am-8pm; Friday to Sunday, 11am-5pm.
Closed: New Year's Day, Independence Day, Thanksgiving Day, Christmas Day.

University of Washington - Henry Art Gallery, cont.

Facilities: **Architecture** (modernist expansion, 1997 design by Charles Gwathmey; collegiate gothic building, 1927 design by Carl F. Gould); **Exhibition Area** (14,000 square feet); **Food Services** Henry Café (pastries, beverages & light fare); **Print Study Room**; **Sculpture Court**; **Shop** (books and local artist-made products).

Activities: **Gallery Talks** (2/month mid-day curatorial talks); **Guided Tours** (for information call (206) 616-8782); **Lectures**; **Temporary/Traveling Exhibitions**.

Publications: exhibition catalogues.

Henri Matisse, *Nu au bracelet*, 1940, linoleum cut on Arches paper, 9 5/8 x 7 inches. Gift of Mr. and Mrs. Frank L. Dobbins, Jr. Henry Art Gallery. From the 1997-1998 exhibition "Unpacking the Collection: 70 Years of Collections at the Henry". Photograph courtesy of Henry Art Gallery, University of Washington, Seattle Washington.

Since its inception, the Henry Art Gallery, the art museum of the University of Washington, has been best known for its progressive exhibition program. The Gallery has presented significant exhibitions and provocative public programs on modern and contemporary art and organized nationally-prominent exhibitions. By the early 1990's, given the range and depth of the museum's programming and exhibitions, the Henry had far exceeded the physical capacity of its building, which provided less than 5,000 square feet of exhibition space. Driven by the critical success of its programs and a growing public and student audience, the Henry initiated a renovation and expansion that increased its overall size from 10,000 to 46,000 square feet. The interior space is sequential, leading visitors through exhibitions of the permanent collection in the renovated galleries of the original building down to special installations and exhibitions of modern and contemporary art in the new galleries on the lower levels. The concept behind this descending procession is to frame the experience of exhibitions of contemporary art with the historical precedents of the permanent collection. The lowest level features the primary exhibition areas. The main 6,000 square-foot gallery is a lofty and expansive sky-lit space, specifically conceived to accommodate large-scale works and installations. An additional 1,000-square-foot gallery was designed for artist projects or small exhibitions, and a 700-square-foot multimedia gallery will support a wide range of technologically-based art installations. Approximately 19,000 objects comprise the museum's permanent collection. Among the holdings in paintings are late 19th- and early 20th-century American and French paintings by such artists as Ralph Albert Blakelock, William Merritt Chase, Charles Daubigny, and Winslow Homer; modern works by artists including Stuart Davis, Lionel Feininger, Morris Graves, Jacob Lawrence, and Robert Motherwell; and works by Northwest artists including Guy Anderson, Kenneth Callahan, Morris Graves, Walter Isaacs, Helmi Juvonen, and Mark Tobey. Other media are represented by an extensive photography collection from the 1840s to the 1970s, with works by such photographers as Diane Arbus, Ansel Adams, Imogen Cunningham, Man Ray, and Garry Winogrand; prints by such artists as Seymour Hayden, William Hogarth, Giovanni Piranesi, Robert Rauschenberg, Georges Rouault, Rembrandt van Rijn, and James McNeill Whistler; a wide range of contemporary Japanese prints and woodblocks; and a significant collection of ethnic costumes and textiles, dating from 1500 BC to the present. Recent acquisitions of photography (including the core portion of the Joseph and Elaine Monsen Collection), sculpture, and video have strengthened these areas of the collection.

Spokane

Eastern Washington University - Spokane Center Gallery ⓒ⒜

Spokane Center, West 705 1st St., Spokane, WA   99204
Tel: (509) 458-6401
Internet Address: http://visual.arts.ewu.edu/galleries/spokane-center/spokane-center.htm
Curator: Mr. Richard L. Twedt
Admission: free.
Attendance: 10,000   *ADA Compliant:* Y

Eastern Washington University - Spokane Center Gallery, cont.

Open: Monday to Thursday, 8am-10pm;
Friday, 8am-5pm.

Facilities: **Exhibition Area**.

Activities: **Permanent Exhibits**.

The Center Gallery is home to the Anne Harder MacKenzie Wyatt Collection of "Modern American Masters". Initially developed over a period of eighteen months, the Collection features prints by American artists who were in the forefront of the major art movements since the 1940's. Included are works by Dine, Sam Francis, Lichtenstein, Oldenburg, Rauschenburg, Ruscha, Stella, Thiebaud, and LeWitt. For information on other Eastern Washington University galleries and collections, see the University's listing under Cheney, Washington.

Buky Schwartz, *Video Space for a Blue House*, 1990, Installation at Spokane Center Gallery. Photograph courtesy of Eastern Washington University, Cheney, Washington.

Gonzaga University - Jundt Art Museum 🕮 (JAM)

Southeast Corner of Desmet Ave. & Pearl St.
Spokane, WA 99258-0001

Tel: (509) 328-4220   *Ext:* 3211

Fax: (509) 323-5525

Internet Address: http://www.gonzaga.edu/jundt/index.html

Director and Curator: Mr. J. Scott Patnode

Admission: free.

Established: 1995

ADA Compliant: Y

Open: Monday to Friday, 10am-4pm; Saturday, noon-4pm.

Closed: Academic Holidays, Summer Session.

Facilities: **Auditorium** (118 seat); **Exhibition Space** (3 areas, total 5,538 square feet); **Print Study Room**.

Activities: **Gallery Talks**; **Lectures**.

The Museum provides space for traveling exhibits and houses Gonzaga University's art collection. The collection includes prints from the Bolker, Baruch, and Jacobs collections; major pieces of glass art by Dale Chihuly, bronze sculptures by Auguste Rodin, and paintings, ceramics, photographs and tapestries. Exhibits of permanent holdings are periodically rotated. The Museum also includes a print study room for Gonzaga's print collection.

Jundt Art Museum Lobby and Reception area with installation of Dale Chihuly glass collection and Red Chandelier, 1995. Photograph by J. Craig Sweat, courtesy of   Jundt Art Museum, Spokane, Washington.

Tacoma

University of Puget Sound - Kittredge Gallery 🕮

1500 N. Lawrence, Tacoma, WA 98416

Tel: (253) 756-3348   *Fax:* (253) 756-3500

Internet Address: http://www.ups.edu

Director: Gregg Bell

Admission: free.

Attendance: 900   *Established:* 1950   *ADA Compliant:* Y

Open: **September to May 15**, Monday to Friday, 10am-4pm; Sunday, 1pm-4pm.

Facilities: **Exhibition Space** (2,100 square feet).

Activities: **Lectures**; **Temporary/Traveling Exhibitions**.

University of Puget Sound - Kittredge Gallery, cont.

The Gallery presents a series of Community and regional art shows, as well as exhibitions of student work. Exhibiting artists generally present public lectures on their work.

Vancouver

Clark College - The Archer Gallery

1800 E. McLoughlin Blvd., Vancouver, WA   98663

Tel: (360) 992-2246   *Fax:* (360) 992-2828

Internet Address: http://www.clark.edu

Director: Ms. Marjorie Hirsch

Admission: free.

Established: 1978

ADA Compliant: Y

Parking: free adjacent to site.

Open: Tuesday to Thursday, 9am-8pm;
          Friday, 9am-4pm;
          Saturday to Sunday, 1pm-5pm.

Facilities: Gallery (2,400 square feet).

Activities: Films; Lectures; Temporary Exhibitions (6/year).

Each year, the Gallery hosts six exhibits by regional and nationally-recognized artists, and at least one faculty/student show. The Archer Gallery has evolved from its inception in 1978 into a showcase for Northwest artists. Focusing on Washington state, the gallery presents the work of established artists as well as emerging talent working in a wide variety of media, including paintings, prints, photography, and sculpture, as well as site-specific installations and video work. Recognized as an alternative venue, the Archer Gallery serves the Clark College faculty and student body as well as the Vancouver-Portland public at large.

Archer Gallery interior. Photograph courtesy of Archer Gallery, Clark College, Vancouver, Washington.

Wenatchee

Wenatchee Valley College - Gallery '76

Wenatchee Valley College, Sexton Hall, 9th St., Wenatchee, WA   98801

Tel: (509) 664-2521   *Fax:* (509) 664-2538

Internet Address: http://wvc.ctc.edu

Coordinator: Ms. Sue DePiro

Admission: voluntary contribution.

Attendance: 2,000   *Established:* 1976   *Membership:* Y   *ADA Compliant:* Y

Open: **September to June**, Monday to Tuesday, 10am-2pm;
          Wednesday to Thursday, 10am-2pm & 7pm-9pm; Friday, 10am-2pm.

Activities: **Education   Program**   (undergraduate);   **Gallery   Talks**;   **Lectures**;
Temporary/Traveling Exhibitions.

Publications: newsletter, "Gallery '76 News" (quarterly).

Gallery '76 is a community supported non-profit art gallery located on the campus of Wenatchee Valley College in Sexton Hall off Ninth Street. North Central Washington's first public art gallery, Gallery '76, promotes the visual arts in North Central Washington through quality exhibitions, workshops, lectures, tours, and children's classes. The gallery provides a vehicle for the exhibition of work by talented local artists and craftspeople, Wenatchee Valley College art students, and artists of national and international repute. In addition the Gallery also brings visual artists to the community to speak about their art so that the public may better understand the artist's motivations and role in society.

Yakima

Yakima Valley Community College - Larson Museum and Gallery

Yakima Valley Community College, South 16th Ave. & Nob Hill Blvd.
Yakima, WA 98902
Tel: (509) 574-4875
Fax: (509) 574-6826
TDDY: (509) 575-2350
Internet Address: http://www.rfttc.org/~yvcc
Director: Ms. Carol Hassen
Admission: voluntary contribution.
Attendance: 10,000   *Established:* 1949   *Membership:* Y   *ADA Compliant:* Y
Parking: free lot on site.
Open: **Academic Sessions**, Monday to Friday, 10am-5pm; Saturday to Sunday, 1pm-5pm.
Activities: **Arts Festival**; **Education Program** (children); **Guided Tours**.
Publications: exhibition catalogues, "Central Washington Artists Exhibition" (annual); newsletter, "ARTicles" (quarterly).

The Larson Gallery presents monthly temporary exhibitions representing a broad range of interests, promotes art education through tours, and provides workshops and lectures. The Gallery also conducts three annual juried exhibitions: the Central Washington Artists Exhibition (restricted to local artists), the Art to Wear exhibit (open to residents of Washington, Oregon, and Idaho), and the National Photography Juried Exhibit.

West Virginia

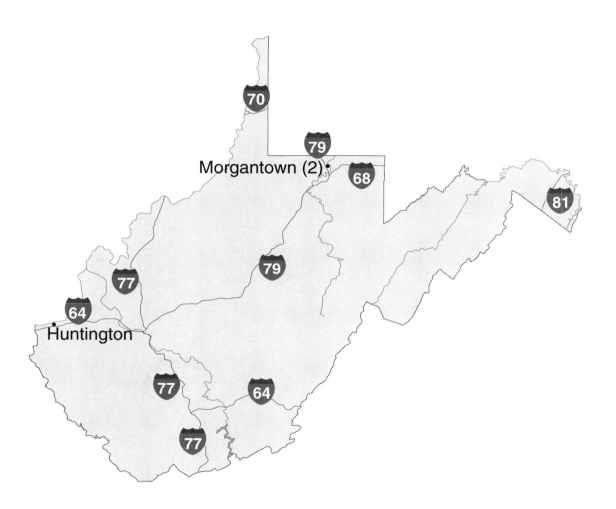

The number in parentheses following the city name indicates the number of museums/galleries in that municipality. If there is no number, one is understood. For example, in the text two listings would be found under Morgantown and one listing under Huntington.

West Virginia

Huntington

Marshall University - Birke Art Gallery ⓒ⁴⁴

Third Avenue, Smith Hall, Huntington, WV   25755-2222
Tel: (304) 696-2296
Internet Address: http://www.marshall.edu
Director: Ms. Beverly Marchant
Open: Monday to Friday, 10am-4pm; Monday, 7pm-9pm; Saturday, 1pm-4pm.

The Birke Art Gallery presents a series of temporary exhibitions each year, including the work of both students and professional artists.

Morgantown

West Virginia University - Paul and Laura Mesaros Galleries ⓒ⁴⁴ (CAC)

West Virginia University,, Evansdale Campus
College of the Creatve Arts, Creative Arts Center
Morgantown, WV   26506-6111
Tel: (304) 291-2140 *Ext:* 3210   *Fax:* (304) 293-5731
Internet Address: http://www.wvu.edu/~ccarts
Dean & Director: Mr. Philip Faini
Admission: free.
Attendance: 16,000   *Established:* 1968   *ADA Compliant:* Y
Parking: guest parking available.
Open: Monday to Saturday, noon-9:30pm.
Closed: Academic Holidays.
Facilities: **Auditorium** (1,500 seat); **Classrooms**; **Exhibition Space** (2 galleries, total 1,100 square feet); **Studios**.
Activities: **Education Program** (undergraduate and graduate students); **Guided Tours** (available on request); **Lectures**; **Temporary Exhibitions** (change monthly).
Publications: exhibition catalogues (biennial).

The Galleries focus on individual and group exhibitions of contemporary artists of regional, national, and international reputation working in all media. Additionally, the Galleries host yearly exhibitions of the work undergraduate senior BFA candidates and graduate student MFA thesis work during the spring semester. Exhibitions are also mounted in the Grandview Gallery, located above the main entrance on the second floor of the Mountainlair. Grandview Gallery is operated by The Student Art Association under the guidance of the Division of Art.

West Virginia University - Permanent Art Collection ⓒ⁴⁴

Colson Hall Library (University Ave. at Hough St)
Morgantown, WV   26506
Tel: (304) 293-0111
Internet Address: http://www.wvu/edu/~library/art.htm
Curator, Permanent Art Collection: Mr. John Cuthbert
Admission: free.
Open: **Call for hours**.

Works from the Permanent Collection are displayed in a series of temporary exhibitions.

Wisconsin

The number in parentheses following the city name indicates the number of museums/galleries in that municipality. If there is no number, one is understood. For example, in the text three listings would be found under Madison and one listing under Sheboygan.

Wisconsin

Appleton

Lawrence University - Wriston Art Center Galleries ⓒ

Lawrence University
613 E. College Ave.
Appleton, WI   54911
Tel: (920) 832-6621
Fax: (920) 832-7362
Internet Address:
  http://cwis.lawrence.edu/ www/campus/wriston/
Curator: Ms. Nadine Wasserman
Admission: free.
Attendance: 5,000   *Established:* 1989
Membership: N   *ADA Compliant:* Y
Parking: next to university's Memorial Chapel,
  access via Lawe St.
Open: **October to May**,
        Tuesday to Friday, 10am-4pm;
        Saturday to Sunday, noon-4pm.
      June to September,
        Tuesday to Friday, 10am-4pm;
        Saturday, noon-4pm.
Closed: Memorial Day, Independence Day,
  Thanksgiving Weekend,
  December 15 to January 2.

Lower Lobby, Wriston Art Center (1989), designed by Jefferson Riley, Centerbrook Architects. Photograph courtesy of Henry M. and Ruth B. Wriston Art Center, Appleton, Wisconsin.

Facilities: **Architecture** (1989 design by architect Jefferson Riley); **Exhibition Area** (3 galleries).
Activities: **Education Program** (undergraduate students); **Films**; **Guided Tours** (by appointment,
  48 hour notice required); **Lectures**; **Temporary/Traveling Exhibitions** (5-6 shows/year).
Publications: exhibition catalogues.

Located in the heart of the campus, the upper level of the Henry M. and Ruth B. Wriston Art Center, devoted to art history and exhibition, includes a serpentine galleria for the display of study reproductions and transitory exhibits, a 150-seat auditorium, and a visual resources suite for an extensive collection of slides. The west side of the lobby features three galleries of increasing size (the Leech Gallery, Hoffmaster Gallery, and Kohler Gallery), each leading into the next. Adjacent to these is the Quirk Print Gallery, a print study room. The Center's lower level is devoted to studios and opens onto an amphitheater. The Galleries coordinate an exhibition schedule of 5-6 shows per year while maintaining a permanent collection of approximately 1,800 works. The collection, which consists primarily of works of art on paper, contains a number of Japanese prints, graphic work from the 1930s, and the LaVera Pohl Collection of German Expressionist Art. The Wriston Art Center also houses the Ottilia Buerger Collection of Ancient and Byzantine Coins. Artwork from the collection can be made available for public inspection with advance notice. Please allow four working days to process any request.

Beloit

Beloit College - Wright Museum of Art ⓒ

Beloit College, 700 College St., Beloit, WI   53511-5595
Tel: (608) 363-2677   *Fax:* (608) 363-2248
Director, Beloit College Museums: Mr. Thomas H. Wilson
Admission: free.
Attendance: 20,000   *Established:* 1892   *Membership:* Y   *ADA Compliant:* Y
Parking: free on site.
Open: Tuesday to Sunday, 11am-4pm.
Closed: Academic Holidays.

Beloit College - Wright Museum of Art, cont.

Facilities: **Auditorium; Classrooms.**

Activities: **Art Classes** (children); **Artist-in-Residence Program; Concerts; Education Program** (undergraduate students); **Films; Guided Tours; Juried Exhibit; Lectures; Temporary/Traveling Exhibitions.**

Publications: exhibition catalogues; newsletter.

The Museum offers both thematic and solo temporary and traveling exhibitions. An annual juried show for regional artists and a student show are held each spring. The Museum's permanent collection includes 15th- to 20th-century paintings, works on paper, sculpture, photographs, and Asian art (e.g., imperial Chinese robes, Korean celadon ceramics, and Japanese sagemono), as well as the collection of plaster casts from the Greek government exhibit at the Columbian Exposition.

Eau Claire

University of Wisconsin-Eau Claire - Foster Gallery Ⓒ⁴⁴

121 Water St.,
Eau Claire, WI   54702-4004
Tel: (715) 836-2328
Fax: (715) 836-4882
Internet Address: http://www.uwec.edu/Academic/Art/featuresc.htm
Director: Dr. Thomas K.. Wagener
Admission: free.
Attendance: 25,000   *Established:* 1970   *Membership:* N   *ADA Compliant:* Y
Parking: permit required weekdays 8am-4pm.
Open: Monday to Friday, 11am-4:30pm; Saturday to Sunday, 1pm-3:30pm.
Closed: Academic Holidays.
Facilities: **Exhibition Area** (2 galleries, 3,200 square feet).
Activities: **Education Program** (undergraduate and graduate students); **Lectures; Temporary/Traveling Exhibitions.**
Publications: exhibition brochures.

The Foster Gallery mounts four major shows annually during the University's academic year. These shows may feature the work of a single artist or pieces by a group of artists from a major commercial gallery. Exhibitions have included the work of both established and emerging artists. Exhibitions of the permanent collection, work of faculty and BFA degree candidates, and an annual juried student art show are also scheduled. The permanent collection consists of over 700 works ranging from 19th-century oriental to late 20th-century modern art including prints, paintings, pen and ink, sculpture, ceramics, photography, fibers, and computer graphics. Its founding collection, the Emil J. Arnold Collection, includes works by Chaim Gross, Karl Knaths, I. Rice Pereira, Joseph Solman, Raphael Soyer, and Theodore Stamos.

Green Bay

University of Wisconsin-Green Bay - Galleries Ⓒ⁴⁴

2420 Nicolet Drive
Green Bay, WI   54302
Tel: (414) 465-2271
Internet Address: http://www.uwgb.edu
Director: Mr. Tomas Galaty
Open: Monday to Friday, 10am-4pm; Saturday to Sunday, noon-4pm.
Facilities: **Exhibition Area** (3 galleries).
Activities: **Temporary Exhibitions.**

Three display galleries are maintained: Lawton Gallery (located at 249 Theater Hall), 407 Gallery (located in Studio Arts Building, Room 407), and Weidner Mezzanine Gallery (located in the Weidner Center for the Performing Arts.

La Crosse

University of Wisconsin - La Crosse - University Art Gallery ⓒⒶ

Center for the Arts, 16th and Vine Streets, La Crosse, WI   54601
Tel: (608) 785-8237
Internet Address: http://www.uwlax.edu
Director: Mr. Joel Eigin
Admission: free.
Open: Monday, 10am-9pm; Tuesday to Thursday, 10am-6pm; Friday to Saturday, 11am-3pm.
Activities: **Demonstrations**; **Lectures** (by visiting artists).

The Gallery displays works by students, faculty, and regionally- and nationally-known artists in all media

Madison

Edgewood College - DeRicci Gallery ⓒⒶ

DeRicci Hall 855 Woodrow St.
Madison, WI   53711-1997
Tel: (608) 257-4861
Fax: (608) 257-1455
Internet Address: http://www.edgewood.edu/
   schedules/galsched.htm
Gallery Director: Ms. Melanie Herzog, Ph.D.
Admission: free.
Attendance: 12,000   *Established:* 1986
Membership: N   *ADA Compliant:* Y
Open: 8am-7pm.
Facilities: **Gallery**.
Activities: **Temporary Exhibitions**.

View of DeRicci Gallery during student art show (1991). Photograph courtesy of DeRicci Gallery, Madison, Wisconsin.

The DeRicci Gallery offers a schedule of art exhibitions by regional artists and students. The is also a small permanent collection of student and faculty works.

University of Wisconsin-Madison - Elvehjem Museum of Art ⓒⒶ (LVM)

800 University Ave. (between Murray & Park Sts.)
Madison, WI   53706
Tel: (608) 263-2246
Fax: (608) 263-8188
Director: Dr. Russell Panczenko
Admission: voluntary contribution.
Attendance: 70,824   *Established:* 1962
Membership: Y   *ADA Compliant:* Y
Parking: university lots #46 and #83 and near-
   by municipal ramps.
Open: Tuesday to Friday, 9am-5pm;
      Saturday to Sunday, 11am-5pm.
Closed: New Year's Day, Thanksgiving Day,
      Christmas Eve to Christmas Day.

Exterior view of Elvehjem Museum of Art. Photograph courtesy of Elvehjem Museum of Art, Madison, Wisconsin.

Facilities: **Architecture** (designed by Chicago architect Harry Weese); **Auditoriums** (4); **Classrooms**; **Exhibition Area** (11 galleries, 26,000 square feet); **Library** (120,000 volumes); **Print Center** (Mayer Print Center - by appointment (608) 263-4421); **Shop** (arts-related items, books, posters, jewelry).
Activities: **Concerts** (Sept-May, Sun, 12:30pm, chamber music, free); **Docent Program**; **Education Program** (adults and undergraduate/graduate students); **Films**; **Guided Tours** (group tours schedule in advance (608) 263-4421; Thurs, 12:20pm, permanent collection; Sun, 2pm, temp exhibits); **Lectures**; **Temporary/Traveling Exhibitions**.

University of Wisconsin-Madison - Elvehjem Museum of Art, cont.

Publications: bulletin (semi-annual); calendar, "Artscene" (bi-monthly); exhibition catalogues (occasional).

The Elvehjem (pronounced L-V-M) Museum of Art was founded in 1970 to conserve, study and exhibit the art collections of the University of Wisconsin-Madison. It serves as an active educational and cultural center for the campus and surrounding communities. Painting, sculpture and decorative arts ranging from Egyptian tomb sculpture to contemporary artwork are on view in the permanent collection galleries. The Museum also provides a schedule of temporary exhibitions to supplement the installations from the permanent collection. Catalogues and gallery notes are regularly published to accompany exhibitions. The Elvehjem also presents numerous educational programs for the public. These include lectures, tours, trips, films, a chamber music series on Sunday afternoons and other performances. In 1991, the Elvehjem commissioned and installed in front of the museum "Generations", a large, outdoor sculpture and plaza designed by Richard Artschwager. The Kohler Art Library on the ground level houses over 100,000 volumes and maintains subscriptions to over 300 periodicals, which can be used by the public, although only staff, faculty, and university students can check out materials. The Mayer Print Center houses the Museum's 6,000 works of art on paper, including old master and contemporary prints, watercolors, Japanese prints and Indian miniature paintings. (The Center is available for research and study by appointment.) The Elvehjem has a permanent collection of over 15,500 works of art ranging from 2300 BC to the present. The primary focus is on the collection of western European and American paintings, sculpture, drawings, prints, and photographs, with examples by Eugène Boudin, Jean Baptiste Corot, Helen Frankenthaler, Hendrick Goltzius, Hans Hofmann, Henri Matisse, Louise Nevelson, Auguste Rodin, David Smith, Bernardo Strozzi, Rembrandt van Rijn, and Giorgio Vasari. Specialized collections offer in-depth studies of printmaking with a focus on Japanese prints (the Edward Burr Van Vleck collection), Russian and Soviet paintings (the Joseph E. Davies collection), 18th- and 19th-century British watercolors, 20th-century painting and sculpture, Indian sculpture and Indian miniature painting (the Earnest C. and Jane Werner Watson collection), ancient Greek vases and coins, European and Chinese export porcelain, European medals (the Vernon Hall collection), Lalique glass, and North American Indian baskets. Several hundred works of art are added each year by gift, bequest, or purchase.

University of Wisconsin-Madison - The Wisconsin Union Galleries Ⓒᴬᴬ

800 Langdon St., Madison, WI 53706
Tel: (608) 262-5969   ***Fax:*** (608) 262-5487
Internet Address: http://www.wisc.edu/union
Director: Mr. Ralph Russo
Admission: free.
Attendance: 85,000   ***Established:*** 1928   ***Membership:*** Y
Open: **Butts & Class of 25 Galleries**, Daily, 10am-8pm.
          Theater Gallery, Daily, during Theater Wing building hours.
Closed: Christmas Eve to New Year's Day.
Facilities: **Food Services** Restaurant; **Reading Room**; **Theatre**.
Activities: **Arts Festival**; **Classes/Workshops**; **Concerts**; **Dance Recitals**; **Education Program** (adults, children, and students); **Films**; **Guided Tours**; **Lectures**; **Temporary/Traveling Exhibitions**.

The Wisconsin Union Galleries present exhibitions by a variety of artists and touring exhibitions. Exhibitions are sponsored and arranged by the Art Committee and usually changed monthly. The Porter Butts Gallery and the Class of 25 Gallery are located on the second floor; the Theater Gallery is on the first and second floors of the Theater Wing. More than 800 works of art by over 500 artists with Wisconsin roots make up the collection of the Wisconsin Union Galleries at the University of Wisconsin in Madison.

Menomonie

University of Wisconsin-Stout- John Furlong Gallery Ⓒᴬᴬ

Micheels Hall (3rd St. East, between 10th and 13th Aves.), Menomonie, WI   54751-0790
Tel: (715) 232-2261   ***Fax:*** (715) 232-1346

University of Wisconsin-Stout- John Furlong Gallery, cont.

Internet Address: http://www.uwstout.edu
Admission: voluntary contribution.
Established: 1965   *ADA Compliant:* Y
Open: Monday to Tuesday, 10am-4:30pm; Wednesday, 10am-4pm & 6pm-9pm;
Thursday to Friday, 10am-4:30pm; Saturday, noon-3pm.
Closed: Legal Holidays.
Facilities: **Gallery**.
Activities: **Temporary/Traveling Exhibitions**.

The John Furlong Gallery and a student gallery, along with other exhibit spaces on campus, provide student, faculty, and outside exhibitions throughout the school year. Also of possible interest on campus is the Brich Gallery, located in the Memorial Student Center.

Mequon

Concordia University-Wisconsin - Art Gallery

12800 N. Lake Shore Drive, Mequon, WI 53097
Tel: (414) 243-4242   *Fax:* (414) 243-4351
Internet Address: http://www.cuw.edu
Director: Dr. Gaylund K. Stone
Admission: free.
Attendance: 600   *Membership:* N   *ADA Compliant:* Y
Parking: large lots throughout campus for parking.
Open: **September to May 15**,
Tuesday to Wednesday, noon-4pm; Thursday, noon-4pm & 5pm-7pm; Friday, noon-4pm;
Sunday, noon-4pm.
Closed: Legal Holidays.
Facilities: **Exhibition Area**.
Activities: **Education Program** (undergraduate and graduate students); **Lectures**; **Temporary/Traveling Exhibitions** (7-8/year).

The Concordia University Gallery hosts 7-8 temporary exhibits per year, mostly featuring regional artists. The permanent collection includes a number of Russian bronzes, the Great Heron Race series by John Doyle, and a large collection of Sidel porcelain.

Milwaukee

Marquette University - The Patrick and Beatrice Haggerty Museum of Art ⓒ

Marquette University, 13th and Cylbourn Sts.
Milwaukee, WI 53233-1881
Tel: (414) 288-1669
Fax: (414) 288-5415
Internet Address: http://www.mu.edu/haggerty
Director: Dr. Curtis L. Carter
Admission: free.
Attendance: 43,500   *Established:* 1955
Membership: Y   *ADA Compliant:* Y
Parking: free at Lot J, 11th & Wisconsin Ave.
Open: Monday to Wednesday, 10am-4:30pm;
Thursday, 10am-8pm;
Friday to Saturday, 10am-4:30pm;
Sunday, noon-5pm.
Closed: New Year's Day, Easter,
Thanksgiving Day, Christmas Day.

Exterior view of Patrick and Beatrice Haggerty Museum of Art. Photograph courtesy of Patrick and Beatrice Haggerty Museum of Art, Marquette University, Milwaukee, Wisconsin.

Facilities: **Architecture** (designed by architects O'Neil Ford and David Kahler); **Library**; **Museum Store**; **Sculpture Garden**.

Marquette University - The Patrick and Beatrice Haggerty Museum of Art, cont.

Activities: **Concerts**; **Docent Program**; **Education Program** (adults and students); **Films**; **Guided Tours** (schedule in advance, free); **Lectures**; **Temporary/Traveling Exhibitions**.
Publications: exhibition catalogues.

Located in a striking building on the campus of Marquette University, the Haggerty Museum's educational program incorporates special exhibitions, visiting scholars, and visiting artists in various media. In addition to the pictorial arts, the museum presents programs that include dance, music, poetry, performance art, film, and video. The permanent collection of over 6,000 objects contains a substantial body of works not typical of other museums in the region. Included are works by Chagall, Dali, Dürer, Wilhelm Lehmbruck, Miró, Picasso, Rouault, Trevisani, and an important collection of Barbara Morgan photographs. The collection is still growing, the most recent acquisitions being Louis Valtat's " Au Cabaret", and Albrecht Dürer's "The Presentation of the Temple".

Milwaukee Institute of Art and Design - Galleries Ⓒᴬᴬ (MIAD)

273 E. Erie St., Milwaukee, WI   53202
Tel: (414) 276-7889   *Fax:* (414) 291-8077
Internet Address: http://www.miad.edu
Director of Institutional Galleries: Mr. Mark Lawson
Admission: free.
Attendance: 6,000   *Established:* 1974
Membership: N   *ADA Compliant:* Y
Parking: metered on street.
Open: Tuesday to Saturday, 10am-5pm.
Facilities: **Exhibition Area**.
Activities: **Temporary Exhibitions**.
Publications: brochures (biennial).

MIAD's Frederick Layton Gallery features changing exhibitions of traditional and contemporary fine art by artists of regional and national reputation, including MIAD faculty, alumni, and students. The Brooks Stevens Gallery features year-long exhibitions of work by nationally- and internationally-known industrial designers.

View of Frederick Layton Gallery during 1999 Student Exhibition. Photograph courtesy of Milwaukee Institute of Art and Design, Milwaukee, Wisconsin.

University of Wisconsin-Milwaukee - Institute of Visual Arts Ⓒᴬᴬ (Inova)

3253 N. Downer Ave., Milwaukee, WI   53211
Tel: (414) 229-5070   *Fax:* (414) 229-6785
Internet Address: http://www.uwm.edu:80/Dept/inova
Director: Mr. Peter Doroshenko
Admission: free.
Attendance: 18,000   *Established:* 1982   *ADA Compliant:* Y
Parking: metered on street.
Open: **Gallery One & Video to Video Gallery**, Wednesday to Sunday, noon-5pm.
       Galleries 2 & 3, Tuesday to Saturday, noon-5pm.
Closed: Legal Holidays.
Facilities: **Print Study Room**.
Activities: **Lectures**.
Publications: calendar; exhibition catalogues; newsletter.

Opened in September 1982 as the UWM Art Museum, the museum and its associated galleries (Art History and Fine Arts Gallery) have been combined under the umbrella of the new Institute of Visual Arts (Inova). Inova focuses on one-person exhibitions of local, national, and international contemporary artists complemented by lectures and gallery talks. The institute also features a monthly video program, screenings of films by artists, adjunct curators, and guest critics. In addition, the

University of Wisconsin-Milwaukee - Institute of Visual Arts, cont.

gallery spaces have been reorganized. "Gallery One" is the main Inova building (formerly the UWM Art Museum) in Vogel Hall, 3253 N. Downer Ave. Gallery Two (formerly the Art History Gallery) has newly renovated space in Mitchell Hall, 3203 N. Downer Ave. "Gallery Three" consists of two distinct areas in the Fine Arts Center, 2400 E. Kenwood Blvd. One space features rotating exhibitions of work by various artists; the other, work by UWM fine arts undergraduate students. "Gallery Four" describes all site-specific, non-traditional projects throughout the campus and city. "Gallery Video" is located in various places in Vogel Hall.

University of Wisconsin-Milwaukee - Union Art Gallery ⓒ⁴⁴

2200 E. Kenwood Blvd., Milwaukee, WI   53201
Tel: (414) 229-6310   *Fax:* (414) 229-6709
Internet Address: http://www.aux.uwm.edu/union/artcraft.htm
Director: Ms. Patricia Kozik
Admission: free.
Attendance: 13,000   *Established:* 1972   *ADA Compliant:* Y
Open: Monday, noon-3pm; Tuesday, 11am-3pm; Wednesday, noon-3pm; Thursday, 11am-7pm;
           Friday to Saturday, noon-3pm.
Closed: Academic Holidays, Legal Holidays.
Facilities: **Exhibition Area.**
Activities: **Classes/Workshops); Dance Recitals; Films; Temporary/Traveling Exhibitions.**
Publications: newsletter (monthly).

The Union Gallery hosts art exhibitions and special events throughout the year. The Gallery also features a sales area, Artworks, for the sale of original art and crafts. The art exhibitions and special events are usually complemented by public receptions.

Oshkosh

University of Wisconsin-Oshkosh - Galleries ⓒ⁴⁴

Priebe Gallery: 800 Algoma Blvd.
Reeve Memorial Union Art Gallery: 748 Algoma
Oshkosh, WI   54901
Tel: (414) 424-2235
Internet Address: http://www.uwosh.edu
Director: Mr. Jeff Lipschutz
Open: **Priebe Gallery**, Monday to Thursday, 10:30am-3pm and 7pm-9pm; Friday, 10:30am-3pm;
           Saturday to Sunday, 1pm-4pm.
           Reeve Memorial Union, Daily, during building hours.
Facilities: **Galleries** (2).
Activities: **Temporary Exhibitions.**

Exhibitions are regularly scheduled in the Allen Priebe Art Gallery. There is also an annex gallery in which student work is displayed. The Reeve Memorial Union Art Gallery, located on the second floor, seeks to integrate art into the daily lives of students through exhibits, educational and enrichment activities. Exhibits consist primarily of work by locally and regionally recognized professional artists, as well as works by students, faculty and staff. The Union also houses a collection of modern art, which are on view in public areas throughout the building. Holdings include works by Denny Dent, Robert Indiana, LeRoy Neiman, George Segal, Ernst Trova, and Victor Vassarely.

Platteville

University of Wisconsin-Platteville - Harry and Laura Nohr Gallery ⓒ⁴⁴

Ullsvik Center, One University Plaza, Platteville, WI   53818
Tel: (608) 342-1398   *Fax:* (608) 342-1478
Internet Address: http://www.uwplatt.edu
Director: Ms. Susan A. Davis
Admission: free.

Platteville, Wisconsin

University of Wisconsin-Platteville - Harry and Laura Nohr Gallery, cont.

Attendance: 6,000
Parking: parking lot across street.
Open: Monday to Thursday, 11am-3pm and 5pm-8pm; Friday to Saturday, noon-3pm.
Facilities: **Exhibition Area** (4,500 square feet of gallery with 1,200 square feet classroom).
Activities: **Temporary Exhibitions**.

The Gallery presents temporary exhibitions of the work of professional artists and university faculty, staff, and students.

River Falls

University of Wisconsin-River Falls - Gallery 101

Kleinpell Fine Arts Building, Cascade Ave., River Falls, WI   54022
Tel: (715) 425-3266   *Fax:* (715) 425-0657
Internet Address: http://www.uwrf.edu
Art Department Chairman: Mr. Michael Padgett
Admission: free.
Established: 1973   *ADA Compliant:* Y
Open: **September to May,**
        Monday to Friday, 9am-5pm & 7pm-9pm; Saturday to Sunday, 2pm-4pm.
Facilities: **Exhibition Area.**
Activities: **Arts Festival** (annual student and faculty outdoor art exhibition); **Temporary Exhibitions**.

The Gallery maintains a collection of W.P.A. graphics, contemporary prints, and regional art.

Sheboygan

Lakeland College - Bradley Gallery of Art

Lakeland College, Sheboygan, WI   53082
Tel: (920) 565-1280
Internet Address: http://www.lakeland.edu
Co-Director: Ms. Denise Presnell-Weidner
Admission: free.
Established: 1988   *ADA Compliant:* Y
Open: **September to May**, Monday to Friday, 1pm-5pm.
Closed: Easter Week, Thanksgiving Day, Christmas Day.
Facilities: **Exhibition Area.**
Activities: **Lectures**; **Temporary Exhibitions** (5/year).

The Gallery presents temporary exhibitions of work by faculty, students and outside artists.

Stevens Point

University of Wisconsin-Stevens Point - Edna Carlsten Gallery Ⓒᴬ

College of Fine Arts Bldg., 2nd Floor, 900 Reserve Street
Stevens Point, WI   54481
Tel: (715) 346-4797
Internet Address: http://www.uwsp.edu
Director: Ms. Suzanne Woods
Admission: free.
Open: Monday to Friday, 10am-4pm; Saturday to Sunday, 1pm-4pm.
Facilities: **Exhibition Area.**
Activities: **Temporary Exhibitions** (10/year).

The Gallery presents a schedule of temporary exhibitions.

Whitewater

University of Wisconsin-Whitewater - Crossman Gallery ⓒ

Center for the Arts, 800 W. Main St.
Whitewater, WI   53190
Tel: (414) 472-5708
Internet Address: http://www.uww.edu
Director: Mr. Michael Flanagan
Admission: free.
Attendance: 6,091   *Established:* 1970   *Membership:* Y
Open: **Academic Year**,
    Monday to Wednesday, 10am-5pm and 7pm-9pm; Thursday to Friday, 10am-5pm;
    Saturday, 1pm-4pm.
Closed: Academic Holidays, Easter, Christmas Day.
Facilities: **Auditorium** (1,300 seats); **Gallery** (2,400 square feet); **Studios**; **Theatres** (2; 425 seats
    and 160 seats).
Activities: **Temporary/Traveling Exhibitions**.

The Gallery offers temporary exhibitions of work by students, faculty, and outside artists. The permanent collection features 20th-century American folk art.

Wyoming

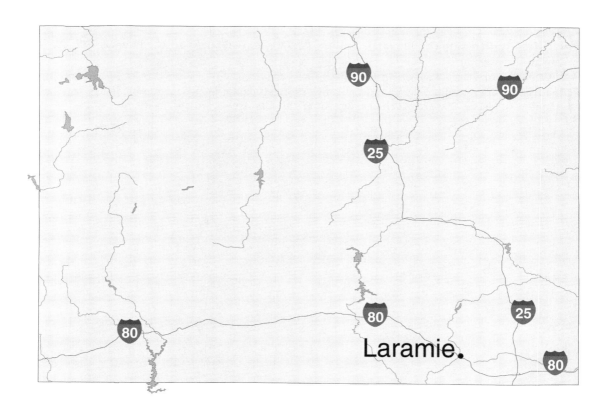

A number in parentheses following a city name indicates the number of museums/galleries in that municipality. If there is no number, one is understood. For example, in the text one listing would be found under each Wyoming city shown on map.

Wyoming

Laramie

The University of Wyoming Art Museum Ⓒᴬᴬ

Centennial Complex, 2111 Willett Drive
Laramie, WY   82071
Tel: (307) 766-6622
Fax: (397) 766-3520
Internet Address: http://www.uwyo.edu/legal/artmus/index.htm
Director: Mr. Charles Guerin

Attendance: 50,000   *Established:* 1968   *Membership:* Y   *ADA Compliant:* Y
Open: **Fall to Spring**,
   Tuesday to Saturday, 10am-5pm; Sunday, noon-4:30pm.
   Summer,
   Tuesday to Friday, 9:30am-4:30pm; Saturday, 10am-4:30pm; Sunday, noon-4:30pm.
Closed: University Holidays.
Facilities: **Galleries** (8; Rotunda Gallery); **Sculpture Terrace** (20,000 square feet); **Shop**.
Activities: **Education Programs** (adults and students); **Films**; **Gallery Talks**; **Lectures**; **Permanent Exhibits**; **Temporary Exhibitions**; **Traveling Exhibitions**.
Publications: exhibition catalogues.

The University of Wyoming Art Museum has a diverse collection of over 7,000 objects. Significant holdings include European and American paintings, prints, and drawings; 19th-century Japanese prints; 18th- and 19th-century Persian and Indian miniature paintings; 20th-century photography; decorative arts; crafts; and African and Native American artifacts.

423

Index

424

Index

Index

Index

Index

Index

437

Index

Also available from
Friar's Lantern, Inc., *Publishers*
in 2000:

Comprehensive Guide
to
American Art Museums and
Exhibition Galleries

Volume 1 - The East and Southeast
and
Volume 2 - The Midwest and West

Presented in the same format as **Art on Campus**, the Guide profiles all major non-profit art venues in the United States - over 1,650 sites (including college and university facilities). Each volume describes approximately 830 institutions, contains over 375 illustrations, is approximately 450 pages in length, and includes a thorough index to both volumes.

Each volume - $24.95
Complete set - $44.95

To order, contact your local bookseller, or order directly from the publisher:
Friar's Lantern, Inc.
P.O. Box 641, 1900 Monkton Road
Monkton, Maryland 21111
Telephone: (800) 752-5408 or (410) 771-4403
Telecopier: (410) 472-3774   E-Mail: flantern@aol.com